RSMeans® Residential Repair & Remodeling Costs

2014 Contractor's Pricing Guide

Senior Editor
Bob Mewis, CCC

Contributing Editors
Christopher Babbitt
Adrian C. Charest, PE
Gary W. Christensen
David G. Drain, PE
Cheryl Elsmore
David Fiske
Robert Fortier, PE
Robert J. Kuchta
Thomas Lane
Robert C. McNichols
Genevieve Medeiros
Melville J. Mossman, PE
Jeannene D. Murphy
Marilyn Phelan, AIA
Stephen C. Plotner
Siobhan Soucie
Phillip R. Waier, PE

Cover Design
Wendy McBay
Paul Robertson
Wayne Engebretson

Chief Operating Officer
Richard Remington

**Vice President,
Business Development**
Steven Ritchie

**Vice President,
Finance & Operations**
Renée Pinczes

Senior Director, Inside Sales
Derek F. Dean

Sales Manager
Reid Clanton

Director, Engineering
Bob Mewis, CCC

**Senior Director, Product
Management**
Jennifer Johnson

**Senior Product
Marketing Manager**
Andrea Sillah

**Senior Director,
Operations**
Rodney L. Sharples

Production Manager
Michael Kokernak

Production
Jill Goodman
Jonathan Forgit
Debbie Panarelli
Sara Rutan
Mary Lou Geary

Technical Support
Christopher Anderson
Gary L. Hoitt
Kathryn S. Rodriguez

RSMeans®
Contractor's Pricing Guide
Residential Repair & Remodeling Costs
2014

Quick costs to help you estimate

Easy-to-use format . . . organized the way you build!

Hundreds of work items with material, labor, and equipment

Built for the small residential contractor/insurance repair specialist

$39.95 per copy (in United States)
Price subject to change without prior notice.

RSMeans
© 2013
A division of Reed Construction Data
Construction Publishers & Consultants
700 Longwater Drive Norwell, MA 02061
www.rsmeans.com

RSMeans, its authors, editors and engineers, apply diligence and
judgment in locating and using reliable sources for the information published.
**However, RSMeans makes no express or implied warranty or guarantee in
connection with the content of the information contained herein, including
the accuracy, correctness, value, sufficiency, or completeness of the data,
methods and other information contained herein. RSMeans makes no express
or implied warranty of merchantability or fitness for a particular purpose.**
RSMeans shall have no liability to any customer or third party for any loss, expense,
or damage, including consequential, incidental, special or punitive damages, including
lost profits or lost revenue, caused directly or indirectly by any error or omission, or
arising out of, or in connection with, the information contained herein.

**No part of this publication may be reproduced, stored in a retrieval system, or
transmitted in any form or by any means without prior written permission of RSMeans.**

Printed in the United States of America

ISSN 1542-9156
ISBN 978-1-940238-19-7

This book is printed on recycled paper,
using soy-based printing ink.
This book is recyclable.

Foreword

Our Mission

Since 1942, RSMeans has been actively engaged in construction cost publishing and consulting throughout North America.

Today, more than 70 years after RSMeans began, our primary objective remains the same: to provide you, the construction and facilities professional, with the most current and comprehensive construction cost data possible.

Whether you are a contractor, owner, architect, engineer, facilities manager, or anyone else who needs a reliable construction cost estimate, you'll find this publication to be a highly useful and necessary tool.

With the constant flow of new construction methods and materials today, it's difficult to find the time to look at and evaluate all the different construction cost possibilities. In addition, because labor and material costs keep changing, last year's cost information is not a reliable basis for today's estimate or budget.

That's why so many construction professionals turn to RSMeans. We keep track of the costs for you, along with a wide range of other key information, from city cost indexes . . . to productivity rates . . . to crew composition . . . to contractor's overhead and profit rates.

RSMeans performs these functions by collecting data from all facets of the industry and organizing it in a format that is instantly accessible to you. From the preliminary budget to the detailed unit price estimate, you'll find the data in this book useful for all phases of construction cost determination.

The Staff, the Organization, and Our Services

When you purchase one of RSMeans' publications, you are, in effect, hiring the services of a full-time staff of construction and engineering professionals.

Our thoroughly experienced and highly qualified staff works daily at collecting, analyzing, and disseminating comprehensive cost information for your needs. These staff members have years of practical construction experience and engineering training prior to joining the firm. As a result, you can count on them not only for accurate cost figures, but also for additional background reference information that will help you create a realistic estimate.

The RSMeans organization is always prepared to help you solve construction problems through its variety of data solutions, including online, CD, and print book formats, as well as cost estimating expertise available via our business solutions, training, and seminars.

Besides a full array of construction cost estimating books, RSMeans also publishes a number of other reference works for the construction industry. Subjects include construction estimating and project and business management, special topics such as green building and job order contracting, and a library of facility management references.

In addition, you can access all of our construction cost data electronically in convenient CD format or on the web. Visit **RSMeansOnline.com** for more information on our 24/7 online cost data.

What's more, you can increase your knowledge and improve your construction estimating and management performance with an RSMeans construction seminar or in-house training program. These two-day seminar programs offer unparalleled opportunities for everyone in your organization to become updated on a wide variety of construction-related issues.

RSMeans is also a worldwide provider of construction cost management and analysis services for commercial and government owners.

In short, RSMeans can provide you with the tools and expertise for constructing accurate and dependable construction estimates and budgets in a variety of ways.

Robert Snow Means Established a Tradition of Quality That Continues Today

Robert Snow Means spent years building RSMeans, making certain he always delivered a quality product.

Today, at RSMeans, we do more than talk about the quality of our data and the usefulness of our books. We stand behind all of our data, from historical cost indexes to construction materials and techniques to current costs.

If you have any questions about our products or services, please call us toll-free at 1-800-334-3509. Our customer service representatives will be happy to assist you. You can also visit our website at **www.rsmeans.com**

Table of Contents

How the Book Is Built: An Overview

A Powerful Construction Tool

You have in your hands one of the most powerful construction tools available today. A successful project is built on the foundation of an accurate and dependable estimate. This book will enable you to construct just such an estimate.

For the casual user the book is designed to be:

- quickly and easily understood so you can get right to your estimate.
- filled with valuable information so you can understand the necessary factors that go into the cost estimate.

For the regular user, the book is designed to be:

- a handy desk reference that can be quickly referred to for key costs.
- a comprehensive, fully reliable source of current construction costs, so you'll be prepared to estimate any project.
- a source book for project cost, product selections, and alternate materials and methods.

To meet all of these requirements we have organized the book into the following clearly defined sections.

Unit Price Section

The cost data has been divided into 23 sections representing the order of construction. Within each section is a listing of components and variations to those components applicable to that section. Costs are shown for the various actions that must be done to that component.

Reference Section

This section includes information on Location Factors and a listing of Abbreviations.

Location Factors

You can adjust total project costs to over 900 locations throughout the U.S. and Canada by using the data in this section.

Abbreviations:

A listing of the abbreviations used throughout this book, along with the terms they represent, is included.

Index

A comprehensive listing of all terms and subjects in this book will help you quickly find what you need when you are not sure where it falls in the order of construction.

The Scope of This Book

This book is designed to be as comprehensive and as easy to use as possible. To that end we have made certain assumptions and limited its scope in two key ways:

1. We have established material prices based on a national average.
2. We have computed labor costs based on a seven major-region average of open shop wage rates.

Project Size

This book is intended for use by those involved primarily in residential repair and remodeling construction costing between $10,000–$100,000.

With reasonable exercise of judgment, the figures can be used for any building work. For other types of projects, such as new home construction or commercial buildings, consult the appropriate RSMeans publication for more information.

How to Use the Book: The Details

What's Behind the Numbers? The Development of Cost Data

The staff at RSMeans continually monitors developments in the construction industry in order to ensure reliable, thorough, and up-to-date cost information.

While *overall* construction costs may vary relative to general economic conditions, price fluctuations within the industry are dependent upon many factors. Individual price variations may, in fact, be opposite to overall economic trends. Therefore, costs are constantly tracked and complete updates are published yearly. Also, new items are frequently added in response to changes in materials and methods.

Costs—$ (U.S.)

All costs represent U.S. national averages and are given in U.S. dollars. The RSMeans Location Factors can be used to adjust costs to a particular location. The Location Factors for Canada can be used to adjust U.S. national averages to local costs in Canadian dollars. No exchange rate conversion is necessary.

Material Costs

The RSMeans staff contacts manufacturers, dealers, distributors, and contractors all across the U.S. and Canada to determine national average material costs. If you have access to current material costs for your specific location, you may wish to make adjustments to reflect differences from the national average.

Included within material costs are fasteners for a normal installation. RSMeans engineers use manufacturers' recommendations, written specifications, and/or standard construction practice for size and spacing of fasteners. Adjustments to material costs may be required for your specific application or location. Material costs do not include sales tax.

Labor Costs

Labor costs are based on the average of residential wages from across the U.S. for the current year. Rates, along with overhead and profit markups, are listed on the inside back cover of this book.

• If wage rates in your area vary from those used in this book, or if rate increases are expected within a given year, labor costs should be adjusted accordingly.

Labor costs reflect productivity based on actual working conditions. These figures include time spent during a normal workday on tasks other than actual installation, such as material receiving and handling, mobilization at site, site movement, breaks, and cleanup.

Productivity data is developed over an extended period so as not to be influenced by abnormal variations and reflects a typical average.

Equipment Costs

Equipment costs include not only rental costs, but also operating costs for equipment under normal use. Equipment and rental rates are obtained from industry sources throughout North America—contractors, suppliers, dealers, manufacturers, and distributors

Factors Affecting Costs

Costs can vary depending upon a number of variables. Here's how we have handled the main factors affecting costs.

Quality——The prices for materials and the workmanship upon which productivity is based represent sound construction work. They are also in line with U.S. government specifications.

Overtime——We have made no allowance for overtime. If you anticipate premium time or work beyond normal working hours, be sure to make an appropriate adjustment to your labor costs.

Productivity——The labor costs for each line item are based on working an eight-hour day in daylight hours in moderate temperatures. For work that extends beyond normal work hours or is performed under adverse conditions, productivity may decrease.

Size of Project——The size, scope of work, and type of construction project will have a significant impact on cost. Economies of scale can reduce costs for large projects. Unit costs can often run higher for small projects. Costs in this book are intended for the size and type of project as previously described in "How the Book Is Built: An Overview." Costs for projects of a significantly different size or type should be adjusted accordingly.

Location——Material prices in this book are for metropolitan areas. However, in dense urban areas, traffic and site storage limitations may increase costs. Beyond a 20-mile radius of large cities, extra trucking or transportation charges may also increase the material costs slightly. On the other hand, lower wage rates may be in effect. Be sure to consider both of these factors when preparing an estimate, particularly if the job site is located in a central city or remote rural location.

In addition, highly specialized subcontract items may require travel and per diem expenses for mechanics.

Other Factors——

• season of year
• contractor management
• weather conditions
• building code requirements
• availability of:
  ○ adequate energy
  ○ skilled labor
  ○ building materials
• owner's special requirements/restrictions
• safety requirements
• environmental considerations

Overhead & Profit——The extreme right-hand column of each chart gives the "Totals." These figures contain the installing contractor's O&P. Therefore, it is necessary for a general contractor to add a percentage of all subcontracted items. For a detailed breakdown of O&P see the inside back cover of this book.

Unpredictable Factors——General business conditions influence "in-place" costs of all items. Substitute materials and construction methods may have to be employed. These may affect the installed cost and/or life cycle costs. Such factors may be difficult to evaluate and cannot necessarily be predicted on the basis of the job's location in a particular section of the country. Thus, where these factors apply, you may find significant but unavoidable cost variations for which you will have to apply a measure of judgment to your estimate.

Final Checklist

Estimating can be a straightforward process provided you remember the basics. Here's a checklist of some of the steps you should remember to complete before finalizing your estimate.

Did you remember to . . .

* factor in the Location Factor for your locale?
* take into consideration which items have been marked up and by how much?
* mark up the entire estimate sufficiently for your purposes?
* include all components of your project in the final estimate?
* double check your figures to be sure of your accuracy?
* call RSMeans if you have any questions about your estimate or the data you've found in our publications?

Remember, RSMeans stands behind its publications. If you have any questions about your estimate . . . about the costs you've used from our books . . . or even about the technical aspects of the job that may affect your estimate, feel free to call the RSMeans editors at 1-800-334-3509.

Free Quarterly Updates

Stay up-to-date throughout 2014 with RSMeans' free cost data updates four times a year. Sign up online to make sure you have access to the newest data. Every quarter we provide the city cost adjustment factors for hundreds of cities and key materials. Register at: **www.rsmeans2014updates.com**

Unit Price Section

Table of Contents

Table of Contents (cont.)

How to Use the Unit Price Pages

The prices in this publication include all overhead and profit mark-ups for the installing contractor. If a general contractor is involved, an additional 10% should be added to the cost shown in the "Total" column.

The costs for material, labor and any equipment are shown here. Material costs include delivery and a 10% mark-up. No sales taxes are included. Labor costs include all mark-ups as shown on the inside back cover of this book. Equipment costs also include a 10% mark-up.

The cost in the total column should be multiplied by the quantity of each item to determine the total cost for that item. The sum of all item's total costs becomes the project's total cost.

The book is arranged into 23 categories that follow the order of construction for residential projects. The category is shown as white letters on a black background at the top of each page.

A brief specification of the cost item is shown here.

Graphics representing some of the cost items are found at the beginning of each category.

The cost data is arranged in a tree structure format. Major cost sections are left justified and are shown as bold headings within a grey background. Cost items and sub-cost items are found under the bold headings. The complete description should read as "bold heading, cost item, sub-cost item."

For example, the identified item's description is "Beam/Girder, Solid Wood Beam, 2" x 8"."

Each action performed to the cost item is conveniently listed to the right of the description. See the explanation below for the scope of work included as part of the action.

The unit of measure upon which all the costs are based is shown here. An abbreviations list is included within the reference section found at the back of this book.

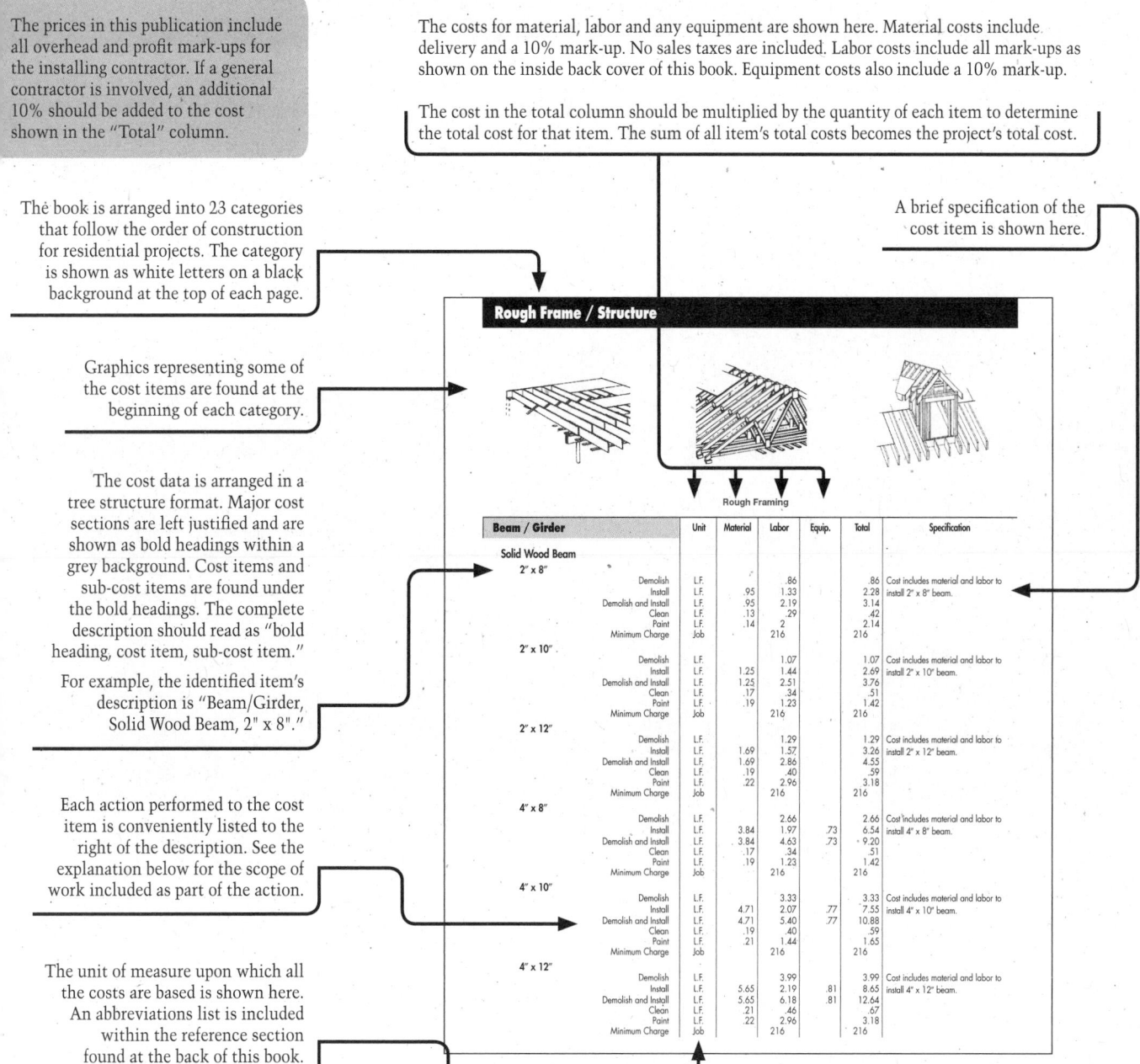

Rough Frame / Structure

Rough Framing

Beam / Girder		Unit	Material	Labor	Equip.	Total	Specification
Solid Wood Beam							
2" x 8"							
	Demolish	L.F.		.86		.86	Cost includes material and labor to
	Install	L.F.	.95	1.33		2.28	install 2" x 8" beam.
	Demolish and Install	L.F.	.95	2.19		3.14	
	Clean	L.F.	.13	.29		.42	
	Paint	L.F.	.14	2		2.14	
	Minimum Charge	Job		216		216	
2" x 10"							
	Demolish	L.F.		1.07		1.07	Cost includes material and labor to
	Install	L.F.	1.25	1.44		2.69	install 2" x 10" beam.
	Demolish and Install	L.F.	1.25	2.51		3.76	
	Clean	L.F.	.17	.34		.51	
	Paint	L.F.	.19	1.23		1.42	
	Minimum Charge	Job		216		216	
2" x 12"							
	Demolish	L.F.		1.29		1.29	Cost includes material and labor to
	Install	L.F.	1.69	1.57		3.26	install 2" x 12" beam.
	Demolish and Install	L.F.	1.69	2.86		4.55	
	Clean	L.F.	.19	.40		.59	
	Paint	L.F.	.22	2.96		3.18	
	Minimum Charge	Job		216		216	
4" x 8"							
	Demolish	L.F.		2.66		2.66	Cost includes material and labor to
	Install	L.F.	3.84	1.97	.73	6.54	install 4" x 8" beam.
	Demolish and Install	L.F.	3.84	4.63	.73	9.20	
	Clean	L.F.	.17	.34		.51	
	Paint	L.F.	.19	1.23		1.42	
	Minimum Charge	Job		216		216	
4" x 10"							
	Demolish	L.F.		3.33		3.33	Cost includes material and labor to
	Install	L.F.	4.71	2.07	.77	7.55	install 4" x 10" beam.
	Demolish and Install	L.F.	4.71	5.40	.77	10.88	
	Clean	L.F.	.19	.40		.59	
	Paint	L.F.	.21	1.44		1.65	
	Minimum Charge	Job		216		216	
4" x 12"							
	Demolish	L.F.		3.99		3.99	Cost includes material and labor to
	Install	L.F.	5.65	2.19	.81	8.65	install 4" x 12" beam.
	Demolish and Install	L.F.	5.65	6.18	.81	12.64	
	Clean	L.F.	.21	.46		.67	
	Paint	L.F.	.22	2.96		3.18	
	Minimum Charge	Job		216		216	

Action	Scope
Demolish	Includes removal of the item and hauling the debris to a truck, dumpster, or storage area.
Install	Includes the installation of the item with normal placement and spacing of fasteners.
Demolish and Install	Includes the demolish action and the install action.
Reinstall	Includes the reinstallation of a removed item.
Clean	Includes cleaning of the item.
Paint	Includes up to two coats of finish on the item (unless otherwise indicated).
Minimum Charge	Includes the minimum labor or the minimum labor and equipment cost. Use this charge for small quantities of material.

Job Costs

Scaffolding	Temporary Electrical Service	Air Compressor

Construction Fees		Unit	Material	Labor	Equip.	Total	Specification
Asbestos Test							
	Minimum Charge	Job		254		254	Minimum charge for testing.
Architectural							
	Minimum Charge	Day	1975			1975	Minimum labor charge for architect.
Engineering							
	Minimum Charge	Day	1850			1850	Minimum labor charge for field engineer.

Construction Permits		Unit	Material	Labor	Equip.	Total	Specification
Job (less than 5K)							
	Minimum Charge	Job	65			65	Permit fees, job less than 5K.
Job (5K to 10K)							
	Minimum Charge	Job	109			109	Permit fees, job more than 5K, but less than 10K.
Job (10K to 25K)							
	Minimum Charge	Job	241			241	Permit fees, job more than 10K, but less than 25K.
Job (25K to 50K)							
	Minimum Charge	Job	460			460	Permit fees, job more than 25K, but less than 50K.
Job (50K to 100K)							
	Minimum Charge	Job	845			845	Permit fees, job more than 50K, but less than 100K.
Job (100K to 250K)							
	Minimum Charge	Job	1750			1750	Permit fees, job more than 100K, but less than 250K.
Job (250K to 500K)							
	Minimum Charge	Job	3300			3300	Permit fees, job more than 250K, but less than 500K.
Job (500K to 1M)							
	Minimum Charge	Job	5925			5925	Permit fees, job more than 500K, but less than 1 million.

Job Costs

Trade Labor		Unit	Material	Labor	Equip.	Total	Specification
Carpenter							
Daily (8 hours)							
	Install	Day		430		430	Daily labor rate for one carpenter.
	Minimum Charge	Job		216		216	
Weekly (40 hours)							
	Install	Week		2150		2150	Weekly labor rate for one carpenter.
	Minimum Charge	Job		216		216	
Drywaller							
Daily (8 hours)							
	Install	Day		430		430	Daily labor rate for one carpenter.
	Minimum Charge	Job		216		216	
Weekly (40 hours)							
	Install	Week		2150		2150	Weekly labor rate for one carpenter.
	Minimum Charge	Job		216		216	
Roofer							
Daily (8 hours)							
	Install	Day		400		400	Daily labor rate for one skilled roofer.
	Minimum Charge	Job		199		199	
Weekly (40 hours)							
	Install	Week		2000		2000	Weekly labor rate for one skilled roofer.
	Minimum Charge	Job		199		199	
Painter							
Daily (8 hours)							
	Install	Day		370		370	Daily labor rate for one painter.
	Minimum Charge	Job		185		185	
Weekly (40 hours)							
	Install	Week		1850		1850	Weekly labor rate for one painter.
	Minimum Charge	Job		185		185	
Mason							
Daily (8 hours)							
	Install	Day		425		425	Daily labor rate for one skilled mason.
	Minimum Charge	Job		212		212	
Weekly (40 hours)							
	Install	Week		2125		2125	Weekly labor rate for one skilled mason.
	Minimum Charge	Job		212		212	
Electrician							
Daily (8 hours)							
	Install	Day		470		470	Daily labor rate for an electrician.
	Minimum Charge	Job		234		234	
Weekly (40 hours)							
	Install	Week		2350		2350	Weekly labor rate for an electrician.
	Minimum Charge	Job		234		234	
Plumber							
Daily (8 hours)							
	Install	Day		500		500	Daily labor rate for a plumber.
	Minimum Charge	Job		251		251	
Weekly (40 hours)							
	Install	Week		2500		2500	Weekly labor rate for a plumber.
	Minimum Charge	Job		251		251	
Common Laborer							
Daily (8 hours)							
	Install	Day		320		320	Daily labor rate for a common laborer.
	Minimum Charge	Job		160		160	

Job Costs

Trade Labor

Trade Labor		Unit	Material	Labor	Equip.	Total	Specification
Weekly (40 hours)							
	Install	Week		1600		1600	Weekly labor rate for a common
	Minimum Charge	Job		160		160	laborer.

Temporary Utilities

Temporary Utilities		Unit	Material	Labor	Equip.	Total	Specification
Power Pole							
Job Site Electricity							
	Install	Month	55			55	Includes average cost of electricity per
	Minimum Charge	Job		234		234	month.
Water Service							
Job Site Water							
	Install	Month	70			70	Includes average costs for water for
	Minimum Charge	Month	70			70	one month.
Telephone							
	Install	Month	89			89	Includes average cost for local and
	Minimum Charge	Month	89			89	long distance telephone service for
							one month.
Chemical Toilet							
	Install	Month			294	294	Monthly rental of portable toilet.
	Minimum Charge	Day			14.70	14.70	
Office Trailer							
Place and Remove							
	Install	Job	375			375	Includes cost to a contractor to deliver,
	Minimum Charge	Job		178		178	place and level an office trailer and
							remove at end of job.
Storage Container							
Place and Remove							
	Install	Job	209			209	Includes cost to a contractor to deliver
	Minimum Charge	Job		178		178	and place a storage container and
							remove at end of job.
Fencing							
	Install	L.F.	4.72			4.72	Includes material costs for temporary
	Minimum Charge	L.F.	275			275	fencing.
Railing							
	Install	L.F.	17.05	12.05	.89	29.99	Includes material and labor to install
	Minimum Charge	L.F.	275			275	primed steel pipe.

Equipment Rental

Equipment Rental		Unit	Material	Labor	Equip.	Total	Specification
Flatbed Truck							
Daily Rental							
	Install	Day			297	297	Daily rental of flatbed truck.
	Minimum Charge	Job			297	297	
Weekly Rental							
	Install	Week			1475	1475	Weekly rental of flatbed truck.
	Minimum Charge	Job			297	297	
Monthly Rental							
	Install	Month			5950	5950	Monthly rental of flatbed truck.
	Minimum Charge	Job			297	297	
Dump Truck							
Daily Rental							
	Install	Day			460	460	Daily rental of dump truck.
	Minimum Charge	Day			460	460	

Equipment Rental		Unit	Material	Labor	Equip.	Total	Specification
Weekly Rental							
	Install	Week			2300	2300	Weekly rental of dump truck.
	Minimum Charge	Day			460	460	
Monthly Rental							
	Install	Month			9175	9175	Monthly rental of dump truck.
	Minimum Charge	Day			460	460	
Forklift							
Daily Rental							
	Install	Day			355	355	Daily rental of forklift.
	Minimum Charge	Day			355	355	
Weekly Rental							
	Install	Week			1775	1775	Weekly rental of forklift.
	Minimum Charge	Day			355	355	
Monthly Rental							
	Install	Month			7150	7150	Monthly rental of forklift.
	Minimum Charge	Day			355	355	
Bobcat							
Daily Rental							
	Install	Day			192	192	Daily rental of wheeled, skid steer loader.
	Minimum Charge	Day			192	192	
Weekly Rental							
	Install	Week			960	960	Weekly rental of wheeled, skid steer loader.
	Minimum Charge	Day			192	192	
Monthly Rental							
	Install	Month			3825	3825	Monthly rental of wheeled, skid steer loader.
	Minimum Charge	Day			192	192	
Air Compressor							
Daily Rental							
	Install	Day			151	151	Daily rental of air compressor.
	Minimum Charge	Day			151	151	
Weekly Rental							
	Install	Week			755	755	Weekly rental of air compressor.
	Minimum Charge	Day			151	151	
Monthly Rental							
	Install	Month			3025	3025	Monthly rental of air compressor.
	Minimum Charge	Day			151	151	
Jackhammer							
Daily Rental							
	Install	Day			10.80	10.80	Daily rental of air tool, jackhammer.
	Minimum Charge	Day			10.80	10.80	
Weekly Rental							
	Install	Week			54	54	Weekly rental of air tool, jackhammer.
	Minimum Charge	Day			10.80	10.80	
Monthly Rental							
	Install	Month			216	216	Monthly rental of air tool, jackhammer.
	Minimum Charge	Day			10.80	10.80	
Concrete Mixer							
Daily Rental							
	Install	Day			158	158	Daily rental of concrete mixer.
	Minimum Charge	Day			158	158	
Weekly Rental							
	Install	Week			790	790	Weekly rental of concrete mixer.
	Minimum Charge	Day			158	158	

Job Costs

Equipment Rental		Unit	Material	Labor	Equip.	Total	Specification
Monthly Rental							
	Install	Month			3150	3150	Monthly rental of concrete mixer.
	Minimum Charge	Day			158	158	
Concrete Bucket							
Daily Rental							
	Install	Day			22	22	Daily rental of concrete bucket.
	Minimum Charge	Day			22	22	
Weekly Rental							
	Install	Week			111	111	Weekly rental of concrete bucket.
	Minimum Charge	Day			22	22	
Monthly Rental							
	Install	Month			445	445	Monthly rental of concrete bucket.
	Minimum Charge	Day			22	22	
Concrete Pump							
Daily Rental							
	Install	Day			780	780	Daily rental of concrete pump.
	Minimum Charge	Day			780	780	
Weekly Rental							
	Install	Week			3900	3900	Weekly rental of concrete pump.
	Minimum Charge	Day			780	780	
Monthly Rental							
	Install	Month			15600	15600	Monthly rental of concrete pump.
	Minimum Charge	Day			780	780	
Generator							
Daily Rental							
	Install	Day			42	42	Daily rental of generator.
	Minimum Charge	Day			42	42	
Weekly Rental							
	Install	Week			211	211	Weekly rental of generator.
	Minimum Charge	Day			42	42	
Monthly Rental							
	Install	Month			845	845	Monthly rental of generator.
	Minimum Charge	Day			42	42	
Welder							
Daily Rental							
	Install	Day			43	43	Daily rental of welder.
	Minimum Charge	Day			43	43	
Weekly Rental							
	Install	Week			214	214	Weekly rental of welder.
	Minimum Charge	Day			43	43	
Monthly Rental							
	Install	Month			855	855	Monthly rental of welder.
	Minimum Charge	Day			43	43	
Sandblaster							
Daily Rental							
	Install	Day			22.50	22.50	Daily rental of sandblaster.
	Minimum Charge	Day			22.50	22.50	
Weekly Rental							
	Install	Week			112	112	Weekly rental of sandblaster.
	Minimum Charge	Day			22.50	22.50	
Monthly Rental							
	Install	Month			450	450	Monthly rental of sandblaster.
	Minimum Charge	Day			22.50	22.50	

Job Costs

Equipment Rental

Equipment Rental		Unit	Material	Labor	Equip.	Total	Specification
Space Heater							
Daily Rental							
	Install	Day			22	22	Daily rental of space heater.
	Minimum Charge	Day			11.35	11.35	
Weekly Rental							
	Install	Day			110	110	Weekly rental of space heater.
	Minimum Charge	Day			11.35	11.35	
Monthly Rental							
	Install	Day			440	440	Monthly rental of space heater.
	Minimum Charge	Day			11.35	11.35	

Move / Reset Contents

Move / Reset Contents		Unit	Material	Labor	Equip.	Total	Specification
Small Room							
	Install	Room		39		39	Includes cost to remove and reset the
	Minimum Charge	Job		160		160	contents of a small room.
Average Room							
	Install	Room		47		47	Includes cost to remove and reset the
	Minimum Charge	Job		160		160	contents of an average room.
Large Room							
	Install	Room		65		65	Includes cost to remove and reset the
	Minimum Charge	Job		160		160	contents of a large room.
Extra Large Room							
	Install	Room		103		103	Includes cost to remove and reset the
	Minimum Charge	Job		160		160	contents of a extra large room.
Store Contents							
Weekly							
	Install	Week	275			275	Storage fee, per week.
Monthly							
	Install	Month	825			825	Storage fee, per month.

Cover and Protect

Cover and Protect		Unit	Material	Labor	Equip.	Total	Specification
Cover / Protect Walls							
	Install	SF Wall		.12		.12	Includes labor costs to cover and
	Minimum Charge	Job		160		160	protect walls.
Cover / Protect Floors							
	Install	SF Flr.		.12		.12	Includes labor costs to cover and
	Minimum Charge	Job		160		160	protect floors.

Temporary Bracing

Temporary Bracing		Unit	Material	Labor	Equip.	Total	Specification
Shim Support Piers							
	Install	Ea.	4.40	126		130.40	Includes labor and material to install
	Minimum Charge	Job		375		375	shims support for piers.

Job Costs

Jack and Relevel

Jack and Relevel		Unit	Material	Labor	Equip.	Total	Specification
Single Story							
	Install	S.F.	1.84	1.51		3.35	Includes labor and equipment to jack
	Minimum Charge	Job		375		375	and relevel single-story building.
Two-story							
	Install	S.F.	1.84	2.51		4.35	Includes labor and equipment to jack
	Minimum Charge	Job		375		375	and relevel two-story building.

Dumpster Rental

Dumpster Rental		Unit	Material	Labor	Equip.	Total	Specification
Small Load							
	Install	Week			685	685	Dumpster, weekly rental, 2 dumps, 5
	Minimum Charge	Week			685	685	yard container.
Medium Load							
	Install	Week			795	795	Dumpster, weekly rental, 2 dumps, 10
	Minimum Charge	Week			795	795	yard container.
Large Load							
	Install	Week			1200	1200	Dumpster, weekly rental, 2 dumps, 30
	Minimum Charge	Week			1200	1200	yard container.

Debris Hauling

Debris Hauling		Unit	Material	Labor	Equip.	Total	Specification
Per Ton							
	Install	Ton		99.50	56.50	156	Includes hauling of debris by trailer or
	Minimum Charge	Ton		745	425	1170	dump truck.
Per Cubic Yard							
	Install	C.Y.		33	18.80	51.80	Includes hauling of debris by trailer or
	Minimum Charge	Job		745	425	1170	dump truck.
Per Pick-up Truck Load							
	Install	Ea.		178		178	Includes hauling of debris by pick-up
	Minimum Charge	Ea.		178		178	truck.

Dump Fees

Dump Fees		Unit	Material	Labor	Equip.	Total	Specification
Per Cubic Yard							
	Install	C.Y.	35			35	Dump charges, building materials.
	Minimum Charge	C.Y.	35			35	
Per Ton							
	Install	Ton	132			132	Dump charges, building materials.
	Minimum Charge	Ton	132			132	

Scaffolding

Scaffolding		Unit	Material	Labor	Equip.	Total	Specification
4' to 6' High							
	Install	Month	67			67	Includes monthly rental of scaffolding,
	Minimum Charge	Month	67			67	steel tubular, 30" wide; 7' long, 5' high.
7' to 11' High							
	Install	Month	80.50			80.50	Includes monthly rental of scaffolding,
	Minimum Charge	Month	80.50			80.50	steel tubular, 30" wide, 7' long, 10' high.

Job Costs

Scaffolding

Scaffolding		Unit	Material	Labor	Equip.	Total	Specification
12' to 16' High							
	Install	Month	93.50			93.50	Includes monthly rental of scaffolding, steel tubular, 30" wide, 7' long, 15' high.
	Minimum Charge	Month	93.50			93.50	
17' to 21' High							
	Install	Month	122			122	Includes monthly rental of scaffolding, steel tubular, 30" wide, 7' long, 20' high.
	Minimum Charge	Month	122			122	
22' to 26' High							
	Install	Month	135			135	Includes monthly rental of scaffolding, steel tubular, 30" wide, 7' long, 25' high.
	Minimum Charge	Month	135			135	
27' to 30' High							
	Install	Month	149			149	Includes monthly rental of scaffolding, steel tubular, 30" wide, 7' long, 30' high.
	Minimum Charge	Month	149			149	

Construction Clean-up

Construction Clean-up		Unit	Material	Labor	Equip.	Total	Specification
Initial							
	Clean	S.F.		.40		.40	Includes labor for general clean-up.
	Minimum Charge	Job		160		160	
Progressive							
	Clean	S.F.		.20		.20	Includes labor for progressive site/job clean-up on a weekly basis.
	Minimum Charge	Job		160		160	

Building Demolition		Unit	Material	Labor	Equip.	Total	Specification
Wood-framed Building							
1 Story Demolition							
	Demolish	S.F.		1.51	1.99	3.50	Includes demolition of 1 floor only
	Minimum Charge	Job		2375	3150	5525	light wood-framed building, including hauling of debris. Dump fees not included.
2nd Story Demolition							
	Demolish	S.F.		1.53	2.02	3.55	Includes demolition of 2nd floor only
	Minimum Charge	Job		2375	3150	5525	light wood-framed building, including hauling of debris. Dump fees not included.
3rd Story Demolition							
	Demolish	S.F.		2	2.64	4.64	Includes demolition of 3rd floor only
	Minimum Charge	Job		2375	3150	5525	light wood-framed building, including hauling of debris. Dump fees not included.
Masonry Building							
	Demolish	S.F.		2.15	2.83	4.98	Includes demolition of one story
	Minimum Charge	Job		2375	3150	5525	masonry building, including hauling of debris. Dump fees not included.
Concrete Building							
Unreinforced							
	Demolish	S.F.		4.41	1.30	5.71	Includes demolition of a one story
	Minimum Charge	Job		2375	3150	5525	non-reinforced concrete building, including hauling of debris. Dump fees not included.
Reinforced							
	Demolish	S.F.		5.05	1.49	6.54	Includes demolition of a one story
	Minimum Charge	Job		2375	3150	5525	reinforced concrete building, including hauling of debris. Dump fees not included.
Steel Building							
	Demolish	S.F.		2.86	3.78	6.64	Includes demolition of a metal
	Minimum Charge	Job		2375	3150	5525	building, including hauling of debris. Dump fees not included. No salvage value assumed for scrap metal.

Job Preparation

General Clean-up		Unit	Material	Labor	Equip.	Total	Specification
Remove Debris							Includes removal of debris caused by the loss including contents items and loose debris.
	Clean	S.F.		.99	.30	1.29	
	Minimum Charge	Job		495	149	644	
Muck-out							Includes labor to remove 2" of muck and mud after a flood loss.
	Clean	S.F.		.62		.62	
	Minimum Charge	Job		160		160	
Deodorize / Disinfect							Includes deodorizing building with application of mildicide and disinfectant to floors and walls - will vary depending on the extent of deodorization required.
	Clean	SF Flr.		.21		.21	
	Minimum Charge	Job		160		160	
Clean Walls							
Heavy							Includes labor and material for heavy cleaning (multiple applications) with detergent and solvent.
	Clean	S.F.		.15		.15	
	Minimum Charge	Job		160		160	
Clean Ceiling							
Light							Includes labor and material to clean light to moderate smoke and soot.
	Clean	S.F.		.25		.25	
	Minimum Charge	Job		160		160	
Heavy							Includes labor and material to clean heavy smoke and soot.
	Clean	S.F.		.37		.37	
	Minimum Charge	Job		160		160	

Flood Clean-up		Unit	Material	Labor	Equip.	Total	Specification
Emergency Service Call							
After Hours / Weekend							Includes minimum charges for deflooding clean-up after hours or on weekends.
	Minimum Charge	Job		214		214	
Grey Water / Sewage							Includes minimum charges for deflooding clean-up.
	Minimum Charge	Job		160		160	
Water Extraction							
Clean (non-grey)							Includes labor to remove clean uncontaminated water from the loss.
	Clean	S.F.	.04	.64		.68	
	Minimum Charge	Job		160		160	
Grey (non-solids)							Includes labor to remove non-solid grey water from the loss.
	Clean	S.F.	.04	1.28		1.32	
	Minimum Charge	Job		160		160	
Sewage / Solids							Includes labor to remove water from the loss that may contain sewage or solids.
	Clean	SF Flr.	.07	1.60		1.67	
	Minimum Charge	Job		160		160	

Flood Clean-up		Unit	Material	Labor	Equip.	Total	Specification
Mildicide Walls							
Topographical							
	Clean	SF Wall		.29		.29	Clean-up of deflooding including
	Minimum Charge	Job		160		160	topographical mildicide application.
Injection Treatments							
	Clean	SF Flr.	39.50	4.93		44.43	Clean-up of deflooding including
	Minimum Charge	Job		160		160	mildicide injection.
Carpet Cleaning							
Uncontaminated							
	Clean	SF Flr.		.20		.20	Includes labor to clean carpet.
	Minimum Charge	Job		160		160	
Contaminated							
	Clean	SF Flr.		.32		.32	Includes labor to clean contaminated
	Minimum Charge	Job		160		160	carpet.
Stairway							
	Clean	Ea.	.11	3.77		3.88	Includes labor to clean contaminated
	Minimum Charge	Job		160		160	carpet on a stairway.
Carpet Treatment							
Disinfect / Deodorize							
	Clean	SF Flr.		.20		.20	Includes disinfecting and deodorizing
	Minimum Charge	Job		160		160	of carpet.
Disinfect For Sewage							
	Clean	SF Flr.		.52		.52	Includes labor to disinfect and
	Minimum Charge	Job		160		160	deodorize carpet exposed to sewage.
Mildicide							
	Clean	SF Flr.	.02	.20		.22	Includes labor and materials to apply
	Minimum Charge	Job		160		160	mildicide to carpet.
Thermal Fog Area							
	Clean	SF Flr.	.03	.49		.52	Includes labor and materials to
	Minimum Charge	Job		160		160	perform thermal fogging during
							deflooding clean-up.
Wet Fog / ULV Area							
	Clean	SF Flr.	.02	.28		.30	Includes labor and materials to
	Minimum Charge	Job		160		160	perform wet fogging / ULV during
							deflooding clean-up.
Steam Clean Fixtures							
	Clean	Ea.	.01	32		32.01	Includes labor and materials to steam
	Minimum Charge	Job		160		160	clean fixtures during deflooding
							clean-up.
Pressure Wash Sewage							
	Clean	SF Flr.		2.91		2.91	Includes labor to pressure wash
	Minimum Charge	Job		160		160	sewage contamination.
Air Mover							
	Minimum Charge	Day			22.50	22.50	Daily rental of air mover.

Job Preparation

Flood Clean-up		Unit	Material	Labor	Equip.	Total	Specification
Dehumidifier							
Medium Size							
	Minimum Charge	Day			49.50	49.50	Daily rental of dehumidifier, medium.
Large Size							
	Minimum Charge	Day			101	101	Daily rental of dehumidifier, large.
Air Purifier							
HEPA Filter-Bacteria							
	Minimum Charge	Ea.	345			345	HEPA filter for air purifier.

Asbestos Removal		Unit	Material	Labor	Equip.	Total	Specification
Asbestos Analysis							
	Minimum Charge	Job		254		254	Minimum charge for testing.
Asbestos Pipe Insulation							
1/2" to 3/4" Diameter							
	Demolish	L.F.	.52	6.60		7.12	Minimum charge to remove asbestos.
	Minimum Charge	Job		4075		4075	Includes full Tyvek suits for workers changed four times per eight-hour shift with respirators, air monitoring and supervision by qualified professionals.
1" to 3" Diameter							
	Demolish	L.F.	1.60	20.50		22.10	Minimum charge to remove asbestos.
	Minimum Charge	Job		4075		4075	Includes full Tyvek suits for workers changed four times per eight-hour shift with respirators, air monitoring and supervision by qualified professionals.
Asbestos-based Siding							
	Demolish	S.F.	3.53	45.50		49.03	Minimum charge to remove asbestos.
	Minimum Charge	Job		4075		4075	Includes full Tyvek suits for workers changed four times per eight-hour shift with respirators, air monitoring and supervision by qualified professionals.
Asbestos-based Plaster							
	Demolish	S.F.	2.72	35		37.72	Minimum charge to remove asbestos.
	Minimum Charge	Job		4075		4075	Includes full Tyvek suits for workers changed four times per eight-hour shift with respirators, air monitoring and supervision by qualified professionals.
Encapsulate Asbestos Ceiling							
	Install	S.F.	.33	.19		.52	Includes encapsulation with penetrating sealant sprayed onto ceiling and walls with airless sprayer.
	Minimum Charge	Job		4075		4075	
Scrape Acoustical Ceiling							
	Demolish	S.F.	.10	1.15		1.25	Minimum charge to remove asbestos.
	Minimum Charge	Job		4075		4075	Includes full Tyvek suits for workers changed four times per eight-hour shift with respirators, air monitoring and supervision by qualified professionals.

Job Preparation

Asbestos Removal

Asbestos Removal		Unit	Material	Labor	Equip.	Total	Specification
Seal Ceiling Asbestos							
	Install	S.F.	2.31	3.84		6.15	Includes attaching plastic cover to ceiling area and sealing where asbestos exists, taping all seams, caulk or foam insulation in cracks and negative air system.
	Minimum Charge	Job		4075		4075	
Seal Wall Asbestos							
	Install	S.F.	2.31	3.41		5.72	Includes attaching plastic cover to wall area and sealing where asbestos exists, taping all seams, caulk or foam insulation in cracks and negative air system.
	Minimum Charge	Job		4075		4075	
Seal Floor Asbestos							
	Install	S.F.	3.70	6.80		10.50	Includes attaching plastic cover to floor area and sealing where asbestos exists, taping all seams, caulk or foam insulation in cracks and negative air system.
	Minimum Charge	Job		4075		4075	
Negative Air Vent System							
	Install	Day			47	47	Daily rental of negative air vent system.
	Minimum Charge	Week			236	236	
HEPA Vacuum Cleaner							
	Install	Day			19.20	19.20	Daily rental of HEPA vacuum, 16 gallon.
	Minimum Charge	Week			96	96	
Airless Sprayer							
	Install	Day			69	69	Daily rental of airless sprayer.
	Minimum Charge	Week			345	345	
Decontamination Unit							
	Install	Day			131	131	Daily rental of decontamination unit.
	Minimum Charge	Week			655	655	
Light Stand							
	Install	Day			16.40	16.40	Daily rental of floodlight w/tripod.
	Minimum Charge	Week			82	82	

Room Demolition

Room Demolition		Unit	Material	Labor	Equip.	Total	Specification
Strip Typical Room							
	Demolish	S.F.		3.20		3.20	Includes 4 labor hours for general demolition.
	Minimum Charge	Job		178		178	
Strip Typical Bathroom							
	Demolish	S.F.		4.27		4.27	Includes 4 labor hours for general demolition.
	Minimum Charge	Job		178		178	
Strip Typical Kitchen							
	Demolish	S.F.		4.11		4.11	Includes 4 labor hours for general demolition.
	Minimum Charge	Job		178		178	
Strip Typical Laundry							
	Demolish	S.F.		3.66		3.66	Includes 4 labor hours for general demolition.
	Minimum Charge	Job		178		178	

Job Preparation

Selective Demolition		Unit	Material	Labor	Equip.	Total	Specification
Concrete Slab							
4″ Unreinforced							
	Demolish	S.F.		2.13	.34	2.47	Includes labor and equipment to
	Minimum Charge	Job		905	143	1048	remove unreinforced concrete slab
							and haul debris to truck or dumpster.
6″ Unreinforced							
	Demolish	S.F.		3.02	.48	3.50	Includes labor and equipment to
	Minimum Charge	Job		905	143	1048	remove unreinforced concrete slab
							and haul debris to truck or dumpster.
8″ Unreinforced							
	Demolish	S.F.		4.96	.78	5.74	Includes labor and equipment to
	Minimum Charge	Job		905	143	1048	remove unreinforced concrete slab
							and haul debris to truck or dumpster.
4″ Reinforced							
	Demolish	S.F.		2.68	.42	3.10	Includes labor and equipment to
	Minimum Charge	Job		905	143	1048	remove reinforced concrete slab and
							haul debris to truck or dumpster.
6″ Reinforced							
	Demolish	S.F.		4.02	.63	4.65	Includes labor and equipment to
	Minimum Charge	Job		905	143	1048	remove reinforced concrete slab and
							haul debris to truck or dumpster.
8″ Reinforced							
	Demolish	S.F.		6.60	1.04	7.64	Includes labor and equipment to
	Minimum Charge	Job		905	143	1048	remove reinforced concrete slab and
							haul debris to truck or dumpster.
Brick Wall							
4″ Thick							
	Demolish	S.F.		2.96	.47	3.43	Includes labor and equipment to
	Minimum Charge	Job		905	143	1048	remove brick wall and haul debris to
							a central location for disposal.
8″ Thick							
	Demolish	S.F.		4.07	.64	4.71	Includes labor and equipment to
	Minimum Charge	Job		905	143	1048	remove brick wall and haul debris to
							a central location for disposal.
12″ Thick							
	Demolish	S.F.		5.45	.86	6.31	Includes labor and equipment to
	Minimum Charge	Job		905	143	1048	remove brick wall and haul debris to
							a central location for disposal.
Concrete Masonry Wall							
4″ Thick							
	Demolish	S.F.		3.29	.52	3.81	Includes minimum labor and
	Minimum Charge	Job		905	143	1048	equipment to remove 4″ block wall
							and haul debris to a central location
							for disposal.
6″ Thick							
	Demolish	S.F.		4.07	.64	4.71	Includes minimum labor and
	Minimum Charge	Job		905	143	1048	equipment to remove 6″ block wall
							and haul debris to a central location
							for disposal.

Job Preparation

Selective Demolition		Unit	Material	Labor	Equip.	Total	Specification
8″ Thick							
	Demolish	S.F.		5	.79	5.79	Includes minimum labor and
	Minimum Charge	Job		905	143	1048	equipment to remove 8″ block wall and haul debris to a central location for disposal.
12″ Thick							
	Demolish	S.F.		7.25	1.14	8.39	Includes minimum labor and
	Minimum Charge	Job		905	143	1048	equipment to remove 12″ block wall and haul debris to a central location for disposal.
Tree Removal							
Small, 4″ - 8″							
	Demolish	Ea.		115	103	218	Minimum charge, common labor
	Minimum Charge	Job		160		160	trade.
Medium, 9″ - 12″							
	Demolish	Ea.		173	154	327	Minimum charge, common labor
	Minimum Charge	Job		160		160	trade.
Large, 13″ - 18″							
	Demolish	Ea.		208	185	393	Minimum charge, tree removal.
	Minimum Charge	Job		535	226	761	
Very Large, 19″ - 24″							
	Demolish	Ea.		260	231	491	Minimum charge, tree removal.
	Minimum Charge	Job		535	226	761	
Stump Removal							
	Demolish	Ea.		72.50	166	238.50	Includes minimum charges for a site
	Minimum Charge	Job		297	112	409	demolition crew and backhoe / loader.

Excavation

Backhoe/Loader - Wheel Type   **Tractor Loader - Wheel Type**   **Backhoe - Crawler Type**

Excavation		Unit	Material	Labor	Equip.	Total	Specification
Footings							
Hand Trenching							
	Install	L.F.		2		2	Includes hand excavation for footing
	Minimum Charge	Job		80		80	or trench up to 10″ deep and 12″ wide.
Machine Trenching							
	Install	L.F.		.77	.40	1.17	Includes machine excavation for
	Minimum Charge	Job		385	201	586	footing or trench up to 10″ deep and 12″ wide.
Trenching w / Backfill							
Hand							
	Install	L.F.		3.20		3.20	Includes hand excavation, backfill and
	Minimum Charge	Job		80		80	compaction.
Machine							
	Install	L.F.		3.84	18.55	22.39	Includes machine excavation, backfill
	Minimum Charge	Job		160	39	199	and compaction.

Backfill		Unit	Material	Labor	Equip.	Total	Specification
Hand (no compaction)							
	Install	L.C.Y.		26.50		26.50	Includes backfill by hand in average
	Minimum Charge	Job		160		160	soil without compaction.
Hand (w / compaction)							
	Install	E.C.Y.		37.50		37.50	Includes backfill by hand in average
	Minimum Charge	Job		160		160	soil with compaction.
Machine (no compaction)							
	Install	L.C.Y.		3.84	2.01	5.85	Includes backfill, by 55 HP wheel
	Minimum Charge	Job		385	201	586	loader, of trenches from loose material piled adjacent without compaction.
Machine (w / compaction)							
	Install	L.C.Y.		10.25	5.35	15.60	Includes backfill, by 55 HP wheel
	Minimum Charge	Job		385	201	586	loader, of trenches from loose material piled adjacent with compaction by vibrating tampers.

17

Concrete Footing and Formwork   **Wood Pile**

Piles	Unit	Material	Labor	Equip.	Total	Specification
Treated Wood, 12″ Butt						
To 30′						
Demolish	L.F.		5.15	1.94	7.09	Includes material, labor and
Install	V.L.F.	18.35	4.73	3.24	26.32	equipment to install up to 30′ long
Demolish and Install	V.L.F.	18.35	9.88	5.18	33.41	treated wood piling.
Paint	L.F.	.42	2.11		2.53	
Minimum Charge	Job		2950	2025	4975	
30′ to 40′						
Demolish	L.F.		5.15	1.94	7.09	Includes material, labor and
Install	V.L.F.	20	4.22	2.89	27.11	equipment to install 30′ to 40′ long
Demolish and Install	V.L.F.	20	9.37	4.83	34.20	treated wood piling.
Paint	L.F.	.42	2.11		2.53	
Minimum Charge	Job		2950	2025	4975	
40′ to 50′						
Demolish	L.F.		5.15	1.94	7.09	Includes material, labor and
Install	V.L.F.	22.50	4.10	2.81	29.41	equipment to install 40′ to 50′ long
Demolish and Install	V.L.F.	22.50	9.25	4.75	36.50	treated wood piling.
Paint	L.F.	.42	2.11		2.53	
Minimum Charge	Job		2950	2025	4975	
50′ to 60′						
Demolish	L.F.		5.15	1.94	7.09	Includes material and
Install	V.L.F.	23.50	3.69	2.53	29.72	equipment to install 50′ to 60′ long
Demolish and Install	V.L.F.	23.50	8.84	4.47	36.81	treated wood piling.
Paint	L.F.	.42	2.11		2.53	
Minimum Charge	Job		2950	2025	4975	
60′ to 80′						
Demolish	L.F.		5.15	1.94	7.09	Includes material, labor and
Install	V.L.F.	31	3.52	2.96	37.48	equipment to install 60′ to 80′ long
Demolish and Install	V.L.F.	31	8.67	4.90	44.57	treated wood piling.
Paint	L.F.	.42	2.11		2.53	
Minimum Charge	Job		2950	2025	4975	
Untreated Wood, 12″ Butt						
To 30′						
Demolish	L.F.		5.15	1.94	7.09	Includes material, labor and
Install	V.L.F.	19.15	4.73	3.24	27.12	equipment to install up to 30′ long
Demolish and Install	V.L.F.	19.15	9.88	5.18	34.21	untreated wood piling.
Paint	L.F.	.42	2.11		2.53	
Minimum Charge	Job		2950	2025	4975	

Foundation

Piles

	Unit	Material	Labor	Equip.	Total	Specification
30' to 40'						
Demolish	L.F.		5.15	1.94	7.09	Includes material, labor and
Install	V.L.F.	19.15	4.22	2.89	26.26	equipment to install 30' to 40' long
Demolish and Install	V.L.F.	19.15	9.37	4.83	33.35	untreated wood piling.
Paint	L.F.	.42	2.11		2.53	
Minimum Charge	Job		2950	2025	4975	
40' to 50'						
Demolish	L.F.		5.15	1.94	7.09	Includes material, labor and
Install	V.L.F.	19.15	4.10	2.81	26.06	equipment to install 40' to 50' long
Demolish and Install	V.L.F.	19.15	9.25	4.75	33.15	untreated wood piling.
Paint	L.F.	.42	2.11		2.53	
Minimum Charge	Job		2950	2025	4975	
50' to 60'						
Demolish	L.F.		5.15	1.94	7.09	Includes material, labor and
Install	V.L.F.	19.15	3.69	2.53	25.37	equipment to install 50' to 60' long
Demolish and Install	V.L.F.	19.15	8.84	4.47	32.46	untreated wood piling.
Paint	L.F.	.42	2.11		2.53	
Minimum Charge	Job		2950	2025	4975	
60' to 80'						
Demolish	L.F.		5.15	1.94	7.09	Includes material, labor and
Install	V.L.F.	24	3.52	2.41	29.93	equipment to install 60' to 80' long
Demolish and Install	V.L.F.	24	8.67	4.35	37.02	untreated wood piling.
Paint	L.F.	.42	2.11		2.53	
Minimum Charge	Job		2950	2025	4975	

Precast Concrete

	Unit	Material	Labor	Equip.	Total	Specification
10" Square						
Demolish	L.F.		5.30	1.98	7.28	Includes material, labor and
Install	V.L.F.	19.85	4.22	2.89	26.96	equipment to install a precast,
Demolish and Install	V.L.F.	19.85	9.52	4.87	34.24	prestressed, 40' long, 10" square
Paint	L.F.	.42	2.11		2.53	concrete pile.
Minimum Charge	Job		2950	2025	4975	
12" Square						
Demolish	L.F.		5.65	2.13	7.78	Includes material, labor and
Install	V.L.F.	23.50	4.35	2.98	30.83	equipment to install a precast,
Demolish and Install	V.L.F.	23.50	10	5.11	38.61	prestressed, 40' long, 12" square
Paint	L.F.	.42	2.11		2.53	concrete pile.
Minimum Charge	Job		2950	2025	4975	
14" Square						
Demolish	L.F.		5.80	2.18	7.98	Includes material, labor and
Install	V.L.F.	27.50	4.93	3.37	35.80	equipment to install a precast,
Demolish and Install	V.L.F.	27.50	10.73	5.55	43.78	prestressed, 40' long, 14" square
Paint	L.F.	.42	2.11		2.53	concrete pile.
Minimum Charge	Job		2950	2025	4975	
16" Square						
Demolish	L.F.		6.10	2.29	8.39	Includes material, labor and
Install	V.L.F.	44.50	5.30	3.62	53.42	equipment to install a precast,
Demolish and Install	V.L.F.	44.50	11.40	5.91	61.81	prestressed, 40' long, 16" square
Paint	L.F.	.42	2.11		2.53	concrete pile.
Minimum Charge	Job		2950	2025	4975	
18" Square						
Demolish	L.F.		6.60	2.48	9.08	Includes material, labor and
Install	V.L.F.	51.50	5.70	4.78	61.98	equipment to install a precast,
Demolish and Install	V.L.F.	51.50	12.30	7.26	71.06	prestressed, 40' long, 18" square
Paint	L.F.	.42	2.11		2.53	concrete pile.
Minimum Charge	Job		2950	2025	4975	

Piles	Unit	Material	Labor	Equip.	Total	Specification
Cross Bracing						
Treated 2" x 6"						
Demolish	L.F.		1.05		1.05	Cost includes material and labor to
Install	L.F.	.84	6.10		6.94	install 2" x 6" lumber for cross-bracing
Demolish and Install	L.F.	.84	7.15		7.99	of foundation piling or posts.
Reinstall	L.F.		4.87		4.87	
Clean	S.F.		.40		.40	
Paint	L.F.	.37	1.42		1.79	
Minimum Charge	Job		755		755	
Treated 2" x 8"						
Demolish	L.F.		1.05		1.05	Cost includes material and labor to
Install	L.F.	1.11	6.30		7.41	install 2" x 8" lumber for cross-bracing
Demolish and Install	L.F.	1.11	7.35		8.46	of foundation piling or posts.
Reinstall	L.F.		5.03		5.03	
Clean	S.F.		.40		.40	
Paint	L.F.	.50	1.48		1.98	
Minimum Charge	Job		755		755	
Treated 2" x 10"						
Demolish	L.F.		1.08		1.08	Cost includes material and labor to
Install	L.F.	1.46	6.50		7.96	install 2" x 10" lumber for
Demolish and Install	L.F.	1.46	7.58		9.04	cross-bracing of foundation piling or
Reinstall	L.F.		5.20		5.20	posts.
Clean	S.F.		.40		.40	
Paint	L.F.	.61	1.51		2.12	
Minimum Charge	Job		755		755	
Treated 2" x 12"						
Demolish	L.F.		1.29		1.29	Cost includes material and labor to
Install	L.F.	2.19	6.75		8.94	install 2" x 12" lumber for
Demolish and Install	L.F.	2.19	8.04		10.23	cross-bracing of foundation piling or
Reinstall	L.F.		5.39		5.39	posts.
Clean	S.F.		.40		.40	
Paint	L.F.	.72	1.54		2.26	
Minimum Charge	Job		755		755	
Metal Pipe						
6" Concrete Filled						
Demolish	L.F.		7.35	2.76	10.11	Includes material, labor and
Install	V.L.F.	26.50	6.15	4.22	36.87	equipment to install concrete filled
Demolish and Install	V.L.F.	26.50	13.50	6.98	46.98	steel pipe pile.
Paint	L.F.	.32	2.11		2.43	
Minimum Charge	Job		2950	2025	4975	
6" Unfilled						
Demolish	L.F.		7.35	2.76	10.11	Includes material, labor and
Install	V.L.F.	22	5.65	3.86	31.51	equipment to install unfilled steel pipe
Demolish and Install	V.L.F.	22	13	6.62	41.62	pile.
Paint	L.F.	.32	2.11		2.43	
Minimum Charge	Job		2950	2025	4975	
8" Concrete Filled						
Demolish	L.F.		7.35	2.76	10.11	Includes material, labor and
Install	V.L.F.	23.50	6.40	4.40	34.30	equipment to install concrete filled
Demolish and Install	V.L.F.	23.50	13.75	7.16	44.41	steel pipe pile.
Paint	L.F.	.32	2.11		2.43	
Minimum Charge	Job		2950	2025	4975	
8" Unfilled						
Demolish	L.F.		7.35	2.76	10.11	Includes material, labor and
Install	V.L.F.	22.50	5.90	4.05	32.45	equipment to install unfilled steel pipe
Demolish and Install	V.L.F.	22.50	13.25	6.81	42.56	pile.
Paint	L.F.	.32	2.11		2.43	
Minimum Charge	Job		2950	2025	4975	

Foundation

Piles

	Unit	Material	Labor	Equip.	Total	Specification
10" Concrete Filled						
Demolish	L.F.		7.60	2.84	10.44	Includes material, labor and
Install	V.L.F.	31.50	6.55	4.50	42.55	equipment to install concrete filled
Demolish and Install	V.L.F.	31.50	14.15	7.34	52.99	steel pipe pile.
Paint	L.F.	.32	2.11		2.43	
Minimum Charge	Job		2950	2025	4975	
10" Unfilled						
Demolish	L.F.		7.60	2.84	10.44	Includes material, labor and
Install	V.L.F.	29.50	5.90	4.05	39.45	equipment to install unfilled steel pipe
Demolish and Install	V.L.F.	29.50	13.50	6.89	49.89	pile.
Paint	L.F.	.32	2.11		2.43	
Minimum Charge	Job		2950	2025	4975	
12" Concrete Filled						
Demolish	L.F.		7.60	2.84	10.44	Includes material, labor and
Install	V.L.F.	40	7.10	4.88	51.98	equipment to install concrete filled
Demolish and Install	V.L.F.	40	14.70	7.72	62.42	steel pipe pile.
Paint	L.F.	.32	2.11		2.43	
Minimum Charge	Job		2950	2025	4975	
12" Unfilled						
Demolish	L.F.		7.60	2.84	10.44	Includes material, labor and
Install	V.L.F.	37	6.20	4.26	47.46	equipment to install unfilled steel pipe
Demolish and Install	V.L.F.	37	13.80	7.10	57.90	pile.
Paint	L.F.	.32	2.11		2.43	
Minimum Charge	Job		2950	2025	4975	
Steel H Section						
H Section 8 x 8 x 36#						
Demolish	L.F.		5.15	1.92	7.07	Includes material, labor and
Install	V.L.F.	17.75	4.62	3.16	25.53	equipment to install steel H section
Demolish and Install	V.L.F.	17.75	9.77	5.08	32.60	pile.
Paint	L.F.	.32	2.11		2.43	
Minimum Charge	Job		2950	2025	4975	
H Section 10 x 10 x 57#						
Demolish	L.F.		5.60	2.11	7.71	Includes material, labor and
Install	V.L.F.	28.50	4.84	3.32	36.66	equipment to install steel H section
Demolish and Install	V.L.F.	28.50	10.44	5.43	44.37	pile.
Paint	L.F.	.32	2.11		2.43	
Minimum Charge	Job		2950	2025	4975	
H Section 12 x 12 x 74#						
Demolish	L.F.		5.80	2.18	7.98	Includes material, labor and
Install	V.L.F.	36.50	5	4.21	45.71	equipment to install steel H section
Demolish and Install	V.L.F.	36.50	10.80	6.39	53.69	pile.
Paint	L.F.	.32	2.11		2.43	
Minimum Charge	Job		2950	2025	4975	
H Section 14 x 14 x 89#						
Demolish	L.F.		6.10	2.29	8.39	Includes material, labor and
Install	V.L.F.	43.50	5.45	4.60	53.55	equipment to install steel H section
Demolish and Install	V.L.F.	43.50	11.55	6.89	61.94	pile.
Paint	L.F.	.32	2.11		2.43	
Minimum Charge	Job		2950	2025	4975	

Foundation

Foundation Post		Unit	Material	Labor	Equip.	Total	Specification
Wood Foundation Post							
4″ x 4″							
	Demolish	L.F.		.83	.31	1.14	Cost includes material and labor to
	Install	L.F.	1.43	5.35		6.78	install 4″ x 4″ treated wood post by
	Demolish and Install	L.F.	1.43	6.18	.31	7.92	hand in normal soil conditions.
	Reinstall	L.F.		4.27		4.27	
	Minimum Charge	Job		755		755	
4″ x 6″							
	Demolish	L.F.		.83	.31	1.14	Cost includes material and labor to
	Install	L.F.	1.71	5.35		7.06	install 4″ x 6″ treated wood post by
	Demolish and Install	L.F.	1.71	6.18	.31	8.20	hand in normal soil conditions.
	Reinstall	L.F.		4.27		4.27	
	Minimum Charge	Job		755		755	
6″ x 6″							
	Demolish	L.F.		.83	.31	1.14	Cost includes material and labor to
	Install	L.F.	2.53	5.35		7.88	install 6″ x 6″ treated wood post by
	Demolish and Install	L.F.	2.53	6.18	.31	9.02	hand in normal soil conditions.
	Reinstall	L.F.		4.27		4.27	
	Minimum Charge	Job		755		755	
Water Jet							
	Demolish	Ea.		95		95	Includes material, labor and
	Install	Ea.	73	730		803	equipment to water jet a 6″ x 6″ wood
	Demolish and Install	Ea.	73	825		898	post under an existing building. Cost
	Reinstall	Ea.		732.34		732.34	may vary depending upon location
	Minimum Charge	Job		640		640	and access.
Shim							
	Install	Ea.	3.58	75.50		79.08	Includes labor and material to trim or
	Minimum Charge	Job		755		755	readjust existing foundation posts under an existing building. Access of 2 - 4 foot assumed.
Cross-bracing							
Treated 2″ x 6″							
	Demolish	L.F.		1.05		1.05	Cost includes material and labor to
	Install	L.F.	.84	6.10		6.94	install 2″ x 6″ lumber for cross-bracing
	Demolish and Install	L.F.	.84	7.15		7.99	of foundation piling or posts.
	Reinstall	L.F.		4.87		4.87	
	Clean	S.F.		.40		.40	
	Paint	L.F.	.37	1.42		1.79	
	Minimum Charge	Job		755		755	
Treated 2″ x 8″							
	Demolish	L.F.		1.05		1.05	Cost includes material and labor to
	Install	L.F.	1.11	6.30		7.41	install 2″ x 8″ lumber for cross-bracing
	Demolish and Install	L.F.	1.11	7.35		8.46	of foundation piling or posts.
	Reinstall	L.F.		5.03		5.03	
	Clean	S.F.		.40		.40	
	Paint	L.F.	.50	1.48		1.98	
	Minimum Charge	Job		755		755	
Treated 2″ x 10″							
	Demolish	L.F.		1.08		1.08	Cost includes material and labor to
	Install	L.F.	1.46	6.50		7.96	install 2″ x 10″ lumber for
	Demolish and Install	L.F.	1.46	7.58		9.04	cross-bracing of foundation piling or
	Reinstall	L.F.		5.20		5.20	posts.
	Clean	S.F.		.40		.40	
	Paint	L.F.	.61	1.51		2.12	
	Minimum Charge	Job		755		755	

Foundation

Foundation Post

	Unit	Material	Labor	Equip.	Total	Specification
Treated 2″ x 12″						
Demolish	L.F.		1.29		1.29	Cost includes material and labor to
Install	L.F.	2.19	6.75		8.94	install 2″ x 12″ lumber for
Demolish and Install	L.F.	2.19	8.04		10.23	cross-bracing of foundation piling or
Reinstall	L.F.		5.39		5.39	posts.
Clean	S.F.		.40		.40	
Paint	L.F.	.72	1.54		2.26	
Minimum Charge	Job		755		755	

Concrete Footing

	Unit	Material	Labor	Equip.	Total	Specification
Continuous						
12″ w x 6″ d						
Demolish	L.F.		1.56	1.39	2.95	Includes material and labor to install
Install	L.F.	4.24	3.54	.02	7.80	continuous reinforced concrete footing
Demolish and Install	L.F.	4.24	5.10	1.41	10.75	poured by chute cast against earth
Minimum Charge	Job		865		865	including reinforcing, forming and
						finishing.
12″ w x 12″ d						
Demolish	L.F.		3	2.68	5.68	Includes material and labor to install
Install	L.F.	9.20	7.10	.04	16.34	continuous reinforced concrete footing
Demolish and Install	L.F.	9.20	10.10	2.72	22.02	poured by chute cast against earth
Minimum Charge	Job		865		865	including reinforcing, forming and
						finishing.
18″ w x 10″ d						
Demolish	L.F.		3.90	3.48	7.38	Includes material and labor to install
Install	L.F.	8.60	8.70	.06	17.36	continuous reinforced concrete footing
Demolish and Install	L.F.	8.60	12.60	3.54	24.74	poured by chute cast against earth
Minimum Charge	Job		865		865	including reinforcing, forming and
						finishing.
24″ w x 24″ d						
Demolish	L.F.		6.50	5.80	12.30	Includes material and labor to install
Install	L.F.	25.50	28.50	.18	54.18	continuous reinforced concrete footing
Demolish and Install	L.F.	25.50	35	5.98	66.48	poured by chute cast against earth
Minimum Charge	Job		865		865	including reinforcing, forming and
						finishing.
Stem Wall						
Single Story						
Demolish	L.F.		14.45	12.90	27.35	Includes material and labor to install
Install	L.F.	22	76.50	68	166.50	stem wall 24″ above and 18″ below
Demolish and Install	L.F.	22	90.95	80.90	193.85	grade for a single story structure.
Minimum Charge	Job		865		865	Includes 12″ wide and 8″ deep
						footing.
Two Story						
Demolish	L.F.		14.45	12.90	27.35	Includes material and labor to install
Install	L.F.	27	110	98	235	stem wall 24″ above and 18″ below
Demolish and Install	L.F.	27	124.45	110.90	262.35	grade typical for a two story structure,
Minimum Charge	Job		865		865	includes 18″ wide and 10″ deep
						footing.

Concrete Slab	Unit	Material	Labor	Equip.	Total	Specification
Reinforced						
4"						
Demolish	S.F.		2.68	.42	3.10	Cost includes material and labor to
Install	S.F.	2.17	.41		2.58	install 4" reinforced concrete
Demolish and Install	S.F.	2.17	3.09	.42	5.68	slab-on-grade poured by chute
Clean	S.F.	.11	.36		.47	including forms, vapor barrier, wire
Paint	S.F.	.18	.80		.98	mesh, 3000 PSI concrete, float finish,
Minimum Charge	Job		200		200	and curing.
6"						
Demolish	S.F.		4.02	.63	4.65	Cost includes material and labor to
Install	S.F.	2.97	.62	.01	3.60	install 6" reinforced concrete
Demolish and Install	S.F.	2.97	4.64	.64	8.25	slab-on-grade poured by chute
Clean	S.F.	.11	.36		.47	including forms, vapor barrier, wire
Paint	S.F.	.18	.80		.98	mesh, 3000 PSI concrete, float finish,
Minimum Charge	Job		200		200	and curing.
8"						
Demolish	S.F.		6.60	1.04	7.64	Cost includes material and labor to
Install	S.F.	3.78	.81	.01	4.60	install 8" reinforced concrete
Demolish and Install	S.F.	3.78	7.41	1.05	12.24	slab-on-grade poured by chute
Clean	S.F.	.11	.36		.47	including forms, vapor barrier, wire
Paint	S.F.	.18	.80		.98	mesh, 3000 PSI concrete, float finish,
Minimum Charge	Job		200		200	and curing.
Unreinforced						
4"						
Demolish	S.F.		2.13	.34	2.47	Cost includes material and labor to
Install	S.F.	1.44	.99	.01	2.44	install 4" concrete slab-on-grade
Demolish and Install	S.F.	1.44	3.12	.35	4.91	poured by chute, including forms,
Clean	S.F.	.11	.36		.47	vapor barrier, 3000 PSI concrete, float
Paint	S.F.	.18	.80		.98	finish, and curing.
Minimum Charge	Job		200		200	
6"						
Demolish	S.F.		3.02	.48	3.50	Cost includes material and labor to
Install	S.F.	2.10	1.01	.01	3.12	install 6" concrete slab-on-grade
Demolish and Install	S.F.	2.10	4.03	.49	6.62	poured by chute, including forms,
Clean	S.F.	.11	.36		.47	vapor barrier, 3000 PSI concrete, float
Paint	S.F.	.18	.80		.98	finish, and curing.
Minimum Charge	Job		200		200	
8"						
Demolish	S.F.		4.96	.78	5.74	Cost includes material and labor to
Install	S.F.	2.88	1.06	.01	3.95	install 8" concrete slab-on-grade
Demolish and Install	S.F.	2.88	6.02	.79	9.69	poured by chute, including forms,
Clean	S.F.	.11	.36		.47	vapor barrier, 3000 PSI concrete, float
Paint	S.F.	.18	.80		.98	finish, and curing.
Minimum Charge	Job		200		200	
Lightweight						
Demolish	S.F.		.95	.27	1.22	Includes material and labor to install
Install	S.F.	1.84	2.98		4.82	lightweight concrete, 3" - 4" thick.
Demolish and Install	S.F.	1.84	3.93	.27	6.04	
Clean	S.F.	.11	.36		.47	
Paint	S.F.	.18	.80		.98	
Minimum Charge	Job		200		200	

Foundation

Concrete Slab		Unit	Material	Labor	Equip.	Total	Specification
Gunite							Includes material and labor to install
	Demolish	S.F.		1.19	.45	1.64	gunite on flat plane per inch of
	Install	S.F.	.35	1.28	.22	1.85	thickness using 1" as base price. No
	Demolish and Install	S.F.	.35	2.47	.67	3.49	forms or reinforcing are included.
	Clean	S.F.	.11	.36		.47	
	Paint	S.F.	.18	.80		.98	
	Minimum Charge	Job		1125		1125	
Epoxy Inject							
	Install	L.F.	5.15	6.65		11.80	Includes labor and material to inject
	Minimum Charge	Job		200		200	epoxy into cracks.
Slabjacking							
	Install	S.F.	.47	1.48	.12	2.07	Includes labor, material and
	Minimum Charge	Job		200		200	equipment to install slabjacking under
							an existing building.
Scrape and Paint							
	Paint	S.F.	.23	.92		1.15	Includes labor and materials to scrape
	Minimum Charge	Job		185		185	and paint a concrete floor.
Vapor Barrier							
	Install	S.F.	.03	.12		.15	Cost includes material and labor to
	Minimum Charge	Job		216		216	install 4 mil polyethylene vapor barrier
							10' wide sheets with 6" overlaps.

Rough Framing

Beam / Girder		Unit	Material	Labor	Equip.	Total	Specification
Solid Wood Beam							
2″ x 8″							
	Demolish	L.F.		.86		.86	Cost includes material and labor to
	Install	L.F.	.95	1.33		2.28	install 2″ x 8″ beam.
	Demolish and Install	L.F.	.95	2.19		3.14	
	Clean	L.F.	.13	.29		.42	
	Paint	L.F.	.14	2		2.14	
	Minimum Charge	Job		216		216	
2″ x 10″							
	Demolish	L.F.		1.07		1.07	Cost includes material and labor to
	Install	L.F.	1.25	1.44		2.69	install 2″ x 10″ beam.
	Demolish and Install	L.F.	1.25	2.51		3.76	
	Clean	L.F.	.17	.34		.51	
	Paint	L.F.	.19	1.23		1.42	
	Minimum Charge	Job		216		216	
2″ x 12″							
	Demolish	L.F.		1.29		1.29	Cost includes material and labor to
	Install	L.F.	1.69	1.57		3.26	install 2″ x 12″ beam.
	Demolish and Install	L.F.	1.69	2.86		4.55	
	Clean	L.F.	.19	.40		.59	
	Paint	L.F.	.22	2.96		3.18	
	Minimum Charge	Job		216		216	
4″ x 8″							
	Demolish	L.F.		2.66		2.66	Cost includes material and labor to
	Install	L.F.	3.84	1.97	.73	6.54	install 4″ x 8″ beam.
	Demolish and Install	L.F.	3.84	4.63	.73	9.20	
	Clean	L.F.	.17	.34		.51	
	Paint	L.F.	.19	1.23		1.42	
	Minimum Charge	Job		216		216	
4″ x 10″							
	Demolish	L.F.		3.33		3.33	Cost includes material and labor to
	Install	L.F.	4.71	2.07	.77	7.55	install 4″ x 10″ beam.
	Demolish and Install	L.F.	4.71	5.40	.77	10.88	
	Clean	L.F.	.19	.40		.59	
	Paint	L.F.	.21	1.44		1.65	
	Minimum Charge	Job		216		216	
4″ x 12″							
	Demolish	L.F.		3.99		3.99	Cost includes material and labor to
	Install	L.F.	5.65	2.19	.81	8.65	install 4″ x 12″ beam.
	Demolish and Install	L.F.	5.65	6.18	.81	12.64	
	Clean	L.F.	.21	.46		.67	
	Paint	L.F.	.22	2.96		3.18	
	Minimum Charge	Job		216		216	

Rough Frame / Structure

Beam / Girder		Unit	Material	Labor	Equip.	Total	Specification
6″ x 8″							
	Demolish	L.F.		3.99		3.99	Cost includes material and labor to
	Install	L.F.	7	3.75	1.39	12.14	install 6″ x 8″ beam.
	Demolish and Install	L.F.	7	7.74	1.39	16.13	
	Clean	L.F.	.19	.40		.59	
	Paint	L.F.	.21	1.44		1.65	
	Minimum Charge	Job		216		216	
6″ x 10″							
	Demolish	L.F.		4.99		4.99	Cost includes material and labor to
	Install	L.F.	3.75	1.73		5.48	install 6″ x 10″ triple beam.
	Demolish and Install	L.F.	3.75	6.72		10.47	
	Clean	L.F.	.21	.46		.67	
	Paint	L.F.	.24	1.64		1.88	
	Minimum Charge	Job		216		216	
6″ x 12″							
	Demolish	L.F.		5.95		5.95	Cost includes material and labor to
	Install	L.F.	5.10	1.82		6.92	install 6″ x 12″ triple beam.
	Demolish and Install	L.F.	5.10	7.77		12.87	
	Clean	L.F.	.24	.52		.76	
	Paint	L.F.	.28	1.85		2.13	
	Minimum Charge	Job		216		216	
Steel I-type							
W8 x 31							
	Demolish	L.F.		9.30	3.65	12.95	Includes material and labor to install
	Install	L.F.	49.50	2.87	1.56	53.93	W shaped steel beam / girder.
	Demolish and Install	L.F.	49.50	12.17	5.21	66.88	
	Minimum Charge	Job		520		520	
W8 x 48							
	Demolish	L.F.		9.30	3.65	12.95	Includes material and labor to install
	Install	L.F.	77	3	1.63	81.63	W shaped steel beam / girder.
	Demolish and Install	L.F.	77	12.30	5.28	94.58	
	Minimum Charge	Job		520		520	
W8 x 67							
	Demolish	L.F.		9.30	3.65	12.95	Includes material and labor to install
	Install	L.F.	107	3.15	1.71	111.86	W shaped steel beam / girder.
	Demolish and Install	L.F.	107	12.45	5.36	124.81	
	Minimum Charge	Job		520		520	
W10 x 45							
	Demolish	L.F.		9.30	3.65	12.95	Includes material and labor to install
	Install	L.F.	72	3	1.63	76.63	W shaped steel beam / girder.
	Demolish and Install	L.F.	72	12.30	5.28	89.58	
	Minimum Charge	Job		520		520	
W10 x 68							
	Demolish	L.F.		9.30	3.65	12.95	Includes material and labor to install
	Install	L.F.	109	3.15	1.71	113.86	W shaped steel beam / girder.
	Demolish and Install	L.F.	109	12.45	5.36	126.81	
	Minimum Charge	Job		520		520	
W12 x 50							
	Demolish	L.F.		9.30	3.65	12.95	Includes material and labor to install
	Install	L.F.	80.50	3	1.63	85.13	W shaped steel beam / girder.
	Demolish and Install	L.F.	80.50	12.30	5.28	98.08	
	Minimum Charge	Job		520		520	
W12 x 87							
	Demolish	L.F.		13.65	5.35	19	Includes material and labor to install
	Install	L.F.	140	3.15	1.71	144.86	W shaped steel beam / girder.
	Demolish and Install	L.F.	140	16.80	7.06	163.86	
	Minimum Charge	Job		520		520	

Rough Frame / Structure

Beam / Girder

Beam / Girder	Unit	Material	Labor	Equip.	Total	Specification
W12 x 120						
Demolish	L.F.		13.65	5.35	19	Includes material and labor to install
Install	L.F.	193	3.23	1.75	197.98	W shaped steel beam / girder.
Demolish and Install	L.F.	193	16.88	7.10	216.98	
Minimum Charge	Job		520		520	
W14 x 74						
Demolish	L.F.		13.65	5.35	19	Includes material and labor to install
Install	L.F.	119	3.15	1.71	123.86	W shaped steel beam / girder.
Demolish and Install	L.F.	119	16.80	7.06	142.86	
Minimum Charge	Job		520		520	
W14 x 120						
Demolish	L.F.		13.65	5.35	19	Includes material and labor to install
Install	L.F.	193	3.23	1.75	197.98	W shaped steel beam / girder.
Demolish and Install	L.F.	193	16.88	7.10	216.98	
Minimum Charge	Job		520		520	

Column

Column	Unit	Material	Labor	Equip.	Total	Specification
Concrete						
Small Diameter						
Demolish	L.F.		15.10	2.38	17.48	Includes material and labor to install
Install	L.F.	150	13.90	2.73	166.63	small diameter concrete column.
Demolish and Install	L.F.	150	29	5.11	184.11	
Minimum Charge	Job		695	137	832	
Large Diameter						
Demolish	L.F.		45	7.15	52.15	Includes material and labor to install
Install	L.F.	267	16.35	3.22	286.57	large diameter concrete column.
Demolish and Install	L.F.	267	61.35	10.37	338.72	
Minimum Charge	Job		695	137	832	

Floor Framing System

Floor Framing System	Unit	Material	Labor	Equip.	Total	Specification
12" O.C.						
2" x 6" Joists						
Demolish	S.F.		.73		.73	Cost includes material and labor to
Install	S.F.	.73	.69		1.42	install 2" x 6" joists, 12" O.C.
Demolish and Install	S.F.	.73	1.42		2.15	including box or band joist. Blocking
Reinstall	S.F.		.55		.55	or bridging not included.
Minimum Charge	Job		216		216	
2" x 8" Joists						
Demolish	S.F.		.76		.76	Cost includes material and labor to
Install	S.F.	1.10	.79		1.89	install 2" x 8" joists, 12" O.C.
Demolish and Install	S.F.	1.10	1.55		2.65	including box or band joist. Blocking
Reinstall	S.F.		.63		.63	or bridging not included.
Minimum Charge	Job		216		216	
2" x 10" Joists						
Demolish	S.F.		.78		.78	Cost includes material and labor to
Install	S.F.	1.46	.96		2.42	install 2" x 10" joists, 12" O.C.
Demolish and Install	S.F.	1.46	1.74		3.20	including box or band joist. Blocking
Reinstall	S.F.		.77		.77	or bridging not included.
Minimum Charge	Job		216		216	

Floor Framing System		Unit	Material	Labor	Equip.	Total	Specification
2" x 12" Joists							
	Demolish	S.F.		.81		.81	Cost includes material and labor to
	Install	S.F.	1.98	.99		2.97	install 2" x 12" joists, 12" O.C.
	Demolish and Install	S.F.	1.98	1.80		3.78	including box or band joist. Blocking
	Reinstall	S.F.		.79		.79	or bridging not included.
	Minimum Charge	Job		216		216	
Block / Bridge							
	Demolish	Ea.		1.11		1.11	Includes material and labor to install
	Install	Ea.	1.67	2.43		4.10	set of cross bridging or per block of
	Demolish and Install	Ea.	1.67	3.54		5.21	solid bridging for 2" x 10" joists cut to
	Minimum Charge	Job		216		216	size on site.
16" O.C.							
2" x 6" Joists							
	Demolish	S.F.		.55		.55	Cost includes material and labor to
	Install	S.F.	.56	.52		1.08	install 2" x 6" joists including box or
	Demolish and Install	S.F.	.56	1.07		1.63	band joist installed 16" O.C. Does not
	Reinstall	S.F.		.41		.41	include beams, blocking or bridging.
	Minimum Charge	Job		216		216	
2" x 8" Joists							
	Demolish	S.F.		.57		.57	Cost includes material and labor to
	Install	S.F.	.85	.59		1.44	install 2" x 8" joists including box or
	Demolish and Install	S.F.	.85	1.16		2.01	band joist installed 16" O.C. Does not
	Reinstall	S.F.		.47		.47	include beams, blocking or bridging.
	Minimum Charge	Job		216		216	
2" x 10" Joists							
	Demolish	S.F.		.59		.59	Cost includes material and labor to
	Install	S.F.	1.12	.72		1.84	install 2" x 10" joists including box or
	Demolish and Install	S.F.	1.12	1.31		2.43	band joist 16" O.C. Does not include
	Reinstall	S.F.		.58		.58	beams, blocking or bridging.
	Minimum Charge	Job		216		216	
2" x 12" Joists							
	Demolish	S.F.		.61		.61	Cost includes material and labor to
	Install	S.F.	1.52	.74		2.26	install 2" x 12" joists including box or
	Demolish and Install	S.F.	1.52	1.35		2.87	band joist installed 16" O.C. Does not
	Reinstall	S.F.		.59		.59	include beams, blocking or bridging.
	Minimum Charge	Job		216		216	
Block / Bridge							
	Demolish	Ea.		1.11		1.11	Includes material and labor to install
	Install	Ea.	1.67	2.43		4.10	set of cross bridging or per block of
	Demolish and Install	Ea.	1.67	3.54		5.21	solid bridging for 2" x 10" joists cut to
	Minimum Charge	Job		216		216	size on site.
24" O.C.							
2" x 6" Joists							
	Demolish	S.F.		.37		.37	Cost includes material and labor to
	Install	S.F.	.40	.35		.75	install 2" x 6" joists including box or
	Demolish and Install	S.F.	.40	.72		1.12	band joist installed 24" O.C. Does not
	Reinstall	S.F.		.28		.28	include beams, blocking or bridging.
	Minimum Charge	Job		216		216	
2" x 8" Joists							
	Demolish	S.F.		.38		.38	Cost includes material and labor to
	Install	S.F.	.61	.39		1	install 2" x 8" joists including box or
	Demolish and Install	S.F.	.61	.77		1.38	band joist installed 24" O.C. Does not
	Reinstall	S.F.		.31		.31	include beams, blocking or bridging.
	Minimum Charge	Job		216		216	

Floor Framing System		Unit	Material	Labor	Equip.	Total	Specification
2" x 10" Joists							Cost includes material and labor to
	Demolish	S.F.		.39		.39	install 2" x 10" joists including box or
	Install	S.F.	.79	.48		1.27	band joist installed 24" O.C. Does not
	Demolish and Install	S.F.	.79	.87		1.66	include beams, blocking or bridging.
	Reinstall	S.F.		.38		.38	
	Minimum Charge	Job		216		216	
2" x 12" Joists							Cost includes material and labor to
	Demolish	S.F.		.40		.40	install 2" x 12" joists including box or
	Install	S.F.	1.08	.49		1.57	band joist installed 24" O.C. Does not
	Demolish and Install	S.F.	1.08	.89		1.97	include beams, blocking or bridging.
	Reinstall	S.F.		.40		.40	
	Minimum Charge	Job		216		216	
Block / Bridge							Includes material and labor to install
	Demolish	Ea.		1.11		1.11	set of cross bridging or per block of
	Install	Ea.	1.67	2.43		4.10	solid bridging for 2" x 10" joists cut to
	Demolish and Install	Ea.	1.67	3.54		5.21	size on site.
	Minimum Charge	Job		216		216	
Engineered Lumber, Joist							
9-1/2"							Includes material and labor to install
	Demolish	S.F.		.59		.59	engineered lumber truss / joists per
	Install	S.F.	1.71	.43		2.14	S.F. of floor area based on joists 16"
	Demolish and Install	S.F.	1.71	1.02		2.73	O.C. Beams, supports and bridging
	Reinstall	S.F.		.35		.35	are not included.
	Minimum Charge	Job		216		216	
11-7/8"							Includes material and labor to install
	Demolish	S.F.		.61		.61	engineered lumber truss / joists per
	Install	S.F.	1.94	.44		2.38	S.F. of floor area based on joists 16"
	Demolish and Install	S.F.	1.94	1.05		2.99	O.C. Beams, supports and bridging
	Reinstall	S.F.		.35		.35	are not included.
	Minimum Charge	Job		216		216	
14"							Includes material and labor to install
	Demolish	S.F.		.63		.63	engineered lumber truss / joists per
	Install	S.F.	2.29	.47		2.76	S.F. of floor area based on joists 16"
	Demolish and Install	S.F.	2.29	1.10		3.39	O.C. Beams, supports and bridging
	Reinstall	S.F.		.38		.38	are not included.
	Minimum Charge	Job		216		216	
16"							Includes material and labor to install
	Demolish	S.F.		.65		.65	engineered lumber truss / joists per
	Install	S.F.	3.40	.50		3.90	S.F. of floor area based on joists 16"
	Demolish and Install	S.F.	3.40	1.15		4.55	O.C. Beams, supports and bridging
	Reinstall	S.F.		.40		.40	are not included.
	Minimum Charge	Job		216		216	
Block / Bridge							Includes material and labor to install
	Demolish	Pr.		1.11		1.11	set of steel, one-nail type cross
	Install	Pr.	1.02	3.20		4.22	bridging for trusses placed 16" O.C.
	Demolish and Install	Pr.	1.02	4.31		5.33	
	Minimum Charge	Job		216		216	
Block / Bridge							
2" x 6"							Includes material and labor to install
	Demolish	Ea.		1.11		1.11	set of cross bridging or per block of
	Install	Ea.	.84	1.95		2.79	solid bridging for 2" x 6" joists cut to
	Demolish and Install	Ea.	.84	3.06		3.90	size on site.
	Minimum Charge	Job		216		216	

Rough Frame / Structure

Floor Framing System		Unit	Material	Labor	Equip.	Total	Specification
2″ x 8″							
	Demolish	Ea.		1.11		1.11	Includes material and labor to install
	Install	Ea.	1.27	2.16		3.43	set of cross bridging or per block of
	Demolish and Install	Ea.	1.27	3.27		4.54	solid bridging for 2″ x 8″ joists cut to
	Minimum Charge	Job		216		216	size on site.
2″ x 10″							
	Demolish	Ea.		1.11		1.11	Includes material and labor to install
	Install	Ea.	1.67	2.43		4.10	set of cross bridging or per block of
	Demolish and Install	Ea.	1.67	3.54		5.21	solid bridging for 2″ x 10″ joists cut to
	Minimum Charge	Job		216		216	size on site.
2″ x 12″							
	Demolish	Ea.		1.11		1.11	Includes material and labor to install
	Install	Ea.	2.27	2.86		5.13	set of cross bridging or per block of
	Demolish and Install	Ea.	2.27	3.97		6.24	solid bridging for 2″ x 12″ joists cut to
	Minimum Charge	Job		216		216	size on site.
Ledger Strips							
1″ x 2″							
	Demolish	L.F.		.30		.30	Cost includes material and labor to
	Install	L.F.	.26	1.25		1.51	install 1″ x 2″ ledger strip nailed to the
	Demolish and Install	L.F.	.26	1.55		1.81	face of studs, beams or joist.
	Minimum Charge	Job		216		216	
1″ x 3″							
	Demolish	L.F.		.30		.30	Includes material and labor to install
	Install	L.F.	.52	1.44		1.96	up to 1″ x 4″ ledger strip nailed to the
	Demolish and Install	L.F.	.52	1.74		2.26	face of studs, beams or joist.
	Minimum Charge	Job		216		216	
1″ x 4″							
	Demolish	L.F.		.30		.30	Includes material and labor to install
	Install	L.F.	.52	1.44		1.96	up to 1″ x 4″ ledger strip nailed to the
	Demolish and Install	L.F.	.52	1.74		2.26	face of studs, beams or joist.
	Minimum Charge	Job		216		216	
2″ x 2″							
	Demolish	L.F.		.32		.32	Cost includes material and labor to
	Install	L.F.	.41	1.31		1.72	install 2″ x 2″ ledger strip nailed to the
	Demolish and Install	L.F.	.41	1.63		2.04	face of studs, beams or joist.
	Minimum Charge	Job		216		216	
2″ x 4″							
	Demolish	L.F.		.36		.36	Cost includes material and labor to
	Install	L.F.	.42	1.73		2.15	install 2″ x 4″ ledger strip nailed to the
	Demolish and Install	L.F.	.42	2.09		2.51	face of studs, beams or joist.
	Reinstall	L.F.		1.38		1.38	
	Minimum Charge	Job		216		216	
Ledger Boards							
2″ x 6″							
	Demolish	L.F.		.36		.36	Cost includes material and labor to
	Install	L.F.	4.75	2.70		7.45	install 2″ x 6″ ledger board fastened to
	Demolish and Install	L.F.	4.75	3.06		7.81	a wall, joists or studs.
	Reinstall	L.F.		2.16		2.16	
	Minimum Charge	Job		216		216	
4″ x 6″							
	Demolish	L.F.		.59		.59	Cost includes material and labor to
	Install	L.F.	8.25	3.09		11.34	install 4″ x 6″ ledger board fastened to
	Demolish and Install	L.F.	8.25	3.68		11.93	a wall, joists or studs.
	Reinstall	L.F.		2.47		2.47	
	Minimum Charge	Job		216		216	

Rough Frame / Structure

Floor Framing System	Unit	Material	Labor	Equip.	Total	Specification
4" x 8"						
Demolish	L.F.		.79		.79	Cost includes material and labor to
Install	L.F.	9.25	3.60		12.85	install 4" x 8" ledger board fastened to
Demolish and Install	L.F.	9.25	4.39		13.64	a wall, joists or studs.
Reinstall	L.F.		2.88		2.88	
Minimum Charge	Job		216		216	
Sill Plate Per L.F.						
2" x 4"						
Demolish	L.F.		.30		.30	Cost includes material and labor to
Install	L.F.	.53	1.57		2.10	install 2" x 4" pressure treated lumber,
Demolish and Install	L.F.	.53	1.87		2.40	drilled and installed on foundation
Reinstall	L.F.		1.26		1.26	bolts 48" O.C. Bolts, nuts and washers
Minimum Charge	Job		216		216	are not included.
2" x 6"						
Demolish	L.F.		.46		.46	Cost includes material and labor to
Install	L.F.	.83	1.73		2.56	install 2" x 6" pressure treated lumber,
Demolish and Install	L.F.	.83	2.19		3.02	drilled and installed on foundation
Reinstall	L.F.		1.38		1.38	bolts 48" O.C. Bolts, nuts and washers
Minimum Charge	Job		216		216	not included.
2" x 8"						
Demolish	L.F.		.61		.61	Cost includes material and labor to
Install	L.F.	1.10	1.92		3.02	install 2" x 8" pressure treated lumber,
Demolish and Install	L.F.	1.10	2.53		3.63	drilled and installed on foundation
Reinstall	L.F.		1.54		1.54	bolts 48" O.C. Bolts, nuts and washers
Minimum Charge	Job		216		216	not included.
Earthquake Strapping						
Install	Ea.	3.26	2.70		5.96	Includes labor and material to replace
Minimum Charge	Job		216		216	an earthquake strap.

Subflooring	Unit	Material	Labor	Equip.	Total	Specification
Plywood						
1/2"						
Demolish	S.F.		.93		.93	Cost includes material and labor to
Install	SF Flr.	.50	.46		.96	install 1/2" plywood subfloor, CD
Demolish and Install	SF Flr.	.50	1.39		1.89	standard interior grade, plugged and
Minimum Charge	Job		216		216	touch sanded.
5/8"						
Demolish	S.F.		.94		.94	Cost includes material and labor to
Install	SF Flr.	.62	.52		1.14	install 5/8" plywood subfloor, CD
Demolish and Install	SF Flr.	.62	1.46		2.08	standard interior grade, plugged and
Reinstall	SF Flr.		.41		.41	touch sanded.
Minimum Charge	Job		216		216	
3/4"						
Demolish	S.F.		.95		.95	Cost includes material and labor to
Install	SF Flr.	.74	.56		1.30	install 3/4" plywood subfloor, CD
Demolish and Install	SF Flr.	.74	1.51		2.25	standard interior grade, plugged and
Reinstall	SF Flr.		.45		.45	touch sanded.
Minimum Charge	Job		216		216	

Rough Frame / Structure

Subflooring

Subflooring		Unit	Material	Labor	Equip.	Total	Specification
Particle Board							
1/2"	Demolish	S.F.		.46		.46	Cost includes material and labor to install 1/2" particle board subfloor.
	Install	SF Flr.	.46	.58		1.04	
	Demolish and Install	SF Flr.	.46	1.04		1.50	
	Minimum Charge	Job		216		216	
5/8"	Demolish	S.F.		.47		.47	Cost includes material and labor to install 5/8" particle board subfloor.
	Install	SF Flr.	.57	.63		1.20	
	Demolish and Install	SF Flr.	.57	1.10		1.67	
	Minimum Charge	Job		216		216	
3/4"	Demolish	S.F.		.47		.47	Cost includes material and labor to install 3/4" particle board subfloor.
	Install	SF Flr.	.68	.69		1.37	
	Demolish and Install	SF Flr.	.68	1.16		1.84	
	Minimum Charge	Job		216		216	
Plank Board	Demolish	S.F.		1.48		1.48	Cost includes material and labor to install 1" x 6" standard grade plank flooring.
	Install	SF Flr.	1.91	.96		2.87	
	Demolish and Install	SF Flr.	1.91	2.44		4.35	
	Reinstall	SF Flr.		.96		.96	
	Minimum Charge	Job		216		216	
Felt Underlay	Demolish	S.F.		.08		.08	Includes material and labor to install #15 felt building paper.
	Install	S.F.	.06	.12		.18	
	Demolish and Install	S.F.	.06	.20		.26	
	Minimum Charge	Job		216		216	
Prep (for flooring)	Install	S.F.		.36		.36	Preparation of subflooring for installation of new finished flooring. Cost reflects average time to prep area.
	Minimum Charge	Job		189		189	

Wall Framing System

Wall Framing System		Unit	Material	Labor	Equip.	Total	Specification
2" x 4"							
8' High	Demolish	L.F.		4.75		4.75	Cost includes material and labor to install 2" x 4" x 8' high wall system, including studs, treated bottom plate, double top plate and one row of fire blocking.
	Install	L.F.	4.29	7.20		11.49	
	Demolish and Install	L.F.	4.29	11.95		16.24	
	Reinstall	L.F.		5.76		5.76	
	Minimum Charge	Job		216		216	
9' High	Demolish	L.F.		5.30		5.30	Cost includes material and labor to install 2" x 4" x 9' wall system including studs, treated bottom plate, double top plate and one row of fire blocking.
	Install	L.F.	4.61	7.20		11.81	
	Demolish and Install	L.F.	4.61	12.50		17.11	
	Reinstall	L.F.		5.76		5.76	
	Minimum Charge	Job		216		216	
10' High	Demolish	L.F.		5.95		5.95	Cost includes material and labor to install 2" x 4" x 10' wall system including studs, treated bottom plate, double top plate and one row of fire blocking.
	Install	L.F.	4.92	7.20		12.12	
	Demolish and Install	L.F.	4.92	13.15		18.07	
	Reinstall	L.F.		5.76		5.76	
	Minimum Charge	Job		216		216	

Rough Frame / Structure

Wall Framing System	Unit	Material	Labor	Equip.	Total	Specification
12' High						
Demolish	L.F.		7.10		7.10	Cost includes material and labor to
Install	L.F.	5.55	9		14.55	install 2" x 4" x 12' wall system
Demolish and Install	L.F.	5.55	16.10		21.65	including studs, treated bottom plate,
Reinstall	L.F.		7.20		7.20	double top plate and one row of fire
Minimum Charge	Job		216		216	blocking.
2" x 6"						
8' High						
Demolish	L.F.		4.45		4.45	Cost includes material and labor to
Install	L.F.	6.50	8		14.50	install 2" x 6" x 8' wall system
Demolish and Install	L.F.	6.50	12.45		18.95	including studs, treated bottom plate,
Reinstall	L.F.		6.40		6.40	double top plate and one row of fire
Minimum Charge	Job		216		216	blocking.
9' High						
Demolish	L.F.		5		5	Cost includes material and labor to
Install	L.F.	6.95	8		14.95	install 2" x 6" x 9' wall system
Demolish and Install	L.F.	6.95	13		19.95	including studs, treated bottom plate,
Reinstall	L.F.		6.40		6.40	double top plate and one row of fire
Minimum Charge	Job		216		216	blocking.
10' High						
Demolish	L.F.		5.50		5.50	Cost includes material and labor to
Install	L.F.	7.45	8		15.45	install 2" x 6" x 10' wall system
Demolish and Install	L.F.	7.45	13.50		20.95	including studs, treated bottom plate,
Reinstall	L.F.		6.40		6.40	double top plate and one row of fire
Minimum Charge	Job		216		216	blocking.
12' High						
Demolish	L.F.		6.45		6.45	Cost includes material and labor to
Install	L.F.	8.35	9.80		18.15	install 2" x 6" x 12' wall system
Demolish and Install	L.F.	8.35	16.25		24.60	including studs, treated bottom plate,
Reinstall	L.F.		7.85		7.85	double top plate and one row of fire
Minimum Charge	Job		216		216	blocking.
Fireblock						
2" x 4", 16" O.C. System						
Demolish	L.F.		.59		.59	Cost includes material and labor to
Install	L.F.	.42	1.44		1.86	install 2" x 4" fireblocks in wood frame
Demolish and Install	L.F.	.42	2.03		2.45	walls per L.F. of wall to be blocked.
Reinstall	L.F.		1.15		1.15	
Minimum Charge	Job		216		216	
2" x 4", 24" O.C. System						
Demolish	L.F.		.59		.59	Cost includes material and labor to
Install	L.F.	.42	1.44		1.86	install 2" x 4" fireblocks in wood frame
Demolish and Install	L.F.	.42	2.03		2.45	walls per L.F. of wall to be blocked.
Reinstall	L.F.		1.15		1.15	
Minimum Charge	Job		216		216	
2" x 6", 16" O.C. System						
Demolish	L.F.		.89		.89	Cost includes material and labor to
Install	L.F.	.63	1.44		2.07	install 2" x 6" fireblocks in wood frame
Demolish and Install	L.F.	.63	2.33		2.96	walls per L.F. of wall to be blocked.
Reinstall	L.F.		1.15		1.15	
Minimum Charge	Job		216		216	
2" x 6", 24" O.C. System						
Demolish	L.F.		.89		.89	Cost includes material and labor to
Install	L.F.	.63	1.44		2.07	install 2" x 6" fireblocks in wood frame
Demolish and Install	L.F.	.63	2.33		2.96	walls per L.F. of wall to be blocked.
Reinstall	L.F.		1.15		1.15	
Minimum Charge	Job		216		216	

Rough Frame / Structure

Wall Framing System		Unit	Material	Labor	Equip.	Total	Specification
Bracing							
1" x 3"							
	Demolish	L.F.		.34		.34	Cost includes material and labor to
	Install	L.F.	.42	2.70		3.12	install 1" x 3" let-in bracing.
	Demolish and Install	L.F.	.42	3.04		3.46	
	Minimum Charge	Job		216		216	
1" x 4"							
	Demolish	L.F.		.34		.34	Cost includes material and labor to
	Install	L.F.	.52	2.70		3.22	install 1" x 4" let-in bracing.
	Demolish and Install	L.F.	.52	3.04		3.56	
	Minimum Charge	Job		216		216	
1" x 6"							
	Demolish	L.F.		.34		.34	Cost includes material and labor to
	Install	L.F.	.88	2.88		3.76	install 1" x 6" let-in bracing.
	Demolish and Install	L.F.	.88	3.22		4.10	
	Minimum Charge	Job		216		216	
2" x 3"							
	Demolish	L.F.		.44		.44	Cost includes material and labor to
	Install	L.F.	.41	2.88		3.29	install 2" x 3" let-in bracing.
	Demolish and Install	L.F.	.41	3.32		3.73	
	Reinstall	L.F.		2.30		2.30	
	Minimum Charge	Job		216		216	
2" x 4"							
	Demolish	L.F.		.44		.44	Cost includes material and labor to
	Install	L.F.	.42	2.88		3.30	install 2" x 4" let-in bracing.
	Demolish and Install	L.F.	.42	3.32		3.74	
	Reinstall	L.F.		2.30		2.30	
	Minimum Charge	Job		216		216	
2" x 6"							
	Demolish	L.F.		.44		.44	Cost includes material and labor to
	Install	L.F.	.63	3.09		3.72	install 2" x 6" let-in bracing.
	Demolish and Install	L.F.	.63	3.53		4.16	
	Reinstall	L.F.		2.47		2.47	
	Minimum Charge	Job		216		216	
2" x 8"							
	Demolish	L.F.		.44		.44	Cost includes material and labor to
	Install	L.F.	.95	3.09		4.04	install 2" x 8" let-in bracing.
	Demolish and Install	L.F.	.95	3.53		4.48	
	Reinstall	L.F.		2.47		2.47	
	Minimum Charge	Job		216		216	
Earthquake Strapping							
	Install	Ea.	3.26	2.70		5.96	Includes labor and material to replace
	Minimum Charge	Job		216		216	an earthquake strap.
Hurricane Clips							
	Install	Ea.	1.22	2.98		4.20	Includes labor and material to install a
	Minimum Charge	Job		216		216	hurricane clip.
Stud							
2" x 4"							
	Demolish	L.F.		.36		.36	Cost includes material and labor to
	Install	L.F.	.41	.79		1.20	install 2" x 4" wall stud per L.F. of stud.
	Demolish and Install	L.F.	.41	1.15		1.56	
	Reinstall	L.F.		.63		.63	
	Minimum Charge	Job		216		216	

Wall Framing System		Unit	Material	Labor	Equip.	Total	Specification
2" x 6"							
	Demolish	L.F.		.44		.44	Cost includes material and labor to
	Install	L.F.	.63	.86		1.49	install 2" x 6" stud per L.F. of stud.
	Demolish and Install	L.F.	.63	1.30		1.93	
	Reinstall	L.F.		.69		.69	
	Minimum Charge	Job		216		216	
Plates							
2" x 4"							
	Demolish	L.F.		.32		.32	Cost includes material and labor to
	Install	L.F.	.42	1.08		1.50	install 2" x 4" plate per L.F. of plate.
	Demolish and Install	L.F.	.42	1.40		1.82	
	Reinstall	L.F.		.86		.86	
	Minimum Charge	Job		216		216	
2" x 6"							
	Demolish	L.F.		.34		.34	Cost includes material and labor to
	Install	L.F.	.63	1.15		1.78	install 2" x 6" plate per L.F. of plate.
	Demolish and Install	L.F.	.63	1.49		2.12	
	Reinstall	L.F.		.92		.92	
	Minimum Charge	Job		216		216	
Headers							
2" x 6"							
	Demolish	L.F.		.32		.32	Includes material and labor to install
	Install	L.F.	.63	2.40		3.03	header over wall openings and
	Demolish and Install	L.F.	.63	2.72		3.35	around floor, ceiling and roof
	Clean	L.F.	.02	.40		.42	openings or flush beam.
	Paint	L.F.	.11	1.48		1.59	
	Minimum Charge	Job		216		216	
2" x 8"							
	Demolish	L.F.		.34		.34	Includes material and labor to install
	Install	L.F.	.95	2.54		3.49	header over wall openings and
	Demolish and Install	L.F.	.95	2.88		3.83	around floor, ceiling and roof
	Clean	L.F.	.02	.41		.43	openings or flush beam.
	Paint	L.F.	.14	2		2.14	
	Minimum Charge	Job		216		216	
2" x 10"							
	Demolish	L.F.		.34		.34	Includes material and labor to install
	Install	L.F.	1.25	2.70		3.95	header over wall openings and
	Demolish and Install	L.F.	1.25	3.04		4.29	around floor, ceiling and roof
	Clean	L.F.	.03	.41		.44	openings or flush beam.
	Paint	L.F.	.19	2.46		2.65	
	Minimum Charge	Job		216		216	
2" x 12"							
	Demolish	L.F.		.36		.36	Includes material and labor to install
	Install	L.F.	1.69	2.88		4.57	header over wall openings and
	Demolish and Install	L.F.	1.69	3.24		4.93	around floor, ceiling and roof
	Clean	L.F.	.04	.41		.45	openings or flush beam.
	Paint	L.F.	.22	2.96		3.18	
	Minimum Charge	Job		216		216	
4" x 8"							
	Demolish	L.F.		.64		.64	Includes material and labor to install
	Install	L.F.	3.84	3.32		7.16	header over wall openings and
	Demolish and Install	L.F.	3.84	3.96		7.80	around floor, ceiling and roof
	Clean	L.F.	.02	.41		.43	openings or flush beam.
	Paint	L.F.	.14	2		2.14	
	Minimum Charge	Job		216		216	

Rough Frame / Structure

Wall Framing System

Wall Framing System	Unit	Material	Labor	Equip.	Total	Specification
4" x 10"						
Demolish	L.F.		.68		.68	Includes material and labor to install
Install	L.F.	4.71	3.60		8.31	header over wall openings and
Demolish and Install	L.F.	4.71	4.28		8.99	around floor, ceiling and roof
Clean	L.F.	.03	.41		.44	openings or flush beam.
Paint	L.F.	.19	2.46		2.65	
Minimum Charge	Job		216		216	
4" x 12"						
Demolish	L.F.		.71		.71	Includes material and labor to install
Install	L.F.	5.65	4.55		10.20	header over wall openings and
Demolish and Install	L.F.	5.65	5.26		10.91	around floor, ceiling and roof
Clean	L.F.	.04	.41		.45	openings or flush beam.
Paint	L.F.	.22	2.96		3.18	
Minimum Charge	Job		216		216	
6" x 8"						
Demolish	L.F.		.64		.64	Includes material and labor to install
Install	L.F.	7	2.40		9.40	header over wall openings and
Demolish and Install	L.F.	7	3.04		10.04	around floor, ceiling and roof
Clean	L.F.	.02	.41		.43	openings or flush beam.
Paint	L.F.	.14	2		2.14	
Minimum Charge	Job		216		216	
6" x 10"						
Demolish	L.F.		.68		.68	Includes material and labor to install
Install	L.F.	8.75	5.25		14	header over wall openings and
Demolish and Install	L.F.	8.75	5.93		14.68	around floor, ceiling and roof
Clean	L.F.	.03	.41		.44	openings or flush beam.
Paint	L.F.	.19	2.46		2.65	
Minimum Charge	Job		216		216	
6" x 12"						
Demolish	L.F.		.71		.71	Includes material and labor to install
Install	L.F.	10.50	6.15		16.65	header over wall openings and
Demolish and Install	L.F.	10.50	6.86		17.36	around floor, ceiling and roof
Clean	L.F.	.04	.41		.45	openings or flush beam.
Paint	L.F.	.22	1.03		1.25	
Minimum Charge	Job		216		216	

Rough-in Opening

Rough-in Opening	Unit	Material	Labor	Equip.	Total	Specification
Door w / 2" x 4" Lumber						
3' Wide						
Demolish	Ea.		11.15		11.15	Includes material and labor to install
Install	Ea.	17.40	13.50		30.90	header, double studs each side,
Demolish and Install	Ea.	17.40	24.65		42.05	cripples, blocking and nails, up to 3'
Reinstall	Ea.		10.80		10.80	opening in 2" x 4" stud wall 8' high.
Minimum Charge	Job		216		216	
4' Wide						
Demolish	Ea.		11.15		11.15	Includes material and labor to install
Install	Ea.	18.65	13.50		32.15	header, double studs each side,
Demolish and Install	Ea.	18.65	24.65		43.30	cripples, blocking and nails, up to 4'
Reinstall	Ea.		10.80		10.80	opening in 2" x 4" stud wall 8' high.
Minimum Charge	Job		216		216	
5' Wide						
Demolish	Ea.		11.15		11.15	Includes material and labor to install
Install	Ea.	23	13.50		36.50	header, double studs each side,
Demolish and Install	Ea.	23	24.65		47.65	cripples, blocking and nails, up to 5'
Reinstall	Ea.		10.80		10.80	opening in 2" x 4" stud wall 8' high.
Minimum Charge	Job		216		216	

Rough Frame / Structure

Rough-in Opening	Unit	Material	Labor	Equip.	Total	Specification
6' Wide						
Demolish	Ea.		11.15		11.15	Includes material and labor to install
Install	Ea.	25.50	13.50		39	header, double studs each side,
Demolish and Install	Ea.	25.50	24.65		50.15	cripples, blocking and nails, up to 6'
Reinstall	Ea.		10.80		10.80	opening in 2" x 4" stud wall 8' high.
Minimum Charge	Job		216		216	
8' Wide						
Demolish	Ea.		11.85		11.85	Includes material and labor to install
Install	Ea.	33.50	14.40		47.90	header, double studs each side,
Demolish and Install	Ea.	33.50	26.25		59.75	cripples, blocking and nails, up to 8'
Reinstall	Ea.		11.52		11.52	opening in 2" x 4" stud wall 8' high.
Minimum Charge	Job		216		216	
10' Wide						
Demolish	Ea.		11.85		11.85	Includes material and labor to install
Install	Ea.	48	14.40		62.40	header, double studs each side,
Demolish and Install	Ea.	48	26.25		74.25	cripples, blocking and nails, up to 10'
Reinstall	Ea.		11.52		11.52	opening in 2" x 4" stud wall 8' high.
Minimum Charge	Job		216		216	
12' Wide						
Demolish	Ea.		11.85		11.85	Includes material and labor to install
Install	Ea.	61.50	14.40		75.90	header, double studs each side,
Demolish and Install	Ea.	61.50	26.25		87.75	cripples, blocking and nails, up to 12'
Reinstall	Ea.		11.52		11.52	opening in 2" x 4" stud wall 8' high.
Minimum Charge	Job		216		216	
Door w / 2" x 6" Lumber						
3' Wide						
Demolish	Ea.		11.15		11.15	Includes material and labor to install
Install	Ea.	24	13.50		37.50	header, double studs each side,
Demolish and Install	Ea.	24	24.65		48.65	cripples, blocking and nails, up to 3'
Reinstall	Ea.		10.80		10.80	opening in 2" x 6" stud wall 8' high.
Minimum Charge	Job		216		216	
4' Wide						
Demolish	Ea.		11.15		11.15	Includes material and labor to install
Install	Ea.	25.50	13.50		39	header, double studs each side,
Demolish and Install	Ea.	25.50	24.65		50.15	cripples, blocking and nails, up to 4'
Reinstall	Ea.		10.80		10.80	opening in 2" x 6" stud wall 8' high.
Minimum Charge	Job		216		216	
5' Wide						
Demolish	Ea.		11.15		11.15	Includes material and labor to install
Install	Ea.	29.50	13.50		43	header, double studs each side,
Demolish and Install	Ea.	29.50	24.65		54.15	cripples, blocking and nails up to 5'
Reinstall	Ea.		10.80		10.80	opening in 2" x 6" stud wall 8' high.
Minimum Charge	Job		216		216	
6' Wide						
Demolish	Ea.		11.15		11.15	Includes material and labor to install
Install	Ea.	32	13.50		45.50	header, double studs each side,
Demolish and Install	Ea.	32	24.65		56.65	cripples, blocking and nails up to 6'
Reinstall	Ea.		10.80		10.80	opening in 2" x 6" stud wall 8' high.
Minimum Charge	Job		216		216	
8' Wide						
Demolish	Ea.		11.85		11.85	Includes material and labor to install
Install	Ea.	40.50	14.40		54.90	header, double studs each side,
Demolish and Install	Ea.	40.50	26.25		66.75	cripples, blocking and nails up to 8'
Reinstall	Ea.		11.52		11.52	opening in 2" x 6" stud wall 8' high.
Minimum Charge	Job		216		216	
10' Wide						
Demolish	Ea.		11.85		11.85	Includes material and labor to install
Install	Ea.	54.50	14.40		68.90	header, double studs each side,
Demolish and Install	Ea.	54.50	26.25		80.75	cripples, blocking and nails up to 10'
Reinstall	Ea.		11.52		11.52	opening in 2" x 6" stud wall 8' high.
Minimum Charge	Job		216		216	

Rough Frame / Structure

Rough-in Opening

Rough-in Opening	Unit	Material	Labor	Equip.	Total	Specification
12′ Wide						
Demolish	Ea.		11.85		11.85	Includes material and labor to install
Install	Ea.	68	14.40		82.40	header, double studs each side,
Demolish and Install	Ea.	68	26.25		94.25	cripples, blocking and nails, up to 12′
Reinstall	Ea.		11.52		11.52	opening in 2″ x 6″ stud wall 8′ high.
Minimum Charge	Job		216		216	

Rough-in Opening

Rough-in Opening	Unit	Material	Labor	Equip.	Total	Specification
Window w / 2″ x 4″ Lumber						
2′ Wide						
Demolish	Ea.		14.85		14.85	Includes material and labor to install
Install	Ea.	18.55	18		36.55	header, double studs each side of
Demolish and Install	Ea.	18.55	32.85		51.40	opening, cripples, blocking, nails and
Reinstall	Ea.		14.40		14.40	sub-sills for opening up to 2′ in a 2″ x
Minimum Charge	Job		216		216	4″ stud wall 8′ high.
3′ Wide						
Demolish	Ea.		14.85		14.85	Includes material and labor to install
Install	Ea.	21.50	18		39.50	header, double studs each side of
Demolish and Install	Ea.	21.50	32.85		54.35	opening, cripples, blocking, nails and
Reinstall	Ea.		14.40		14.40	sub-sills for opening up to 3′ in a 2″ x
Minimum Charge	Job		216		216	4″ stud wall 8′ high.
4′ Wide						
Demolish	Ea.		14.85		14.85	Includes material and labor to install
Install	Ea.	23.50	18		41.50	header, double studs each side of
Demolish and Install	Ea.	23.50	32.85		56.35	opening, cripples, blocking, nails and
Reinstall	Ea.		14.40		14.40	sub-sills for opening up to 4′ in a 2″ x
Minimum Charge	Job		216		216	4″ stud wall 8′ high.
5′ Wide						
Demolish	Ea.		14.85		14.85	Includes material and labor to install
Install	Ea.	28	18		46	header, double studs each side of
Demolish and Install	Ea.	28	32.85		60.85	opening, cripples, blocking, nails and
Reinstall	Ea.		14.40		14.40	sub-sills for opening up to 5′ in a 2″ x
Minimum Charge	Job		216		216	4″ stud wall 8′ high.
6′ Wide						
Demolish	Ea.		14.85		14.85	Includes material and labor to install
Install	Ea.	31.50	18		49.50	header, double studs each side of
Demolish and Install	Ea.	31.50	32.85		64.35	opening, cripples, blocking, nails and
Reinstall	Ea.		14.40		14.40	sub-sills for opening up to 6′ in a 2″ x
Minimum Charge	Job		216		216	4″ stud wall 8′ high.
7′ Wide						
Demolish	Ea.		14.85		14.85	Includes material and labor to install
Install	Ea.	38.50	18		56.50	header, double studs each side of
Demolish and Install	Ea.	38.50	32.85		71.35	opening, cripples, blocking, nails and
Reinstall	Ea.		14.40		14.40	sub-sills for opening up to 7′ in a 2″ x
Minimum Charge	Job		216		216	4″ stud wall 8′ high.
8′ Wide						
Demolish	Ea.		16.20		16.20	Includes material and labor to install
Install	Ea.	42.50	19.65		62.15	header, double studs each side of
Demolish and Install	Ea.	42.50	35.85		78.35	opening, cripples, blocking, nails and
Reinstall	Ea.		15.71		15.71	sub-sills for opening up to 8′ in a 2″ x
Minimum Charge	Job		216		216	4″ stud wall 8′ high.

Rough Frame / Structure

Rough-in Opening	Unit	Material	Labor	Equip.	Total	Specification
10' Wide						
Demolish	Ea.		16.20		16.20	Includes material and labor to install
Install	Ea.	58	19.65		77.65	header, double studs each side of
Demolish and Install	Ea.	58	35.85		93.85	opening, cripples, blocking, nails and
Reinstall	Ea.		15.71		15.71	sub-sills for opening up to 10' in a 2"
Minimum Charge	Job		216		216	x 4" stud wall 8' high.
12' Wide						
Demolish	Ea.		16.20		16.20	Includes material and labor to install
Install	Ea.	73.50	19.65		93.15	header, double studs each side of
Demolish and Install	Ea.	73.50	35.85		109.35	opening, cripples, blocking, nails and
Reinstall	Ea.		15.71		15.71	sub-sills for opening up to 12' in a 2"
Minimum Charge	Job		216		216	x 4" stud wall 8' high.

Window w / 2" x 6" Lumber

Rough-in Opening	Unit	Material	Labor	Equip.	Total	Specification
2' Wide						
Demolish	Ea.		14.85		14.85	Includes material and labor to install
Install	Ea.	27	18		45	header, double studs each side of
Demolish and Install	Ea.	27	32.85		59.85	opening, cripples, blocking, nails and
Reinstall	Ea.		14.40		14.40	sub-sills for opening up to 2' in a 2" x
Minimum Charge	Job		216		216	6" stud wall 8' high.
3' Wide						
Demolish	Ea.		14.85		14.85	Includes material and labor to install
Install	Ea.	29.50	18		47.50	header, double studs each side of
Demolish and Install	Ea.	29.50	32.85		62.35	opening, cripples, blocking, nails and
Reinstall	Ea.		14.40		14.40	sub-sills for opening up to 3' in a 2" x
Minimum Charge	Job		216		216	6" stud wall 8' high.
4' Wide						
Demolish	Ea.		14.85		14.85	Includes material and labor to install
Install	Ea.	32.50	18		50.50	header, double studs each side of
Demolish and Install	Ea.	32.50	32.85		65.35	opening, cripples, blocking, nails and
Reinstall	Ea.		14.40		14.40	sub-sills for opening up to 4' in a 2" x
Minimum Charge	Job		216		216	6" stud wall 8' high.
5' Wide						
Demolish	Ea.		14.85		14.85	Includes material and labor to install
Install	Ea.	37.50	18		55.50	header, double studs each side of
Demolish and Install	Ea.	37.50	32.85		70.35	opening, cripples, blocking, nails and
Reinstall	Ea.		14.40		14.40	sub-sills for opening up to 5' in a 2" x
Minimum Charge	Job		216		216	6" stud wall 8' high.
6' Wide						
Demolish	Ea.		14.85		14.85	Includes material and labor to install
Install	Ea.	41.50	18		59.50	header, double studs each side of
Demolish and Install	Ea.	41.50	32.85		74.35	opening, cripples, blocking, nails and
Reinstall	Ea.		14.40		14.40	sub-sills for opening up to 6' in a 2" x
Minimum Charge	Job		216		216	6" stud wall 8' high.
7' Wide						
Demolish	Ea.		14.85		14.85	Includes material and labor to install
Install	Ea.	49.50	18		67.50	header, double studs each side of
Demolish and Install	Ea.	49.50	32.85		82.35	opening, cripples, blocking, nails and
Reinstall	Ea.		14.40		14.40	sub-sills for opening up to 7' in a 2" x
Minimum Charge	Job		216		216	6" stud wall 8' high.

Rough Frame / Structure

Rough-in Opening

	Unit	Material	Labor	Equip.	Total	Specification
8' Wide						
Demolish	Ea.		16.20		16.20	Includes material and labor to install
Install	Ea.	54	19.65		73.65	header, double studs each side of
Demolish and Install	Ea.	54	35.85		89.85	opening, cripples, blocking, nails and
Reinstall	Ea.		15.71		15.71	sub-sills for opening up to 8' in a 2" x
Minimum Charge	Job		216		216	6" stud wall 8' high.
10' Wide						
Demolish	Ea.		16.20		16.20	Includes material and labor to install
Install	Ea.	70	19.65		89.65	header, double studs each side of
Demolish and Install	Ea.	70	35.85		105.85	opening, cripples, blocking, nails and
Reinstall	Ea.		15.71		15.71	sub-sills for opening up to 10' in a 2"
Minimum Charge	Job		216		216	x 6" stud wall 8' high.
12' Wide						
Demolish	Ea.		16.20		16.20	Includes material and labor to install
Install	Ea.	87	19.65		106.65	header, double studs each side of
Demolish and Install	Ea.	87	35.85		122.85	opening, cripples, blocking, nails and
Reinstall	Ea.		15.71		15.71	sub-sills for opening up to 12' in a 2"
Minimum Charge	Job		216		216	x 6" stud wall 8' high.

Glue-Laminated Beams

	Unit	Material	Labor	Equip.	Total	Specification
3-1/2" x 6"						
Demolish	L.F.		2.66		2.66	Includes material and labor to install
Install	L.F.	5.45	3.28	1.22	9.95	glue-laminated wood beam.
Demolish and Install	L.F.	5.45	5.94	1.22	12.61	
Reinstall	L.F.		2.62	.97	3.59	
Clean	L.F.	.13	.40		.53	
Paint	L.F.	.37	1.09		1.46	
Minimum Charge	Job		216		216	
3-1/2" x 9"						
Demolish	L.F.		2.66		2.66	Includes material and labor to install
Install	L.F.	7.30	3.28	1.22	11.80	glue-laminated wood beam.
Demolish and Install	L.F.	7.30	5.94	1.22	14.46	
Reinstall	L.F.		2.62	.97	3.59	
Clean	L.F.	.18	.41		.59	
Paint	L.F.	.48	1.41		1.89	
Minimum Charge	Job		216		216	
3-1/2" x 12"						
Demolish	L.F.		3.99		3.99	Includes material and labor to install
Install	L.F.	9.75	3.28	1.22	14.25	glue-laminated wood beam.
Demolish and Install	L.F.	9.75	7.27	1.22	18.24	
Reinstall	L.F.		2.62	.97	3.59	
Clean	L.F.	.21	.43		.64	
Paint	L.F.	.61	1.76		2.37	
Minimum Charge	Job		216		216	
3-1/2" x 15"						
Demolish	L.F.		3.99		3.99	Includes material and labor to install
Install	L.F.	12.15	3.39	1.26	16.80	glue-laminated wood beam.
Demolish and Install	L.F.	12.15	7.38	1.26	20.79	
Reinstall	L.F.		2.71	1.01	3.72	
Clean	L.F.	.25	.44		.69	
Paint	L.F.	.70	2.05		2.75	
Minimum Charge	Job		216		216	

Glue-Laminated Beams		Unit	Material	Labor	Equip.	Total	Specification
3-1/2″ x 18″							
	Demolish	L.F.		4.99		4.99	Includes material and labor to install
	Install	L.F.	16.35	3.39	1.26	21	glue-laminated wood beam.
	Demolish and Install	L.F.	16.35	8.38	1.26	25.99	
	Reinstall	L.F.		2.71	1.01	3.72	
	Clean	L.F.	.30	.46		.76	
	Paint	L.F.	.83	2.38		3.21	
	Minimum Charge	Job		216		216	
5-1/8″ x 6″							
	Demolish	L.F.		3.99		3.99	Includes material and labor to install
	Install	L.F.	8	3.28	1.22	12.50	glue-laminated wood beam.
	Demolish and Install	L.F.	8	7.27	1.22	16.49	
	Reinstall	L.F.		2.62	.97	3.59	
	Clean	L.F.	.14	.40		.54	
	Paint	L.F.	.41	1.19		1.60	
	Minimum Charge	Job		216		216	
5-1/8″ x 9″							
	Demolish	L.F.		4.99		4.99	Includes material and labor to install
	Install	L.F.	12	3.28	1.22	16.50	glue-laminated wood beam.
	Demolish and Install	L.F.	12	8.27	1.22	21.49	
	Reinstall	L.F.		2.62	.97	3.59	
	Clean	L.F.	.19	.41		.60	
	Paint	L.F.	.53	1.53		2.06	
	Minimum Charge	Job		216		216	
5-1/8″ x 12″							
	Demolish	L.F.		5.95		5.95	Includes material and labor to install
	Install	L.F.	15.95	3.28	1.22	20.45	glue-laminated wood beam.
	Demolish and Install	L.F.	15.95	9.23	1.22	26.40	
	Reinstall	L.F.		2.62	.97	3.59	
	Clean	L.F.	.23	.43		.66	
	Paint	L.F.	.64	1.85		2.49	
	Minimum Charge	Job		216		216	
5-1/8″ x 18″							
	Demolish	L.F.		10		10	Includes material and labor to install
	Install	L.F.	24	3.39	1.26	28.65	glue-laminated wood beam.
	Demolish and Install	L.F.	24	13.39	1.26	38.65	
	Reinstall	L.F.		2.71	1.01	3.72	
	Clean	L.F.	.31	.46		.77	
	Paint	L.F.	.75	2.50		3.25	
	Minimum Charge	Job		216		216	
6-3/4″ x 12″							
	Demolish	L.F.		5.95		5.95	Includes material and labor to install
	Install	L.F.	21	3.39	1.26	25.65	glue-laminated wood beam.
	Demolish and Install	L.F.	21	9.34	1.26	31.60	
	Reinstall	L.F.		2.71	1.01	3.72	
	Clean	L.F.	.25	.44		.69	
	Paint	L.F.	.70	2.05		2.75	
	Minimum Charge	Job		216		216	
6-3/4″ x 15″							
	Demolish	L.F.		10		10	Includes material and labor to install
	Install	L.F.	26.50	3.39	1.26	31.15	glue-laminated wood beam.
	Demolish and Install	L.F.	26.50	13.39	1.26	41.15	
	Reinstall	L.F.		2.71	1.01	3.72	
	Clean	L.F.	.30	.46		.76	
	Paint	L.F.	.83	2.38		3.21	
	Minimum Charge	Job		216		216	

Rough Frame / Structure

Glue-Laminated Beams

Glue-Laminated Beams	Unit	Material	Labor	Equip.	Total	Specification
6-3/4" x 18"						
Demolish	L.F.		10		10	Includes material and labor to install
Install	L.F.	31.50	3.51	1.30	36.31	glue-laminated wood beam.
Demolish and Install	L.F.	31.50	13.51	1.30	46.31	
Reinstall	L.F.		2.81	1.04	3.85	
Clean	L.F.	.34	.47		.81	
Paint	L.F.	.95	2.72		3.67	
Minimum Charge	Job		216		216	
Hardware						
5-1/4" Glue-Lam Seat						
Install	Ea.	230	2.40		232.40	Includes labor and material to install
Minimum Charge	Job		216		216	beam hangers.
6-3/4" Glue-Lam Seat						
Install	Ea.	235	2.40		237.40	Includes labor and material to install
Minimum Charge	Job		216		216	beam hangers.
Earthquake Strapping						
Install	Ea.	3.26	2.70		5.96	Includes labor and material to replace
Minimum Charge	Job		216		216	an earthquake strap.
Hurricane Clips						
Install	Ea.	1.22	2.98		4.20	Includes labor and material to install a
Minimum Charge	Job		216		216	hurricane clip.

Metal Stud Framing

Metal Stud Framing	Unit	Material	Labor	Equip.	Total	Specification
16" O.C. System						
4", 16 Ga.						
Demolish	S.F.		1.31		1.31	Includes material and labor to install
Install	S.F.	1.32	1.33		2.65	load bearing cold rolled metal stud
Demolish and Install	S.F.	1.32	2.64		3.96	walls, to 10' high, including studs, top
Reinstall	S.F.		1.06		1.06	and bottom track and screws.
Minimum Charge	Job		216		216	
6", 16 Ga.						
Demolish	S.F.		1.31		1.31	Includes material and labor to install
Install	S.F.	1.65	1.35		3	load bearing cold rolled metal stud
Demolish and Install	S.F.	1.65	2.66		4.31	walls, to 10' high, including studs, top
Reinstall	S.F.		1.08		1.08	and bottom track and screws.
Minimum Charge	Job		216		216	
4", 25 Ga.						
Demolish	S.F.		.91		.91	Includes material and labor to install
Install	S.F.	.44	.91		1.35	cold rolled metal stud walls, to 10'
Demolish and Install	S.F.	.44	1.82		2.26	high, including studs, top and bottom
Reinstall	S.F.		.73		.73	track and screws.
Minimum Charge	Job		216		216	
6", 25 Ga.						
Demolish	S.F.		.91		.91	Includes material and labor to install
Install	S.F.	.55	.92		1.47	cold rolled metal stud walls, to 10'
Demolish and Install	S.F.	.55	1.83		2.38	high, including studs, top and bottom
Reinstall	S.F.		.74		.74	track and screws.
Minimum Charge	Job		216		216	
24" O.C. System						
4", 25 Ga.						
Demolish	S.F.		.77		.77	Includes material and labor to install
Install	S.F.	.33	.58		.91	cold rolled metal stud walls, to 10'
Demolish and Install	S.F.	.33	1.35		1.68	high, including studs, top and bottom
Reinstall	S.F.		.47		.47	track and screws.
Minimum Charge	Job		216		216	

Rough Frame / Structure

Metal Stud Framing

	Unit	Material	Labor	Equip.	Total	Specification
6", 25 Ga.						Includes material and labor to install
Demolish	S.F.		.77		.77	cold rolled metal stud walls, to 10'
Install	S.F.	.41	.60		1.01	high, including studs, top and bottom
Demolish and Install	S.F.	.41	1.37		1.78	track and screws.
Reinstall	S.F.		.48		.48	
Minimum Charge	Job		216		216	
4", 16 Ga.						Includes material and labor to install
Demolish	L.F.		8.80		8.80	load bearing cold rolled metal stud
Install	S.F.	.96	.96		1.92	walls, to 10' high, including studs, top
Demolish and Install	S.F.	.96	9.76		10.72	and bottom track and screws.
Reinstall	S.F.		.77		.77	
Minimum Charge	Job		216		216	
6", 16 Ga.						Includes material and labor to install
Demolish	L.F.		8.80		8.80	load bearing cold rolled metal stud
Install	S.F.	1.20	.98		2.18	walls, to 10' high, including studs, top
Demolish and Install	S.F.	1.20	9.78		10.98	and bottom track and screws.
Reinstall	S.F.		.79		.79	
Minimum Charge	Job		216		216	

Metal Joist

	Unit	Material	Labor	Equip.	Total	Specification
Bar Joist						
18K9						Includes material, labor and
Demolish	L.F.		1.05	.41	1.46	equipment to install open web joist.
Install	L.F.	9.30	2.33	1	12.63	
Demolish and Install	L.F.	9.30	3.38	1.41	14.09	
Reinstall	L.F.		1.87	.80	2.67	
Minimum Charge	Job		1975	730	2705	
16K6						Includes material, labor and
Demolish	L.F.		1.05	.41	1.46	equipment to install open web joist.
Install	L.F.	5.10	1.57	.12	6.79	
Demolish and Install	L.F.	5.10	2.62	.53	8.25	
Reinstall	L.F.		1.26	.09	1.35	
Minimum Charge	Job		1975	730	2705	

Exterior Sheathing

	Unit	Material	Labor	Equip.	Total	Specification
CDX Plywood						
5/16"						Cost includes material and labor to
Demolish	S.F.		.61		.61	install 5/16" CDX plywood sheathing.
Install	S.F.	.61	.54		1.15	
Demolish and Install	S.F.	.61	1.15		1.76	
Minimum Charge	Job		216		216	
3/8"						Cost includes material and labor to
Demolish	S.F.		.62		.62	install 3/8" CDX plywood sheathing.
Install	S.F.	.55	.72		1.27	
Demolish and Install	S.F.	.55	1.34		1.89	
Minimum Charge	Job		216		216	
1/2"						Cost includes material and labor to
Demolish	S.F.		.63		.63	install 1/2" CDX plywood sheathing.
Install	S.F.	.66	.77		1.43	
Demolish and Install	S.F.	.66	1.40		2.06	
Minimum Charge	Job		216		216	

Rough Frame / Structure

Exterior Sheathing

Exterior Sheathing	Unit	Material	Labor	Equip.	Total	Specification
5/8″						
Demolish	S.F.		.65		.65	Cost includes material and labor to
Install	S.F.	.81	.82		1.63	install 5/8″ CDX plywood sheathing.
Demolish and Install	S.F.	.81	1.47		2.28	
Minimum Charge	Job		216		216	
3/4″						
Demolish	S.F.		.66		.66	Cost includes material and labor to
Install	S.F.	.97	.89		1.86	install 3/4″ CDX plywood sheathing.
Demolish and Install	S.F.	.97	1.55		2.52	
Minimum Charge	Job		216		216	
OSB						
1/2″						
Demolish	S.F.		.63		.63	Cost includes material and labor to
Install	S.F.	.55	.62		1.17	install 4′ x 8′ x 1/2″ OSB sheathing.
Demolish and Install	S.F.	.55	1.25		1.80	
Minimum Charge	Job		216		216	
5/8″						
Demolish	S.F.		.65		.65	Cost includes material and labor to
Install	S.F.	.55	.50		1.05	install 4′ x 8′ x 5/8″ OSB sheathing.
Demolish and Install	S.F.	.55	1.15		1.70	
Minimum Charge	Job		216		216	
Vapor Barrier						
Black Paper						
Install	S.F.	.06	.12		.18	Includes material and labor to install
Minimum Charge	Job		216		216	#15 felt building paper.

Plywood Sheathing

Plywood Sheathing	Unit	Material	Labor	Equip.	Total	Specification
Finish Plywood						
5/16″						
Demolish	S.F.		.61		.61	Includes material and labor to install
Install	S.F.	1.02	.27		1.29	exterior 5/16″ AC plywood on walls.
Demolish and Install	S.F.	1.02	.88		1.90	
Minimum Charge	Job		216		216	
3/8″						
Demolish	S.F.		.62		.62	Includes material and labor to install
Install	S.F.	1.02	.36		1.38	exterior 3/8″ AC plywood on walls.
Demolish and Install	S.F.	1.02	.98		2	
Minimum Charge	Job		216		216	
1/2″						
Demolish	S.F.		.63		.63	Includes material and labor to install
Install	S.F.	1.17	.38		1.55	exterior 1/2″ AC plywood on walls.
Demolish and Install	S.F.	1.17	1.01		2.18	
Minimum Charge	Job		216		216	
5/8″						
Demolish	S.F.		.65		.65	Includes material and labor to install
Install	S.F.	1.30	.38		1.68	exterior 5/8″ AC plywood on walls.
Demolish and Install	S.F.	1.30	1.03		2.33	
Reinstall	S.F.		.38		.38	
Minimum Charge	Job		216		216	
3/4″						
Demolish	S.F.		.66		.66	Includes material and labor to install
Install	S.F.	1.54	.38		1.92	exterior 3/4″ AC plywood on walls.
Demolish and Install	S.F.	1.54	1.04		2.58	
Reinstall	S.F.		.38		.38	
Minimum Charge	Job		216		216	

Rough Frame / Structure

Stairs

Stairs	Unit	Material	Labor	Equip.	Total	Specification
Job-built						
Treads and Risers						
Demolish	Ea.		44.50		44.50	Includes material and labor to install
Install	Ea.	615	430		1045	three 2″ x 12″ stringers, treads and
Demolish and Install	Ea.	615	474.50		1089.50	risers of 3/4″ CDX plywood, installed
Clean	Flight	4.03	27.50		31.53	in a straight or "L" shaped run
Paint	Ea.	.11	74		74.11	including carpet.
Minimum Charge	Job		216		216	
Landing						
Demolish	S.F.		.36		.36	Includes material and labor to install
Install	S.F.	75	3		78	landing framing, 3/4″ CDX plywood
Demolish and Install	S.F.	75	3.36		78.36	surface and carpet.
Clean	S.F.		.40		.40	
Paint	S.F.	.44	.91		1.35	
Minimum Charge	Job		216		216	

Ceiling Framing

Ceiling Framing	Unit	Material	Labor	Equip.	Total	Specification
16″ O.C. System						
2″ x 6″ Joists						
Demolish	S.F.		.55		.55	Cost includes material and labor to
Install	S.F.	.47	.71		1.18	install 2″ x 6″ joists including end and
Demolish and Install	S.F.	.47	1.26		1.73	header joist installed 16″ O.C. Does
Reinstall	S.F.		.57		.57	not include beams, ledger strips,
Minimum Charge	Job		216		216	blocking or bridging.
2″ x 8″ Joists						
Demolish	S.F.		.57		.57	Cost includes material and labor to
Install	S.F.	.72	.87		1.59	install 2″ x 8″ joists including end and
Demolish and Install	S.F.	.72	1.44		2.16	header joist installed 16″ O.C. Does
Reinstall	S.F.		.70		.70	not include beams, ledger strips,
Minimum Charge	Job		216		216	blocking or bridging.
2″ x 10″ Joists						
Demolish	S.F.		.59		.59	Cost includes material and labor to
Install	S.F.	.95	1.03		1.98	install 2″ x 10″ joists including end
Demolish and Install	S.F.	.95	1.62		2.57	and header joist installed 16″ O.C.
Reinstall	S.F.		.83		.83	Does not include beams, ledger strips,
Minimum Charge	Job		216		216	blocking or bridging.
2″ x 12″ Joists						
Demolish	S.F.		.61		.61	Cost includes material and labor to
Install	S.F.	1.29	1.26		2.55	install 2″ x 12″ joists including end
Demolish and Install	S.F.	1.29	1.87		3.16	and header joist installed 16″ O.C.
Reinstall	S.F.		1.01		1.01	Does not include beams, ledger strips,
Minimum Charge	Job		216		216	blocking or bridging.
Block / Bridge						
Demolish	Ea.		1.11		1.11	Includes material and labor to install
Install	Ea.	1.67	2.43		4.10	set of cross bridging or per block of
Demolish and Install	Ea.	1.67	3.54		5.21	solid bridging for 2″ x 10″ joists cut to
Minimum Charge	Job		216		216	size on site.

Rough Frame / Structure

Ceiling Framing		Unit	Material	Labor	Equip.	Total	Specification
24″ O.C. System							
2″ x 6″ Joists							
	Demolish	S.F.		.37		.37	Cost includes material and labor to
	Install	S.F.	.32	.47		.79	install 2″ x 6″ joists including end and
	Demolish and Install	S.F.	.32	.84		1.16	header joist installed 24″ O.C. Does
	Reinstall	S.F.		.38		.38	not include beams, ledger strips,
	Minimum Charge	Job		216		216	blocking or bridging.
2″ x 8″ Joists							
	Demolish	S.F.		.38		.38	Cost includes material and labor to
	Install	S.F.	.48	.58		1.06	install 2″ x 8″ joists including end and
	Demolish and Install	S.F.	.48	.96		1.44	header joist installed 24″ O.C. Does
	Reinstall	S.F.		.47		.47	not include beams, ledger strips,
	Minimum Charge	Job		216		216	blocking or bridging.
2″ x 10″ Joists							
	Demolish	S.F.		.39		.39	Cost includes material and labor to
	Install	S.F.	.64	.69		1.33	install 2″ x 10″ joists including end
	Demolish and Install	S.F.	.64	1.08		1.72	and header joist installed 24″ O.C.
	Reinstall	S.F.		.55		.55	Does not include beams, ledger strips,
	Minimum Charge	Job		216		216	blocking or bridging.
2″ x 12″ Joists							
	Demolish	S.F.		.40		.40	Cost includes material and labor to
	Install	S.F.	.87	.84		1.71	install 2″ x 12″ joists including end
	Demolish and Install	S.F.	.87	1.24		2.11	and header joist installed 24″ O.C.
	Reinstall	S.F.		.67		.67	Does not include beams, ledger strips,
	Minimum Charge	Job		216		216	blocking or bridging.
Block / Bridge							
	Demolish	Ea.		1.11		1.11	Includes material and labor to install
	Install	Ea.	1.67	2.43		4.10	set of cross bridging or per block of
	Demolish and Install	Ea.	1.67	3.54		5.21	solid bridging for 2″ x 10″ joists cut to
	Minimum Charge	Job		216		216	size on site.
Ledger Strips							
1″ x 2″							
	Demolish	L.F.		.30		.30	Cost includes material and labor to
	Install	L.F.	.26	1.25		1.51	install 1″ x 2″ ledger strip nailed to the
	Demolish and Install	L.F.	.26	1.55		1.81	face of studs, beams or joist.
	Minimum Charge	Job		216		216	
1″ x 3″							
	Demolish	L.F.		.30		.30	Includes material and labor to install
	Install	L.F.	.52	1.44		1.96	up to 1″ x 4″ ledger strip nailed to the
	Demolish and Install	L.F.	.52	1.74		2.26	face of studs, beams or joist.
	Minimum Charge	Job		216		216	
1″ x 4″							
	Demolish	L.F.		.30		.30	Includes material and labor to install
	Install	L.F.	.52	1.44		1.96	up to 1″ x 4″ ledger strip nailed to the
	Demolish and Install	L.F.	.52	1.74		2.26	face of studs, beams or joist.
	Minimum Charge	Job		216		216	
2″ x 2″							
	Demolish	L.F.		.32		.32	Cost includes material and labor to
	Install	L.F.	.41	1.31		1.72	install 2″ x 2″ ledger strip nailed to the
	Demolish and Install	L.F.	.41	1.63		2.04	face of studs, beams or joist.
	Minimum Charge	Job		216		216	
2″ x 4″							
	Demolish	L.F.		.36		.36	Cost includes material and labor to
	Install	L.F.	.42	1.73		2.15	install 2″ x 4″ ledger strip nailed to the
	Demolish and Install	L.F.	.42	2.09		2.51	face of studs, beams or joist.
	Reinstall	L.F.		1.38		1.38	
	Minimum Charge	Job		216		216	

Rough Frame / Structure

Ceiling Framing

Ceiling Framing	Unit	Material	Labor	Equip.	Total	Specification
Ledger Boards						
2" x 4"						
Demolish	L.F.		.36		.36	Cost includes material and labor to
Install	L.F.	4.75	2.40		7.15	install 2" x 4" ledger board fastened to
Demolish and Install	L.F.	4.75	2.76		7.51	a wall, joists or studs.
Reinstall	L.F.		1.92		1.92	
Minimum Charge	Job		216		216	
4" x 6"						
Demolish	L.F.		.59		.59	Cost includes material and labor to
Install	L.F.	8.25	3.09		11.34	install 4" x 6" ledger board fastened to
Demolish and Install	L.F.	8.25	3.68		11.93	a wall, joists or studs.
Reinstall	L.F.		2.47		2.47	
Minimum Charge	Job		216		216	
4" x 8"						
Demolish	L.F.		.79		.79	Cost includes material and labor to
Install	L.F.	9.25	3.60		12.85	install 4" x 8" ledger board fastened to
Demolish and Install	L.F.	9.25	4.39		13.64	a wall, joists or studs.
Reinstall	L.F.		2.88		2.88	
Minimum Charge	Job		216		216	
Earthquake Strapping						
Install	Ea.	3.26	2.70		5.96	Includes labor and material to replace
Minimum Charge	Job		216		216	an earthquake strap.
Hurricane Clips						
Install	Ea.	1.22	2.98		4.20	Includes labor and material to install a
Minimum Charge	Job		216		216	hurricane clip.

Roof Framing

Roof Framing	Unit	Material	Labor	Equip.	Total	Specification
16" O.C. System						
2" x 4" Rafters						
Demolish	S.F.		.81		.81	Cost includes material and labor to
Install	S.F.	.31	.77		1.08	install 2" x 4", 16" O.C. rafter framing
Demolish and Install	S.F.	.31	1.58		1.89	for flat, shed or gable roofs, 25' span,
Reinstall	S.F.		.62		.62	up to 5/12 slope, per S.F. of roof.
Minimum Charge	Job		216		216	
2" x 6" Rafters						
Demolish	S.F.		.85		.85	Cost includes material and labor to
Install	S.F.	.47	.81		1.28	install 2" x 6", 16" O.C. rafter framing
Demolish and Install	S.F.	.47	1.66		2.13	for flat, shed or gable roofs, 25' span,
Reinstall	S.F.		.65		.65	up to 5/12 slope, per S.F. of roof.
Minimum Charge	Job		216		216	
2" x 8" Rafters						
Demolish	S.F.		.87		.87	Cost includes material and labor to
Install	S.F.	.70	.86		1.56	install 2" x 8", 16" O.C. rafter framing
Demolish and Install	S.F.	.70	1.73		2.43	for flat, shed or gable roofs, 25' span,
Reinstall	S.F.		.69		.69	up to 5/12 slope, per S.F. of roof.
Minimum Charge	Job		216		216	
2" x 10" Rafters						
Demolish	S.F.		.87		.87	Cost includes material and labor to
Install	S.F.	.94	1.31		2.25	install 2" x 10", 16" O.C. rafter
Demolish and Install	S.F.	.94	2.18		3.12	framing for flat, shed or gable roofs,
Reinstall	S.F.		1.05		1.05	25' span, up to 5/12 slope, per S.F.
Minimum Charge	Job		216		216	of roof.

Rough Frame / Structure

Roof Framing

Roof Framing		Unit	Material	Labor	Equip.	Total	Specification
2" x 12" Rafters							
	Demolish	S.F.		.88		.88	Cost includes material and labor to
	Install	S.F.	1.28	1.42		2.70	install 2" x 12", 16" O.C. rafter
	Demolish and Install	S.F.	1.28	2.30		3.58	framing for flat, shed or gable roofs,
	Reinstall	S.F.		1.14		1.14	25' span, up to 5/12 slope, per S.F.
	Minimum Charge	Job		216		216	of roof.
24" O.C. System							
2" x 4" Rafters							
	Demolish	S.F.		.61		.61	Cost includes material and labor to
	Install	S.F.	.21	.58		.79	install 2" x 4", 24" O.C. rafter framing
	Demolish and Install	S.F.	.21	1.19		1.40	for flat, shed or gable roofs, 25' span,
	Reinstall	S.F.		.46		.46	up to 5/12 slope, per S.F. of roof.
	Minimum Charge	Job		216		216	
2" x 6" Rafters							
	Demolish	S.F.		.64		.64	Cost includes material and labor to
	Install	S.F.	.31	.61		.92	install 2" x 6", 24" O.C. rafter framing
	Demolish and Install	S.F.	.31	1.25		1.56	for flat, shed or gable roofs, 25' span,
	Reinstall	S.F.		.49		.49	up to 5/12 slope, per S.F. of roof.
	Minimum Charge	Job		216		216	
2" x 8" Rafters							
	Demolish	S.F.		.65		.65	Cost includes material and labor to
	Install	S.F.	.47	.65		1.12	install 2" x 8", 24" O.C. rafter framing
	Demolish and Install	S.F.	.47	1.30		1.77	for flat, shed or gable roofs, 25' span,
	Reinstall	S.F.		.52		.52	up to 5/12 slope, per S.F. of roof.
	Minimum Charge	Job		216		216	
2" x 10" Rafters							
	Demolish	S.F.		.65		.65	Cost includes material and labor to
	Install	S.F.	.63	.98		1.61	install 2" x 10", 24" O.C. rafter
	Demolish and Install	S.F.	.63	1.63		2.26	framing for flat, shed or gable roofs,
	Reinstall	S.F.		.79		.79	25' span, up to 5/12 slope, per S.F.
	Minimum Charge	Job		216		216	of roof.
2" x 12" Rafters							
	Demolish	S.F.		.66		.66	Cost includes material and labor to
	Install	S.F.	.85	1.07		1.92	install 2" x 12", 24" O.C. rafter
	Demolish and Install	S.F.	.85	1.73		2.58	framing for flat, shed or gable roofs,
	Reinstall	S.F.		.86		.86	25' span, up to 5/12 slope, per S.F.
	Minimum Charge	Job		216		216	of roof.
Rafter							
2" x 4"							
	Demolish	L.F.		.83		.83	Cost includes material and labor to
	Install	L.F.	.42	1.08		1.50	install 2" x 4" rafters for flat, shed or
	Demolish and Install	L.F.	.42	1.91		2.33	gable roofs, up to 5/12 slope, 25'
	Reinstall	L.F.		.86		.86	span, per L.F.
	Minimum Charge	Job		216		216	
2" x 6"							
	Demolish	L.F.		.84		.84	Cost includes material and labor to
	Install	L.F.	.63	1.08		1.71	install 2" x 6" rafters for flat, shed or
	Demolish and Install	L.F.	.63	1.92		2.55	gable roofs, up to 5/12 slope, 25'
	Reinstall	L.F.		.86		.86	span, per L.F.
	Minimum Charge	Job		216		216	
2" x 8"							
	Demolish	L.F.		.85		.85	Cost includes material and labor to
	Install	L.F.	.95	1.15		2.10	install 2" x 8" rafters for flat, shed or
	Demolish and Install	L.F.	.95	2		2.95	gable roofs, up to 5/12 slope, 25'
	Reinstall	L.F.		.92		.92	span, per L.F.
	Minimum Charge	Job		216		216	

Rough Frame / Structure

Roof Framing		Unit	Material	Labor	Equip.	Total	Specification
2″ x 10″							
	Demolish	L.F.		.86		.86	Cost includes material and labor to
	Install	L.F.	1.25	1.75		3	install 2″ x 10″ rafters for flat, shed or
	Demolish and Install	L.F.	1.25	2.61		3.86	gable roofs, up to 5/12 slope, 25′
	Reinstall	L.F.		1.40		1.40	span, per L.F.
	Minimum Charge	Job		216		216	
2″ x 12″							
	Demolish	L.F.		.88		.88	Cost includes material and labor to
	Install	L.F.	1.69	1.90		3.59	install 2″ x 12″ rafters for flat, shed or
	Demolish and Install	L.F.	1.69	2.78		4.47	gable roofs, up to 5/12 slope, 25′
	Reinstall	L.F.		1.52		1.52	span, per L.F.
	Minimum Charge	Job		216		216	
2″x 4″ Valley / Jack							
	Demolish	L.F.		.83		.83	Includes material and labor to install
	Install	L.F.	.63	1.82		2.45	up to 2″ x 6″ valley/jack rafters for
	Demolish and Install	L.F.	.63	2.65		3.28	flat, shed or gable roofs, up to 5/12
	Reinstall	L.F.		1.46		1.46	slope, 25′ span, per L.F.
	Minimum Charge	Job		216		216	
2″x 6″ Valley / Jack							
	Demolish	L.F.		.84		.84	Includes material and labor to install
	Install	L.F.	.63	1.82		2.45	up to 2″ x 6″ valley/jack rafters for
	Demolish and Install	L.F.	.63	2.66		3.29	flat, shed or gable roofs, up to 5/12
	Reinstall	L.F.		1.46		1.46	slope, 25′ span, per L.F.
	Minimum Charge	Job		216		216	
Ridgeboard							
2″ x 4″							
	Demolish	L.F.		.79		.79	Cost includes material and labor to
	Install	L.F.	.42	1.57		1.99	install 2″ x 4″ ridgeboard for flat, shed
	Demolish and Install	L.F.	.42	2.36		2.78	or gable roofs, up to 5/12 slope, 25′
	Reinstall	L.F.		1.26		1.26	span, per L.F.
	Minimum Charge	Job		216		216	
2″ x 6″							
	Demolish	L.F.		.81		.81	Cost includes material and labor to
	Install	L.F.	.63	1.73		2.36	install 2″ x 6″ ridgeboard for flat, shed
	Demolish and Install	L.F.	.63	2.54		3.17	or gable roofs, up to 5/12 slope, 25′
	Reinstall	L.F.		1.38		1.38	span, per L.F.
	Minimum Charge	Job		216		216	
2″ x 8″							
	Demolish	L.F.		.84		.84	Cost includes material and labor to
	Install	L.F.	.95	1.92		2.87	install 2″ x 8″ ridgeboard for flat, shed
	Demolish and Install	L.F.	.95	2.76		3.71	or gable roofs, up to 5/12 slope, 25′
	Reinstall	L.F.		1.54		1.54	span, per L.F.
	Minimum Charge	Job		216		216	
2″ x 10″							
	Demolish	L.F.		.86		.86	Cost includes material and labor to
	Install	L.F.	1.25	2.16		3.41	install 2″ x 10″ ridgeboard for flat,
	Demolish and Install	L.F.	1.25	3.02		4.27	shed or gable roofs, up to 5/12
	Reinstall	L.F.		1.73		1.73	slope, 25′ span, per L.F.
	Minimum Charge	Job		216		216	
2″ x 12″							
	Demolish	L.F.		.89		.89	Cost includes material and labor to
	Install	L.F.	1.69	1.23		2.92	install 2″ x 12″ ridgeboard for flat,
	Demolish and Install	L.F.	1.69	2.12		3.81	shed or gable roofs, up to 5/12
	Reinstall	L.F.		.99		.99	slope, 25′ span, per L.F.
	Minimum Charge	Job		216		216	

Roof Framing	Unit	Material	Labor	Equip.	Total	Specification
Collar Beam						
1" x 6"						
Demolish	L.F.		.63		.63	Cost includes material and labor to
Install	L.F.	.88	.54		1.42	install 1" x 6" collar beam or tie for
Demolish and Install	L.F.	.88	1.17		2.05	roof framing.
Reinstall	L.F.		.43		.43	
Minimum Charge	Job		216		216	
2" x 6"						
Demolish	L.F.		.73		.73	Cost includes material and labor to
Install	L.F.	.63	.54		1.17	install 2" x 6" collar beam or tie for
Demolish and Install	L.F.	.63	1.27		1.90	roof framing.
Reinstall	L.F.		.43		.43	
Minimum Charge	Job		216		216	
Purlins						
2" x 6"						
Demolish	L.F.		.71		.71	Cost includes material and labor to
Install	L.F.	.63	.48		1.11	install 2" x 6" purlins below roof
Demolish and Install	L.F.	.63	1.19		1.82	rafters.
Reinstall	L.F.		.38		.38	
Minimum Charge	Job		216		216	
2" x 8"						
Demolish	L.F.		.72		.72	Cost includes material and labor to
Install	L.F.	.95	.49		1.44	install 2" x 8" purlins below roof
Demolish and Install	L.F.	.95	1.21		2.16	rafters.
Reinstall	L.F.		.39		.39	
Minimum Charge	Job		216		216	
2" x 10"						
Demolish	L.F.		.73		.73	Cost includes material and labor to
Install	L.F.	1.25	.49		1.74	install 2" x 10" purlins below roof
Demolish and Install	L.F.	1.25	1.22		2.47	rafters.
Reinstall	L.F.		.39		.39	
Minimum Charge	Job		216		216	
2" x 12"						
Demolish	L.F.		.73		.73	Cost includes material and labor to
Install	L.F.	1.69	.50		2.19	install 2" x 12" purlins below roof
Demolish and Install	L.F.	1.69	1.23		2.92	rafters.
Reinstall	L.F.		.40		.40	
Minimum Charge	Job		216		216	
4" x 6"						
Demolish	L.F.		.73		.73	Cost includes material and labor to
Install	L.F.	2.85	.50		3.35	install 4" x 6" purlins below roof
Demolish and Install	L.F.	2.85	1.23		4.08	rafters.
Reinstall	L.F.		.40		.40	
Minimum Charge	Job		216		216	
4" x 8"						
Demolish	L.F.		.74		.74	Cost includes material and labor to
Install	L.F.	3.84	.51		4.35	install 4" x 8" purlins below roof
Demolish and Install	L.F.	3.84	1.25		5.09	rafters.
Reinstall	L.F.		.41		.41	
Minimum Charge	Job		216		216	
Ledger Board						
2" x 6"						
Demolish	L.F.		.36		.36	Cost includes material and labor to
Install	L.F.	.63	1.95		2.58	install 2" x 6" ledger board nailed to
Demolish and Install	L.F.	.63	2.31		2.94	the face of a rafter.
Reinstall	L.F.		1.56		1.56	
Minimum Charge	Job		216		216	

Rough Frame / Structure

Roof Framing		Unit	Material	Labor	Equip.	Total	Specification
4″ x 6″							
	Demolish	L.F.		.59		.59	Cost includes material and labor to
	Install	L.F.	2.85	2.86		5.71	install 4″ x 6″ ledger board nailed to
	Demolish and Install	L.F.	2.85	3.45		6.30	the face of a rafter.
	Reinstall	L.F.		2.29		2.29	
	Minimum Charge	Job		216		216	
4″ x 8″							
	Demolish	L.F.		.79		.79	Cost includes material and labor to
	Install	L.F.	3.84	3.30		7.14	install 4″ x 8″ ledger board nailed to
	Demolish and Install	L.F.	3.84	4.09		7.93	the face of a rafter.
	Reinstall	L.F.		2.64		2.64	
	Minimum Charge	Job		216		216	
Outriggers							
2″ x 4″							
	Demolish	L.F.		.24		.24	Cost includes material and labor to
	Install	L.F.	.42	1.73		2.15	install 2″ x 4″ outrigger rafters for flat,
	Demolish and Install	L.F.	.42	1.97		2.39	shed or gabled roofs, up to 5/12
	Reinstall	L.F.		1.38		1.38	slope, per L.F.
	Minimum Charge	Job		216		216	
2″ x 6″							
	Demolish	L.F.		.37		.37	Cost includes material and labor to
	Install	L.F.	.63	1.73		2.36	install 2″ x 6″ outrigger rafters for flat,
	Demolish and Install	L.F.	.63	2.10		2.73	shed or gabled roofs, up to 5/12
	Reinstall	L.F.		1.38		1.38	slope, per L.F.
	Minimum Charge	Job		216		216	
Lookout Rafter							
2″ x 4″							
	Demolish	L.F.		.83		.83	Cost includes material and labor to
	Install	L.F.	.42	.72		1.14	install 2″ x 4″ lookout rafters for flat,
	Demolish and Install	L.F.	.42	1.55		1.97	shed or gabled roofs, up to 5/12
	Reinstall	L.F.		.58		.58	slope, per L.F.
	Minimum Charge	Job		216		216	
2″ x 6″							
	Demolish	L.F.		.84		.84	Cost includes material and labor to
	Install	L.F.	.63	.73		1.36	install 2″ x 6″ lookout rafters for flat,
	Demolish and Install	L.F.	.63	1.57		2.20	shed or gabled roofs, up to 5/12
	Reinstall	L.F.		.59		.59	slope, per L.F.
	Minimum Charge	Job		216		216	
Fly Rafter							
2″ x 4″							
	Demolish	L.F.		.83		.83	Cost includes material and labor to
	Install	L.F.	.42	.72		1.14	install 2″ x 4″ fly rafters for flat, shed
	Demolish and Install	L.F.	.42	1.55		1.97	or gabled roofs, up to 5/12 slope,
	Reinstall	L.F.		.58		.58	per L.F.
	Minimum Charge	Job		216		216	
2″ x 6″							
	Demolish	L.F.		.84		.84	Cost includes material and labor to
	Install	L.F.	.62	.73		1.35	install 2″ x 6″ fly rafters for flat, shed
	Demolish and Install	L.F.	.62	1.57		2.19	or gabled roofs, up to 5/12 slope,
	Reinstall	L.F.		.59		.59	per L.F.
	Minimum Charge	Job		216		216	

Rough Frame / Structure

Residential Trusses	Unit	Material	Labor	Equip.	Total	Specification
W or Fink Truss						
24' Span						
Demolish	Ea.		33	12.30	45.30	Includes material, labor and
Install	Ea.	84.50	32.50	12.15	129.15	equipment to install wood gang-nailed
Demolish and Install	Ea.	84.50	65.50	24.45	174.45	residential truss, up to 24' span.
Reinstall	Ea.		32.73	12.15	44.88	
Minimum Charge	Job		216		216	
28' Span						
Demolish	Ea.		35.50	13.05	48.55	Includes material, labor and
Install	Ea.	102	37	13.75	152.75	equipment to install wood gang-nailed
Demolish and Install	Ea.	102	72.50	26.80	201.30	residential truss, up to 28' span.
Reinstall	Ea.		37.06	13.76	50.82	
Minimum Charge	Job		216		216	
32' Span						
Demolish	Ea.		39	14.45	53.45	Includes material, labor and
Install	Ea.	120	39.50	14.60	174.10	equipment to install wood gang-nailed
Demolish and Install	Ea.	120	78.50	29.05	227.55	residential truss, up to 32' span.
Reinstall	Ea.		39.28	14.58	53.86	
Minimum Charge	Job		216		216	
36' Span						
Demolish	Ea.		42	15.60	57.60	Includes material, labor and
Install	Ea.	146	42.50	15.85	204.35	equipment to install wood gang-nailed
Demolish and Install	Ea.	146	84.50	31.45	261.95	residential truss, up to 36' span.
Reinstall	Ea.		42.70	15.85	58.55	
Minimum Charge	Job		216		216	
Gable End						
24' Span						
Demolish	Ea.		33	12.30	45.30	Includes material, labor and
Install	Ea.	118	35	13	166	equipment to install wood gang-nailed
Demolish and Install	Ea.	118	68	25.30	211.30	residential gable end truss, up to 24'
Reinstall	Ea.		35.07	13.02	48.09	span.
Clean	Ea.	1.68	42.50		44.18	
Paint	Ea.	4.71	49.50		54.21	
Minimum Charge	Job		216		216	
28' Span						
Demolish	Ea.		35.50	13.05	48.55	Includes material, labor and
Install	Ea.	145	42	15.50	202.50	equipment to install wood gang-nailed
Demolish and Install	Ea.	145	77.50	28.55	251.05	residential gable end truss, up to 30'
Reinstall	Ea.		41.79	15.51	57.30	span.
Clean	Ea.	1.75	58.50		60.25	
Paint	Ea.	4.91	67		71.91	
Minimum Charge	Job		216		216	
32' Span						
Demolish	Ea.		39	14.45	53.45	Includes material, labor and
Install	Ea.	160	42.50	15.85	218.35	equipment to install wood gang-nailed
Demolish and Install	Ea.	160	81.50	30.30	271.80	residential gable end truss, up to 32'
Reinstall	Ea.		42.70	15.85	58.55	span.
Clean	Ea.	1.84	76.50		78.34	
Paint	Ea.	5.15	88		93.15	
Minimum Charge	Job		216		216	
36' Span						
Demolish	Ea.		42	15.60	57.60	Includes material, labor and
Install	Ea.	206	49	18.25	273.25	equipment to install wood gang-nailed
Demolish and Install	Ea.	206	91	33.85	330.85	residential gable end truss, up to 36'
Reinstall	Ea.		49.10	18.23	67.33	span.
Clean	Ea.	1.91	96		97.91	
Paint	Ea.	5.40	111		116.40	
Minimum Charge	Job		216		216	

Residential Trusses

Residential Trusses	Unit	Material	Labor	Equip.	Total	Specification
Truss Hardware						
5-1/4" Glue-Lam Seat						
Install	Ea.	230	2.40		232.40	Includes labor and material to install
Minimum Charge	Job		216		216	beam hangers.
6-3/4" Glue-Lam Seat						
Install	Ea.	235	2.40		237.40	Includes labor and material to install
Minimum Charge	Job		216		216	beam hangers.
2" x 4" Joist Hanger						
Install	Ea.	.80	2.47		3.27	Includes labor and material to install
Minimum Charge	Job		216		216	joist and beam hangers.
2" x 12" Joist Hanger						
Install	Ea.	1.53	2.62		4.15	Cost includes labor and material to
Minimum Charge	Job		216		216	install 2" x 12" joist hanger.

Commercial Trusses

Commercial Trusses	Unit	Material	Labor	Equip.	Total	Specification
Engineered Lumber, Truss / Joist						
9-1/2"						
Demolish	S.F.		.59		.59	Includes material and labor to install
Install	S.F.	1.71	.43		2.14	engineered lumber truss / joists per
Demolish and Install	S.F.	1.71	1.02		2.73	S.F. of floor area based on joists 16"
Reinstall	S.F.		.35		.35	O.C. Beams, supports and bridging
Minimum Charge	Job		216		216	are not included.
11-7/8"						
Demolish	S.F.		.61		.61	Includes material and labor to install
Install	S.F.	1.94	.44		2.38	engineered lumber truss / joists per
Demolish and Install	S.F.	1.94	1.05		2.99	S.F. of floor area based on joists 16"
Reinstall	S.F.		.35		.35	O.C. Beams, supports and bridging
Minimum Charge	Job		216		216	are not included.
14"						
Demolish	S.F.		.63		.63	Includes material and labor to install
Install	S.F.	2.29	.47		2.76	engineered lumber truss / joists per
Demolish and Install	S.F.	2.29	1.10		3.39	S.F. of floor area based on joists 16"
Reinstall	S.F.		.38		.38	O.C. Beams, supports and bridging
Minimum Charge	Job		216		216	are not included.
16"						
Demolish	S.F.		.65		.65	Includes material and labor to install
Install	S.F.	3.40	.50		3.90	engineered lumber truss / joists per
Demolish and Install	S.F.	3.40	1.15		4.55	S.F. of floor area based on joists 16"
Reinstall	S.F.		.40		.40	O.C. Beams, supports and bridging
Minimum Charge	Job		216		216	are not included.
Bowstring Truss						
100' Clear Span						
Demolish	SF Flr.		.60	.50	1.10	Includes material, labor and
Install	SF Flr.	7.15	.49	.31	7.95	equipment to install bow string truss
Demolish and Install	SF Flr.	7.15	1.09	.81	9.05	system up to 100' clear span per S.F.
Minimum Charge	Job		216		216	of floor area.
120' Clear Span						
Demolish	SF Flr.		.67	.56	1.23	Includes material, labor and
Install	SF Flr.	7.70	.55	.35	8.60	equipment to install bow string truss
Demolish and Install	SF Flr.	7.70	1.22	.91	9.83	system up to 120' clear span per S.F.
Minimum Charge	Job		216		216	of floor area.

Rough Frame / Structure

Roof Sheathing	Unit	Material	Labor	Equip.	Total	Specification
Plywood						
3/8"						
Demolish	S.F.		.46		.46	Cost includes material and labor to
Install	S.F.	.55	.57		1.12	install 3/8" CDX plywood roof
Demolish and Install	S.F.	.55	1.03		1.58	sheathing.
Reinstall	S.F.		.57		.57	
Minimum Charge	Job		216		216	
1/2"						
Demolish	S.F.		.46		.46	Cost includes material and labor to
Install	S.F.	.66	.62		1.28	install 1/2" CDX plywood roof
Demolish and Install	S.F.	.66	1.08		1.74	sheathing.
Minimum Charge	Job		216		216	
5/8"						
Demolish	S.F.		.46		.46	Cost includes material and labor to
Install	S.F.	.81	.66		1.47	install 5/8" CDX plywood roof
Demolish and Install	S.F.	.81	1.12		1.93	sheathing.
Minimum Charge	Job		216		216	
3/4"						
Demolish	S.F.		.46		.46	Cost includes material and labor to
Install	S.F.	.97	.72		1.69	install 3/4" CDX plywood roof
Demolish and Install	S.F.	.97	1.18		2.15	sheathing.
Minimum Charge	Job		216		216	
OSB						
1/2"						
Demolish	S.F.		.46		.46	Cost includes material and labor to
Install	S.F.	.55	.62		1.17	install 4' x 8' x 1/2" OSB sheathing.
Demolish and Install	S.F.	.55	1.08		1.63	
Minimum Charge	Job		216		216	
5/8"						
Demolish	S.F.		.46		.46	Cost includes material and labor to
Install	S.F.	.55	.50		1.05	install 4' x 8' x 5/8" OSB sheathing.
Demolish and Install	S.F.	.55	.96		1.51	
Minimum Charge	Job		216		216	
Plank						
Demolish	S.F.		.46		.46	Cost includes material and labor to
Install	S.F.	2.09	1.19		3.28	install 1" x 6" or 1" x 8" utility T&G
Demolish and Install	S.F.	2.09	1.65		3.74	board sheathing laid diagonal.
Reinstall	S.F.		1.19		1.19	
Minimum Charge	Job		216		216	
Skip-type						
1" x 4"						
Demolish	S.F.		.71		.71	Includes material and labor to install
Install	S.F.	.64	.36		1	sheathing board material 1" x 4", 7"
Demolish and Install	S.F.	.64	1.07		1.71	O.C.
Minimum Charge	Job		216		216	
1" x 6"						
Demolish	S.F.		.71		.71	Includes material and labor to install
Install	S.F.	.88	.30		1.18	sheathing board material 1" x 6", 7"
Demolish and Install	S.F.	.88	1.01		1.89	or 9" O.C.
Minimum Charge	Job		216		216	

Rough Frame / Structure

Wood Deck

Wood Deck	Unit	Material	Labor	Equip.	Total	Specification
Stairs						
Demolish	Ea.		420		420	Includes material and labor to install
Install	Ea.	150	755		905	wood steps. 5 - 7 risers included.
Demolish and Install	Ea.	150	1175		1325	
Reinstall	Ea.		602.75		602.75	
Clean	Flight	4.03	27.50		31.53	
Paint	Flight	21	49.50		70.50	
Minimum Charge	Job		216		216	
Bench Seating						
Demolish	L.F.		5.95		5.95	Includes material and labor to install
Install	L.F.	2.21	21.50		23.71	pressure treated bench seating.
Demolish and Install	L.F.	2.21	27.45		29.66	
Reinstall	L.F.		17.28		17.28	
Clean	L.F.	.17	1.60		1.77	
Paint	L.F.	.67	2.96		3.63	
Minimum Charge	Job		216		216	
Privacy Wall						
Demolish	SF Flr.		1.42		1.42	Includes material, labor and
Install	SF Flr.	1.57	.74	.23	2.54	equipment to install privacy wall.
Demolish and Install	SF Flr.	1.57	2.16	.23	3.96	
Reinstall	SF Flr.		.59	.18	.77	
Clean	SF Flr.	.08	.33		.41	
Paint	S.F.	.13	.28		.41	
Minimum Charge	Job		216		216	
Treated Column or Post						
4″ x 4″						
Demolish	L.F.		.89		.89	Includes material and labor to install
Install	L.F.	1.34	2.22		3.56	4″ x 4″ treated column or post.
Demolish and Install	L.F.	1.34	3.11		4.45	
Reinstall	L.F.		1.77		1.77	
Clean	L.F.	.13	.29		.42	
Paint	L.F.	.19	.92		1.11	
Minimum Charge	Job		216		216	
4″ x 6″						
Demolish	L.F.		1.29		1.29	Includes material and labor to install
Install	L.F.	1.95	3.14		5.09	4″ x 6″ treated column or post.
Demolish and Install	L.F.	1.95	4.43		6.38	
Reinstall	L.F.		2.51		2.51	
Clean	L.F.	.19	.40		.59	
Paint	L.F.	.19	.92		1.11	
Minimum Charge	Job		216		216	
Cedar Columns or Posts						
4″ x 4″						
Demolish	L.F.		.89		.89	Includes material and labor to install
Install	L.F.	4.18	2.22		6.40	4″ x 4″ cedar columns or posts.
Demolish and Install	L.F.	4.18	3.11		7.29	
Reinstall	L.F.		1.77		1.77	
Clean	L.F.	.13	.29		.42	
Paint	L.F.	.19	.92		1.11	
Minimum Charge	Job		216		216	
4″ x 6″						
Demolish	L.F.		1.29		1.29	Includes material and labor to install
Install	L.F.	6.50	3.14		9.64	4″ x 6″ cedar columns or posts.
Demolish and Install	L.F.	6.50	4.43		10.93	
Reinstall	L.F.		2.51		2.51	
Clean	L.F.	.19	.40		.59	
Paint	L.F.	.19	.92		1.11	
Minimum Charge	Job		216		216	

Rough Frame / Structure

Wood Deck	Unit	Material	Labor	Equip.	Total	Specification
Redwood Columns or Posts						
4" x 4"						
Demolish	L.F.		.89		.89	Includes material and labor to install
Install	L.F.	7.10	2.22		9.32	4" x 4" redwood columns or posts.
Demolish and Install	L.F.	7.10	3.11		10.21	
Reinstall	L.F.		1.77		1.77	
Clean	L.F.	.13	.29		.42	
Paint	L.F.	.19	.92		1.11	
Minimum Charge	Job		216		216	
4" x 6"						
Demolish	L.F.		1.29		1.29	Includes material and labor to install
Install	L.F.	12.30	3.14		15.44	4" x 6" redwood columns or posts.
Demolish and Install	L.F.	12.30	4.43		16.73	
Reinstall	L.F.		2.51		2.51	
Clean	L.F.	.19	.40		.59	
Paint	L.F.	.19	.92		1.11	
Minimum Charge	Job		216		216	
Treated Girder - Single						
4" x 8"						
Demolish	L.F.		2.66		2.66	Includes material and labor to install a
Install	L.F.	3.38	1.65		5.03	treated lumber girder consisting of one
Demolish and Install	L.F.	3.38	4.31		7.69	4" x 8" for porch or deck construction.
Reinstall	L.F.		1.32		1.32	
Clean	L.F.	.17	.34		.51	
Minimum Charge	Job		216		216	
Treated Girder - Double						
2" x 8"						
Demolish	L.F.		2.66		2.66	Includes material and labor to install a
Install	L.F.	2.29	1.50		3.79	treated lumber girder consisting of two
Demolish and Install	L.F.	2.29	4.16		6.45	2" x 8"s for porch or deck
Reinstall	L.F.		1.20		1.20	construction.
Clean	L.F.	.17	.34		.51	
Minimum Charge	Job		216		216	
2" x 10"						
Demolish	L.F.		3.33		3.33	Includes material and labor to install a
Install	L.F.	2.99	1.57		4.56	treated lumber girder consisting of two
Demolish and Install	L.F.	2.99	4.90		7.89	2" x 10"s for porch or deck
Reinstall	L.F.		1.26		1.26	construction.
Clean	L.F.	.19	.40		.59	
Minimum Charge	Job		216		216	
2" x 12"						
Demolish	L.F.		3.99		3.99	Includes material and labor to install a
Install	L.F.	4.48	1.65		6.13	treated lumber girder consisting of two
Demolish and Install	L.F.	4.48	5.64		10.12	2" x 12"s for porch or deck
Reinstall	L.F.		1.32		1.32	construction.
Clean	L.F.	.21	.46		.67	
Minimum Charge	Job		216		216	
Treated Girder - Triple						
2" x 8"						
Demolish	L.F.		3.99		3.99	Includes material and labor to install a
Install	L.F.	3.43	1.65		5.08	treated lumber girder consisting of
Demolish and Install	L.F.	3.43	5.64		9.07	three 2" x 8"s for porch or deck
Reinstall	L.F.		1.32		1.32	construction.
Clean	L.F.	.19	.40		.59	
Minimum Charge	Job		216		216	

Rough Frame / Structure

Wood Deck

	Unit	Material	Labor	Equip.	Total	Specification
2″ x 10″						
Demolish	L.F.		4.99		4.99	Includes material and labor to install a
Install	L.F.	4.49	1.73		6.22	treated lumber girder consisting of
Demolish and Install	L.F.	4.49	6.72		11.21	three 2″ x 10″s for porch or deck
Reinstall	L.F.		1.38		1.38	construction.
Clean	L.F.	.21	.46		.67	
Minimum Charge	Job		216		216	
2″ x 12″						
Demolish	L.F.		5.95		5.95	Includes material and labor to install a
Install	L.F.	6.70	1.82		8.52	treated lumber girder consisting of
Demolish and Install	L.F.	6.70	7.77		14.47	three 2″ x 12″s for porch or deck
Reinstall	L.F.		1.46		1.46	construction.
Clean	L.F.	.24	.52		.76	
Minimum Charge	Job		216		216	

Treated Ledger - Bolted

	Unit	Material	Labor	Equip.	Total	Specification
2″ x 8″						
Demolish	L.F.		.44		.44	Includes material and labor to install a
Install	L.F.	1.28	2.22		3.50	treated lumber 2″ x 8″ ledger with
Demolish and Install	L.F.	1.28	2.66		3.94	carriage bolts 4′ on center for porch
Reinstall	L.F.		1.77		1.77	or deck construction.
Clean	L.F.	.03	.23		.26	
Minimum Charge	Job		216		216	
2″ x 10″						
Demolish	L.F.		.44		.44	Includes material and labor to install a
Install	L.F.	1.62	2.24		3.86	treated lumber 2″ x 10″ ledger with
Demolish and Install	L.F.	1.62	2.68		4.30	carriage bolts 4′ on center for porch
Reinstall	L.F.		1.80		1.80	or deck construction.
Clean	L.F.	.04	.27		.31	
Minimum Charge	Job		216		216	
2″ x 12″						
Demolish	L.F.		.44		.44	Includes material and labor to install a
Install	L.F.	2.34	2.27		4.61	treated lumber 2″ x 12″ ledger with
Demolish and Install	L.F.	2.34	2.71		5.05	carriage bolts 4′ on center for porch
Reinstall	L.F.		1.82		1.82	or deck construction.
Clean	L.F.	.04	.27		.31	
Minimum Charge	Job		216		216	

Treated Joists

	Unit	Material	Labor	Equip.	Total	Specification
2″ x 8″						
Demolish	L.F.		.76		.76	Includes material and labor to install
Install	L.F.	1.14	.79		1.93	treated lumber 2″ x 8″ deck or floor
Demolish and Install	L.F.	1.14	1.55		2.69	joists for porch or deck construction.
Reinstall	L.F.		.63		.63	
Clean	L.F.	.13	.29		.42	
Minimum Charge	Job		216		216	
2″ x 10″						
Demolish	L.F.		.78		.78	Includes material and labor to install
Install	L.F.	1.50	.96		2.46	treated lumber 2″ x 10″ deck or floor
Demolish and Install	L.F.	1.50	1.74		3.24	joists for porch or deck construction.
Reinstall	L.F.		.77		.77	
Clean	L.F.	.17	.34		.51	
Minimum Charge	Job		216		216	
2″ x 12″						
Demolish	L.F.		.81		.81	Includes material and labor to install
Install	L.F.	1.79	.99		2.78	treated lumber 2″ x 12″ deck or floor
Demolish and Install	L.F.	1.79	1.80		3.59	joists for porch or deck construction.
Reinstall	L.F.		.79		.79	
Clean	L.F.	.19	.40		.59	
Minimum Charge	Job		216		216	

Rough Frame / Structure

Wood Deck	Unit	Material	Labor	Equip.	Total	Specification
Treated Railings and Trim						
2" x 2"						
Demolish	L.F.		.30		.30	Includes material and labor to install
Install	L.F.	.36	1.44		1.80	treated lumber 2" x 2" railings and
Demolish and Install	L.F.	.36	1.74		2.10	trim for porch or deck construction.
Reinstall	L.F.		1.15		1.15	
Clean	L.F.	.01	.21		.22	
Paint	L.F.	.19	.92		1.11	
Minimum Charge	Job		216		216	
2" x 4"						
Demolish	L.F.		.30		.30	Includes material and labor to install
Install	L.F.	.55	1.44		1.99	treated lumber 2" x 4" railings and
Demolish and Install	L.F.	.55	1.74		2.29	trim for porch or deck construction.
Reinstall	L.F.		1.15		1.15	
Clean	L.F.	.03	.23		.26	
Paint	L.F.	.19	.92		1.11	
Minimum Charge	Job		216		216	
2" x 6"						
Demolish	L.F.		.30		.30	Includes material and labor to install
Install	L.F.	.85	1.44		2.29	treated lumber 2" x 6" railings and
Demolish and Install	L.F.	.85	1.74		2.59	trim for porch or deck construction.
Reinstall	L.F.		1.15		1.15	
Clean	L.F.	.02	.27		.29	
Paint	L.F.	.19	.92		1.11	
Minimum Charge	Job		216		216	
Cedar Railings and Trim						
1" x 4"						
Demolish	L.F.		.30		.30	Includes material and labor to install
Install	L.F.	1.99	1.44		3.43	cedar 1" x 4" railings and trim for
Demolish and Install	L.F.	1.99	1.74		3.73	porch or deck construction.
Reinstall	L.F.		1.15		1.15	
Clean	L.F.	.01	.21		.22	
Paint	L.F.	.19	.92		1.11	
Minimum Charge	Job		216		216	
2" x 4"						
Demolish	L.F.		.30		.30	Includes material and labor to install
Install	L.F.	3.99	1.44		5.43	cedar 2" x 4" railings and trim for
Demolish and Install	L.F.	3.99	1.74		5.73	porch or deck construction.
Reinstall	L.F.		1.15		1.15	
Clean	L.F.	.03	.23		.26	
Paint	L.F.	.19	.92		1.11	
Minimum Charge	Job		216		216	
2" x 6"						
Demolish	L.F.		.30		.30	Includes material and labor to install
Install	L.F.	7.25	1.44		8.69	cedar 2" x 6" railings and trim for
Demolish and Install	L.F.	7.25	1.74		8.99	porch or deck construction.
Reinstall	L.F.		1.15		1.15	
Clean	L.F.	.02	.27		.29	
Paint	L.F.	.19	.92		1.11	
Minimum Charge	Job		216		216	
Redwood Railings and Trim						
1" x 4"						
Demolish	L.F.		.30		.30	Includes material and labor to install
Install	L.F.	1.29	1.44		2.73	redwood 1" x 4" railings and trim for
Demolish and Install	L.F.	1.29	1.74		3.03	porch or deck construction.
Reinstall	L.F.		1.15		1.15	
Clean	L.F.	.01	.21		.22	
Paint	L.F.	.19	.92		1.11	
Minimum Charge	Job		216		216	

Wood Deck	Unit	Material	Labor	Equip.	Total	Specification
2″ x 6″						
Demolish	L.F.		.30		.30	Includes material and labor to install
Install	L.F.	8.25	1.44		9.69	redwood 2″ x 6″ railings and trim for
Demolish and Install	L.F.	8.25	1.74		9.99	porch or deck construction.
Reinstall	L.F.		1.15		1.15	
Clean	L.F.	.02	.27		.29	
Paint	L.F.	.19	.92		1.11	
Minimum Charge	Job		216		216	
Treated Decking						
1″ x 4″						
Demolish	L.F.		.43		.43	Includes material and labor to install
Install	S.F.	2.15	1.57		3.72	treated lumber 1″ x 4″ decking for
Demolish and Install	S.F.	2.15	2		4.15	porch or deck construction.
Reinstall	S.F.		1.26		1.26	
Clean	S.F.	.08	.33		.41	
Paint	S.F.	.23	.74		.97	
Minimum Charge	Job		216		216	
2″ x 4″						
Demolish	L.F.		.43		.43	Includes material and labor to install
Install	S.F.	1.84	1.44		3.28	treated lumber 2″ x 4″ decking for
Demolish and Install	S.F.	1.84	1.87		3.71	porch or deck construction.
Reinstall	S.F.		1.15		1.15	
Clean	S.F.	.08	.33		.41	
Paint	S.F.	.23	.74		.97	
Minimum Charge	Job		216		216	
2″ x 6″						
Demolish	L.F.		.43		.43	Includes material and labor to install
Install	S.F.	1.82	1.35		3.17	treated lumber 2″ x 6″ decking for
Demolish and Install	S.F.	1.82	1.78		3.60	porch or deck construction.
Reinstall	S.F.		1.08		1.08	
Clean	S.F.	.08	.33		.41	
Paint	S.F.	.23	.74		.97	
Minimum Charge	Job		216		216	
5/4″ x 6″						
Demolish	L.F.		.43		.43	Includes material and labor to install
Install	S.F.	2.24	1.35		3.59	treated lumber 5/4″ x 6″ decking for
Demolish and Install	S.F.	2.24	1.78		4.02	porch or deck construction.
Reinstall	S.F.		1.08		1.08	
Clean	S.F.	.08	.33		.41	
Paint	S.F.	.23	.74		.97	
Minimum Charge	Job		216		216	
Wood / Plastic Composite Decking						
5/4″ x 6″						
Demolish	L.F.		.43		.43	Includes material and labor to install
Install	L.F.	3.34	1.35		4.69	wood/plastic composite 5/4″ x 6″
Demolish and Install	L.F.	3.34	1.78		5.12	decking for porch or deck
Reinstall	L.F.		1.08		1.08	construction.
Clean	S.F.	.08	.33		.41	
Paint	S.F.	.23	.74		.97	
Minimum Charge	Job		216		216	
Square Edge Fir Decking						
1″ x 4″						
Demolish	L.F.		.43		.43	Includes material and labor to install
Install	L.F.	2.17	1.57		3.74	square edge fir 1″ x 4″ decking for
Demolish and Install	L.F.	2.17	2		4.17	porch or deck construction.
Reinstall	L.F.		1.26		1.26	
Clean	S.F.	.08	.33		.41	
Paint	S.F.	.23	.74		.97	
Minimum Charge	Job		216		216	

Rough Frame / Structure

Wood Deck	Unit	Material	Labor	Equip.	Total	Specification
Tongue and Groove Fir Decking						
1″ x 4″						
Demolish	L.F.		.43		.43	Includes material and labor to install
Install	L.F.	1.44	1.92		3.36	treated lumber 1″ x 4″ decking for
Demolish and Install	L.F.	1.44	2.35		3.79	porch or deck construction.
Reinstall	L.F.		1.54		1.54	
Clean	S.F.	.08	.33		.41	
Paint	S.F.	.23	.74		.97	
Minimum Charge	Job		216		216	
Mahogany Decking						
1″ x 4″						
Demolish	L.F.		.43		.43	Includes material and labor to install
Install	L.F.	1.99	1.57		3.56	treated lumber 1″ x 4″ decking for
Demolish and Install	L.F.	1.99	2		3.99	porch or deck construction.
Reinstall	L.F.		1.26		1.26	
Clean	S.F.	.08	.33		.41	
Paint	S.F.	.23	.74		.97	
Minimum Charge	Job		216		216	
PVC Decking						
5/4″ x 6″						
Demolish	L.F.		.43		.43	Includes material and labor to install
Install	L.F.	3.98	1.57		5.55	PVC 5/4″ x 6″ decking for porch or
Demolish and Install	L.F.	3.98	2		5.98	deck construction.
Reinstall	L.F.		1.26		1.26	
Clean	S.F.	.08	.33		.41	
Minimum Charge	Job		216		216	
PVC Handrails and Balusters						
Straight						
Demolish	L.F.		2.97		2.97	Includes material and labor to install
Install	L.F.	27.50	4.50		32	straight PVC handrails and balusters
Demolish and Install	L.F.	27.50	7.47		34.97	for porch or deck construction.
Reinstall	L.F.		3.60		3.60	
Clean	L.F.	.80	2.50		3.30	
Minimum Charge	Job		216		216	
Angled						
Demolish	L.F.		2.97		2.97	Includes material and labor to install
Install	L.F.	31.50	6		37.50	angled PVC handrails and balusters
Demolish and Install	L.F.	31.50	8.97		40.47	for porch or deck construction.
Reinstall	L.F.		4.80		4.80	
Clean	L.F.	.80	2.50		3.30	
Minimum Charge	Job		216		216	
PVC Post Sleeve						
for 4″ x 4″ post						
Demolish	L.F.		.89		.89	Includes material and labor to install
Install	L.F.	15.40	4.50		19.90	PVC post sleeves over 4″ x 4″ porch
Demolish and Install	L.F.	15.40	5.39		20.79	or deck posts.
Reinstall	L.F.		3.60		3.60	
Clean	L.F.	.13	.29		.42	
Minimum Charge	Job		216		216	
Post Cap						
Demolish	Ea.		4.45		4.45	Includes material and labor to install
Install	Ea.	26	9		35	PVC post caps for porch or deck
Demolish and Install	Ea.	26	13.45		39.45	construction.
Reinstall	Ea.		7.20		7.20	
Clean	L.F.	.13	.29		.42	
Minimum Charge	Job		216		216	

Rough Frame / Structure

Porch

	Unit	Material	Labor	Equip.	Total	Specification
Stairs						
Demolish	Ea.		420		420	Includes material and labor to install
Install	Ea.	150	755		905	wood steps. 5 - 7 risers included.
Demolish and Install	Ea.	150	1175		1325	
Reinstall	Ea.		602.75		602.75	
Clean	Flight	4.03	27.50		31.53	
Paint	Flight	.21	49.50		70.50	
Minimum Charge	Job		216		216	
Bench Seating						
Demolish	L.F.		5.95		5.95	Includes material and labor to install
Install	L.F.	2.21	21.50		23.71	pressure treated bench seating.
Demolish and Install	L.F.	2.21	27.45		29.66	
Reinstall	L.F.		17.28		17.28	
Clean	L.F.	.17	1.60		1.77	
Paint	L.F.	.67	2.96		3.63	
Minimum Charge	Job		216		216	
Privacy Wall						
Demolish	SF Flr.		1.42		1.42	Includes material, labor and
Install	SF Flr.	1.57	.74	.23	2.54	equipment to install privacy wall.
Demolish and Install	SF Flr.	1.57	2.16	.23	3.96	
Reinstall	SF Flr.		.59	.18	.77	
Clean	SF Flr.	.08	.33		.41	
Paint	S.F.	.13	.28		.41	
Minimum Charge	Job		216		216	
Wood Board Ceiling						
Demolish	S.F.		.59		.59	Includes material and labor to install
Install	S.F.	3.40	1.92		5.32	wood board on ceiling.
Demolish and Install	S.F.	3.40	2.51		5.91	
Clean	S.F.	.03	.19		.22	
Paint	S.F.	.21	.46		.67	
Minimum Charge	Job		216		216	
Re-screen						
Install	S.F.	1.77	1.73		3.50	Includes labor and material to
Minimum Charge	Job		216		216	re-screen wood frame.

Exterior Trim

Exterior Trim	Unit	Material	Labor	Equip.	Total	Specification
Stock Lumber						
1″ x 2″						
Demolish	L.F.		.30		.30	Cost includes material and labor to
Install	L.F.	.28	1.31		1.59	install 1″ x 2″ pine trim.
Demolish and Install	L.F.	.28	1.61		1.89	
Clean	L.F.	.01	.21		.22	
Paint	L.F.	.02	.58		.60	
Minimum Charge	Job		216		216	
1″ x 3″						
Demolish	L.F.		.30		.30	Cost includes material and labor to
Install	L.F.	.30	1.49		1.79	install 1″ x 3″ pine trim.
Demolish and Install	L.F.	.30	1.79		2.09	
Clean	L.F.	.01	.21		.22	
Paint	L.F.	.02	.58		.60	
Minimum Charge	Job		216		216	
1″ x 4″						
Demolish	L.F.		.30		.30	Cost includes material and labor to
Install	L.F.	.54	1.73		2.27	install 1″ x 4″ pine trim.
Demolish and Install	L.F.	.54	2.03		2.57	
Clean	L.F.	.01	.21		.22	
Paint	L.F.	.02	.58		.60	
Minimum Charge	Job		216		216	
1″ x 6″						
Demolish	L.F.		.30		.30	Cost includes material and labor to
Install	L.F.	.91	1.73		2.64	install 1″ x 6″ pine trim.
Demolish and Install	L.F.	.91	2.03		2.94	
Clean	L.F.	.02	.21		.23	
Paint	L.F.	.09	.58		.67	
Minimum Charge	Job		216		216	
1″ x 8″						
Demolish	L.F.		.32		.32	Cost includes material and labor to
Install	L.F.	1.34	2.16		3.50	install 1″ x 8″ pine trim.
Demolish and Install	L.F.	1.34	2.48		3.82	
Reinstall	L.F.		1.73		1.73	
Clean	L.F.	.03	.23		.26	
Paint	L.F.	.09	.58		.67	
Minimum Charge	Job		216		216	

Exterior Trim

Exterior Trim	Unit	Material	Labor	Equip.	Total	Specification
1″ x 10″						
Demolish	L.F.		.49		.49	Cost includes material and labor to
Install	L.F.	1.75	2.40		4.15	install 1″ x 10″ pine trim.
Demolish and Install	L.F.	1.75	2.89		4.64	
Minimum Charge	Job		216		216	
1″ x 12″						
Demolish	L.F.		.49		.49	Cost includes material and labor to
Install	L.F.	2.26	2.40		4.66	install 1″ x 12″ pine trim.
Demolish and Install	L.F.	2.26	2.89		5.15	
Minimum Charge	Job		216		216	
Polyvinyl Chloride (PVC)						
1″ x 4″						
Demolish	L.F.		.30		.30	Includes material and labor to install
Install	L.F.	1.49	1.73		3.22	1″ x 4″ PVC exterior trim.
Demolish and Install	L.F.	1.49	2.03		3.52	
Reinstall	L.F.		1.38		1.38	
Clean	L.F.	.01	.21		.22	
Paint	L.F.	.02	.58		.60	
Minimum Charge	Job		216		216	
1″ x 6″						
Demolish	L.F.		.30		.30	Includes material and labor to install
Install	L.F.	2.33	1.73		4.06	1″ x 6″ PVC exterior trim.
Demolish and Install	L.F.	2.33	2.03		4.36	
Reinstall	L.F.		1.38		1.38	
Clean	L.F.	.02	.21		.23	
Paint	L.F.	.09	.58		.67	
Minimum Charge	Job		216		216	
1″ x 8″						
Demolish	L.F.		.32		.32	Includes material and labor to install
Install	L.F.	3.08	1.92		5	1″ x 8″ PVC exterior trim.
Demolish and Install	L.F.	3.08	2.24		5.32	
Reinstall	L.F.		1.54		1.54	
Clean	L.F.	.03	.23		.26	
Paint	L.F.	.09	.58		.67	
Minimum Charge	Job		216		216	
1″ x 10″						
Demolish	L.F.		.34		.34	Includes material and labor to install
Install	L.F.	3.91	1.92		5.83	1″ x 10″ PVC exterior trim.
Demolish and Install	L.F.	3.91	2.26		6.17	
Reinstall	L.F.		1.54		1.54	
Clean	L.F.	.04	.27		.31	
Paint	L.F.	.09	.58		.67	
Minimum Charge	Job		216		216	
1″ x 12″						
Demolish	L.F.		.36		.36	Includes material and labor to install
Install	L.F.	4.77	2.16		6.93	1″ x 12″ PVC exterior trim.
Demolish and Install	L.F.	4.77	2.52		7.29	
Reinstall	L.F.		1.73		1.73	
Clean	L.F.	.04	.27		.31	
Paint	L.F.	.09	.58		.67	
Minimum Charge	Job		216		216	

Exterior Trim

Fascia

	Unit	Material	Labor	Equip.	Total	Specification
Aluminum						
Demolish	L.F.		.62		.62	Includes material and labor to install
Install	S.F.	2.06	2.06		4.12	aluminum fascia.
Demolish and Install	S.F.	2.06	2.68		4.74	
Reinstall	S.F.		1.65		1.65	
Clean	L.F.		.40		.40	
Minimum Charge	Job		216		216	
Vinyl						
Demolish	L.F.		.62		.62	Cost includes material and labor to
Install	L.F.	4.79	2.47		7.26	install 6″ vinyl fascia with 12″ vinyl
Demolish and Install	L.F.	4.79	3.09		7.88	soffit and J-channel.
Reinstall	L.F.		1.97		1.97	
Clean	L.F.		.40		.40	
Minimum Charge	Job		216		216	
Plywood						
Demolish	L.F.		.61		.61	Cost includes material and labor to
Install	L.F.	1.58	.96		2.54	install 12″ wide plywood fascia.
Demolish and Install	L.F.	1.58	1.57		3.15	
Reinstall	L.F.		.77		.77	
Clean	L.F.	.04	.27		.31	
Paint	L.F.	.19	.92		1.11	
Minimum Charge	Job		216		216	
Cedar						
Demolish	L.F.		.61		.61	Cost includes material and labor to
Install	L.F.	3.53	.96		4.49	install 12″ wide cedar fascia.
Demolish and Install	L.F.	3.53	1.57		5.10	
Reinstall	L.F.		.77		.77	
Clean	L.F.	.04	.27		.31	
Paint	L.F.	.19	.92		1.11	
Minimum Charge	Job		216		216	
Redwood						
1″ x 6″						
Demolish	L.F.		.48		.48	Cost includes material and labor to
Install	L.F.	1.96	1.73		3.69	install 1″ x 6″ redwood fascia board.
Demolish and Install	L.F.	1.96	2.21		4.17	
Reinstall	L.F.		1.38		1.38	
Minimum Charge	Job		216		216	
1″ x 8″						
Demolish	L.F.		.54		.54	Cost includes material and labor to
Install	L.F.	2.60	1.88		4.48	install 1″ x 8″ redwood fascia board.
Demolish and Install	L.F.	2.60	2.42		5.02	
Reinstall	L.F.		1.50		1.50	
Minimum Charge	Job		216		216	
2″ x 6″						
Demolish	L.F.		.48		.48	Cost includes material and labor to
Install	L.F.	.63	3.46		4.09	install 2″ x 6″ hem-fir exterior trim
Demolish and Install	L.F.	.63	3.94		4.57	board.
Reinstall	L.F.		2.76		2.76	
Minimum Charge	Job		216		216	
2″ x 8″						
Demolish	L.F.		.54		.54	Cost includes material and labor to
Install	L.F.	.95	3.84		4.79	install 2″ x 8″ hem-fir exterior trim
Demolish and Install	L.F.	.95	4.38		5.33	board.
Reinstall	L.F.		3.07		3.07	
Minimum Charge	Job		216		216	

Exterior Trim

Fascia	Unit	Material	Labor	Equip.	Total	Specification
Hem-fir Std & Better						
2″ x 6″						
Demolish	L.F.		.48		.48	Cost includes material and labor to
Install	L.F.	.63	3.46		4.09	install 2″ x 6″ hem-fir exterior trim
Demolish and Install	L.F.	.63	3.94		4.57	board.
Reinstall	L.F.		2.76		2.76	
Clean	L.F.	.02	.27		.29	
Paint	L.F.	.19	.92		1.11	
Minimum Charge	Job		216		216	
2″ x 8″						
Demolish	L.F.		.54		.54	Cost includes material and labor to
Install	L.F.	.95	3.84		4.79	install 2″ x 8″ hem-fir exterior trim
Demolish and Install	L.F.	.95	4.38		5.33	board.
Reinstall	L.F.		3.07		3.07	
Clean	L.F.	.03	.27		.30	
Paint	L.F.	.19	.92		1.11	
Minimum Charge	Job		216		216	
2″ x 10″						
Demolish	L.F.		.61		.61	Cost includes material and labor to
Install	L.F.	1.25	4.80		6.05	install 2″ x 10″ hem-fir exterior trim
Demolish and Install	L.F.	1.25	5.41		6.66	board.
Reinstall	L.F.		3.84		3.84	
Clean	L.F.	.04	.29		.33	
Paint	L.F.	.19	.92		1.11	
Minimum Charge	Job		216		216	
Barge Rafter						
2″ x 6″						
Demolish	L.F.		.95		.95	Cost includes material and labor to
Install	L.F.	.63	.48		1.11	install 2″ x 6″ barge rafters.
Demolish and Install	L.F.	.63	1.43		2.06	
Reinstall	L.F.		.38		.38	
Clean	L.F.	.02	.27		.29	
Paint	L.F.	.19	.92		1.11	
Minimum Charge	Job		216		216	
2″ x 8″						
Demolish	L.F.		.97		.97	Cost includes material and labor to
Install	L.F.	.95	.51		1.46	install 2″ x 8″ barge rafters.
Demolish and Install	L.F.	.95	1.48		2.43	
Reinstall	L.F.		.41		.41	
Clean	L.F.	.03	.27		.30	
Paint	L.F.	.19	.92		1.11	
Minimum Charge	Job		216		216	
2″ x 10″						
Demolish	L.F.		.98		.98	Cost includes material and labor to
Install	L.F.	1.25	.52		1.77	install 2″ x 10″ barge rafters.
Demolish and Install	L.F.	1.25	1.50		2.75	
Reinstall	L.F.		.42		.42	
Clean	L.F.	.04	.29		.33	
Paint	L.F.	.19	.92		1.11	
Minimum Charge	Job		216		216	

Exterior Trim

Soffit

	Unit	Material	Labor	Equip.	Total	Specification
Aluminum						
12″ w / Fascia						
Demolish	L.F.		.62		.62	Cost includes material and labor to
Install	L.F.	4.84	2.47		7.31	install 12″ aluminum soffit with 6″
Demolish and Install	L.F.	4.84	3.09		7.93	fascia and J-channel.
Reinstall	L.F.		1.97		1.97	
Clean	L.F.		.40		.40	
Paint	L.F.	.24	.92		1.16	
Minimum Charge	Job		216		216	
18″ w / Fascia						
Demolish	L.F.		.62		.62	Cost includes material and labor to
Install	L.F.	5.90	2.88		8.78	install 18″ aluminum soffit with 6″
Demolish and Install	L.F.	5.90	3.50		9.40	fascia and J-channel.
Reinstall	L.F.		2.30		2.30	
Clean	L.F.		.40		.40	
Paint	L.F.	.24	.92		1.16	
Minimum Charge	Job		216		216	
24″ w / Fascia						
Demolish	L.F.		.62		.62	Cost includes material and labor to
Install	L.F.	6.90	3.20		10.10	install 24″ aluminum soffit with 6″
Demolish and Install	L.F.	6.90	3.82		10.72	fascia and J-channel.
Reinstall	L.F.		2.56		2.56	
Clean	L.F.		.58		.58	
Paint	L.F.	.24	.92		1.16	
Minimum Charge	Job		216		216	
Vinyl						
Demolish	L.F.		.62		.62	Cost includes material and labor to
Install	L.F.	4.79	2.47		7.26	install 6″ vinyl fascia with 12″ vinyl
Demolish and Install	L.F.	4.79	3.09		7.88	soffit and J-channel.
Reinstall	L.F.		1.97		1.97	
Clean	L.F.		.40		.40	
Paint	L.F.	.24	.92		1.16	
Minimum Charge	Job		216		216	
Plywood						
Demolish	L.F.		.68		.68	Cost includes material and labor to
Install	L.F.	1.54	1.23		2.77	install 12″ wide plywood soffit.
Demolish and Install	L.F.	1.54	1.91		3.45	
Reinstall	L.F.		.99		.99	
Clean	L.F.	.04	.27		.31	
Paint	L.F.	.19	.92		1.11	
Minimum Charge	Job		216		216	
Redwood						
Demolish	L.F.		.68		.68	Cost includes material and labor to
Install	L.F.	5.20	1.23		6.43	install 12″ wide redwood soffit.
Demolish and Install	L.F.	5.20	1.91		7.11	
Reinstall	L.F.		.99		.99	
Clean	L.F.	.04	.27		.31	
Paint	L.F.	.19	.92		1.11	
Minimum Charge	Job		216		216	
Cedar						
Demolish	L.F.		.68		.68	Cost includes material and labor to
Install	L.F.	3.49	1.23		4.72	install 12″ wide cedar soffit.
Demolish and Install	L.F.	3.49	1.91		5.40	
Reinstall	L.F.		.99		.99	
Clean	L.F.	.04	.27		.31	
Paint	L.F.	.19	.92		1.11	
Minimum Charge	Job		216		216	

Exterior Trim

Soffit

Douglas Fir

	Unit	Material	Labor	Equip.	Total	Specification
Demolish	L.F.		.68		.68	Cost includes material and labor to install 12″ wide Douglas fir soffit.
Install	L.F.	2.21	1.23		3.44	
Demolish and Install	L.F.	2.21	1.91		4.12	
Reinstall	L.F.		.99		.99	
Clean	L.F.	.04	.27		.31	
Paint	L.F.	.19	.92		1.11	
Minimum Charge	Job		216		216	

Roofing and Flashing

Tile Roofing

Metal Flashing	Unit	Material	Labor	Equip.	Total	Specification
Galvanized						
6″						
Demolish	L.F.		.24		.24	Includes material and labor to install
Install	L.F.	.69	1		1.69	flat galvanized steel flashing, 6″ wide.
Demolish and Install	L.F.	.69	1.24		1.93	
Paint	L.F.	.13	.46		.59	
Minimum Charge	Job		199		199	
14″						
Demolish	L.F.		.24		.24	Includes material and labor to install
Install	L.F.	1.61	1		2.61	flat galvanized steel flashing, 14″
Demolish and Install	L.F.	1.61	1.24		2.85	wide.
Paint	L.F.	.13	.46		.59	
Minimum Charge	Job		199		199	
20″						
Demolish	L.F.		.24		.24	Includes material and labor to install
Install	L.F.	2.29	1		3.29	flat galvanized steel flashing, 20″
Demolish and Install	L.F.	2.29	1.24		3.53	wide.
Paint	L.F.	.13	.46		.59	
Minimum Charge	Job		199		199	
Aluminum						
6″						
Demolish	L.F.		.24		.24	Includes material and labor to install
Install	L.F.	.44	1		1.44	flat aluminum flashing, 6″ wide.
Demolish and Install	L.F.	.44	1.24		1.68	
Paint	L.F.	.13	.46		.59	
Minimum Charge	Job		199		199	
14″						
Demolish	L.F.		.24		.24	Includes material and labor to install
Install	L.F.	.80	1		1.80	flat aluminum flashing, 14″ wide.
Demolish and Install	L.F.	.80	1.24		2.04	
Paint	L.F.	.13	.46		.59	
Minimum Charge	Job		199		199	
20″						
Demolish	L.F.		.24		.24	Includes material and labor to install
Install	L.F.	1.12	1		2.12	flat aluminum flashing, 20″ wide.
Demolish and Install	L.F.	1.12	1.24		2.36	
Paint	L.F.	.13	.46		.59	
Minimum Charge	Job		199		199	

Metal Flashing	Unit	Material	Labor	Equip.	Total	Specification
Copper						
6"						
Demolish	L.F.		.24		.24	Includes material and labor to install
Install	L.F.	3.83	1.33		5.16	flat copper flashing, 6" wide.
Demolish and Install	L.F.	3.83	1.57		5.40	
Minimum Charge	Job		241		241	
14"						
Demolish	L.F.		.24		.24	Includes material and labor to install
Install	L.F.	8.95	1.33		10.28	flat copper flashing, 14" wide.
Demolish and Install	L.F.	8.95	1.57		10.52	
Minimum Charge	Job		241		241	
18"						
Demolish	L.F.		.24		.24	Includes material and labor to install
Install	L.F.	12.75	1.33		14.08	flat copper flashing, 18" wide.
Demolish and Install	L.F.	12.75	1.57		14.32	
Minimum Charge	Job		241		241	
Aluminum Valley						
Demolish	L.F.		.24		.24	Includes material and labor to install
Install	L.F.	3.77	2.54		6.31	aluminum valley flashing, .024" thick.
Demolish and Install	L.F.	3.77	2.78		6.55	
Paint	L.F.	.13	.46		.59	
Minimum Charge	Job		216		216	
Gravel Stop						
Demolish	L.F.		.37		.37	Includes material and labor to install
Install	L.F.	6.60	3.32		9.92	aluminum gravel stop, .050" thick, 4"
Demolish and Install	L.F.	6.60	3.69		10.29	high, mill finish.
Reinstall	L.F.		2.66		2.66	
Paint	L.F.	.21	.46		.67	
Minimum Charge	Job		216		216	
Drip Edge						
Demolish	L.F.		.36		.36	Includes material and labor to install
Install	L.F.	.44	1.08		1.52	aluminum drip edge, .016" thick, 5"
Demolish and Install	L.F.	.44	1.44		1.88	wide, mill finish.
Reinstall	L.F.		.86		.86	
Paint	L.F.	.21	.46		.67	
Minimum Charge	Job		216		216	
End Wall						
Demolish	L.F.		1.10		1.10	Includes material and labor to install
Install	L.F.	2.19	2.54		4.73	aluminum end wall flashing, .024"
Demolish and Install	L.F.	2.19	3.64		5.83	thick.
Minimum Charge	Job		216		216	
Side Wall						
Demolish	L.F.		.21		.21	Includes material and labor to install
Install	L.F.	2.19	2.54		4.73	aluminum side wall flashing, .024"
Demolish and Install	L.F.	2.19	2.75		4.94	thick.
Minimum Charge	Job		216		216	
Coping and Wall Cap						
Demolish	L.F.		1.48		1.48	Includes material and labor to install
Install	L.F.	2.54	2.74		5.28	aluminum flashing, mill finish, 0.40
Demolish and Install	L.F.	2.54	4.22		6.76	thick, 12" wide.
Clean	L.F.	.10	1		1.10	
Minimum Charge	Job		199		199	

Roofing

Roof Shingles

Roof Shingles	Unit	Material	Labor	Equip.	Total	Specification
Underlayment						
15#						
Demolish	Sq.		11.85		11.85	Includes material and labor to install
Install	Sq.	5.95	6.20		12.15	#15 felt underlayment.
Demolish and Install	Sq.	5.95	18.05		24	
Minimum Charge	Job		199		199	
30#						
Demolish	Sq.		11.85		11.85	Includes material and labor to install
Install	Sq.	11.90	6.85		18.75	#30 felt underlayment.
Demolish and Install	Sq.	11.90	18.70		30.60	
Minimum Charge	Job		199		199	
Self Adhering						
Demolish	Sq.		29.50		29.50	Includes material and labor to install
Install	Sq.	84.50	18.10		102.60	self adhering ice barrier roofing
Demolish and Install	Sq.	84.50	47.60		132.10	underlayment.
Minimum Charge	Job		199		199	

Rolled Roofing

Rolled Roofing	Unit	Material	Labor	Equip.	Total	Specification
90 lb						
Demolish	Sq.		29.50		29.50	Cost includes material and labor to
Install	Sq.	38.50	33		71.50	install 90 lb mineral surface rolled
Demolish and Install	Sq.	38.50	62.50		101	roofing.
Minimum Charge	Job		199		199	

Composition Shingles

Composition Shingles	Unit	Material	Labor	Equip.	Total	Specification
Fiberglass (3-tab)						
225 lb, 20 Year						
Demolish	Sq.		32.50		32.50	Cost includes material and labor to
Install	Sq.	83	77.50		160.50	install 225 lb, 20 year fiberglass
Demolish and Install	Sq.	83	110		193	shingles.
Minimum Charge	Job		199		199	
300 lb, 25 Year						
Demolish	Sq.		32.50		32.50	Cost includes material and labor to
Install	Sq.	83	77.50		160.50	install 300 lb, 25 year fiberglass
Demolish and Install	Sq.	83	110		193	shingles.
Minimum Charge	Job		199		199	
Emergency Repairs						
Install	Ea.	154	199		353	Includes labor and material for
Minimum Charge	Job		199		199	emergency repairs.
Architectural						
Laminated, 25 Year						
Demolish	Sq.		32.50		32.50	Cost includes material and labor to
Install	Sq.	129	77.50		206.50	install 25 year fiberglass roof shingles.
Demolish and Install	Sq.	129	110		239	
Minimum Charge	Job		199		199	
Laminated, 30 Year						
Demolish	Sq.		32.50		32.50	Cost includes material and labor to
Install	Sq.	108	69		177	install 30 year laminated roof
Demolish and Install	Sq.	108	101.50		209.50	shingles.
Minimum Charge	Job		199		199	

Roofing

Composition Shingles		Unit	Material	Labor	Equip.	Total	Specification
Laminated, 40 Year							
	Demolish	Sq.		32.50		32.50	Cost includes material and labor to
	Install	Sq.	143	77.50		220.50	install 40 year fiberglass roof shingles.
	Demolish and Install	Sq.	143	110		253	
	Minimum Charge	Job		199		199	
Laminated Shake, 40 Year							
	Demolish	Sq.		32.50		32.50	Cost includes material and labor to
	Install	Sq.	169	88.50		257.50	install 40 year laminated roof
	Demolish and Install	Sq.	169	121		290	shingles.
	Minimum Charge	Job		199		199	
Emergency Repairs							
	Install	Ea.	154	199		353	Includes labor and material for
	Minimum Charge	Job		199		199	emergency repairs.
Roof Jack							
	Demolish	Ea.		6.45		6.45	Includes material and labor to install
	Install	Ea.	27.50	44		71.50	residential roof jack, w/bird screen,
	Demolish and Install	Ea.	27.50	50.45		77.95	backdraft damper, 3" & 4" dia. round
	Paint	Ea.	.07	4.62		4.69	duct.
	Minimum Charge	Job		234		234	
Ridge Vent							
	Demolish	L.F.		1.15		1.15	Includes material and labor to install a
	Install	L.F.	3.28	3.11		6.39	mill finish aluminum ridge vent strip.
	Demolish and Install	L.F.	3.28	4.26		7.54	
	Minimum Charge	Job		216		216	
Shingle Molding							
1" x 2"							
	Demolish	L.F.		.22		.22	Cost includes material and labor to
	Install	L.F.	.28	1.31		1.59	install 1" x 2" pine trim.
	Demolish and Install	L.F.	.28	1.53		1.81	
	Paint	L.F.	.02	.58		.60	
	Minimum Charge	Job		216		216	
1" x 3"							
	Demolish	L.F.		.22		.22	Cost includes material and labor to
	Install	L.F.	.30	1.49		1.79	install 1" x 3" pine trim.
	Demolish and Install	L.F.	.30	1.71		2.01	
	Paint	L.F.	.02	.58		.60	
	Minimum Charge	Job		216		216	
1" x 4"							
	Demolish	L.F.		.22		.22	Cost includes material and labor to
	Install	L.F.	.54	1.73		2.27	install 1" x 4" pine trim.
	Demolish and Install	L.F.	.54	1.95		2.49	
	Paint	L.F.	.02	.58		.60	
	Minimum Charge	Job		216		216	
Add for Steep Pitch							
	Install	Sq.		25		25	Includes labor and material added for
Add for Additional Story							2nd story or steep roofs.
	Install	Sq.		25		25	Includes labor and material added for 2nd story or steep roofs.

Roofing

Wood Shingles		Unit	Material	Labor	Equip.	Total	Specification
Cedar Wood Shingles							
16" Red Label (#2)							
	Demolish	Sq.		79		79	Includes material and labor to install
	Install	Sq.	152	173		325	wood shingles/shakes.
	Demolish and Install	Sq.	152	252		404	
	Minimum Charge	Job		216		216	
16" Blue Label (#1)							
	Demolish	Sq.		79		79	Includes material and labor to install
	Install	Sq.	290	133		423	wood shingles/shakes.
	Demolish and Install	Sq.	290	212		502	
	Minimum Charge	Job		216		216	
18" Red Label (#2)							
	Demolish	Sq.		79		79	Includes material and labor to install
	Install	Sq.	310	111		421	wood shingles/shakes.
	Demolish and Install	Sq.	310	190		500	
	Minimum Charge	Job		216		216	
18" Blue Label (#1)							
	Demolish	Sq.		79		79	Includes material and labor to install
	Install	Sq.	250	121		371	wood shingles/shakes.
	Demolish and Install	Sq.	250	200		450	
	Minimum Charge	Job		216		216	
Replace Shingle							
	Install	Ea.	71.50	10.80		82.30	Includes labor and material to replace
	Minimum Charge	Job		216		216	individual wood shingle/shake. Cost is per shingle.
Cedar Shake							
18" Medium Handsplit							
	Demolish	Sq.		79		79	Includes material and labor to install
	Install	Sq.	197	166		363	wood shingles/shakes.
	Demolish and Install	Sq.	197	245		442	
	Minimum Charge	Job		216		216	
18" Heavy Handsplit							
	Demolish	Sq.		79		79	Includes material and labor to install
	Install	Sq.	197	185		382	wood shingles/shakes.
	Demolish and Install	Sq.	197	264		461	
	Minimum Charge	Job		216		216	
24" Heavy Handsplit							
	Demolish	Sq.		79		79	Includes material and labor to install
	Install	Sq.	278	148		426	wood shingles/shakes.
	Demolish and Install	Sq.	278	227		505	
	Minimum Charge	Job		216		216	
24" Medium Handsplit							
	Demolish	Sq.		79		79	Includes material and labor to install
	Install	Sq.	278	133		411	wood shingles/shakes.
	Demolish and Install	Sq.	278	212		490	
	Minimum Charge	Job		216		216	
24" Straight Split							
	Demolish	Sq.		79		79	Includes material and labor to install
	Install	Sq.	305	196		501	wood shingles/shakes.
	Demolish and Install	Sq.	305	275		580	
	Minimum Charge	Job		216		216	
24" Tapersplit							
	Demolish	Sq.		79		79	Includes material and labor to install
	Install	Sq.	305	196		501	wood shingles/shakes.
	Demolish and Install	Sq.	305	275		580	
	Minimum Charge	Job		216		216	

Roofing

Wood Shingles

Wood Shingles		Unit	Material	Labor	Equip.	Total	Specification
18″ Straight Split							
	Demolish	Sq.		79		79	Includes material and labor to install
	Install	Sq.	305	196		501	wood shingles/shakes.
	Demolish and Install	Sq.	305	275		580	
	Minimum Charge	Job		216		216	
Replace Shingle							
	Install	Ea.	71.50	10.80		82.30	Includes labor and material to replace
	Minimum Charge	Job		216		216	individual wood shingle/shake. Cost is per shingle.

Slate Tile Roofing

Slate Tile Roofing		Unit	Material	Labor	Equip.	Total	Specification
Unfading Green							
	Demolish	Sq.		71		71	Includes material and labor to install
	Install	Sq.	530	229		759	clear Vermont slate tile.
	Demolish and Install	Sq.	530	300		830	
	Reinstall	Sq.		182.86		182.86	
	Minimum Charge	Job		200		200	
Unfading Purple							
	Demolish	Sq.		71		71	Includes material and labor to install
	Install	Sq.	470	229		699	clear Vermont slate tile.
	Demolish and Install	Sq.	470	300		770	
	Reinstall	Sq.		182.86		182.86	
	Minimum Charge	Job		200		200	
Replace Slate Tiles							
	Install	Ea.	6.50	21		27.50	Includes labor and material to replace
	Minimum Charge	Job		200		200	individual slate tiles. Cost is per tile.
Variegated Purple							
	Demolish	Sq.		71		71	Includes material and labor to install
	Install	Sq.	455	229		684	clear Vermont slate tile.
	Demolish and Install	Sq.	455	300		755	
	Reinstall	Sq.		182.86		182.86	
	Minimum Charge	Job		200		200	
Unfading Grey / Black							
	Demolish	Sq.		71		71	Includes material and labor to install
	Install	Sq.	505	229		734	clear Vermont slate tile.
	Demolish and Install	Sq.	505	300		805	
	Reinstall	Sq.		182.86		182.86	
	Minimum Charge	Job		200		200	
Unfading Red							
	Demolish	Sq.		71		71	Includes material and labor to install
	Install	Sq.	1300	229		1529	clear Vermont slate tile.
	Demolish and Install	Sq.	1300	300		1600	
	Reinstall	Sq.		182.86		182.86	
	Minimum Charge	Job		200		200	
Weathering Black							
	Demolish	Sq.		71		71	Includes material and labor to install
	Install	Sq.	540	229		769	clear Pennsylvania slate tile.
	Demolish and Install	Sq.	540	300		840	
	Reinstall	Sq.		182.86		182.86	
	Minimum Charge	Job		200		200	

Roofing

Slate Tile Roofing

Slate Tile Roofing	Unit	Material	Labor	Equip.	Total	Specification
Weathering Green						
Demolish	Sq.		71		71	Includes material and labor to install
Install	Sq.	385	229		614	clear Vermont slate tile.
Demolish and Install	Sq.	385	300		685	
Reinstall	Sq.		182.86		182.86	
Minimum Charge	Job		200		200	

Flat Clay Tile Roofing

Flat Clay Tile Roofing	Unit	Material	Labor	Equip.	Total	Specification
Glazed						
Demolish	Sq.		79		79	Includes material and labor to install
Install	Sq.	560	200		760	tile roofing. Cost based on terra cotta
Demolish and Install	Sq.	560	279		839	red flat clay tile and includes ridge
Reinstall	Sq.		160		160	and rake tiles.
Minimum Charge	Job		200		200	
Terra Cotta Red						
Demolish	Sq.		79		79	Includes material and labor to install
Install	Sq.	560	200		760	tile roofing. Cost based on terra cotta
Demolish and Install	Sq.	560	279		839	red flat clay tile and includes ridge
Reinstall	Sq.		160		160	and rake tiles.
Minimum Charge	Job		200		200	

Mission Tile Roofing

Mission Tile Roofing	Unit	Material	Labor	Equip.	Total	Specification
Glazed Red						
Demolish	Sq.		79		79	Includes material and labor to install
Install	Sq.	550	218		768	tile roofing. Cost based on glazed red
Demolish and Install	Sq.	550	297		847	tile and includes birdstop, ridge and
Reinstall	Sq.		174.55		174.55	rake tiles.
Minimum Charge	Job		200		200	
Unglazed Red						
Demolish	Sq.		79		79	Includes material and labor to install
Install	Sq.	445	218		663	tile roofing. Cost based on unglazed
Demolish and Install	Sq.	445	297		742	red tile and includes birdstop, ridge
Reinstall	Sq.		174.55		174.55	and rake tiles.
Minimum Charge	Job		200		200	
Glazed Blue						
Demolish	Sq.		79		79	Includes material and labor to install
Install	Sq.	550	218		768	tile roofing. Cost based on glazed
Demolish and Install	Sq.	550	297		847	blue tile and includes birdstop, ridge
Reinstall	Sq.		174.55		174.55	and rake tiles.
Minimum Charge	Job		200		200	
Glazed White						
Demolish	Sq.		79		79	Includes material and labor to install
Install	Sq.	550	218		768	tile roofing. Cost based on glazed
Demolish and Install	Sq.	550	297		847	white tile and includes birdstop, ridge
Reinstall	Sq.		174.55		174.55	and rake tiles.
Minimum Charge	Job		200		200	
Unglazed White						
Demolish	Sq.		79		79	Includes material and labor to install
Install	Sq.	550	218		768	tile roofing. Cost based on unglazed
Demolish and Install	Sq.	550	297		847	white tile and includes birdstop, ridge
Reinstall	Sq.		174.55		174.55	and rake tiles.
Minimum Charge	Job		200		200	

Roofing

Mission Tile Roofing

Mission Tile Roofing	Unit	Material	Labor	Equip.	Total	Specification
Color Blend						
Demolish	Sq.		79		79	Includes material and labor to install
Install	Sq.	550	218		768	tile roofing. Cost based on color blend
Demolish and Install	Sq.	550	297		847	tile and includes birdstop, ridge and
Reinstall	Sq.		174.55		174.55	rake tiles.
Minimum Charge	Job		200		200	
Accessories / Extras						
Add for Cap Furring Strips						
Install	Sq.	99	250		349	Includes labor and material to install vertically placed wood furring strips under cap tiles.
Add for Tile Adhesive						
Install	Sq.	23	14.60		37.60	Includes material and labor for adhesive material placed between tiles.
Add for Wire Attachment						
Install	Sq.	15.40	174		189.40	Includes labor and material to install single wire anchors for attaching tile.
Add for Braided Runners						
Install	Sq.	38.50	167		205.50	Includes labor and material to install braided wire runners for secure attachment in high wind areas.
Add for Stainless Steel Nails						
Install	Sq.	25.50			25.50	Includes material only for stainless steel nails.
Add for Brass Nails						
Install	Sq.	44			44	Includes material only for brass nails.
Add for Hurricane Clips						
Install	Sq.	23	235		258	Includes material and labor for Hurricane or wind clips for high wind areas.
Add for Copper Nails						
Install	Sq.	44			44	Includes material only for copper nails.
Add for Vertical Furring Strips						
Install	Sq.	19.30	46.50		65.80	Includes labor and material to install vertically placed wood furring strips under tiles.
Add for Horizontal Furring Strips						
Install	Sq.	13.20	21		34.20	Includes labor and material to install horizontally placed wood furring strips under tiles.

Spanish Tile Roofing

Spanish Tile Roofing	Unit	Material	Labor	Equip.	Total	Specification
Glazed Red						
Demolish	Sq.		79		79	Includes material and labor to install
Install	Sq.	770	167		937	tile roofing. Cost based on glazed red
Demolish and Install	Sq.	770	246		1016	tile and includes birdstop, ridge and
Reinstall	Sq.		133.33		133.33	rake tiles.
Minimum Charge	Job		200		200	

Roofing

Spanish Tile Roofing		Unit	Material	Labor	Equip.	Total	Specification
Glazed White							
	Demolish	Sq.		79		79	Includes material and labor to install
	Install	Sq.	770	222		992	tile roofing. Cost based on glazed
	Demolish and Install	Sq.	770	301		1071	white tile and includes birdstop, ridge
	Reinstall	Sq.		177.78		177.78	and rake tiles.
	Minimum Charge	Job		200		200	
Glazed Blue							
	Demolish	Sq.		79		79	Includes material and labor to install
	Install	Sq.	770	167		937	tile roofing. Cost based on glazed
	Demolish and Install	Sq.	770	246		1016	blue tile and includes birdstop, ridge
	Reinstall	Sq.		133.33		133.33	and rake tiles.
	Minimum Charge	Job		200		200	
Unglazed Red							
	Demolish	Sq.		79		79	Includes material and labor to install
	Install	Sq.	615	167		782	tile roofing. Cost based on unglazed
	Demolish and Install	Sq.	615	246		861	red tile and includes birdstop, ridge
	Reinstall	Sq.		133.33		133.33	and rake tiles.
	Minimum Charge	Job		200		200	
Unglazed White							
	Demolish	Sq.		79		79	Includes material and labor to install
	Install	Sq.	670	167		837	tile roofing. Cost based on unglazed
	Demolish and Install	Sq.	670	246		916	white tile and includes birdstop, ridge
	Reinstall	Sq.		133.33		133.33	and rake tiles.
	Minimum Charge	Job		200		200	
Color Blend							
	Demolish	Sq.		79		79	Includes material and labor to install
	Install	Sq.	670	167		837	tile roofing. Cost based on color blend
	Demolish and Install	Sq.	670	246		916	tile and includes birdstop, ridge and
	Reinstall	Sq.		133.33		133.33	rake tiles.
	Minimum Charge	Job		200		200	
Accessories / Extras							
Add for Vertical Furring Strips							
	Install	Sq.	19.30	46.50		65.80	Includes labor and material to install vertically placed wood furring strips under tiles.
Add for Wire Attachment							
	Install	Sq.	8.25	133		141.25	Includes labor and material to install single wire ties.
Add for Braided Runners							
	Install	Sq.	29.50	114		143.50	Includes labor and material to install braided wire runners for secure attachment in high wind areas.
Add for Stainless Steel Nails							
	Install	Sq.	21			21	Includes material only for stainless steel nails.
Add for Copper Nails							
	Install	Sq.	33			33	Includes material only for copper nails.
Add for Brass Nails							
	Install	Sq.	33			33	Includes material only for brass nails.
Add for Hurricane Clips							
	Install	Sq.	12.10	138		150.10	Includes material and labor to install hurricane or wind clips for high wind areas.

Roofing

Spanish Tile Roofing		Unit	Material	Labor	Equip.	Total	Specification
Add for Mortar Set Tiles	Install	Sq.	48.50	200		248.50	Includes material and labor to install setting tiles by using mortar material placed between tiles.
Add for Tile Adhesive	Install	Sq.	12.10	13		25.10	Includes material and labor for adhesive placed between tiles.
Add for Cap Furring Strips	Install	Sq.	99	250		349	Includes labor and material to install vertically placed wood furring strips under cap tiles.
Add for Horizontal Furring Strips	Install	Sq.	13.20	21		34.20	Includes labor and material to install horizontally placed wood furring strips under tiles.

Concrete Tile Roofing		Unit	Material	Labor	Equip.	Total	Specification
Corrugated Red / Brown							
	Demolish	Sq.		79		79	Includes material and labor to install tile roofing. Cost includes birdstop, booster, ridge and rake tiles.
	Install	Sq.	114	296		410	
	Demolish and Install	Sq.	114	375		489	
	Reinstall	Sq.		237.04		237.04	
	Minimum Charge	Job		200		200	
Corrugated Gray							
	Demolish	Sq.		79		79	Includes material and labor to install tile roofing. Cost includes birdstop, booster, ridge and rake tiles.
	Install	Sq.	114	296		410	
	Demolish and Install	Sq.	114	375		489	
	Reinstall	Sq.		237.04		237.04	
	Minimum Charge	Job		200		200	
Corrugated Bright Red							
	Demolish	Sq.		79		79	Includes material and labor to install tile roofing. Cost includes birdstop, booster, ridge and rake tiles.
	Install	Sq.	119	296		415	
	Demolish and Install	Sq.	119	375		494	
	Reinstall	Sq.		237.04		237.04	
	Minimum Charge	Job		200		200	
Corrugated Black							
	Demolish	Sq.		79		79	Includes material and labor to install tile roofing. Cost includes birdstop, booster, ridge and rake tiles.
	Install	Sq.	119	296		415	
	Demolish and Install	Sq.	119	375		494	
	Reinstall	Sq.		237.04		237.04	
	Minimum Charge	Job		200		200	
Corrugated Green							
	Demolish	Sq.		79		79	Includes material and labor to install tile roofing. Cost includes birdstop, booster, ridge and rake tiles.
	Install	Sq.	119	296		415	
	Demolish and Install	Sq.	119	375		494	
	Reinstall	Sq.		237.04		237.04	
	Minimum Charge	Job		200		200	
Corrugated Blue							
	Demolish	Sq.		79		79	Includes material and labor to install tile roofing. Cost includes birdstop, booster, ridge and rake tiles.
	Install	Sq.	119	296		415	
	Demolish and Install	Sq.	119	375		494	
	Reinstall	Sq.		237.04		237.04	
	Minimum Charge	Job		200		200	

Roofing

Concrete Tile Roofing

Concrete Tile Roofing	Unit	Material	Labor	Equip.	Total	Specification
Flat Natural Gray						
Demolish	Sq.		79		79	Includes material and labor to install
Install	Sq.	108	296		404	tile roofing. Cost includes birdstop,
Demolish and Install	Sq.	108	375		483	booster, ridge and rake tiles.
Reinstall	Sq.		237.04		237.04	
Minimum Charge	Job		200		200	
Flat Red / Brown						
Demolish	Sq.		79		79	Includes material and labor to install
Install	Sq.	108	296		404	tile roofing. Cost includes birdstop,
Demolish and Install	Sq.	108	375		483	booster, ridge and rake tiles.
Reinstall	Sq.		237.04		237.04	
Minimum Charge	Job		200		200	
Flat Bright Red						
Demolish	Sq.		79		79	Includes material and labor to install
Install	Sq.	108	296		404	tile roofing. Cost includes birdstop,
Demolish and Install	Sq.	108	375		483	booster, ridge and rake tiles.
Reinstall	Sq.		237.04		237.04	
Minimum Charge	Job		200		200	
Flat Green						
Demolish	Sq.		79		79	Includes material and labor to install
Install	Sq.	108	296		404	tile roofing. Cost includes birdstop,
Demolish and Install	Sq.	108	375		483	booster, ridge and rake tiles.
Minimum Charge	Job		200		200	
Flat Blue						
Demolish	Sq.		79		79	Includes material and labor to install
Install	Sq.	108	296		404	tile roofing. Cost includes birdstop,
Demolish and Install	Sq.	108	375		483	booster, ridge and rake tiles.
Reinstall	Sq.		237.04		237.04	
Minimum Charge	Job		200		200	
Flat Black						
Demolish	Sq.		79		79	Includes material and labor to install
Install	Sq.	108	296		404	tile roofing. Cost includes birdstop,
Demolish and Install	Sq.	108	375		483	booster, ridge and rake tiles.
Reinstall	Sq.		237.04		237.04	
Minimum Charge	Job		200		200	

Aluminum Sheet

Aluminum Sheet	Unit	Material	Labor	Equip.	Total	Specification
Corrugated						
.019" Thick Natural						
Demolish	S.F.		.84		.84	Includes material and labor to install
Install	S.F.	1.43	2.01		3.44	aluminum sheet metal roofing.
Demolish and Install	S.F.	1.43	2.85		4.28	
Reinstall	S.F.		1.61		1.61	
Minimum Charge	Job		480		480	
.016" Thick Natural						
Demolish	S.F.		.84		.84	Includes material and labor to install
Install	S.F.	1.09	2.01		3.10	aluminum sheet metal roofing.
Demolish and Install	S.F.	1.09	2.85		3.94	
Reinstall	S.F.		1.61		1.61	
Minimum Charge	Job		480		480	
.016" Colored Finish						
Demolish	S.F.		.84		.84	Includes material and labor to install
Install	S.F.	1.58	2.01		3.59	aluminum sheet metal roofing.
Demolish and Install	S.F.	1.58	2.85		4.43	
Reinstall	S.F.		1.61		1.61	
Minimum Charge	Job		480		480	

Roofing

Aluminum Sheet	Unit	Material	Labor	Equip.	Total	Specification
.019″ Colored Finish						
Demolish	S.F.		.84		.84	Includes material and labor to install
Install	S.F.	1.76	2.01		3.77	aluminum sheet metal roofing.
Demolish and Install	S.F.	1.76	2.85		4.61	
Reinstall	S.F.		1.61		1.61	
Minimum Charge	Job		480		480	
Ribbed						
.019″ Thick Natural						
Demolish	S.F.		.84		.84	Includes material and labor to install
Install	S.F.	1.43	2.01		3.44	aluminum sheet metal roofing.
Demolish and Install	S.F.	1.43	2.85		4.28	
Reinstall	S.F.		1.61		1.61	
Minimum Charge	Job		480		480	
.016″ Thick Natural						
Demolish	S.F.		.84		.84	Includes material and labor to install
Install	S.F.	1.09	2.01		3.10	aluminum sheet metal roofing.
Demolish and Install	S.F.	1.09	2.85		3.94	
Reinstall	S.F.		1.61		1.61	
Minimum Charge	Job		480		480	
.050″ Colored Finish						
Demolish	S.F.		.84		.84	Includes material and labor to install
Install	S.F.	4.90	2.01		6.91	aluminum sheet metal roofing.
Demolish and Install	S.F.	4.90	2.85		7.75	
Reinstall	S.F.		1.61		1.61	
Minimum Charge	Job		480		480	
.032″ Thick Natural						
Demolish	S.F.		.84		.84	Includes material and labor to install
Install	S.F.	2.78	2.01		4.79	aluminum sheet metal roofing.
Demolish and Install	S.F.	2.78	2.85		5.63	
Reinstall	S.F.		1.61		1.61	
Minimum Charge	Job		480		480	
.040″ Thick Natural						
Demolish	S.F.		.84		.84	Includes material and labor to install
Install	S.F.	3.38	2.01		5.39	aluminum sheet metal roofing.
Demolish and Install	S.F.	3.38	2.85		6.23	
Reinstall	S.F.		1.61		1.61	
Minimum Charge	Job		480		480	
.050″ Thick Natural						
Demolish	S.F.		.84		.84	Includes material and labor to install
Install	S.F.	4.06	2.01		6.07	aluminum sheet metal roofing.
Demolish and Install	S.F.	4.06	2.85		6.91	
Reinstall	S.F.		1.61		1.61	
Minimum Charge	Job		480		480	
.016″ Colored Finish						
Demolish	S.F.		.84		.84	Includes material and labor to install
Install	S.F.	1.58	2.01		3.59	aluminum sheet metal roofing.
Demolish and Install	S.F.	1.58	2.85		4.43	
Reinstall	S.F.		1.61		1.61	
Minimum Charge	Job		480		480	
.019″ Colored Finish						
Demolish	S.F.		.84		.84	Includes material and labor to install
Install	S.F.	1.76	2.01		3.77	aluminum sheet metal roofing.
Demolish and Install	S.F.	1.76	2.85		4.61	
Reinstall	S.F.		1.61		1.61	
Minimum Charge	Job		480		480	

Roofing

Aluminum Sheet

Aluminum Sheet	Unit	Material	Labor	Equip.	Total	Specification
.032" Colored Finish						
Demolish	S.F.		.84		.84	Includes material and labor to install
Install	S.F.	3.41	2.01		5.42	aluminum sheet metal roofing.
Demolish and Install	S.F.	3.41	2.85		6.26	
Reinstall	S.F.		1.61		1.61	
Minimum Charge	Job		480		480	
.040" Colored Finish						
Demolish	S.F.		.84		.84	Includes material and labor to install
Install	S.F.	4.07	2.01		6.08	aluminum sheet metal roofing.
Demolish and Install	S.F.	4.07	2.85		6.92	
Reinstall	S.F.		1.61		1.61	
Minimum Charge	Job		480		480	

Fiberglass Sheet

Fiberglass Sheet	Unit	Material	Labor	Equip.	Total	Specification
12 Ounce Corrugated						
Demolish	S.F.		1.51		1.51	Cost includes material and labor to
Install	S.F.	3.91	1.60		5.51	install 12 ounce corrugated fiberglass
Demolish and Install	S.F.	3.91	3.11		7.02	sheet roofing.
Reinstall	S.F.		1.28		1.28	
Minimum Charge	Job		199		199	
8 Ounce Corrugated						
Demolish	S.F.		1.51		1.51	Cost includes material and labor to
Install	S.F.	2.29	1.60		3.89	install 8 ounce corrugated fiberglass
Demolish and Install	S.F.	2.29	3.11		5.40	roofing.
Reinstall	S.F.		1.28		1.28	
Minimum Charge	Job		199		199	

Galvanized Steel

Galvanized Steel	Unit	Material	Labor	Equip.	Total	Specification
Corrugated						
24 Gauge						
Demolish	S.F.		.84		.84	Includes material and labor to install
Install	S.F.	3.19	1.69		4.88	galvanized steel sheet metal roofing.
Demolish and Install	S.F.	3.19	2.53		5.72	Cost based on 24 gauge corrugated
Reinstall	S.F.		1.35		1.35	or ribbed steel roofing.
Minimum Charge	Job		199		199	
26 Gauge						
Demolish	S.F.		.84		.84	Includes material and labor to install
Install	S.F.	2.04	1.60		3.64	galvanized steel sheet metal roofing.
Demolish and Install	S.F.	2.04	2.44		4.48	Cost based on 26 gauge corrugated
Reinstall	S.F.		1.28		1.28	or ribbed steel roofing.
Minimum Charge	Job		199		199	
28 Gauge						
Demolish	S.F.		.84		.84	Includes material and labor to install
Install	S.F.	1.97	1.53		3.50	galvanized steel sheet metal roofing.
Demolish and Install	S.F.	1.97	2.37		4.34	Cost based on 28 gauge corrugated
Reinstall	S.F.		1.22		1.22	or ribbed steel roofing.
Minimum Charge	Job		199		199	
30 Gauge						
Demolish	S.F.		.84		.84	Includes material and labor to install
Install	S.F.	1.84	1.46		3.30	galvanized steel sheet metal roofing.
Demolish and Install	S.F.	1.84	2.30		4.14	Cost based on 30 gauge corrugated
Reinstall	S.F.		1.17		1.17	or ribbed steel roofing.
Minimum Charge	Job		199		199	

Roofing

Galvanized Steel

Galvanized Steel	Unit	Material	Labor	Equip.	Total	Specification
Ribbed						
24 Gauge						
Demolish	S.F.		.84		.84	Includes material and labor to install
Install	S.F.	3.19	1.69		4.88	galvanized steel sheet metal roofing.
Demolish and Install	S.F.	3.19	2.53		5.72	Cost based on 24 gauge corrugated
Reinstall	S.F.		1.35		1.35	or ribbed steel roofing.
Minimum Charge	Job		199		199	
26 Gauge						
Demolish	S.F.		.84		.84	Includes material and labor to install
Install	S.F.	2.04	1.60		3.64	galvanized steel sheet metal roofing.
Demolish and Install	S.F.	2.04	2.44		4.48	Cost based on 26 gauge corrugated
Reinstall	S.F.		1.28		1.28	or ribbed steel roofing.
Minimum Charge	Job		199		199	
28 Gauge						
Demolish	S.F.		.84		.84	Includes material and labor to install
Install	S.F.	1.97	1.53		3.50	galvanized steel sheet metal roofing.
Demolish and Install	S.F.	1.97	2.37		4.34	Cost based on 28 gauge corrugated
Reinstall	S.F.		1.22		1.22	or ribbed steel roofing.
Minimum Charge	Job		199		199	
30 Gauge						
Demolish	S.F.		.84		.84	Includes material and labor to install
Install	S.F.	1.84	1.46		3.30	galvanized steel sheet metal roofing.
Demolish and Install	S.F.	1.84	2.30		4.14	Cost based on 30 gauge corrugated
Reinstall	S.F.		1.17		1.17	or ribbed steel roofing.
Minimum Charge	Job		199		199	

Standing Seam

Standing Seam	Unit	Material	Labor	Equip.	Total	Specification
Copper						
16 Ounce						
Demolish	Sq.		84		84	Includes material and labor to install
Install	Sq.	955	370		1325	copper standing seam metal roofing.
Demolish and Install	Sq.	955	454		1409	Cost based on 16 ounce copper
Reinstall	Sq.		296.37		296.37	roofing.
Minimum Charge	Job		241		241	
18 Ounce						
Demolish	Sq.		84		84	Includes material and labor to install
Install	Sq.	1075	400		1475	copper standing seam metal roofing.
Demolish and Install	Sq.	1075	484		1559	Cost based on 18 ounce copper
Reinstall	Sq.		321.07		321.07	roofing.
Minimum Charge	Job		241		241	
20 Ounce						
Demolish	Sq.		84		84	Includes material and labor to install
Install	Sq.	1350	440		1790	copper standing seam metal roofing.
Demolish and Install	Sq.	1350	524		1874	Cost based on 20 ounce copper
Reinstall	Sq.		350.25		350.25	roofing.
Stainless Steel						
26 Gauge						
Demolish	Sq.		84		84	Cost includes material and labor to
Install	Sq.	565	420		985	install 26 gauge stainless steel
Demolish and Install	Sq.	565	504		1069	standing seam metal roofing.
Reinstall	Sq.		335.03		335.03	
Minimum Charge	Job		241		241	

Roofing

Standing Seam	Unit	Material	Labor	Equip.	Total	Specification
28 Gauge						
Demolish	Sq.		84		84	Includes material and labor to install standing seam metal roofing. Cost based on 28 gauge stainless steel roofing.
Install	Sq.	610	400		1010	
Demolish and Install	Sq.	610	484		1094	
Reinstall	Sq.		321.07		321.07	
Minimum Charge	Job		241		241	

Elastomeric Roofing	Unit	Material	Labor	Equip.	Total	Specification
Neoprene						
1/16″						
Demolish	Sq.		29		29	Includes material and labor to install neoprene membrane, fully adhered, 1/16″ thick.
Install	Sq.	245	190	44.50	479.50	
Demolish and Install	Sq.	245	219	44.50	508.50	
Minimum Charge	Job		910	110	1020	
GRM Membrane						
1/16″						
Demolish	Sq.		29		29	Includes material and labor to install coal tar based elastomeric roofing membrane, polyester fiber reinforced.
Install	Sq.	81	305	36.50	422.50	
Demolish and Install	Sq.	81	334	36.50	451.50	
Minimum Charge	Job		910	110	1020	
Cant Strips						
3″						
Demolish	L.F.		.90		.90	Includes material and labor to install cants 3″ x 3″, treated timber, cut diagonally.
Install	L.F.	.92	1.22		2.14	
Demolish and Install	L.F.	.92	2.12		3.04	
Minimum Charge	Job		99.50		99.50	
4″						
Demolish	L.F.		.90		.90	Includes material and labor to install cants 4″ x 4″, treated timber, cut diagonally.
Install	L.F.	1.93	1.22		3.15	
Demolish and Install	L.F.	1.93	2.12		4.05	
Minimum Charge	Job		99.50		99.50	
Polyvinyl Chloride (PVC)						
45 mil (loose laid)						
Demolish	Sq.		29		29	Cost includes material and labor to install 45 mil PVC elastomeric roofing, loose-laid with stone.
Install	Sq.	106	35.50	4.30	145.80	
Demolish and Install	Sq.	106	64.50	4.30	174.80	
Minimum Charge	Job		910	110	1020	
48 mil (loose laid)						
Demolish	Sq.		29		29	Cost includes material and labor to install 48 mil PVC elastomeric roofing, loose-laid with stone.
Install	Sq.	129	35.50	4.30	168.80	
Demolish and Install	Sq.	129	64.50	4.30	197.80	
Minimum Charge	Job		910	110	1020	
60 mil (loose laid)						
Demolish	Sq.		29		29	Cost includes material and labor to install 60 mil PVC elastomeric roofing, loose-laid with stone.
Install	Sq.	130	35.50	4.30	169.80	
Demolish and Install	Sq.	130	64.50	4.30	198.80	
Minimum Charge	Job		910	110	1020	
45 mil (attached)						
Demolish	Sq.		46.50		46.50	Cost includes material and labor to install 45 mil PVC elastomeric roofing fully attached to roof deck.
Install	Sq.	97.50	70	8.45	175.95	
Demolish and Install	Sq.	97.50	116.50	8.45	222.45	
Minimum Charge	Job		910	110	1020	

Roofing

Elastomeric Roofing	Unit	Material	Labor	Equip.	Total	Specification
48 mil (attached)						
Demolish	Sq.		46.50		46.50	Cost includes material and labor to
Install	Sq.	168	70	8.45	246.45	install 48 mil PVC elastomeric roofing
Demolish and Install	Sq.	168	116.50	8.45	292.95	fully attached to roof deck.
Minimum Charge	Job		910	110	1020	
60 mil (attached)						
Demolish	Sq.		46.50		46.50	Cost includes material and labor to
Install	Sq.	169	70	8.45	247.45	install 60 mil PVC elastomeric roofing
Demolish and Install	Sq.	169	116.50	8.45	293.95	fully attached to roof deck.
Minimum Charge	Job		910	110	1020	
CSPE Type						
45 mil (loose laid w / stone)						
Demolish	Sq.		29		29	Cost includes material and labor to
Install	Sq.	350	70	8.45	428.45	install 45 mil CSPE (chlorosulfonated
Demolish and Install	Sq.	350	99	8.45	457.45	polyethylene-hypalon) roofing material
Minimum Charge	Job		910	110	1020	loose laid on deck and ballasted with
						stone.
45 mil (attached at seams)						
Demolish	Sq.		35		35	Cost includes material and labor to
Install	Sq.	450	52	6.25	508.25	install 45 mil CSPE (chlorosulfonated
Demolish and Install	Sq.	450	87	6.25	543.25	polyethylene-hypalon) roofing material
Minimum Charge	Job		910	110	1020	attached to deck at seams with batten
						strips.
45 mil (fully attached)						
Demolish	Sq.		46.50		46.50	Cost includes material and labor to
Install	Sq.	340	52	6.25	398.25	install 45 mil CSPE (chlorosulfonated
Demolish and Install	Sq.	340	98.50	6.25	444.75	polyethylene-hypalon) roofing material
Minimum Charge	Job		910	110	1020	fully attached to deck.
EPDM Type						
45 mil (attached at seams)						
Demolish	Sq.		35		35	Cost includes material and labor to
Install	Sq.	86.50	52	6.25	144.75	install 45 mil EPDM (ethylene
Demolish and Install	Sq.	86.50	87	6.25	179.75	propylene diene monomer) roofing
Minimum Charge	Job		910	110	1020	material attached to deck at seams.
45 mil (fully attached)						
Demolish	Sq.		46.50		46.50	Cost includes material and labor to
Install	Sq.	122	70	8.45	200.45	install 45 mil EPDM (ethylene
Demolish and Install	Sq.	122	116.50	8.45	246.95	propylene diene monomer) roofing
Minimum Charge	Job		910	110	1020	material fully attached to deck.
45 mil (loose laid w / stone)						
Demolish	Sq.		29		29	Cost includes material and labor to
Install	Sq.	91.50	35.50	4.30	131.30	install 45 mil EPDM (ethylene
Demolish and Install	Sq.	91.50	64.50	4.30	160.30	propylene diene monomer) roofing
Minimum Charge	Job		910	110	1020	material loose laid on deck and
						ballasted with stones (approx. 1/2 ton
						of stone per square).
60 mil (attached at seams)						
Demolish	Sq.		35		35	Cost includes material and labor to
Install	Sq.	101	52	6.25	159.25	install 60 mil EPDM (ethylene
Demolish and Install	Sq.	101	87	6.25	194.25	propylene diene monomer) roofing
Minimum Charge	Job		910	110	1020	material attached to deck at seams.
60 mil (fully attached)						
Demolish	Sq.		46.50		46.50	Cost includes material and labor to
Install	Sq.	136	70	8.45	214.45	install 60 mil EPDM (ethylene
Demolish and Install	Sq.	136	116.50	8.45	260.95	propylene diene monomer) roofing
Minimum Charge	Job		910	110	1020	material fully attached to deck.

Roofing

Elastomeric Roofing

	Unit	Material	Labor	Equip.	Total	Specification
60 mil (loose laid w / stone)						Cost includes material and labor to
Demolish	Sq.		29		29	install 60 mil EPDM (ethylene
Install	Sq.	107	35.50	4.30	146.80	propylene diene monomer) roofing
Demolish and Install	Sq.	107	64.50	4.30	175.80	material loose laid on deck and
Minimum Charge	Job		910	110	1020	ballasted with stones (approx. 1/2 ton of stone per square).

Modified Bitumen Roofing

	Unit	Material	Labor	Equip.	Total	Specification
Fully Attached						
120 mil						
Demolish	Sq.		69.50		69.50	Cost includes material and labor to
Install	Sq.	76	8.85	2.07	86.92	install 120 mil modified bitumen
Demolish and Install	Sq.	76	78.35	2.07	156.42	roofing, fully attached to deck by
Minimum Charge	Job		99.50		99.50	torch.
150 mil						
Demolish	Sq.		69.50		69.50	Cost includes material and labor to
Install	Sq.	83.50	22	5.10	110.60	install 150 mil modified bitumen
Demolish and Install	Sq.	83.50	91.50	5.10	180.10	roofing, fully attached to deck by
Minimum Charge	Job		99.50		99.50	torch.
160 mil						
Demolish	Sq.		69.50		69.50	Cost includes material and labor to
Install	Sq.	95.50	22.50	5.30	123.30	install 160 mil modified bitumen
Demolish and Install	Sq.	95.50	92	5.30	192.80	roofing, fully attached to deck by
Minimum Charge	Job		99.50		99.50	torch.

Built-up Roofing

	Unit	Material	Labor	Equip.	Total	Specification
Emergency Repairs						
Install	Ea.	220	1875	435	2530	Minimum charge for work requiring
Minimum Charge	Job		1300	305	1605	hot asphalt.
Asphalt						
3-ply Asphalt						
Demolish	Sq.		72.50		72.50	Cost includes material and labor to
Install	Sq.	80	109	25.50	214.50	install 3-ply asphalt built-up roof
Demolish and Install	Sq.	80	181.50	25.50	287	including one 30 lb and two 15 lb
Minimum Charge	Job		1300	305	1605	layers of felt.
4-ply Asphalt						
Demolish	Sq.		86		86	Cost includes material and labor to
Install	Sq.	108	119	27.50	254.50	install 4-ply asphalt built-up roof
Demolish and Install	Sq.	108	205	27.50	340.50	including one 30 lb and three 15 lb
Minimum Charge	Job		1300	305	1605	layers of felt.
5-ply Asphalt						
Demolish	Sq.		113		113	Cost includes material and labor to
Install	Sq.	147	131	30.50	308.50	install 5-ply asphalt built-up roof
Demolish and Install	Sq.	147	244	30.50	421.50	including one 30 lb and four 15 lb
Minimum Charge	Job		1300	305	1605	layers of felt.

Roofing

Built-up Roofing		Unit	Material	Labor	Equip.	Total	Specification
Components / Accessories							
Flood Coat	Install	Sq.	30.50	61		91.50	Includes labor and material to install flood coat.
R / R Gravel and Flood Coat	Install	Sq.	35	199		234	Includes labor and material to install flood coat and gravel.
Aluminum UV Coat	Install	Sq.	32.50	227	27.50	287	Includes labor and material to install aluminum-based UV coating.
Gravel Coat	Demolish	Sq.		36		36	Includes labor and material to install gravel coat.
	Install	Sq.	4.71	33		37.71	
	Demolish and Install	Sq.	4.71	69		73.71	
Mineral Surface Cap Sheet	Install	Sq.	88	6.85		94.85	Cost includes labor and material to install 50 # mineral surfaced cap sheet.
Fibrated Aluminum UV Coating	Install	Sq.	34.50	61		95.50	Includes labor and material to install fibered aluminum-based UV coating.
Impregnated Walk							
1"	Install	S.F.	3.14	2.12		5.26	Cost includes labor and material to install 1" layer of asphalt coating.
1/2"	Install	S.F.	2.26	1.68		3.94	Cost includes labor and material to install 1/2" layer of asphalt coating.
3/4"	Install	S.F.	2.81	1.77		4.58	Cost includes labor and material to install 3/4" layer of asphalt coating.

Exterior Doors and Windows

Doors	Roof Window	Double Hung Window

Exterior Type Door	Unit	Material	Labor	Equip.	Total	Specification
Entry						
Flush (1-3/4")						
Demolish	Ea.		40		40	Cost includes material and labor to
Install	Ea.	252	27		279	install 3' x 6' 8" pre-hung 1-3/4"
Demolish and Install	Ea.	252	67		319	door, including casing and stop,
Reinstall	Ea.		27		27	hinges, jamb, aluminum sill,
Clean	Ea.	4.03	13.35		17.38	weatherstripped.
Paint	Ea.	10.30	53		63.30	
Minimum Charge	Job		216		216	
Raised Panel						
Demolish	Ea.		40		40	Cost includes material and labor to
Install	Ea.	485	24		509	install 3' x 6' 8" pre-hung 1-3/4"
Demolish and Install	Ea.	485	64		549	door, jamb, including casing and
Reinstall	Ea.		24		24	stop, hinges, aluminum sill,
Clean	Ea.	4.03	13.35		17.38	weatherstripping.
Paint	Ea.	10.30	53		63.30	
Minimum Charge	Job		216		216	
Entry w / Lights						
Good Quality						
Demolish	Ea.		40		40	Cost includes material and labor to
Install	Ea.	350	54		404	install 3' x 6' 8" pre-hung 1-3/4"
Demolish and Install	Ea.	350	94		444	door, solid wood lower panel, with up
Reinstall	Ea.		54		54	to 9-light glass panels, casing, sill,
Clean	Ea.	4.03	13.35		17.38	weatherstripped.
Paint	Ea.	7.55	24.50		32.05	
Minimum Charge	Job		216		216	
Better Quality						
Demolish	Ea.		40		40	Cost includes material and labor to
Install	Ea.	360	54		414	install 3' x 6' 8" pre-hung 1-3/4" Ash
Demolish and Install	Ea.	360	94		454	door, solid wood, raised panel door
Reinstall	Ea.		54		54	without glass panels.
Clean	Ea.	4.03	13.35		17.38	
Paint	Ea.	10.30	53		63.30	
Minimum Charge	Job		216		216	
Premium Quality						
Demolish	Ea.		40		40	Cost includes material and labor to
Install	Ea.	970	25.50		995.50	install 3' x 6' 8" pre-hung 1-3/4" Oak
Demolish and Install	Ea.	970	65.50		1035.50	door, solid wood, raised panel door
Reinstall	Ea.		25.41		25.41	without glass panels.
Clean	Ea.	4.03	13.35		17.38	
Paint	Ea.	10.30	53		63.30	
Minimum Charge	Job		216		216	

Exterior Doors and Windows

Exterior Type Door	Unit	Material	Labor	Equip.	Total	Specification
Custom Quality						
Demolish	Ea.		40		40	Cost includes material and labor to
Install	Ea.	510	57.50		567.50	install 3′ x 6′ 8″ pre-hung 1-3/4″
Demolish and Install	Ea.	510	97.50		607.50	hand-made, solid wood, raised panel
Reinstall	Ea.		57.60		57.60	door with custom stained glass.
Clean	Ea.	.28	13.35		13.63	
Paint	Ea.	2.61	123		125.61	
Minimum Charge	Job		216		216	
Miami Style						
Demolish	Ea.		40		40	Cost includes material and labor to
Install	Ea.	232	25.50		257.50	install 3′ x 6′ 8″ pre-hung 1-3/4″
Demolish and Install	Ea.	232	65.50		297.50	lauan door of solid wood.
Reinstall	Ea.		25.41		25.41	
Clean	Ea.	.28	13.35		13.63	
Paint	Ea.	10.30	53		63.30	
Minimum Charge	Job		216		216	
French Style						
1-Light						
Demolish	Ea.		40		40	Cost includes material and labor to
Install	Ea.	660	72		732	install 3′ x 6′ 8″ pre-hung 1-3/4″
Demolish and Install	Ea.	660	112		772	French style door with 1 light.
Reinstall	Ea.		72		72	
Clean	Ea.	2.52	20		22.52	
Paint	Ea.	11.60	92.50		104.10	
Minimum Charge	Job		216		216	
9-Light						
Demolish	Ea.		40		40	Cost includes material and labor to
Install	Ea.	725	31		756	install 3′ x 6′ 8″ pre-hung 1-3/4″
Demolish and Install	Ea.	725	71		796	French style door with 9 lights.
Reinstall	Ea.		30.86		30.86	
Clean	Ea.	.55	26.50		27.05	
Paint	Ea.	11.60	92.50		104.10	
Minimum Charge	Job		216		216	
15-Light						
Demolish	Ea.		44.50		44.50	Cost includes material and labor to
Install	Ea.	705	61.50		766.50	install 3′ x 6′ 8″ pre-hung 1-3/4″
Demolish and Install	Ea.	705	106		811	french style door with 15 lights.
Reinstall	Ea.		61.71		61.71	
Clean	Ea.	.55	26.50		27.05	
Paint	Ea.	11.60	92.50		104.10	
Minimum Charge	Job		216		216	
Jamb						
Wood						
Demolish	Ea.		30		30	Includes material and labor to install
Install	Ea.	146	11.70		157.70	flat pine jamb with square cut heads
Demolish and Install	Ea.	146	41.70		187.70	and rabbeted sides for 6′ 8″ high and
Clean	Ea.	.13	8		8.13	3-9/16″ door including trim sets for
Paint	Ea.	7.55	24.50		32.05	both sides.
Minimum Charge	Job		216		216	
Metal 6′ 8″ High						
Demolish	Ea.		24		24	Cost includes material and labor to
Install	Ea.	171	27		198	install 18 gauge hollow metal door
Demolish and Install	Ea.	171	51		222	frame to fit a 4-1/2″ jamb 6′ 8″ high
Reinstall	Ea.		27		27	and up to 3′ 6″ opening.
Clean	Ea.	.84	6.70		7.54	
Paint	Ea.	1.77	7.40		9.17	
Minimum Charge	Job		216		216	

Exterior Doors and Windows

Exterior Type Door		Unit	Material	Labor	Equip.	Total	Specification
Metal 7' High							
	Demolish	Ea.		24		24	Cost includes material and labor to
	Install	Ea.	178	29		207	install 18 gauge hollow metal door
	Demolish and Install	Ea.	178	53		231	frame to fit a 4-1/2" jamb 7' high and
	Reinstall	Ea.		28.80		28.80	up to 3' 6" opening.
	Clean	Ea.	.84	6.70		7.54	
	Paint	Ea.	1.77	7.40		9.17	
	Minimum Charge	Job		216		216	
Metal 8' High							
	Demolish	Ea.		24		24	Cost includes material and labor to
	Install	Ea.	220	36		256	install 18 gauge hollow metal door
	Demolish and Install	Ea.	220	60		280	frame to fit a 4-1/2" jamb 8' high and
	Reinstall	Ea.		36		36	up to 3' 6" opening.
	Clean	Ea.	1.19	8		9.19	
	Paint	Ea.	1.98	8.20		10.18	
	Minimum Charge	Job		216		216	
Metal 9' High							
	Demolish	Ea.		24		24	Cost includes material and labor to
	Install	Ea.	282	43		325	install 18 gauge hollow metal door
	Demolish and Install	Ea.	282	67		349	frame to fit a 4-1/2" jamb 9' high and
	Reinstall	Ea.		43.20		43.20	up to 3' 6" opening.
	Clean	Ea.	1.19	8		9.19	
	Paint	Ea.	1.98	8.20		10.18	
	Minimum Charge	Job		216		216	
Casing Trim							
Single Width							
	Demolish	Ea.		7.60		7.60	Cost includes material and labor to
	Install	Opng.	28	36		64	install 11/16" x 2-1/2" pine ranch
	Demolish and Install	Opng.	28	43.60		71.60	style casing for one side of a standard
	Reinstall	Opng.		28.80		28.80	door opening.
	Clean	Opng.	.57	3.20		3.77	
	Paint	Ea.	5.20	7.40		12.60	
	Minimum Charge	Job		216		216	
Double Width							
	Demolish	Ea.		9.05		9.05	Cost includes material and labor to
	Install	Opng.	33	43		76	install 11/16" x 2-1/2" pine ranch
	Demolish and Install	Opng.	33	52.05		85.05	style door casing for one side of a
	Reinstall	Opng.		34.56		34.56	double door opening.
	Clean	Opng.	.67	6.40		7.07	
	Paint	Ea.	5.20	8.40		13.60	
	Minimum Charge	Job		216		216	

Residential Metal Door		Unit	Material	Labor	Equip.	Total	Specification
Pre-hung, Steel-clad							
2' 8" x 6' 8"							
	Demolish	Ea.		40		40	Cost includes material and labor to
	Install	Ea.	335	51		386	install 2' 6" x 6' 8" pre-hung 1-3/4"
	Demolish and Install	Ea.	335	91		426	24 gauge steel clad door with 4-1/2"
	Reinstall	Ea.		50.82		50.82	wood frame, trims, hinges, aluminum
	Clean	Ea.	4.03	13.35		17.38	sill, weatherstripped.
	Paint	Ea.	11.60	53		64.60	
	Minimum Charge	Job		216		216	

Exterior Doors and Windows

Residential Metal Door

	Unit	Material	Labor	Equip.	Total	Specification
3' x 6' 8"						
Demolish	Ea.		40		40	Cost includes material and labor to
Install	Ea.	290	57.50		347.50	install 3' x 6' 8" pre-hung 1-3/4" 24
Demolish and Install	Ea.	290	97.50		387.50	gauge steel clad door with 4-1/2"
Reinstall	Ea.		57.60		57.60	wood frame, trims, hinges, aluminum
Clean	Ea.	4.03	13.35		17.38	sill, weatherstripped.
Paint	Ea.	11.60	53		64.60	
Minimum Charge	Job		216		216	

Metal Door

	Unit	Material	Labor	Equip.	Total	Specification
Steel, Door Only						
2' 8" x 6' 8", 18 Gauge						
Demolish	Ea.		8.55		8.55	Cost includes material and labor to
Install	Ea.	555	27		582	install 18 gauge 2' 8" x 6' 8" steel
Demolish and Install	Ea.	555	35.55		590.55	door only, 1-3/4" thick, hinges.
Reinstall	Ea.		27		27	
Clean	Ea.	1.68	10		11.68	
Paint	Ea.	6.40	31		37.40	
Minimum Charge	Job		216		216	
3' x 6' 8", 18 Gauge						
Demolish	Ea.		8.55		8.55	Cost includes material and labor to
Install	Ea.	540	29		569	install 18 gauge 3' x 6' 8" steel door
Demolish and Install	Ea.	540	37.55		577.55	only, 1-3/4" thick, hinges.
Reinstall	Ea.		28.80		28.80	
Clean	Ea.	1.68	10		11.68	
Paint	Ea.	6.40	31		37.40	
Minimum Charge	Job		216		216	
2' 8" x 7', 18 Gauge						
Demolish	Ea.		8.55		8.55	Cost includes material and labor to
Install	Ea.	570	29		599	install 18 gauge 2' 8" x 7' steel door
Demolish and Install	Ea.	570	37.55		607.55	only, 1-3/4" thick, hinges.
Reinstall	Ea.		28.80		28.80	
Clean	Ea.	1.68	10		11.68	
Paint	Ea.	6.40	31		37.40	
Minimum Charge	Job		216		216	
3' x 7', 18 Gauge						
Demolish	Ea.		8.55		8.55	Cost includes material and labor to
Install	Ea.	585	31		616	install 18 gauge 3' x 7' steel door
Demolish and Install	Ea.	585	39.55		624.55	only, 1-3/4" thick, hinges.
Reinstall	Ea.		30.86		30.86	
Clean	Ea.	1.68	10		11.68	
Paint	Ea.	6.40	31		37.40	
Minimum Charge	Job		216		216	
3' 6" x 7', 18 Gauge						
Demolish	Ea.		8.55		8.55	Cost includes material and labor to
Install	Ea.	645	33		678	install 18 gauge 3' 6" x 7' steel door
Demolish and Install	Ea.	645	41.55		686.55	only, 1-3/4" thick, hinges.
Reinstall	Ea.		33.23		33.23	
Clean	Ea.	1.68	10		11.68	
Paint	Ea.	6.40	31		37.40	
Minimum Charge	Job		216		216	

Exterior Doors and Windows

Metal Door		Unit	Material	Labor	Equip.	Total	Specification
Casing Trim							
Single Width							
	Demolish	Ea.		7.60		7.60	Cost includes material and labor to
	Install	Opng.	28	36		64	install 11/16" x 2-1/2" pine ranch
	Demolish and Install	Opng.	28	43.60		71.60	style casing for one side of a standard
	Reinstall	Opng.		28.80		28.80	door opening.
	Clean	Opng.	.57	3.20		3.77	
	Paint	Ea.	5.20	7.40		12.60	
	Minimum Charge	Job		216		216	
Double Width							
	Demolish	Ea.		9.05		9.05	Cost includes material and labor to
	Install	Opng.	33	43		76	install 11/16" x 2-1/2" pine ranch
	Demolish and Install	Opng.	33	52.05		85.05	style door casing for one side of a
	Reinstall	Opng.		34.56		34.56	double door opening.
	Clean	Opng.	.67	6.40		7.07	
	Paint	Ea.	5.20	8.40		13.60	
	Minimum Charge	Job		216		216	

Solid Core Door		Unit	Material	Labor	Equip.	Total	Specification
Exterior Type							
Flush (1-3/4")							
	Demolish	Ea.		40		40	Cost includes material and labor to
	Install	Ea.	415	54		469	install 3' x 6' 8" pre-hung 1-3/4"
	Demolish and Install	Ea.	415	94		509	door, including casing and stop,
	Reinstall	Ea.		54		54	hinges, jamb, aluminum sill,
	Clean	Ea.	4.03	13.35		17.38	weatherstripped.
	Paint	Ea.	11.60	53		64.60	
	Minimum Charge	Job		216		216	
Raised Panel							
	Demolish	Ea.		40		40	Cost includes material and labor to
	Install	Ea.	485	24		509	install 3' x 6' 8" pre-hung 1-3/4"
	Demolish and Install	Ea.	485	64		549	door, jamb, including casing and
	Reinstall	Ea.		24		24	stop, hinges, aluminum sill,
	Clean	Ea.	4.03	13.35		17.38	weatherstripping.
	Paint	Ea.	11.60	123		134.60	
	Minimum Charge	Job		216		216	
Entry w / Lights							
	Demolish	Ea.		40		40	Cost includes material and labor to
	Install	Ea.	350	54		404	install 3' x 6' 8" pre-hung 1-3/4"
	Demolish and Install	Ea.	350	94		444	door, solid wood lower panel, with up
	Reinstall	Ea.		54		54	to 9-light glass panels, casing, sill,
	Clean	Ea.	4.03	13.35		17.38	weatherstripped.
	Paint	Ea.	2.61	123		125.61	
	Minimum Charge	Job		216		216	
Custom Entry							
	Demolish	Ea.		40		40	Cost includes material and labor to
	Install	Ea.	1975	86.50		2061.50	install prehung, fir, single glazed with
	Demolish and Install	Ea.	1975	126.50		2101.50	lead caming, 1-3/4" x 6' 8" x 3'.
	Reinstall	Ea.		86.40		86.40	
	Clean	Ea.	4.03	13.35		17.38	
	Paint	Ea.	6.40	31		37.40	
	Minimum Charge	Job		216		216	

Solid Core Door		Unit	Material	Labor	Equip.	Total	Specification
Dutch Style							
	Demolish	Ea.		40		40	Includes material and labor to install
	Install	Ea.	870	72		942	dutch door, pine, 1-3/4" x 6' 8" x 2'
	Demolish and Install	Ea.	870	112		982	8" wide.
	Reinstall	Ea.		72		72	
	Clean	Ea.	4.03	13.35		17.38	
	Paint	Ea.	2.61	123		125.61	
	Minimum Charge	Job		216		216	
Miami Style							
	Demolish	Ea.		40		40	Cost includes material and labor to
	Install	Ea.	232	25.50		257.50	install 3' x 6' 8" pre-hung 1-3/4"
	Demolish and Install	Ea.	232	65.50		297.50	lauan door of solid wood.
	Reinstall	Ea.		25.41		25.41	
	Clean	Ea.	4.03	13.35		17.38	
	Paint	Ea.	10.30	53		63.30	
	Minimum Charge	Job		216		216	
French Style							
	Demolish	Ea.		44.50		44.50	Cost includes material and labor to
	Install	Ea.	705	61.50		766.50	install 3' x 6' 8" pre-hung 1-3/4"
	Demolish and Install	Ea.	705	106		811	french style door with 15 lights.
	Reinstall	Ea.		61.71		61.71	
	Clean	Ea.	.28	13.35		13.63	
	Paint	Ea.	7.90	185		192.90	
	Minimum Charge	Job		216		216	
Double							
	Demolish	Ea.		29.50		29.50	Includes material and labor to install a
	Install	Ea.	1475	108		1583	pre-hung double entry door including
	Demolish and Install	Ea.	1475	137.50		1612.50	frame and exterior trim.
	Clean	Ea.	.15	47		47.15	
	Paint	Ea.	23	185		208	
	Minimum Charge	Job		108		108	
Commercial Grade							
3' x 6' 8"							
	Demolish	Ea.		40		40	Includes material and labor to install
	Install	Ea.	325	25.50		350.50	flush solid core 1-3/4" hardwood
	Demolish and Install	Ea.	325	65.50		390.50	veneer 3' x 6' 8' door only.
	Reinstall	Ea.		25.41		25.41	
	Clean	Ea.	4.03	13.35		17.38	
	Paint	Ea.	10.65	31		41.65	
	Minimum Charge	Job		216		216	
3' 6" x 6' 8"							
	Demolish	Ea.		40		40	Includes material and labor to install
	Install	Ea.	400	25.50		425.50	flush solid core 1-3/4" hardwood
	Demolish and Install	Ea.	400	65.50		465.50	veneer 3' 6" x 6' 8' door only.
	Reinstall	Ea.		25.41		25.41	
	Clean	Ea.	4.03	13.35		17.38	
	Paint	Ea.	10.65	31		41.65	
	Minimum Charge	Job		216		216	
3' x 7'							
	Demolish	Ea.		40		40	Includes material and labor to install
	Install	Ea.	350	61.50		411.50	flush solid core 1-3/4" hardwood
	Demolish and Install	Ea.	350	101.50		451.50	veneer 3' x 7' door only.
	Reinstall	Ea.		61.71		61.71	
	Clean	Ea.	4.03	13.35		17.38	
	Paint	Ea.	10.65	31		41.65	
	Minimum Charge	Job		216		216	

Exterior Doors and Windows

Solid Core Door		Unit	Material	Labor	Equip.	Total	Specification
3' 6" x 7'							
	Demolish	Ea.		40		40	Includes material and labor to install
	Install	Ea.	460	31		491	flush solid core 1-3/4" hardwood
	Demolish and Install	Ea.	460	71		531	veneer 3' 6" x 7' door only.
	Reinstall	Ea.		30.86		30.86	
	Clean	Ea.	4.03	13.35		17.38	
	Paint	Ea.	10.65	31		41.65	
	Minimum Charge	Job		216		216	
3' x 8'							
	Demolish	Ea.		40		40	Includes material and labor to install
	Install	Ea.	415	54		469	flush solid core 1-3/4" hardwood
	Demolish and Install	Ea.	415	94		509	veneer 3' x 8' door only.
	Reinstall	Ea.		54		54	
	Clean	Ea.	4.84	20		24.84	
	Paint	Ea.	10.65	31		41.65	
	Minimum Charge	Job		216		216	
3' 6" x 8'							
	Demolish	Ea.		40		40	Includes material and labor to install
	Install	Ea.	495	54		549	flush solid core 1-3/4" hardwood
	Demolish and Install	Ea.	495	94		589	veneer 3' 6" x 8' door only.
	Reinstall	Ea.		54		54	
	Clean	Ea.	4.84	20		24.84	
	Paint	Ea.	10.65	31		41.65	
	Minimum Charge	Job		216		216	
3' x 9'							
	Demolish	Ea.		40		40	Includes material and labor to install
	Install	Ea.	555	61.50		616.50	flush solid core 1-3/4" hardwood
	Demolish and Install	Ea.	555	101.50		656.50	veneer 3' x 9' door only.
	Reinstall	Ea.		61.71		61.71	
	Clean	Ea.	4.84	20		24.84	
	Paint	Ea.	10.65	31		41.65	
	Minimum Charge	Job		216		216	
Stain							
	Install	Ea.	9.85	41		50.85	Includes labor and material to stain
	Minimum Charge	Job		185		185	exterior type door and trim on both sides.
Door Only (SC)							
2' 4" x 6' 8"							
	Demolish	Ea.		8.55		8.55	Cost includes material and labor to
	Install	Ea.	215	24		239	install 2' 4" x 6' 8" lauan solid core
	Demolish and Install	Ea.	215	32.55		247.55	door slab.
	Reinstall	Ea.		24		24	
	Clean	Ea.	1.68	10		11.68	
	Paint	Ea.	4.86	46		50.86	
	Minimum Charge	Job		216		216	
2' 8" x 6' 8"							
	Demolish	Ea.		8.55		8.55	Cost includes material and labor to
	Install	Ea.	222	24		246	install 2' 8" x 6' 8" lauan solid core
	Demolish and Install	Ea.	222	32.55		254.55	door slab.
	Reinstall	Ea.		24		24	
	Clean	Ea.	1.68	10		11.68	
	Paint	Ea.	4.86	46		50.86	
	Minimum Charge	Job		216		216	

Exterior Doors and Windows

Solid Core Door	Unit	Material	Labor	Equip.	Total	Specification
3' x 6' 8"						
Demolish	Ea.		8.55		8.55	Cost includes material and labor to
Install	Ea.	229	25.50		254.50	install 3' x 6' 8" lauan solid core door
Demolish and Install	Ea.	229	34.05		263.05	slab.
Reinstall	Ea.		25.41		25.41	
Clean	Ea.	1.68	10		11.68	
Paint	Ea.	4.86	46		50.86	
Minimum Charge	Job		216		216	
3' 6" x 6' 8"						
Demolish	Ea.		8.55		8.55	Cost includes material and labor to
Install	Ea.	262	27		289	install 3' 6" x 6' 8" lauan solid core
Demolish and Install	Ea.	262	35.55		297.55	door slab.
Reinstall	Ea.		27		27	
Clean	Ea.	1.68	10		11.68	
Paint	Ea.	4.86	46		50.86	
Minimum Charge	Job		216		216	
Panel						
Demolish	Ea.		8.55		8.55	Cost includes material and labor to
Install	Ea.	224	51		275	install 3' x 6' 8" six (6) panel interior
Demolish and Install	Ea.	224	59.55		283.55	door.
Reinstall	Ea.		50.82		50.82	
Clean	Ea.	2.01	10		12.01	
Paint	Ea.	4.86	46		50.86	
Minimum Charge	Job		216		216	
Casing Trim						
Single Width						
Demolish	Ea.		7.60		7.60	Cost includes material and labor to
Install	Opng.	28	36		64	install 11/16" x 2-1/2" pine ranch
Demolish and Install	Opng.	28	43.60		71.60	style casing for one side of a standard
Reinstall	Opng.		28.80		28.80	door opening.
Clean	Opng.	.57	3.20		3.77	
Paint	Ea.	5.20	7.40		12.60	
Minimum Charge	Job		216		216	
Double Width						
Demolish	Ea.		9.05		9.05	Cost includes material and labor to
Install	Opng.	33	43		76	install 11/16" x 2-1/2" pine ranch
Demolish and Install	Opng.	33	52.05		85.05	style door casing for one side of a
Reinstall	Opng.		34.56		34.56	double door opening.
Clean	Opng.	.67	6.40		7.07	
Paint	Ea.	5.20	8.40		13.60	
Minimum Charge	Job		216		216	

Components	Unit	Material	Labor	Equip.	Total	Specification
Hardware						
Doorknob						
Demolish	Ea.		17.15		17.15	Includes material and labor to install
Install	Ea.	38	27		65	residential passage lockset, keyless
Demolish and Install	Ea.	38	44.15		82.15	bored type.
Reinstall	Ea.		21.60		21.60	
Clean	Ea.	.41	10		10.41	
Minimum Charge	Job		216		216	

Exterior Doors and Windows

Components		Unit	Material	Labor	Equip.	Total	Specification
Doorknob w / Lock							
	Demolish	Ea.		17.15		17.15	Includes material and labor to install
	Install	Ea.	39	27		66	privacy lockset.
	Demolish and Install	Ea.	39	44.15		83.15	
	Reinstall	Ea.		21.60		21.60	
	Clean	Ea.	.41	10		10.41	
	Minimum Charge	Job		216		216	
Lever Handle							
	Demolish	Ea.		17.15		17.15	Includes material and labor to install
	Install	Ea.	36.50	43		79.50	residential passage lockset, keyless
	Demolish and Install	Ea.	36.50	60.15		96.65	bored type with lever handle.
	Reinstall	Ea.		34.56		34.56	
	Clean	Ea.	.41	10		10.41	
	Minimum Charge	Job		216		216	
Deadbolt							
	Demolish	Ea.		15		15	Includes material and labor to install a
	Install	Ea.	70	31		101	deadbolt.
	Demolish and Install	Ea.	70	46		116	
	Reinstall	Ea.		24.69		24.69	
	Clean	Ea.	.41	10		10.41	
	Minimum Charge	Job		216		216	
Grip Handle Entry							
	Demolish	Ea.		13.70		13.70	Includes material and labor to install
	Install	Ea.	92.50	48		140.50	residential keyed entry lock set with
	Demolish and Install	Ea.	92.50	61.70		154.20	grip type handle.
	Reinstall	Ea.		38.40		38.40	
	Clean	Ea.	.41	10		10.41	
	Minimum Charge	Job		216		216	
Panic Device							
	Demolish	Ea.		35.50		35.50	Includes material and labor to install
	Install	Ea.	390	72		462	touch bar, low profile, exit only.
	Demolish and Install	Ea.	390	107.50		497.50	
	Reinstall	Ea.		57.60		57.60	
	Clean	Ea.	.20	17.80		18	
	Minimum Charge	Job		216		216	
Closer							
	Demolish	Ea.		9		9	Includes material and labor to install
	Install	Ea.	257	72		329	pneumatic heavy duty closer for
	Demolish and Install	Ea.	257	81		338	exterior type doors.
	Reinstall	Ea.		57.60		57.60	
	Clean	Ea.	.20	13.35		13.55	
	Minimum Charge	Job		216		216	
Peep-hole							
	Demolish	Ea.		7.90		7.90	Includes material and labor to install
	Install	Ea.	17.40	13.50		30.90	peep-hole for door.
	Demolish and Install	Ea.	17.40	21.40		38.80	
	Reinstall	Ea.		10.80		10.80	
	Clean	Ea.	.03	3.61		3.64	
	Minimum Charge	Job		216		216	
Exit Sign							
	Demolish	Ea.		23.50		23.50	Includes material and labor to install a
	Install	Ea.	113	58.50		171.50	wall mounted interior electric exit sign.
	Demolish and Install	Ea.	113	82		195	
	Reinstall	Ea.		46.80		46.80	
	Clean	Ea.	.03	7.35		7.38	
	Minimum Charge	Job		216		216	

Exterior Doors and Windows

Components		Unit	Material	Labor	Equip.	Total	Specification
Kickplate							
	Demolish	Ea.		13.35		13.35	Includes material and labor to install
	Install	Ea.	24	29		53	aluminum kickplate, 10" x 28".
	Demolish and Install	Ea.	24	42.35		66.35	
	Reinstall	Ea.		23.04		23.04	
	Clean	Ea.	.41	10		10.41	
	Minimum Charge	Job		216		216	
Threshold							
	Install	L.F.	3.92	4.32		8.24	Includes labor and material to install
	Minimum Charge	Job		108		108	oak threshold.
Weatherstripping							
	Install	L.F.	.58	1.08		1.66	Includes labor and material to install
	Minimum Charge	Job		108		108	rubber weatherstripping for door.
Metal Jamb							
6' 8" High							
	Demolish	Ea.		24		24	Cost includes material and labor to
	Install	Ea.	171	27		198	install 18 gauge hollow metal door
	Demolish and Install	Ea.	171	51		222	frame to fit a 4-1/2" jamb 6' 8" high
	Reinstall	Ea.		27		27	and up to 3' 6" opening.
	Clean	Ea.	.84	6.70		7.54	
	Paint	Ea.	1.77	7.40		9.17	
	Minimum Charge	Job		216		216	
7' High							
	Demolish	Ea.		24		24	Cost includes material and labor to
	Install	Ea.	178	29		207	install 18 gauge hollow metal door
	Demolish and Install	Ea.	178	53		231	frame to fit a 4-1/2" jamb 7' high and
	Reinstall	Ea.		28.80		28.80	up to 3' 6" opening.
	Clean	Ea.	.84	6.70		7.54	
	Paint	Ea.	1.77	7.40		9.17	
	Minimum Charge	Job		216		216	
8' High							
	Demolish	Ea.		24		24	Cost includes material and labor to
	Install	Ea.	220	36		256	install 18 gauge hollow metal door
	Demolish and Install	Ea.	220	60		280	frame to fit a 4-1/2" jamb 8' high and
	Reinstall	Ea.		36		36	up to 3' 6" opening.
	Clean	Ea.	1.19	8		9.19	
	Paint	Ea.	1.98	8.20		10.18	
	Minimum Charge	Job		216		216	
9' High							
	Demolish	Ea.		24		24	Cost includes material and labor to
	Install	Ea.	282	43		325	install 18 gauge hollow metal door
	Demolish and Install	Ea.	282	67		349	frame to fit a 4-1/2" jamb 9' high and
	Reinstall	Ea.		43.20		43.20	up to 3' 6" opening.
	Clean	Ea.	1.19	8		9.19	
	Paint	Ea.	1.98	8.20		10.18	
	Minimum Charge	Job		216		216	
Wood Jamb							
	Demolish	Ea.		30		30	Includes material and labor to install
	Install	Ea.	146	11.70		157.70	flat pine jamb with square cut heads
	Demolish and Install	Ea.	146	41.70		187.70	and rabbeted sides for 6' 8" high and
	Clean	Ea.	.13	8		8.13	3-9/16" door including trim sets for
	Paint	Ea.	7.55	24.50		32.05	both sides.
	Minimum Charge	Job		216		216	
Stain							
	Install	Ea.	6.80	31		37.80	Includes labor and material to stain
	Minimum Charge	Job		185		185	single door and trim on both sides.

Exterior Doors and Windows

Components		Unit	Material	Labor	Equip.	Total	Specification
Shave & Refit							
	Install	Ea.		36		36	Includes labor to shave and rework
	Minimum Charge	Job		108		108	door to fit opening at the job site.

Sliding Patio Door		Unit	Material	Labor	Equip.	Total	Specification
Aluminum							
6' Single Pane							
	Demolish	Ea.		60		60	Cost includes material and labor to
	Install	Ea.	500	216		716	install 6' x 6' 8" sliding anodized
	Demolish and Install	Ea.	500	276		776	aluminum patio door with single pane
	Reinstall	Ea.		172.80		172.80	tempered safety glass, anodized
	Clean	Ea.	2.52	20		22.52	frame, screen, weatherstripped.
	Minimum Charge	Job		216		216	
8' Single Pane							
	Demolish	Ea.		60		60	Cost includes material and labor to
	Install	Ea.	635	288		923	install 8' x 6' 8" sliding aluminum
	Demolish and Install	Ea.	635	348		983	patio door with single pane tempered
	Reinstall	Ea.		230.40		230.40	safety glass, anodized frame, screen,
	Clean	Ea.	2.52	20		22.52	weatherstripped.
	Minimum Charge	Job		216		216	
10' Single Pane							
	Demolish	Ea.		60		60	Cost includes material and labor to
	Install	Ea.	710	430		1140	install 10' x 6' 8" sliding aluminum
	Demolish and Install	Ea.	710	490		1200	patio door with single pane tempered
	Reinstall	Ea.		345.60		345.60	safety glass, anodized frame, screen,
	Clean	Ea.	2.52	20		22.52	weatherstripped.
	Minimum Charge	Job		216		216	
6' Insulated							
	Demolish	Ea.		60		60	Cost includes material and labor to
	Install	Ea.	1000	216		1216	install 6' x 6' 8" sliding aluminum
	Demolish and Install	Ea.	1000	276		1276	patio door with double insulated
	Reinstall	Ea.		172.80		172.80	tempered glass, baked-on enamel
	Clean	Ea.	2.52	20		22.52	finish, screen, weatherstripped.
	Minimum Charge	Job		216		216	
8' Insulated							
	Demolish	Ea.		60		60	Cost includes material and labor to
	Install	Ea.	1175	288		1463	install 8' x 6' 8" sliding aluminum
	Demolish and Install	Ea.	1175	348		1523	patio door with insulated tempered
	Reinstall	Ea.		230.40		230.40	glass, baked-on enamel finish, screen,
	Clean	Ea.	2.52	20		22.52	weatherstripped.
	Minimum Charge	Job		216		216	
10' Insulated							
	Demolish	Ea.		60		60	Cost includes material and labor to
	Install	Ea.	1450	430		1880	install 10' x 6' 8" sliding aluminum
	Demolish and Install	Ea.	1450	490		1940	patio door with double insulated
	Reinstall	Ea.		345.60		345.60	tempered glass, baked-on enamel
	Clean	Ea.	2.52	20		22.52	finish, screen, weatherstripped.
	Minimum Charge	Job		216		216	

Exterior Doors and Windows

Sliding Patio Door	Unit	Material	Labor	Equip.	Total	Specification
Vinyl						
6' Single Pane						
Demolish	Ea.		60		60	Cost includes material and labor to
Install	Ea.	460	216		676	install 6' x 6' 8" sliding vinyl patio
Demolish and Install	Ea.	460	276		736	door with single pane tempered safety
Reinstall	Ea.		172.80		172.80	glass, anodized frame, screen,
Clean	Ea.	2.52	20		22.52	weatherstripped.
Minimum Charge	Job		216		216	
8' Single Pane						
Demolish	Ea.		60		60	Cost includes material and labor to
Install	Ea.	645	288		933	install 8' x 6' 8" sliding vinyl patio
Demolish and Install	Ea.	645	348		993	door with single pane tempered safety
Reinstall	Ea.		230.40		230.40	glass, anodized frame, screen,
Clean	Ea.	2.52	20		22.52	weatherstripped.
Minimum Charge	Job		216		216	
10' Single Pane						
Demolish	Ea.		60		60	Cost includes material and labor to
Install	Ea.	700	430		1130	install 10' x 6' 8" sliding vinyl patio
Demolish and Install	Ea.	700	490		1190	door with single pane tempered safety
Reinstall	Ea.		345.60		345.60	glass, anodized frame, screen,
Clean	Ea.	2.52	20		22.52	weatherstripped.
Minimum Charge	Job		216		216	
6' Insulated						
Demolish	Ea.		60		60	Cost includes material and labor to
Install	Ea.	1250	216		1466	install 6' x 6' 8" sliding vinyl patio
Demolish and Install	Ea.	1250	276		1526	door with double insulated tempered
Reinstall	Ea.		172.80		172.80	glass, anodized frame, screen,
Clean	Ea.	2.52	20		22.52	weatherstripped.
Minimum Charge	Job		216		216	
8' Insulated						
Demolish	Ea.		60		60	Cost includes material and labor to
Install	Ea.	1025	288		1313	install 8' x 6' 8" sliding vinyl patio
Demolish and Install	Ea.	1025	348		1373	door with double insulated tempered
Reinstall	Ea.		230.40		230.40	glass, anodized frame, screen,
Clean	Ea.	2.52	20		22.52	weatherstripped.
Minimum Charge	Job		216		216	
10' Insulated						
Demolish	Ea.		60		60	Cost includes material and labor to
Install	Ea.	1850	216		2066	install 10' x 6' 8" sliding vinyl patio
Demolish and Install	Ea.	1850	276		2126	door with double insulated tempered
Reinstall	Ea.		172.80		172.80	glass, anodized frame, screen,
Clean	Ea.	2.52	20		22.52	weatherstripped.
Minimum Charge	Job		216		216	
Wood Framed						
6' Premium Insulated						
Demolish	Ea.		60		60	Cost includes material and labor to
Install	Ea.	1575	216		1791	install 6' x 6' 8" sliding wood patio
Demolish and Install	Ea.	1575	276		1851	door with pine frame, double insulated
Reinstall	Ea.		172.80		172.80	glass, screen, lock and dead bolt,
Clean	Ea.	2.52	20		22.52	weatherstripped. Add for casing and
Minimum Charge	Job		216		216	finishing.

Exterior Doors and Windows

Sliding Patio Door	Unit	Material	Labor	Equip.	Total	Specification
8' Premium Insulated						Cost includes material and labor to
Demolish	Ea.		60		60	install 8' x 6' 8" sliding wood patio
Install	Ea.	2000	288		2288	door with pine frame, double insulated
Demolish and Install	Ea.	2000	348		2348	glass, screen, lock and dead bolt,
Reinstall	Ea.		230.40		230.40	weatherstripped. Add for casing and
Clean	Ea.	2.52	20		22.52	finishing.
Minimum Charge	Job		216		216	
9' Premium Insulated						Cost includes material and labor to
Demolish	Ea.		60		60	install 9' x 6' 8" sliding wood patio
Install	Ea.	2000	288		2288	door with pine frame, double insulated
Demolish and Install	Ea.	2000	348		2348	glass, screen, lock and dead bolt,
Reinstall	Ea.		230.40		230.40	weatherstripped. Add for casing and
Clean	Ea.	2.52	20		22.52	finishing.
Minimum Charge	Job		216		216	
Stain						Includes labor and material to stain
Install	Ea.	9.85	41		50.85	exterior type door and trim on both
Minimum Charge	Job		185		185	sides.
Casing Trim						Cost includes material and labor to
Demolish	Ea.		9.05		9.05	install 11/16" x 2-1/2" pine ranch
Install	Opng.	33	43		76	style door casing for one side of a
Demolish and Install	Opng.	33	52.05		85.05	double door opening.
Reinstall	Opng.		34.56		34.56	
Clean	Opng.	.67	6.40		7.07	
Paint	Ea.	5.20	8.40		13.60	
Minimum Charge	Job		216		216	
Sliding Screen						Includes material and labor to install
Demolish	Ea.		8.55		8.55	sliding screen door, 6' 8" x 3'.
Install	Ea.	139	21.50		160.50	
Demolish and Install	Ea.	139	30.05		169.05	
Reinstall	Ea.		17.28		17.28	
Clean	Ea.	.84	6.70		7.54	
Minimum Charge	Job		216		216	

Screen Door	Unit	Material	Labor	Equip.	Total	Specification
Aluminum						Includes material and labor to install
Demolish	Ea.		40		40	aluminum frame screen door with
Install	Ea.	163	61.50		224.50	fiberglass screen cloth, closer, hinges,
Demolish and Install	Ea.	163	101.50		264.50	latch.
Reinstall	Ea.		49.37		49.37	
Clean	Ea.	4.03	13.35		17.38	
Paint	Ea.	4.99	14.80		19.79	
Minimum Charge	Job		216		216	
Wood						Includes material and labor to install
Demolish	Ea.		40		40	wood screen door with aluminum cloth
Install	Ea.	360	72		432	screen. Frame and hardware not
Demolish and Install	Ea.	360	112		472	included.
Reinstall	Ea.		57.60		57.60	
Clean	Ea.	4.03	13.35		17.38	
Paint	Ea.	4.99	14.80		19.79	
Minimum Charge	Job		216		216	
Shave & Refit						Includes labor to shave and rework
Install	Ea.		36		36	door to fit opening at the job site.
Minimum Charge	Job		216		216	

Exterior Doors and Windows

Storm Door		Unit	Material	Labor	Equip.	Total	Specification
Good Grade							
	Demolish	Ea.		40		40	Includes material and labor to install
	Install	Ea.	234	61.50		295.50	aluminum frame storm door with
	Demolish and Install	Ea.	234	101.50		335.50	fiberglass screen cloth, upper glass
	Reinstall	Ea.		49.37		49.37	panel, closer, hinges, latch.
	Clean	Ea.	4.03	13.35		17.38	
	Paint	Ea.	4.99	14.80		19.79	
	Minimum Charge	Job		216		216	
Better Grade							
	Demolish	Ea.		40		40	Includes material and labor to install
	Install	Ea.	279	61.50		340.50	aluminum frame storm door with
	Demolish and Install	Ea.	279	101.50		380.50	fiberglass screen cloth, upper and
	Reinstall	Ea.		49.37		49.37	lower glass panel, closer, latch.
	Clean	Ea.	4.03	13.35		17.38	
	Paint	Ea.	4.99	14.80		19.79	
	Minimum Charge	Job		216		216	
Premium Grade							
	Demolish	Ea.		40		40	Includes material and labor to install
	Install	Ea.	300	61.50		361.50	aluminum frame storm door with
	Demolish and Install	Ea.	300	101.50		401.50	fiberglass screen cloth, upper and
	Reinstall	Ea.		49.37		49.37	lower glass panel, closer, latch.
	Clean	Ea.	4.03	13.35		17.38	
	Paint	Ea.	4.99	14.80		19.79	
	Minimum Charge	Job		216		216	
Insulated							
	Demolish	Ea.		40		40	Includes material and labor to install
	Install	Ea.	277	31		308	aluminum frame storm door with
	Demolish and Install	Ea.	277	71		348	fiberglass screen cloth, upper and
	Reinstall	Ea.		24.69		24.69	lower glass panel, closer, latch.
	Clean	Ea.	4.03	13.35		17.38	
	Paint	Ea.	4.99	14.80		19.79	
	Minimum Charge	Job		216		216	

Garage Door		Unit	Material	Labor	Equip.	Total	Specification
9' One Piece Metal							
	Demolish	Ea.		101		101	Includes material and labor to install
	Install	Ea.	660	108		768	one piece steel garage door 9' x 7'
	Demolish and Install	Ea.	660	209		869	primed including hardware.
	Reinstall	Ea.		86.40		86.40	
	Clean	Ea.	5.05	40		45.05	
	Paint	Ea.	9.25	92.50		101.75	
	Minimum Charge	Job		216		216	
16' One Piece Metal							
	Demolish	Ea.		120		120	Includes material and labor to install
	Install	Ea.	880	144		1024	one piece steel garage door 16' x 7'
	Demolish and Install	Ea.	880	264		1144	primed including hardware.
	Reinstall	Ea.		115.20		115.20	
	Clean	Ea.	10.05	53.50		63.55	
	Paint	Ea.	18.50	106		124.50	
	Minimum Charge	Job		216		216	

Exterior Doors and Windows

Garage Door		Unit	Material	Labor	Equip.	Total	Specification
9' Metal Sectional							
	Demolish	Ea.		101		101	Includes material and labor to install
	Install	Ea.	755	164		919	sectional metal garage door 9' x 7'
	Demolish and Install	Ea.	755	265		1020	primed including hardware.
	Reinstall	Ea.		130.91		130.91	
	Clean	Ea.	5.15	46		51.15	
	Paint	Ea.	18.50	106		124.50	
	Minimum Charge	Job		216		216	
16' Metal Sectional							
	Demolish	Ea.		120		120	Includes material and labor to install
	Install	Ea.	955	288		1243	sectional metal garage door 16' x 7'
	Demolish and Install	Ea.	955	408		1363	primed including hardware.
	Reinstall	Ea.		230.40		230.40	
	Clean	Ea.	10.05	53.50		63.55	
	Paint	Ea.	18.50	106		124.50	
	Minimum Charge	Job		216		216	
Metal / Steel Roll Up							
8' x 8' Steel							
	Demolish	Ea.		137		137	Cost includes material and labor to
	Install	Ea.	1250	655		1905	install 8' x 8' steel overhead roll-up,
	Demolish and Install	Ea.	1250	792		2042	chain hoist operated service door.
	Reinstall	Ea.		522		522	
	Clean	Ea.	5.15	46		51.15	
	Paint	Ea.	19.70	123		142.70	
	Minimum Charge	Job		1050		1050	
10' x 10' Steel							
	Demolish	Ea.		160		160	Cost includes material and labor to
	Install	Ea.	2025	745		2770	install 10' x 10' steel overhead roll-up,
	Demolish and Install	Ea.	2025	905		2930	chain hoist operated service door.
	Reinstall	Ea.		596.57		596.57	
	Clean	Ea.	8.10	64		72.10	
	Paint	Ea.	31	123		154	
	Minimum Charge	Job		1050		1050	
12' x 12' Steel							
	Demolish	Ea.		192		192	Cost includes material and labor to
	Install	Ea.	2075	870		2945	install 12' x 12' steel overhead roll-up,
	Demolish and Install	Ea.	2075	1062		3137	chain hoist operated service door.
	Reinstall	Ea.		696		696	
	Clean	Ea.	11.60	71		82.60	
	Paint	Ea.	44.50	148		192.50	
	Minimum Charge	Job		1050		1050	
14' x 14' Steel							
	Demolish	Ea.		240		240	Cost includes material and labor to
	Install	Ea.	3350	1300		4650	install 14' x 14' steel overhead roll-up,
	Demolish and Install	Ea.	3350	1540		4890	chain hoist operated service door.
	Reinstall	Ea.		1044		1044	
	Clean	Ea.	15.80	91.50		107.30	
	Paint	Ea.	51.50	185		236.50	
	Minimum Charge	Job		1050		1050	
18' x 18' Steel							
	Demolish	Ea.		267		267	Cost includes material and labor to
	Install	Opng.	2650	1750		4400	install 18' x 18' steel overhead roll-up,
	Demolish and Install	Opng.	2650	2017		4667	chain hoist operated service door.
	Reinstall	Opng.		1392		1392	
	Clean	Ea.	15.80	53.50		69.30	
	Paint	Ea.	99.50	370		469.50	
	Minimum Charge	Job		1050		1050	
Automatic Motor							
	Install	Ea.	525	43		568	Includes labor and material to install
	Minimum Charge	Job		216		216	electric opener motor, 1/3 HP.

Exterior Doors and Windows

Garage Door		Unit	Material	Labor	Equip.	Total	Specification
9' One Piece Wood							
	Demolish	Ea.		101		101	Includes material and labor to install
	Install	Ea.	770	108		878	one piece wood garage door 9' x 7'
	Demolish and Install	Ea.	770	209		979	primed including hardware.
	Reinstall	Ea.		86.40		86.40	
	Clean	Ea.	5.05	40		45.05	
	Paint	Ea.	9.25	92.50		101.75	
	Minimum Charge	Job		216		216	
9' Wood Sectional							
	Demolish	Ea.		101		101	Includes material and labor to install
	Install	Ea.	1000	108		1108	sectional wood garage door 9' x 7'
	Demolish and Install	Ea.	1000	209		1209	unfinished including hardware.
	Reinstall	Ea.		86.40		86.40	
	Clean	Ea.	5.05	40		45.05	
	Paint	Ea.	9.25	92.50		101.75	
	Minimum Charge	Job		216		216	
16' Wood Sectional							
	Demolish	Ea.		120		120	Includes material and labor to install
	Install	Ea.	1725	144		1869	sectional fiberglass garage door 16' x
	Demolish and Install	Ea.	1725	264		1989	7' unfinished including hardware.
	Reinstall	Ea.		115.20		115.20	
	Clean	Ea.	10.05	53.50		63.55	
	Paint	Ea.	18.50	106		124.50	
	Minimum Charge	Job		216		216	
Electric Opener							
	Demolish	Ea.		71		71	Includes material and labor to install
	Install	Ea.	345	81		426	electric opener, 1/3 HP economy.
	Demolish and Install	Ea.	345	152		497	
	Reinstall	Ea.		64.84		64.84	
	Clean	Ea.	.20	17.80		18	
	Minimum Charge	Job		216		216	
Springs							
	Install	Pr.	87	108		195	Includes labor and material to replace
	Minimum Charge	Job		216		216	springs for garage door.

Commercial Metal Door		Unit	Material	Labor	Equip.	Total	Specification
Pre-hung Steel Door							
2' 8" x 6' 8"							
	Demolish	Ea.		60		60	Cost includes material and labor to
	Install	Ea.	730	27		757	install 2' 8" x 6' 8" pre-hung 1-3/4"
	Demolish and Install	Ea.	730	87		817	18 gauge steel door with steel frame,
	Reinstall	Ea.		27		27	hinges, aluminum sill,
	Clean	Ea.	4.03	13.35		17.38	weather-stripped.
	Paint	Ea.	6.40	31		37.40	
	Minimum Charge	Job		216		216	
3' x 6' 8"							
	Demolish	Ea.		60		60	Cost includes material and labor to
	Install	Ea.	680	29		709	install 3' x 6' 8" pre-hung 1-3/4" 18
	Demolish and Install	Ea.	680	89		769	gauge steel door with steel frame,
	Reinstall	Ea.		28.80		28.80	hinges, aluminum sill,
	Clean	Ea.	4.03	13.35		17.38	weather-stripped.
	Paint	Ea.	6.40	31		37.40	
	Minimum Charge	Job		216		216	

Exterior Doors and Windows

Commercial Metal Door		Unit	Material	Labor	Equip.	Total	Specification
3' 6" x 6' 8"							
	Demolish	Ea.		60		60	Cost includes material and labor to
	Install	Ea.	780	33		813	install 3' 6" x 6' 8" pre-hung 1-3/4"
	Demolish and Install	Ea.	780	93		873	18 gauge steel door with steel frame,
	Reinstall	Ea.		33.23		33.23	hinges, aluminum sill,
	Clean	Ea.	4.03	13.35		17.38	weather-stripped.
	Paint	Ea.	6.40	31		37.40	
	Minimum Charge	Job		216		216	
4' x 6' 8"							
	Demolish	Ea.		60		60	Cost includes material and labor to
	Install	Ea.	845	43		888	install 4' x 6' 8" pre-hung 1-3/4" 18
	Demolish and Install	Ea.	845	103		948	gauge steel door with steel frame,
	Reinstall	Ea.		43.20		43.20	hinges, aluminum sill,
	Clean	Ea.	4.03	13.35		17.38	weather-stripped.
	Paint	Ea.	6.40	31		37.40	
	Minimum Charge	Job		216		216	
Metal Jamb							
6' 8" High							
	Demolish	Ea.		24		24	Cost includes material and labor to
	Install	Ea.	171	27		198	install 18 gauge hollow metal door
	Demolish and Install	Ea.	171	51		222	frame to fit a 4-1/2" jamb 6' 8" high
	Reinstall	Ea.		27		27	and up to 3' 6" opening.
	Clean	Ea.	.84	6.70		7.54	
	Paint	Ea.	1.77	7.40		9.17	
	Minimum Charge	Job		216		216	
7' High							
	Demolish	Ea.		24		24	Cost includes material and labor to
	Install	Ea.	178	29		207	install 18 gauge hollow metal door
	Demolish and Install	Ea.	178	53		231	frame to fit a 4-1/2" jamb 7' high and
	Reinstall	Ea.		28.80		28.80	up to 3' 6" opening.
	Clean	Ea.	.84	6.70		7.54	
	Paint	Ea.	1.77	7.40		9.17	
	Minimum Charge	Job		216		216	
8' High							
	Demolish	Ea.		24		24	Cost includes material and labor to
	Install	Ea.	220	36		256	install 18 gauge hollow metal door
	Demolish and Install	Ea.	220	60		280	frame to fit a 4-1/2" jamb 8' high and
	Reinstall	Ea.		36		36	up to 3' 6" opening.
	Clean	Ea.	1.19	8		9.19	
	Paint	Ea.	1.98	8.20		10.18	
	Minimum Charge	Job		216		216	
9' High							
	Demolish	Ea.		24		24	Cost includes material and labor to
	Install	Ea.	282	43		325	install 18 gauge hollow metal door
	Demolish and Install	Ea.	282	67		349	frame to fit a 4-1/2" jamb 9' high and
	Reinstall	Ea.		43.20		43.20	up to 3' 6" opening.
	Clean	Ea.	1.19	8		9.19	
	Paint	Ea.	1.98	8.20		10.18	
	Minimum Charge	Job		216		216	
Hardware							
Doorknob w / Lock							
	Demolish	Ea.		17.15		17.15	Includes material and labor to install
	Install	Ea.	180	36		216	keyed entry lock set, bored type
	Demolish and Install	Ea.	180	53.15		233.15	including knob trim, strike and strike
	Reinstall	Ea.		28.80		28.80	box for standard commercial
	Clean	Ea.	.41	10		10.41	application.
	Minimum Charge	Job		216		216	

Exterior Doors and Windows

Commercial Metal Door	Unit	Material	Labor	Equip.	Total	Specification
Lever Handle						
Demolish	Ea.		17.15		17.15	Includes material and labor to install
Install	Ea.	135	43		178	passage lockset, keyless bored type
Demolish and Install	Ea.	135	60.15		195.15	with lever handle, non-locking
Reinstall	Ea.		34.56		34.56	standard commercial latchset.
Clean	Ea.	.41	10		10.41	
Minimum Charge	Job		216		216	
Deadbolt						
Demolish	Ea.		15		15	Includes material and labor to install a
Install	Ea.	70	31		101	deadbolt.
Demolish and Install	Ea.	70	46		116	
Reinstall	Ea.		24.69		24.69	
Clean	Ea.	.41	10		10.41	
Minimum Charge	Job		216		216	
Panic Device						
Demolish	Ea.		35.50		35.50	Includes material and labor to install
Install	Ea.	390	72		462	touch bar, low profile, exit only.
Demolish and Install	Ea.	390	107.50		497.50	
Reinstall	Ea.		57.60		57.60	
Clean	Ea.	.20	17.80		18	
Minimum Charge	Job		216		216	
Closer						
Demolish	Ea.		9		9	Includes material and labor to install
Install	Ea.	300	72		372	pneumatic heavy duty model for
Demolish and Install	Ea.	300	81		381	exterior type doors.
Reinstall	Ea.		57.60		57.60	
Clean	Ea.	.20	13.35		13.55	
Minimum Charge	Job		216		216	
Peep-Hole						
Demolish	Ea.		7.90		7.90	Includes material and labor to install
Install	Ea.	17.40	13.50		30.90	peep-hole for door.
Demolish and Install	Ea.	17.40	21.40		38.80	
Reinstall	Ea.		10.80		10.80	
Clean	Ea.	.03	3.61		3.64	
Minimum Charge	Job		216		216	
Exit Sign						
Demolish	Ea.		23.50		23.50	Includes material and labor to install a
Install	Ea.	113	58.50		171.50	wall mounted interior electric exit sign.
Demolish and Install	Ea.	113	82		195	
Reinstall	Ea.		46.80		46.80	
Clean	Ea.	.03	7.35		7.38	
Minimum Charge	Job		216		216	
Kickplate						
Demolish	Ea.		13.35		13.35	Includes material and labor to install
Install	Ea.	87	29		116	stainless steel kickplate, 10" x 36".
Demolish and Install	Ea.	87	42.35		129.35	
Reinstall	Ea.		23.04		23.04	
Clean	Ea.	.41	10		10.41	
Minimum Charge	Job		216		216	

Aluminum Window	Unit	Material	Labor	Equip.	Total	Specification
Single Hung Two Light						
2' x 2'						
Demolish	Ea.		22.50		22.50	Cost includes material and labor to
Install	Ea.	189	95		284	install 2' x 2' single hung, two light,
Demolish and Install	Ea.	189	117.50		306.50	double glazed aluminum window
Reinstall	Ea.		75.93		75.93	including screen.
Clean	Ea.	.04	8.35		8.39	
Minimum Charge	Job		261		261	

Exterior Doors and Windows

Aluminum Window		Unit	Material	Labor	Equip.	Total	Specification
2' x 2' 6"							
	Demolish	Ea.		22.50		22.50	Cost includes material and labor to
	Install	Ea.	78.50	95		173.50	install 2' x 2' 6" single hung, two
	Demolish and Install	Ea.	78.50	117.50		196	light, double glazed aluminum
	Reinstall	Ea.		75.93		75.93	window including screen.
	Clean	Ea.	.04	8.35		8.39	
	Minimum Charge	Job		261		261	
3' x 1' 6"							
	Demolish	Ea.		22.50		22.50	Cost includes material and labor to
	Install	Ea.	74.50	104		178.50	install 3' x 1' 6" single hung, two
	Demolish and Install	Ea.	74.50	126.50		201	light, double glazed aluminum
	Reinstall	Ea.		83.52		83.52	window including screen.
	Clean	Ea.	.03	7.35		7.38	
	Minimum Charge	Job		261		261	
3' x 2'							
	Demolish	Ea.		22.50		22.50	Cost includes material and labor to
	Install	Ea.	89	104		193	install 3' x 2' single hung, two light,
	Demolish and Install	Ea.	89	126.50		215.50	double glazed aluminum window
	Reinstall	Ea.		83.52		83.52	including screen.
	Clean	Ea.	.03	7.35		7.38	
	Minimum Charge	Job		261		261	
3' x 2' 6"							
	Demolish	Ea.		22.50		22.50	Cost includes material and labor to
	Install	Ea.	95	104		199	install 3' x 2' 6" single hung, two
	Demolish and Install	Ea.	95	126.50		221.50	light, double glazed aluminum
	Reinstall	Ea.		83.52		83.52	window including screen.
	Clean	Ea.	.04	8.35		8.39	
	Minimum Charge	Job		261		261	
3' x 3'							
	Demolish	Ea.		22.50		22.50	Cost includes material and labor to
	Install	Ea.	105	104		209	install 3' x 3' single hung, two light,
	Demolish and Install	Ea.	105	126.50		231.50	double glazed aluminum window
	Reinstall	Ea.		83.52		83.52	including screen.
	Clean	Ea.	.04	8.35		8.39	
	Minimum Charge	Job		261		261	
3' x 3' 6"							
	Demolish	Ea.		22.50		22.50	Cost includes material and labor to
	Install	Ea.	264	104		368	install 3' x 3' 6" single hung, two
	Demolish and Install	Ea.	264	126.50		390.50	light, double glazed aluminum
	Reinstall	Ea.		83.52		83.52	window including screen.
	Clean	Ea.	.06	9.75		9.81	
	Minimum Charge	Job		261		261	
3' x 4'							
	Demolish	Ea.		22.50		22.50	Cost includes material and labor to
	Install	Ea.	276	104		380	install 3' x 4' single hung, two light,
	Demolish and Install	Ea.	276	126.50		402.50	double glazed aluminum window
	Reinstall	Ea.		83.52		83.52	including screen.
	Clean	Ea.	.06	9.75		9.81	
	Minimum Charge	Job		261		261	
3' x 5'							
	Demolish	Ea.		32.50		32.50	Cost includes material and labor to
	Install	Ea.	133	104		237	install 3' x 5' single hung, two light,
	Demolish and Install	Ea.	133	136.50		269.50	double glazed aluminum window
	Reinstall	Ea.		83.52		83.52	including screen.
	Clean	Ea.	.08	11.70		11.78	
	Minimum Charge	Job		261		261	

Exterior Doors and Windows

Aluminum Window	Unit	Material	Labor	Equip.	Total	Specification
3' x 6'						
Demolish	Ea.		32.50		32.50	Cost includes material and labor to
Install	Ea.	375	116		491	install 3' x 6' single hung, two light,
Demolish and Install	Ea.	375	148.50		523.50	double glazed aluminum window
Reinstall	Ea.		92.80		92.80	including screen.
Clean	Ea.	.09	13.80		13.89	
Minimum Charge	Job		261		261	
Double Hung Two Light						
2' x 2'						
Demolish	Ea.		22.50		22.50	Cost includes material and labor to
Install	Ea.	127	95		222	install 2' x 2' double hung, two light,
Demolish and Install	Ea.	127	117.50		244.50	double glazed aluminum window
Reinstall	Ea.		75.93		75.93	including screen.
Clean	Ea.	.03	7.35		7.38	
Minimum Charge	Job		261		261	
2' x 2' 6"						
Demolish	Ea.		22.50		22.50	Cost includes material and labor to
Install	Ea.	136	95		231	install 2' x 2' 6" double hung, two
Demolish and Install	Ea.	136	117.50		253.50	light, double glazed aluminum
Reinstall	Ea.		75.93		75.93	window including screen.
Clean	Ea.	.03	7.35		7.38	
Minimum Charge	Job		261		261	
3' x 1' 6"						
Demolish	Ea.		22.50		22.50	Cost includes material and labor to
Install	Ea.	297	104		401	install 3' x 1' 6" double hung, two
Demolish and Install	Ea.	297	126.50		423.50	light, double glazed aluminum
Reinstall	Ea.		83.52		83.52	window including screen.
Clean	Ea.	.03	7.35		7.38	
Minimum Charge	Job		261		261	
3' x 2'						
Demolish	Ea.		22.50		22.50	Cost includes material and labor to
Install	Ea.	345	104		449	install 3' x 2' double hung, two light,
Demolish and Install	Ea.	345	126.50		471.50	double glazed aluminum window
Reinstall	Ea.		83.52		83.52	including screen.
Clean	Ea.	.03	7.35		7.38	
Minimum Charge	Job		261		261	
3' x 2' 6"						
Demolish	Ea.		22.50		22.50	Cost includes material and labor to
Install	Ea.	420	104		524	install 3' x 2' 6" double hung, two
Demolish and Install	Ea.	420	126.50		546.50	light, double glazed aluminum
Reinstall	Ea.		83.52		83.52	window including screen.
Clean	Ea.	.04	8.35		8.39	
Minimum Charge	Job		261		261	
3' x 3'						
Demolish	Ea.		22.50		22.50	Cost includes material and labor to
Install	Ea.	470	104		574	install 3' x 3' double hung, two light,
Demolish and Install	Ea.	470	126.50		596.50	double glazed aluminum window
Reinstall	Ea.		83.52		83.52	including screen.
Clean	Ea.	.04	8.35		8.39	
Minimum Charge	Job		261		261	
3' x 3' 6"						
Demolish	Ea.		22.50		22.50	Cost includes material and labor to
Install	Ea.	490	104		594	install 3' x 3' 6" double hung, two
Demolish and Install	Ea.	490	126.50		616.50	light, double glazed aluminum
Reinstall	Ea.		83.52		83.52	window including screen.
Clean	Ea.	.06	9.75		9.81	
Minimum Charge	Job		261		261	

Exterior Doors and Windows

Aluminum Window

Aluminum Window		Unit	Material	Labor	Equip.	Total	Specification
3' x 4'							
	Demolish	Ea.		22.50		22.50	Cost includes material and labor to
	Install	Ea.	530	104		634.	install 3' x 4' double hung, two light,
	Demolish and Install	Ea.	530	126.50		656.50	double glazed aluminum window
	Reinstall	Ea.		83.52		83.52	including screen.
	Clean	Ea.	.06	9.75		9.81	
	Minimum Charge	Job		261		261	
3' x 5'							
	Demolish	Ea.		32.50		32.50	Cost includes material and labor to
	Install	Ea.	585	104		689	install 3' x 5' double hung, two light,
	Demolish and Install	Ea.	585	136.50		721.50	double glazed aluminum window
	Reinstall	Ea.		83.52		83.52	including screen.
	Clean	Ea.	.08	11.70		11.78	
	Minimum Charge	Job		261		261	
3' x 6'							
	Demolish	Ea.		32.50		32.50	Cost includes material and labor to
	Install	Ea.	615	116		731	install 3' x 6' double hung, two light,
	Demolish and Install	Ea.	615	148.50		763.50	double glazed aluminum window
	Reinstall	Ea.		92.80		92.80	including screen.
	Clean	Ea.	.09	13.80		13.89	
	Minimum Charge	Job		261		261	

Sliding Sash

Sliding Sash		Unit	Material	Labor	Equip.	Total	Specification
1' 6" x 3'							
	Demolish	Ea.		22.50		22.50	Cost includes material and labor to
	Install	Ea.	239	95		334	install 1' 6" x 3' sliding sash, two
	Demolish and Install	Ea.	239	117.50		356.50	light, double glazed aluminum
	Reinstall	Ea.		75.93		75.93	window including screen.
	Clean	Ea.	.03	7.35		7.38	
	Minimum Charge	Job		261		261	
2' x 2'							
	Demolish	Ea.		22.50		22.50	Cost includes material and labor to
	Install	Ea.	64	104		168	install 2' x 2' sliding sash, two light,
	Demolish and Install	Ea.	64	126.50		190.50	double glazed aluminum window
	Reinstall	Ea.		83.52		83.52	including screen.
	Clean	Ea.	.03	7.35		7.38	
	Minimum Charge	Job		261		261	
3' x 2'							
	Demolish	Ea.		22.50		22.50	Cost includes material and labor to
	Install	Ea.	252	104		356	install 3' x 2' sliding sash, two light,
	Demolish and Install	Ea.	252	126.50		378.50	double glazed aluminum window
	Reinstall	Ea.		83.52		83.52	including screen.
	Clean	Ea.	.03	7.35		7.38	
	Minimum Charge	Job		261		261	
3' x 2' 6"							
	Demolish	Ea.		22.50		22.50	Cost includes material and labor to
	Install	Ea.	87	104		191	install 3' x 2' 6" sliding sash, two
	Demolish and Install	Ea.	87	126.50		213.50	light, double glazed aluminum
	Reinstall	Ea.		83.52		83.52	window including screen.
	Clean	Ea.	.04	8.35		8.39	
	Minimum Charge	Job		261		261	
3' x 3'							
	Demolish	Ea.		22.50		22.50	Cost includes material and labor to
	Install	Ea.	305	104		409	install 3' x 3' sliding sash, two light,
	Demolish and Install	Ea.	305	126.50		431.50	double glazed aluminum window
	Reinstall	Ea.		83.52		83.52	including screen.
	Clean	Ea.	.04	8.35		8.39	
	Minimum Charge	Job		261		261	

Aluminum Window	Unit	Material	Labor	Equip.	Total	Specification
3' x 3' 6"						
Demolish	Ea.		22.50		22.50	Cost includes material and labor to
Install	Ea.	103	104		207	install 3' x 3' 6" sliding sash, two
Demolish and Install	Ea.	103	126.50		229.50	light, double glazed aluminum
Reinstall	Ea.		83.52		83.52	window including screen.
Clean	Ea.	.06	9.75		9.81	
Minimum Charge	Job		261		261	
3' x 4'						
Demolish	Ea.		22.50		22.50	Cost includes material and labor to
Install	Ea.	112	116		228	install 3' x 4' sliding sash, two light,
Demolish and Install	Ea.	112	138.50		250.50	double glazed aluminum window
Reinstall	Ea.		92.80		92.80	including screen.
Clean	Ea.	.06	9.75		9.81	
Minimum Charge	Job		261		261	
3' x 5'						
Demolish	Ea.		32.50		32.50	Cost includes material and labor to
Install	Ea.	143	116		259	install 3' x 5' sliding sash, two light,
Demolish and Install	Ea.	143	148.50		291.50	double glazed aluminum window
Reinstall	Ea.		92.80		92.80	including screen.
Clean	Ea.	.08	11.70		11.78	
Minimum Charge	Job		261		261	
4' x 5'						
Demolish	Ea.		32.50		32.50	Cost includes material and labor to
Install	Ea.	145	149		294	install 4' x 5' sliding sash, two light,
Demolish and Install	Ea.	145	181.50		326.50	double glazed aluminum window
Reinstall	Ea.		119.31		119.31	including screen.
Clean	Ea.	.12	16.75		16.87	
Minimum Charge	Job		261		261	
5' x 5'						
Demolish	Ea.		32.50		32.50	Cost includes material and labor to
Install	Ea.	350	149		499	install 5' x 5' sliding sash, two light,
Demolish and Install	Ea.	350	181.50		531.50	double glazed aluminum window
Reinstall	Ea.		119.31		119.31	including screen.
Clean	Ea.	.12	16.75		16.87	
Minimum Charge	Job		261		261	
Awning Sash						
26" x 26", 2 Light						
Demolish	Ea.		22.50		22.50	Cost includes material and labor to
Install	Ea.	320	116		436	install 26" x 26" two light awning,
Demolish and Install	Ea.	320	138.50		458.50	double glazed aluminum window
Reinstall	Ea.		92.80		92.80	including screen.
Clean	Ea.	.04	8.35		8.39	
Minimum Charge	Job		261		261	
26" x 37", 2 Light						
Demolish	Ea.		22.50		22.50	Cost includes material and labor to
Install	Ea.	360	116		476	install 26" x 37" two light awning,
Demolish and Install	Ea.	360	138.50		498.50	double glazed aluminum window
Reinstall	Ea.		92.80		92.80	including screen.
Clean	Ea.	.04	8.35		8.39	
Minimum Charge	Job		261		261	
38" x 26", 3 Light						
Demolish	Ea.		22.50		22.50	Cost includes material and labor to
Install	Ea.	395	116		511	install 38" x 26" three light awning,
Demolish and Install	Ea.	395	138.50		533.50	double glazed aluminum window
Reinstall	Ea.		92.80		92.80	including screen.
Clean	Ea.	.06	9.75		9.81	
Minimum Charge	Job		261		261	

Exterior Doors and Windows

Aluminum Window		Unit	Material	Labor	Equip.	Total	Specification
38" x 37", 3 Light							
	Demolish	Ea.		22.50		22.50	Cost includes material and labor to
	Install	Ea.	400	131		531	install 38" x 37" three light awning,
	Demolish and Install	Ea.	400	153.50		553.50	double glazed aluminum window
	Reinstall	Ea.		104.40		104.40	including screen.
	Clean	Ea.	.06	9.75		9.81	
	Minimum Charge	Job		261		261	
38" x 53", 3 Light							
	Demolish	Ea.		32.50		32.50	Cost includes material and labor to
	Install	Ea.	670	131		801	install 38" x 53" three light awning,
	Demolish and Install	Ea.	670	163.50		833.50	double glazed aluminum window
	Reinstall	Ea.		104.40		104.40	including screen.
	Clean	Ea.	.08	11.70		11.78	
	Minimum Charge	Job		261		261	
50" x 37", 4 Light							
	Demolish	Ea.		32.50		32.50	Cost includes material and labor to
	Install	Ea.	660	131		791	install 50" x 37" four light awning,
	Demolish and Install	Ea.	660	163.50		823.50	double glazed aluminum window
	Reinstall	Ea.		104.40		104.40	including screen.
	Clean	Ea.	.08	11.70		11.78	
	Minimum Charge	Job		261		261	
50" x 53", 4 Light							
	Demolish	Ea.		32.50		32.50	Cost includes material and labor to
	Install	Ea.	1100	149		1249	install 50" x 53" four light awning,
	Demolish and Install	Ea.	1100	181.50		1281.50	double glazed aluminum window
	Reinstall	Ea.		119.31		119.31	including screen.
	Clean	Ea.	.09	13.80		13.89	
	Minimum Charge	Job		261		261	
63" x 37", 5 Light							
	Demolish	Ea.		32.50		32.50	Cost includes material and labor to
	Install	Ea.	860	149		1009	install 63" x 37" five light awning,
	Demolish and Install	Ea.	860	181.50		1041.50	double glazed aluminum window
	Reinstall	Ea.		119.31		119.31	including screen.
	Clean	Ea.	.09	13.80		13.89	
	Minimum Charge	Job		261		261	
63" x 53", 5 Light							
	Demolish	Ea.		32.50		32.50	Cost includes material and labor to
	Install	Ea.	1200	149		1349	install 63" x 53" five light awning,
	Demolish and Install	Ea.	1200	181.50		1381.50	double glazed aluminum window
	Reinstall	Ea.		119.31		119.31	including screen.
	Clean	Ea.	.12	16.75		16.87	
	Minimum Charge	Job		261		261	
Mullion Bars							
	Install	Ea.	13.40	42		55.40	Includes labor and material to install
	Minimum Charge	Job		261		261	mullions for sliding aluminum window.
Bay							
4' 8" x 6' 4"							
	Demolish	Ea.		23.50		23.50	Cost includes material and labor to
	Install	Ea.	1600	108		1708	install 4' 8" x 6' 4" angle bay double
	Demolish and Install	Ea.	1600	131.50		1731.50	hung unit, pine frame with aluminum
	Reinstall	Ea.		86.40		86.40	cladding, picture center sash,
	Clean	Ea.	.18	19.55		19.73	hardware, screens.
	Minimum Charge	Job		261		261	

Exterior Doors and Windows

Aluminum Window	Unit	Material	Labor	Equip.	Total	Specification
4' 8" x 7' 2"						
Demolish	Ea.		23.50		23.50	Cost includes material and labor to
Install	Ea.	1650	108		1758	install 4' 8" x 7' 2" angle bay double
Demolish and Install	Ea.	1650	131.50		1781.50	hung unit, pine frame with aluminum
Reinstall	Ea.		86.40		86.40	cladding, picture center sash,
Clean	Ea.	.18	19.55		19.73	hardware, screens.
Minimum Charge	Job		261		261	
4' 8" x 7' 10"						
Demolish	Ea.		23.50		23.50	Cost includes material and labor to
Install	Ea.	1675	108		1783	install 4' 8" x 7' 10" angle bay
Demolish and Install	Ea.	1675	131.50		1806.50	double hung unit, pine frame with
Reinstall	Ea.		86.40		86.40	aluminum cladding, picture center
Clean	Ea.	.18	19.55		19.73	sash, hardware, screens.
Minimum Charge	Job		261		261	
4' 8" x 8' 6"						
Demolish	Ea.		27.50		27.50	Cost includes material and labor to
Install	Ea.	1650	123		1773	install 4' 8" x 8' 6" angle bay double
Demolish and Install	Ea.	1650	150.50		1800.50	hung unit, pine frame with aluminum
Reinstall	Ea.		98.74		98.74	cladding, picture center sash,
Clean	Ea.	.02	26		26.02	hardware, screens.
Minimum Charge	Job		261		261	
4' 8" x 8' 10"						
Demolish	Ea.		27.50		27.50	Cost includes material and labor to
Install	Ea.	1675	123		1798	install 4' 8" x 8' 10" angle bay
Demolish and Install	Ea.	1675	150.50		1825.50	double hung unit, pine frame with
Reinstall	Ea.		98.74		98.74	aluminum cladding, picture center
Clean	Ea.	.02	26		26.02	sash, hardware, screens.
Minimum Charge	Job		261		261	
4' 8" x 9' 2"						
Demolish	Ea.		27.50		27.50	Cost includes material and labor to
Install	Ea.	1725	216		1941	install 4' 8" x 9' 2" angle bay double
Demolish and Install	Ea.	1725	243.50		1968.50	hung unit, pine frame with aluminum
Reinstall	Ea.		172.80		172.80	cladding, picture center sash,
Clean	Ea.	.02	26		26.02	hardware, screens.
Minimum Charge	Job		261		261	
4' 8" x 9' 10"						
Demolish	Ea.		27.50		27.50	Cost includes material and labor to
Install	Ea.	1825	216		2041	install 4' 8" x 9' 10" angle bay
Demolish and Install	Ea.	1825	243.50		2068.50	double hung unit, pine frame with
Reinstall	Ea.		172.80		172.80	aluminum cladding, picture center
Clean	Ea.	.02	26		26.02	sash, hardware, screens.
Minimum Charge	Job		261		261	
Casing						
Demolish	Ea.		10		10	Cost includes material and labor to
Install	Opng.	40.50	33		73.50	install 11/16" x 2-1/2" pine ranch
Demolish and Install	Opng.	40.50	43		83.50	style window casing.
Reinstall	Opng.		26.58		26.58	
Clean	Opng.	.57	3.20		3.77	
Paint	Ea.	5.20	7.40		12.60	
Minimum Charge	Job		261		261	
Storm Window						
2' x 3' 6"						
Demolish	Ea.		13.20		13.20	Includes material and labor to install
Install	Ea.	84.50	29		113.50	residential aluminum storm window
Demolish and Install	Ea.	84.50	42.20		126.70	with mill finish, 2' x 3' 5" high.
Reinstall	Ea.		23.04		23.04	
Clean	Ea.	.03	7.35		7.38	
Minimum Charge	Job		261		261	

Exterior Doors and Windows

Aluminum Window

		Unit	Material	Labor	Equip.	Total	Specification
2' 6" x 5'							
	Demolish	Ea.		13.20		13.20	Includes material and labor to install
	Install	Ea.	94.50	31		125.50	residential aluminum storm window
	Demolish and Install	Ea.	94.50	44.20		138.70	with mill finish, 2' 6" x 5' high.
	Reinstall	Ea.		24.69		24.69	
	Clean	Ea.	.06	9.75		9.81	
	Minimum Charge	Job		261		261	
4' x 6'							
	Demolish	Ea.		25.50		25.50	Includes material and labor to install
	Install	Ea.	110	34.50		144.50	residential aluminum storm window, 4'
	Demolish and Install	Ea.	110	60		170	x 6' high.
	Reinstall	Ea.		27.65		27.65	
	Clean	Ea.	.12	14.65		14.77	
	Minimum Charge	Job		261		261	

Hardware
Weatherstripping

		Unit	Material	Labor	Equip.	Total	Specification
	Install	L.F.	.68	3.60		4.28	Includes labor and material to install
	Minimum Charge	Job		144		144	vinyl V strip weatherstripping for double-hung window.

Trim Set

		Unit	Material	Labor	Equip.	Total	Specification
	Demolish	Ea.		10		10	Cost includes material and labor to
	Install	Opng.	40.50	33		73.50	install 11/16" x 2-1/2" pine ranch
	Demolish and Install	Opng.	40.50	43		83.50	style window casing.
	Reinstall	Opng.		26.58		26.58	
	Clean	Opng.	.57	3.20		3.77	
	Paint	Ea.	5.20	7.40		12.60	
	Minimum Charge	Job		216		216	

Vinyl Window

		Unit	Material	Labor	Equip.	Total	Specification
Double Hung							
2' x 2' 6"							
	Demolish	Ea.		16.20		16.20	Cost includes material and labor to
	Install	Ea.	219	57.50		276.50	install 2' x 2' 6" double hung, two
	Demolish and Install	Ea.	219	73.70		292.70	light, vinyl window with screen.
	Reinstall	Ea.		46.08		46.08	
	Clean	Ea.	.03	7.35		7.38	
	Minimum Charge	Job		144		144	
2' x 3' 6"							
	Demolish	Ea.		16.20		16.20	Cost includes material and labor to
	Install	Ea.	233	61.50		294.50	install 2' x 3' 6" double hung, two
	Demolish and Install	Ea.	233	77.70		310.70	light, vinyl window with screen.
	Reinstall	Ea.		49.37		49.37	
	Clean	Ea.	.04	8.35		8.39	
	Minimum Charge	Job		144		144	
2' 6" x 4' 6"							
	Demolish	Ea.		16.20		16.20	Cost includes material and labor to
	Install	Ea.	275	66.50		341.50	install 2' 6" x 4' 6" double hung, two
	Demolish and Install	Ea.	275	82.70		357.70	light, vinyl window with screen.
	Reinstall	Ea.		53.17		53.17	
	Clean	Ea.	.06	9.75		9.81	
	Minimum Charge	Job		144		144	
3' x 4'							
	Demolish	Ea.		16.20		16.20	Includes material and labor to install
	Install	Ea.	238	86.50		324.50	medium size double hung, 3' x 4',
	Demolish and Install	Ea.	238	102.70		340.70	two light, vinyl window with screen.
	Reinstall	Ea.		69.12		69.12	
	Clean	Ea.	.06	9.75		9.81	
	Minimum Charge	Job		144		144	

Exterior Doors and Windows

Vinyl Window	Unit	Material	Labor	Equip.	Total	Specification
3' x 4' 6"						
Demolish	Ea.		19.80		19.80	Cost includes material and labor to
Install	Ea.	305	96		401	install 3' x 4' 6" double hung, two
Demolish and Install	Ea.	305	115.80		420.80	light, vinyl window with screen.
Reinstall	Ea.		76.80		76.80	
Clean	Ea.	.08	11.70		11.78	
Minimum Charge	Job		144		144	
4' x 4' 6"						
Demolish	Ea.		19.80		19.80	Cost includes material and labor to
Install	Ea.	320	108		428	install 4' x 4' 6" double hung, two
Demolish and Install	Ea.	320	127.80		447.80	light, vinyl window with screen.
Reinstall	Ea.		86.40		86.40	
Clean	Ea.	.09	13.80		13.89	
Minimum Charge	Job		144		144	
4' x 6'						
Demolish	Ea.		19.80		19.80	Includes material and labor to install
Install	Ea.	375	123		498	large double hung, 4' x 6', two light,
Demolish and Install	Ea.	375	142.80		517.80	vinyl window with screen.
Reinstall	Ea.		98.74		98.74	
Clean	Ea.	.12	16.75		16.87	
Minimum Charge	Job		144		144	
Trim Set						
Demolish	Ea.		10		10	Cost includes material and labor to
Install	Opng.	40.50	33		73.50	install 11/16" x 2-1/2" pine ranch
Demolish and Install	Opng.	40.50	43		83.50	style window casing.
Reinstall	Opng.		26.58		26.58	
Clean	Opng.	.57	3.20		3.77	
Paint	Ea.	5.20	7.40		12.60	
Minimum Charge	Job		261		261	

Wood Window	Unit	Material	Labor	Equip.	Total	Specification
Double Hung						
2' 2" x 3' 4"						
Demolish	Ea.		16.20		16.20	Cost includes material and labor to
Install	Ea.	231	57.50		288.50	install 2' 2" x 3' 4" double hung, two
Demolish and Install	Ea.	231	73.70		304.70	light, double glazed wood window
Reinstall	Ea.		46.08		46.08	with screen.
Clean	Ea.	.04	8.35		8.39	
Paint	Ea.	3.26	15.40		18.66	
Minimum Charge	Job		216		216	
2' 2" x 4' 4"						
Demolish	Ea.		16.20		16.20	Cost includes material and labor to
Install	Ea.	252	61.50		313.50	install 2' 2" x 4' 4" double hung, two
Demolish and Install	Ea.	252	77.70		329.70	light, double glazed wood window
Reinstall	Ea.		49.37		49.37	with screen.
Clean	Ea.	.04	8.35		8.39	
Paint	Ea.	3.26	15.40		18.66	
Minimum Charge	Job		216		216	
2' 6" x 3' 4"						
Demolish	Ea.		16.20		16.20	Cost includes material and labor to
Install	Ea.	241	66.50		307.50	install 2' 6" x 3' 4" double hung, two
Demolish and Install	Ea.	241	82.70		323.70	light, double glazed wood window
Reinstall	Ea.		53.17		53.17	with screen.
Clean	Ea.	.06	9.75		9.81	
Paint	Ea.	4.17	18.50		22.67	
Minimum Charge	Job		216		216	

Wood Window		Unit	Material	Labor	Equip.	Total	Specification
2' 6" x 4'							
	Demolish	Ea.		16.20		16.20	Cost includes material and labor to
	Install	Ea.	252	72		324	install 2' 6" x 4' double hung, two
	Demolish and Install	Ea.	252	88.20		340.20	light, double glazed wood window
	Reinstall	Ea.		57.60		57.60	with screen.
	Clean	Ea.	.06	9.75		9.81	
	Paint	Ea.	4.17	18.50		22.67	
	Minimum Charge	Job		216		216	
2' 6" x 4' 8"							
	Demolish	Ea.		16.20		16.20	Cost includes material and labor to
	Install	Ea.	275	72		347	install 2' 6" x 4' 8" double hung, two
	Demolish and Install	Ea.	275	88.20		363.20	light, double glazed wood window
	Reinstall	Ea.		57.60		57.60	with screen.
	Clean	Ea.	.06	9.75		9.81	
	Paint	Ea.	4.17	18.50		22.67	
	Minimum Charge	Job		216		216	
2' 10" x 3' 4"							
	Demolish	Ea.		16.20		16.20	Cost includes material and labor to
	Install	Ea.	246	86.50		332.50	install 2' 10" x 3' 4" double hung, two
	Demolish and Install	Ea.	246	102.70		348.70	light, double glazed wood window
	Reinstall	Ea.		69.12		69.12	with screen.
	Clean	Ea.	.06	9.75		9.81	
	Paint	Ea.	4.17	18.50		22.67	
	Minimum Charge	Job		216		216	
2' 10" x 4'							
	Demolish	Ea.		16.20		16.20	Cost includes material and labor to
	Install	Ea.	272	86.50		358.50	install 2' 10" x 4' double hung, two
	Demolish and Install	Ea.	272	102.70		374.70	light, double glazed wood window
	Reinstall	Ea.		69.12		69.12	with screen.
	Clean	Ea.	.06	9.75		9.81	
	Paint	Ea.	4.17	18.50		22.67	
	Minimum Charge	Job		216		216	
3' 7" x 3' 4"							
	Demolish	Ea.		16.20		16.20	Cost includes material and labor to
	Install	Ea.	279	96		375	install 3' 7" x 3' 4" double hung, two
	Demolish and Install	Ea.	279	112.20		391.20	light, double glazed wood window
	Reinstall	Ea.		76.80		76.80	with screen.
	Clean	Ea.	.06	9.75		9.81	
	Paint	Ea.	4.17	18.50		22.67	
	Minimum Charge	Job		216		216	
3' 7" x 5' 4"							
	Demolish	Ea.		19.80		19.80	Cost includes material and labor to
	Install	Ea.	310	96		406	install 3' 7" x 5' 4" double hung, two
	Demolish and Install	Ea.	310	115.80		425.80	light, double glazed wood window
	Reinstall	Ea.		76.80		76.80	with screen.
	Clean	Ea.	.12	16.75		16.87	
	Paint	Ea.	6.95	31		37.95	
	Minimum Charge	Job		216		216	
4' 3" x 5' 4"							
	Demolish	Ea.		19.80		19.80	Cost includes material and labor to
	Install	Ea.	560	108		668	install 4' 3" x 5' 4" double hung, two
	Demolish and Install	Ea.	560	127.80		687.80	light, double glazed wood window
	Reinstall	Ea.		86.40		86.40	with screen.
	Clean	Ea.	.12	16.75		16.87	
	Paint	Ea.	4.61	37		41.61	
	Minimum Charge	Job		216		216	

Exterior Doors and Windows

Wood Window	Unit	Material	Labor	Equip.	Total	Specification
Casement						
2' x 3' 4"						
Demolish	Ea.		16.20		16.20	Cost includes material and labor to
Install	Ea.	288	43		331	install 2' x 3' 4 " casement window
Demolish and Install	Ea.	288	59.20		347.20	with 3/4" insulated glass, screens,
Reinstall	Ea.		34.56		34.56	weatherstripping, hardware.
Clean	Ea.	.04	8.35		8.39	
Paint	Ea.	3.26	15.40		18.66	
Minimum Charge	Job		430		430	
2' x 4'						
Demolish	Ea.		16.20		16.20	Cost includes material and labor to
Install	Ea.	305	48		353	install 2' x 4' casement window with
Demolish and Install	Ea.	305	64.20		369.20	3/4" insulated glass, screens,
Reinstall	Ea.		38.40		38.40	weatherstripping, hardware.
Clean	Ea.	.04	8.35		8.39	
Paint	Ea.	3.26	15.40		18.66	
Minimum Charge	Job		430		430	
2' x 5'						
Demolish	Ea.		16.20		16.20	Cost includes material and labor to
Install	Ea.	335	51		386	install 2' x 5' casement window with
Demolish and Install	Ea.	335	67.20		402.20	3/4" insulated glass, screens,
Reinstall	Ea.		40.66		40.66	weatherstripping, hardware.
Clean	Ea.	.06	9.75		9.81	
Paint	Ea.	4.17	18.50		22.67	
Minimum Charge	Job		430		430	
2' x 6'						
Demolish	Ea.		16.20		16.20	Cost includes material and labor to
Install	Ea.	335	54		389	install 2' x 6' casement window with
Demolish and Install	Ea.	335	70.20		405.20	3/4" insulated glass, screens,
Reinstall	Ea.		43.20		43.20	weatherstripping, hardware.
Clean	Ea.	.06	9.75		9.81	
Paint	Ea.	4.17	18.50		22.67	
Minimum Charge	Job		430		430	
4' x 3' 4"						
Demolish	Ea.		19.80		19.80	Cost includes material and labor to
Install	Ea.	645	57.50		702.50	install 4' x 3' 4 " casement windows
Demolish and Install	Ea.	645	77.30		722.30	with 3/4" insulated glass, screens,
Reinstall	Ea.		46.08		46.08	weatherstripping, hardware.
Clean	Ea.	.06	9.75		9.81	
Paint	Ea.	2.31	18.50		20.81	
Minimum Charge	Job		430		430	
4' x 4'						
Demolish	Ea.		19.80		19.80	Cost includes material and labor to
Install	Ea.	720	57.50		777.50	install 4' x 4' casement windows with
Demolish and Install	Ea.	720	77.30		797.30	3/4" insulated glass, screens,
Reinstall	Ea.		46.08		46.08	weatherstripping, hardware.
Clean	Ea.	.09	13.80		13.89	
Paint	Ea.	2.73	23		25.73	
Minimum Charge	Job		430		430	
4' x 5'						
Demolish	Ea.		19.80		19.80	Cost includes material and labor to
Install	Ea.	815	61.50		876.50	install 4' x 5' casement windows with
Demolish and Install	Ea.	815	81.30		896.30	3/4" insulated glass, screens,
Reinstall	Ea.		49.37		49.37	weatherstripping, hardware.
Clean	Ea.	.12	16.75		16.87	
Paint	Ea.	3.56	31		34.56	
Minimum Charge	Job		430		430	

Exterior Doors and Windows

Wood Window	Unit	Material	Labor	Equip.	Total	Specification
4' x 6'						
Demolish	Ea.		19.80		19.80	Cost includes material and labor to
Install	Ea.	920	72		992	install 4' x 6' casement windows with
Demolish and Install	Ea.	920	91.80		1011.80	3/4" insulated glass, screens,
Reinstall	Ea.		57.60		57.60	weatherstripping, hardware.
Clean	Ea.	.12	16.75		16.87	
Paint	Ea.	4.19	37		41.19	
Minimum Charge	Job		430		430	
Casement Bow						
4' 8" x 8' 1"						
Demolish	Ea.		27.50		27.50	Includes material and labor to install
Install	Ea.	1725	162		1887	casement bow window unit with 4
Demolish and Install	Ea.	1725	189.50		1914.50	lights, pine frame, 1/2" insulated
Reinstall	Ea.		129.60		129.60	glass, weatherstripping, hardware,
Clean	Ea.	.18	19.55		19.73	screens.
Paint	Ea.	7.75	74		81.75	
Minimum Charge	Job		430		430	
4' 8" x 10'						
Demolish	Ea.		27.50		27.50	Includes material and labor to install
Install	Ea.	2125	216		2341	casement bow window unit with 5
Demolish and Install	Ea.	2125	243.50		2368.50	lights, pine frame, 1/2" insulated
Reinstall	Ea.		172.80		172.80	glass, weatherstripping, hardware,
Clean	Ea.	.02	26		26.02	screens.
Paint	Ea.	9.65	92.50		102.15	
Minimum Charge	Job		430		430	
5' 4" x 8' 1"						
Demolish	Ea.		27.50		27.50	Includes material and labor to install
Install	Ea.	1875	162		2037	casement bow window unit with 4
Demolish and Install	Ea.	1875	189.50		2064.50	lights, pine frame, 1/2" insulated
Reinstall	Ea.		129.60		129.60	glass, weatherstripping, hardware,
Clean	Ea.	.02	26		26.02	screens.
Paint	Ea.	8.80	74		82.80	
Minimum Charge	Job		430		430	
5' 4" x 10'						
Demolish	Ea.		27.50		27.50	Includes material and labor to install
Install	Ea.	2100	216		2316	casement bow window unit with 5
Demolish and Install	Ea.	2100	243.50		2343.50	lights, pine frame, 1/2" insulated
Reinstall	Ea.		172.80		172.80	glass, weatherstripping, hardware,
Clean	Ea.	.02	26		26.02	screens.
Paint	Ea.	11.10	92.50		103.60	
Minimum Charge	Job		430		430	
6' x 8' 1"						
Demolish	Ea.		27.50		27.50	Includes material and labor to install
Install	Ea.	2125	216		2341	casement bow window unit with 5
Demolish and Install	Ea.	2125	243.50		2368.50	lights, pine frame, 1/2" insulated
Reinstall	Ea.		172.80		172.80	glass, weatherstripping, hardware,
Clean	Ea.	.02	26		26.02	screens.
Paint	Ea.	10.05	92.50		102.55	
Minimum Charge	Job		430		430	
6' x 10'						
Demolish	Ea.		27.50		27.50	Includes material and labor to install
Install	Ea.	2200	216		2416	casement bow window unit with 5
Demolish and Install	Ea.	2200	243.50		2443.50	lights, pine frame, 1/2" insulated
Reinstall	Ea.		172.80		172.80	glass, weatherstripping, hardware,
Clean	Ea.	.02	26		26.02	screens.
Paint	Ea.	12.60	123		135.60	
Minimum Charge	Job		430		430	

Exterior Doors and Windows

Wood Window

Wood Window		Unit	Material	Labor	Equip.	Total	Specification
Casing							
	Demolish	Ea.		10		10	Cost includes material and labor to
	Install	Opng.	40.50	33		73.50	install 11/16" x 2-1/2" pine ranch
	Demolish and Install	Opng.	40.50	43		83.50	style window casing.
	Reinstall	Opng.		26.58		26.58	
	Clean	Opng.	.57	3.20		3.77	
	Paint	Ea.	5.20	7.40		12.60	
	Minimum Charge	Job		261		261	
Trim Set							
	Demolish	Ea.		7.60		7.60	Cost includes material and labor to
	Install	Opng.	40.50	33		73.50	install 11/16" x 2-1/2" pine ranch
	Demolish and Install	Opng.	40.50	40.60		81.10	style window casing.
	Reinstall	Opng.		26.58		26.58	
	Clean	Opng.	.57	3.20		3.77	
	Paint	Ea.	5.20	7.40		12.60	
	Minimum Charge	Job		216		216	
Wood Picture Window							
3' 6" x 4'							
	Demolish	Ea.		19.80		19.80	Includes material and labor to install a
	Install	Ea.	480	72		552	wood framed picture window
	Demolish and Install	Ea.	480	91.80		571.80	including exterior trim.
	Clean	Ea.	.12	16.75		16.87	
	Paint	Ea.	3.47	28.50		31.97	
	Minimum Charge	Job		430		430	
4' x 4' 6"							
	Demolish	Ea.		19.80		19.80	Includes material and labor to install a
	Install	Ea.	585	78.50		663.50	wood framed picture window
	Demolish and Install	Ea.	585	98.30		683.30	including exterior trim.
	Clean	Ea.	.12	16.75		16.87	
	Paint	Ea.	3.47	28.50		31.97	
	Minimum Charge	Job		430		430	
5' x 4'							
	Demolish	Ea.		19.80		19.80	Includes material and labor to install a
	Install	Ea.	665	78.50		743.50	wood framed picture window
	Demolish and Install	Ea.	665	98.30		763.30	including exterior trim.
	Clean	Ea.	.12	16.75		16.87	
	Paint	Ea.	7.45	46		53.45	
	Minimum Charge	Job		430		430	
6' x 4' 6"							
	Demolish	Ea.		19.80		19.80	Includes material and labor to install a
	Install	Ea.	700	86.50		786.50	wood framed picture window
	Demolish and Install	Ea.	700	106.30		806.30	including exterior trim.
	Clean	Ea.	.12	16.75		16.87	
	Paint	Ea.	7.45	46		53.45	
	Minimum Charge	Job		430		430	

Window Screens

Window Screens		Unit	Material	Labor	Equip.	Total	Specification
Small							
	Demolish	Ea.		3.71		3.71	Includes material and labor to install
	Install	Ea.	21	13.10		34.10	small window screen, 4 S.F.
	Demolish and Install	Ea.	21	16.81		37.81	
	Reinstall	Ea.		10.47		10.47	
	Clean	Ea.	.41	6.70		7.11	
	Minimum Charge	Job		108		108	

Exterior Doors and Windows

Window Screens	Unit	Material	Labor	Equip.	Total	Specification
Standard Size						
Demolish	Ea.		3.71		3.71	Includes material and labor to install
Install	Ea.	49.50	13.10		62.60	medium window screen, 12 S.F.
Demolish and Install	Ea.	49.50	16.81		66.31	
Reinstall	Ea.		10.47		10.47	
Clean	Ea.	.41	6.70		7.11	
Minimum Charge	Job		108		108	
Large						
Demolish	Ea.		3.71		3.71	Includes material and labor to install
Install	Ea.	66.50	13.10		79.60	large window screen, 16 S.F.
Demolish and Install	Ea.	66.50	16.81		83.31	
Reinstall	Ea.		10.47		10.47	
Clean	Ea.	.41	6.70		7.11	
Minimum Charge	Job		108		108	

Window Glass	Unit	Material	Labor	Equip.	Total	Specification
Plate, Clear, 1/4"						
Demolish	S.F.		1.78		1.78	Includes material and labor to install
Install	S.F.	9.55	6.95		16.50	clear glass.
Demolish and Install	S.F.	9.55	8.73		18.28	
Reinstall	S.F.		5.55		5.55	
Clean	S.F.	.03	.19		.22	
Minimum Charge	Job		208		208	
Insulated						
Demolish	S.F.		1.78		1.78	Includes material and labor to install
Install	S.F.	15.40	11.90		27.30	insulated glass.
Demolish and Install	S.F.	15.40	13.68		29.08	
Reinstall	S.F.		9.51		9.51	
Clean	S.F.	.03	.19		.22	
Minimum Charge	Job		208		208	
Tinted						
Demolish	S.F.		1.78		1.78	Includes material and labor to install
Install	S.F.	8.60	6.40		15	tinted glass.
Demolish and Install	S.F.	8.60	8.18		16.78	
Reinstall	S.F.		5.12		5.12	
Clean	S.F.	.03	.19		.22	
Minimum Charge	Job		208		208	
Obscure / Florentine						
Demolish	S.F.		1.78		1.78	Includes material and labor to install
Install	S.F.	12.75	5.95		18.70	obscure glass.
Demolish and Install	S.F.	12.75	7.73		20.48	
Reinstall	S.F.		4.75		4.75	
Clean	S.F.	.03	.19		.22	
Minimum Charge	Job		208		208	
Laminated Safety						
Demolish	S.F.		1.78		1.78	Includes material and labor to install
Install	S.F.	13.30	9.25		22.55	clear laminated glass.
Demolish and Install	S.F.	13.30	11.03		24.33	
Reinstall	S.F.		7.40		7.40	
Clean	S.F.	.03	.19		.22	
Minimum Charge	Job		208		208	

Exterior Doors and Windows

Window Glass		Unit	Material	Labor	Equip.	Total	Specification
Wired							
	Demolish	S.F.		1.78		1.78	Includes material and labor to install
	Install	S.F.	26	6.15		32.15	rough obscure wire glass.
	Demolish and Install	S.F.	26	7.93		33.93	
	Reinstall	S.F.		4.93		4.93	
	Clean	S.F.	.03	.19		.22	
	Minimum Charge	Job		208		208	
Tempered							
	Demolish	S.F.		1.78		1.78	Includes material and labor to install
	Install	S.F.	9.55	6.95		16.50	clear glass.
	Demolish and Install	S.F.	9.55	8.73		18.28	
	Reinstall	S.F.		5.55		5.55	
	Clean	S.F.	.03	.19		.22	
	Minimum Charge	Job		208		208	
Stained							
	Demolish	S.F.		1.78		1.78	Includes material and labor to install
	Install	S.F.	67	6.95		73.95	stained glass.
	Demolish and Install	S.F.	67	8.73		75.73	
	Reinstall	S.F.		5.55		5.55	
	Clean	S.F.	.03	.19		.22	
	Minimum Charge	Job		208		208	
Etched							
	Demolish	S.F.		1.78		1.78	Includes material and labor to install
	Install	S.F.	55	6.95		61.95	etched glass.
	Demolish and Install	S.F.	55	8.73		63.73	
	Reinstall	S.F.		5.55		5.55	
	Clean	S.F.	.03	.19		.22	
	Minimum Charge	Job		208		208	
Wall Mirror							
	Demolish	S.F.		1.78		1.78	Includes material and labor to install
	Install	S.F.	10.45	6.65		17.10	distortion-free float glass mirror, 1/4"
	Demolish and Install	S.F.	10.45	8.43		18.88	thick, cut and polished edges.
	Reinstall	S.F.		5.32		5.32	
	Clean	S.F.	.03	.19		.22	
	Minimum Charge	Job		208		208	
Bullet Resistant							
	Demolish	S.F.		1.78		1.78	Includes material and labor to install
	Install	S.F.	127	83		210	bullet resistant clear laminated glass.
	Demolish and Install	S.F.	127	84.78		211.78	
	Reinstall	S.F.		66.56		66.56	
	Clean	S.F.	.03	.19		.22	
	Minimum Charge	Job		208		208	

Storefront System		Unit	Material	Labor	Equip.	Total	Specification
Clear Glass							
Stub Wall to 8'							
	Demolish	S.F.		2.78		2.78	Includes material and labor to install
	Install	S.F.	24	11.50		35.50	commercial grade 4-1/2" section,
	Demolish and Install	S.F.	24	14.28		38.28	anodized aluminum with clear glass in
	Reinstall	S.F.		9.22		9.22	upper section and safety glass in
	Clean	S.F.		.39		.39	lower section.
	Minimum Charge	Job		261		261	

Exterior Doors and Windows

Storefront System	Unit	Material	Labor	Equip.	Total	Specification
Floor to 10'						
Demolish	S.F.		2.78		2.78	Includes material and labor to install
Install	S.F.	25	11.50		36.50	commercial grade 4-1/2" section,
Demolish and Install	S.F.	25	14.28		39.28	anodized aluminum with clear glass in
Reinstall	S.F.		9.22		9.22	upper section and safety glass in
Clean	S.F.		.39		.39	lower section.
Minimum Charge	Job		261		261	
Polished Plate Glass						
Stub Wall to 9'						
Demolish	S.F.		2.78		2.78	Cost includes material and labor to
Install	S.F.	15.95	11.50		27.45	install 4' x 9' polished plate glass
Demolish and Install	S.F.	15.95	14.28		30.23	window built on 8" stub wall.
Reinstall	S.F.		9.22		9.22	
Clean	S.F.		.39		.39	
Minimum Charge	Job		261		261	
Stub Wall to 13'						
Demolish	S.F.		2.78		2.78	Cost includes material and labor to
Install	S.F.	17.25	11.50		28.75	install 4' x 13' polished plate glass
Demolish and Install	S.F.	17.25	14.28		31.53	window built on 8" stub wall.
Reinstall	S.F.		9.22		9.22	
Clean	S.F.		.39		.39	
Minimum Charge	Job		261		261	
Floor to 9'						
Demolish	S.F.		2.78		2.78	Cost includes material and labor to
Install	S.F.	17.80	11.50		29.30	install 4' x 9' polished plate glass
Demolish and Install	S.F.	17.80	14.28		32.08	window built on floor.
Reinstall	S.F.		9.22		9.22	
Clean	S.F.		.39		.39	
Minimum Charge	Job		261		261	
Floor to 13'						
Demolish	S.F.		2.78		2.78	Cost includes material and labor to
Install	S.F.	19.15	11.50		30.65	install 4' x 13' polished plate glass
Demolish and Install	S.F.	19.15	14.28		33.43	window built on floor.
Reinstall	S.F.		9.22		9.22	
Clean	S.F.		.39		.39	
Minimum Charge	Job		261		261	
Clear Plate Glass						
Floor to 9'						
Demolish	S.F.		2.78		2.78	Cost includes material and labor to
Install	S.F.	25.50	11.50		37	install 4' x 9' clear plate glass window
Demolish and Install	S.F.	25.50	14.28		39.78	built on floor.
Reinstall	S.F.		9.22		9.22	
Clean	S.F.		.39		.39	
Minimum Charge	Job		261		261	
Floor to 11'						
Demolish	S.F.		2.78		2.78	Cost includes material and labor to
Install	S.F.	25	11.50		36.50	install 4' x 11' clear plate glass
Demolish and Install	S.F.	25	14.28		39.28	window built on floor.
Reinstall	S.F.		9.22		9.22	
Clean	S.F.		.39		.39	
Minimum Charge	Job		261		261	
Floor to 13'						
Demolish	S.F.		2.78		2.78	Cost includes material and labor to
Install	S.F.	25	11.50		36.50	install 4' x 13' clear plate glass
Demolish and Install	S.F.	25	14.28		39.28	window built on floor.
Reinstall	S.F.		9.22		9.22	
Clean	S.F.		.39		.39	
Minimum Charge	Job		261		261	

Exterior Doors and Windows

Storefront System

Storefront System	Unit	Material	Labor	Equip.	Total	Specification
Entrance						
Narrow Stile 3' x 7"						
Demolish	Ea.		24		24	Cost includes material and labor to
Install	Ea.	995	288		1283	install 3' x 7' narrow stile door, center
Demolish and Install	Ea.	995	312		1307	pivot concealed closer.
Reinstall	Ea.		230.40		230.40	
Clean	Ea.	5.05	40		45.05	
Minimum Charge	Job		261		261	
Tempered Glass						
Demolish	Ea.		24		24	Cost includes material and labor to
Install	Ea.	3475	565		4040	install 3' x 7' tempered glass door,
Demolish and Install	Ea.	3475	589		4064	center pivot concealed closer,.
Reinstall	Ea.		451.46		451.46	
Clean	Ea.	5.05	40		45.05	
Minimum Charge	Job		261		261	
Heavy Section						
Demolish	Ea.		24		24	Includes material and labor to install
Install	Ea.	1325	520		1845	wide stile door with 3' 6" x 7'
Demolish and Install	Ea.	1325	544		1869	opening.
Reinstall	Ea.		417.60		417.60	
Clean	Ea.	1.01	13.35		14.36	
Minimum Charge	Job		830		830	

Curtain Wall System

Curtain Wall System	Unit	Material	Labor	Equip.	Total	Specification
Regular Weight						
Bronze Anodized						
Demolish	S.F.		2.78		2.78	Includes material and labor to install
Install	S.F.	39.50	11.50		51	structural curtain wall system with
Demolish and Install	S.F.	39.50	14.28		53.78	bronze anodized frame of heavy
Clean	S.F.		.39		.39	weight, float glass.
Minimum Charge	Job		216		216	
Black Anodized						
Demolish	S.F.		2.78		2.78	Includes material and labor to install
Install	S.F.	43	11.50		54.50	structural curtain wall system with
Demolish and Install	S.F.	43	14.28		57.28	black anodized frame of regular
Clean	S.F.		.39		.39	weight, float glass.
Minimum Charge	Job		216		216	
Heavy Weight						
Bronze Anodized						
Demolish	S.F.		2.78		2.78	Includes material and labor to install
Install	S.F.	39.50	11.50		51	structural curtain wall system with
Demolish and Install	S.F.	39.50	14.28		53.78	bronze anodized frame of heavy
Clean	S.F.		.39		.39	weight, float glass.
Minimum Charge	Job		216		216	
Black Anodized						
Demolish	S.F.		2.78		2.78	Includes material and labor to install
Install	S.F.	40.50	11.50		52	structural curtain wall system with
Demolish and Install	S.F.	40.50	14.28		54.78	black anodized frame of heavy
Clean	S.F.		.39		.39	weight, float glass.
Minimum Charge	Job		216		216	
Glass						
1" Insulated						
Install	S.F.	18.25	11.10		29.35	Cost includes labor and material to
Minimum Charge	Job		208		208	install 1" insulated glass.

Exterior Doors and Windows

Skylight	Unit	Material	Labor	Equip.	Total	Specification
Dome						
22″ x 22″						
Demolish	Ea.		83.50		83.50	Cost includes material and labor to
Install	Ea.	231	134		365	install 22″ x 22″ fixed dome skylight.
Demolish and Install	Ea.	231	217.50		448.50	
Reinstall	Ea.		106.94		106.94	
Clean	Ea.	.45	11.45		11.90	
Minimum Charge	Job		800		800	
22″ x 46″						
Demolish	Ea.		83.50		83.50	Cost includes material and labor to
Install	Ea.	255	160		415	install 22″ x 46″ fixed dome skylight.
Demolish and Install	Ea.	255	243.50		498.50	
Reinstall	Ea.		128.33		128.33	
Clean	Ea.		17.80		17.80	
Minimum Charge	Job		800		800	
30″ x 30″						
Demolish	Ea.		83.50		83.50	Cost includes material and labor to
Install	Ea.	259	134		393	install 30″ x 30″ fixed dome skylight.
Demolish and Install	Ea.	259	217.50		476.50	
Reinstall	Ea.		106.94		106.94	
Clean	Ea.		17.80		17.80	
Minimum Charge	Job		800		800	
30″ x 46″						
Demolish	Ea.		83.50		83.50	Cost includes material and labor to
Install	Ea.	340	160		500	install 30″ x 46″ fixed dome skylight.
Demolish and Install	Ea.	340	243.50		583.50	
Reinstall	Ea.		128.33		128.33	
Clean	Ea.		17.80		17.80	
Minimum Charge	Job		800		800	
Fixed						
22″ x 27″						
Demolish	Ea.		83.50		83.50	Includes material and labor to install
Install	Ea.	253	134		387	double glazed skylight, 22″ x 27″,
Demolish and Install	Ea.	253	217.50		470.50	fixed.
Reinstall	Ea.		106.94		106.94	
Clean	Ea.	.45	11.45		11.90	
Minimum Charge	Job		800		800	
22″ x 46″						
Demolish	Ea.		83.50		83.50	Includes material and labor to install
Install	Ea.	310	160		470	double glazed skylight, 22″ x 46″,
Demolish and Install	Ea.	310	243.50		553.50	fixed.
Reinstall	Ea.		128.33		128.33	
Clean	Ea.		17.80		17.80	
Minimum Charge	Job		800		800	
44″ x 46″						
Demolish	Ea.		83.50		83.50	Includes material and labor to install
Install	Ea.	475	160		635	double glazed skylight, 44″ x 46″,
Demolish and Install	Ea.	475	243.50		718.50	fixed.
Reinstall	Ea.		128.33		128.33	
Clean	Ea.		20		20	
Minimum Charge	Job		800		800	
Operable						
22″ x 27″						
Demolish	Ea.		83.50		83.50	Includes material and labor to install
Install	Ea.	360	134		494	double glazed skylight, 22″ x 27″,
Demolish and Install	Ea.	360	217.50		577.50	operable.
Reinstall	Ea.		106.94		106.94	
Clean	Ea.	.45	11.45		11.90	
Minimum Charge	Job		800		800	

Exterior Doors and Windows

Skylight		Unit	Material	Labor	Equip.	Total	Specification
22" x 46"							
	Demolish	Ea.		83.50		83.50	Includes material and labor to install
	Install	Ea.	430	160		590	double glazed skylight, 22" x 46",
	Demolish and Install	Ea.	430	243.50		673.50	operable.
	Reinstall	Ea.		128.33		128.33	
	Clean	Ea.		17.80		17.80	
	Minimum Charge	Job		800		800	
44" x 46"							
	Demolish	Ea.		83.50		83.50	Includes material and labor to install
	Install	Ea.	915	160		1075	double glazed skylight, 44" x 46",
	Demolish and Install	Ea.	915	243.50		1158.50	operable.
	Reinstall	Ea.		128.33		128.33	
	Clean	Ea.		20		20	
	Minimum Charge	Job		800		800	

Industrial Steel Window		Unit	Material	Labor	Equip.	Total	Specification
100% Fixed							
	Demolish	S.F.		2.28		2.28	Includes material and labor to install
	Install	S.F.	31.50	5.20		36.70	commercial grade steel windows,
	Demolish and Install	S.F.	31.50	7.48		38.98	including glazing.
	Reinstall	S.F.		4.18		4.18	
	Clean	Ea.	.18	1.22		1.40	
	Paint	S.F.	.18	.82		1	
	Minimum Charge	Job		261		261	
50% Vented							
	Demolish	S.F.		2.28		2.28	Includes material and labor to install
	Install	S.F.	59	5.20		64.20	commercial grade steel windows,
	Demolish and Install	S.F.	59	7.48		66.48	including glazing.
	Reinstall	S.F.		4.18		4.18	
	Clean	Ea.	.18	1.22		1.40	
	Paint	S.F.	.18	.82		1	
	Minimum Charge	Job		261		261	

Masonry

Brick Veneer

Concrete Masonry Units

Masonry Wall	Unit	Material	Labor	Equip.	Total	Specification
Unreinforced CMU						
4″ x 8″ x 16″						
Demolish	S.F.		1.98		1.98	Includes material and labor to install
Install	S.F.	1.83	4.27		6.10	normal weight 4″ x 8″ x 16″ block.
Demolish and Install	S.F.	1.83	6.25		8.08	
Clean	S.F.	.11	.49		.60	
Paint	S.F.	.15	.84		.99	
Minimum Charge	Job		212		212	
6″ x 8″ x 16″						
Demolish	S.F.		2.09		2.09	Includes material and labor to install
Install	S.F.	2.40	4.46		6.86	normal weight 6″ x 8″ x 16″ block.
Demolish and Install	S.F.	2.40	6.55		8.95	
Clean	S.F.	.11	.49		.60	
Paint	S.F.	.15	.84		.99	
Minimum Charge	Job		212		212	
8″ x 8″ x 16″						
Demolish	S.F.		2.37		2.37	Includes material and labor to install
Install	S.F.	2.70	4.91		7.61	normal weight 8″ x 8″ x 16″ block.
Demolish and Install	S.F.	2.70	7.28		9.98	
Clean	S.F.	.11	.49		.60	
Paint	S.F.	.15	.84		.99	
Minimum Charge	Job		212		212	
12″ x 8″ x 16″						
Demolish	S.F.		2.37		2.37	Includes material and labor to install
Install	S.F.	4.14	7.45		11.59	normal weight 12″ x 8″ x 16″ block.
Demolish and Install	S.F.	4.14	9.82		13.96	
Clean	S.F.	.11	.49		.60	
Paint	S.F.	.15	.84		.99	
Minimum Charge	Job		212		212	
Reinforced CMU						
4″ x 8″ x 16″						
Demolish	S.F.		1.98	1.19	3.17	Includes material and labor to install
Install	S.F.	2	4.36		6.36	normal weight 4″ x 8″ x 16″ block,
Demolish and Install	S.F.	2	6.34	1.19	9.53	mortar and 1/2″ re-bar installed
Clean	S.F.	.11	.49		.60	vertically every 24″ O.C.
Paint	S.F.	.15	.84		.99	
Minimum Charge	Job		385		385	
6″ x 8″ x 16″						
Demolish	S.F.		2.08	.60	2.68	Includes material and labor to install
Install	S.F.	2.57	4.57		7.14	normal weight 6″ x 8″ x 16″ block,
Demolish and Install	S.F.	2.57	6.65	.60	9.82	mortar and 1/2″ re-bar installed
Clean	S.F.	.11	.49		.60	vertically every 24″ O.C.
Paint	S.F.	.15	.84		.99	
Minimum Charge	Job		385		385	

Masonry

Masonry Wall		Unit	Material	Labor	Equip.	Total	Specification
8" x 8" x 16"							
	Demolish	S.F.		2.20	.63	2.83	Includes material and labor to install
	Install	S.F.	2.88	4.97		7.85	normal weight 8" x 8" x 16" block,
	Demolish and Install	S.F.	2.88	7.17	.63	10.68	mortar and 1/2" re-bar installed
	Clean	S.F.	.11	.49		.60	vertically every 24" O.C.
	Paint	S.F.	.15	.84		.99	
	Minimum Charge	Job		385		385	
12" x 8" x 16"							
	Demolish	S.F.		2.27	.65	2.92	Includes material and labor to install
	Install	S.F.	4.31	7.70		12.01	normal weight 12" x 8" x 16" block,
	Demolish and Install	S.F.	4.31	9.97	.65	14.93	mortar and 1/2" re-bar installed
	Clean	S.F.	.11	.49		.60	vertically every 24" O.C.
	Paint	S.F.	.15	.84		.99	
	Minimum Charge	Job		385		385	

Structural Brick

		Unit	Material	Labor	Equip.	Total	Specification
4" Single Row							
	Demolish	S.F.		2.85		2.85	Cost includes material and labor to
	Install	S.F.	4.32	9.15		13.47	install 4" red brick wall, running bond
	Demolish and Install	S.F.	4.32	12		16.32	with 3/8" concave joints, mortar and
	Clean	S.F.	.11	.42		.53	ties.
	Paint	S.F.	.15	.84		.99	
	Minimum Charge	Job		385		385	
8" Double Row							
	Demolish	S.F.		2.85		2.85	Cost includes material and labor to
	Install	S.F.	8.90	14.55		23.45	install 8" red brick wall, running bond,
	Demolish and Install	S.F.	8.90	17.40		26.30	with 3/8" concave joints, mortar and
	Clean	S.F.	.11	.42		.53	wall ties.
	Paint	S.F.	.15	.84		.99	
	Minimum Charge	Job		385		385	
12" Triple Row							
	Demolish	S.F.		3.96		3.96	Cost includes material and labor to
	Install	S.F.	13.40	20.50		33.90	install 12" red brick wall, running
	Demolish and Install	S.F.	13.40	24.46		37.86	bond, with 3/8" concave joints,
	Clean	S.F.	.11	.42		.53	mortar and wall ties.
	Paint	S.F.	.15	.84		.99	
	Minimum Charge	Job		385		385	

Brick Veneer

		Unit	Material	Labor	Equip.	Total	Specification
4" Red Common							
	Demolish	S.F.		2.85		2.85	Cost includes material and labor to
	Install	S.F.	4.22	8.55		12.77	install 4" common red face brick,
	Demolish and Install	S.F.	4.22	11.40		15.62	running bond with 3/8" concave
	Clean	S.F.	.11	.42		.53	joints, mortar and wall ties.
	Paint	S.F.	.15	.84		.99	
	Minimum Charge	Job		212		212	
4" Used							
	Demolish	S.F.		2.85		2.85	Cost includes material and labor to
	Install	S.F.	4.32	9.15		13.47	install 4" red brick wall, running bond
	Demolish and Install	S.F.	4.32	12		16.32	with 3/8" concave joints, mortar and
	Clean	S.F.	.11	.42		.53	ties.
	Paint	S.F.	.15	.84		.99	
	Minimum Charge	Job		212		212	

Masonry

Masonry Wall		Unit	Material	Labor	Equip.	Total	Specification
6" Jumbo							
	Demolish	S.F.		2.85		2.85	Cost includes material and labor to
	Install	S.F.	4.96	4.51		9.47	install 6" red jumbo brick veneer,
	Demolish and Install	S.F.	4.96	7.36		12.32	running bond with 3/8" concave
	Clean	S.F.	.11	.42		.53	joints, mortar and ties.
	Paint	S.F.	.15	.84		.99	
	Minimum Charge	Job		212		212	
Norman (11-1/2")							
	Demolish	S.F.		2.85		2.85	Cost includes material and labor to
	Install	S.F.	6.40	6.15		12.55	install 4" norman red brick wall,
	Demolish and Install	S.F.	6.40	9		15.40	running bond with 3/8" concave
	Clean	S.F.	.11	.42		.53	joints, mortar and ties.
	Paint	S.F.	.15	.84		.99	
	Minimum Charge	Job		212		212	
Glazed							
	Demolish	S.F.		2.85		2.85	Includes material, labor and
	Install	S.F.	18.30	9.35		27.65	equipment to install glazed brick.
	Demolish and Install	S.F.	18.30	12.20		30.50	
	Clean	S.F.	.11	.42		.53	
	Paint	S.F.	.15	.84		.99	
	Minimum Charge	Job		212		212	
Slumpstone							
6" x 4"							
	Demolish	S.F.		1.98		1.98	Cost includes material and labor to
	Install	S.F.	5.85	4.81		10.66	install 6" x 4" x 16" concrete slump
	Demolish and Install	S.F.	5.85	6.79		12.64	block.
	Clean	S.F.	.11	.49		.60	
	Paint	S.F.	.15	.84		.99	
	Minimum Charge	Job		212		212	
6" x 6"							
	Demolish	S.F.		2.09		2.09	Cost includes material and labor to
	Install	S.F.	5.55	4.97		10.52	install 6" x 6" x 16" concrete slump
	Demolish and Install	S.F.	5.55	7.06		12.61	block.
	Clean	S.F.	.11	.49		.60	
	Paint	S.F.	.15	.84		.99	
	Minimum Charge	Job		212		212	
8" x 6"							
	Demolish	S.F.		2.09		2.09	Cost includes material and labor to
	Install	S.F.	8.20	5.15		13.35	install 8" x 6" x 16" concrete slump
	Demolish and Install	S.F.	8.20	7.24		15.44	block.
	Clean	S.F.	.11	.49		.60	
	Paint	S.F.	.15	.84		.99	
	Minimum Charge	Job		212		212	
12" x 4"							
	Demolish	S.F.		1.98		1.98	Cost includes material and labor to
	Install	S.F.	12.15	5.90		18.05	install 12" x 4" x 16" concrete slump
	Demolish and Install	S.F.	12.15	7.88		20.03	block.
	Clean	S.F.	.11	.49		.60	
	Paint	S.F.	.15	.84		.99	
	Minimum Charge	Job		212		212	
12" x 6"							
	Demolish	S.F.		2.09		2.09	Cost includes material and labor to
	Install	S.F.	12.40	6.40		18.80	install 12" x 6" x 16" concrete slump
	Demolish and Install	S.F.	12.40	8.49		20.89	block.
	Clean	S.F.	.11	.49		.60	
	Paint	S.F.	.15	.84		.99	
	Minimum Charge	Job		212		212	

Masonry

Masonry Wall		Unit	Material	Labor	Equip.	Total	Specification
Stucco							
Three Coat							
	Demolish	S.Y.		2.46		2.46	Includes material and labor to install
	Install	S.Y.	3.94	9.20	.79	13.93	stucco on exterior masonry walls.
	Demolish and Install	S.Y.	3.94	11.66	.79	16.39	
	Clean	S.Y.		4.45		4.45	
	Paint	S.F.	.28	.60		.88	
	Minimum Charge	Job		193		193	
Three Coat w / Wire Mesh							
	Demolish	S.Y.		4.45		4.45	Includes material and labor to install
	Install	S.Y.	7.20	35	2.51	44.71	stucco on wire mesh over wood
	Demolish and Install	S.Y.	7.20	39.45	2.51	49.16	framing.
	Clean	S.Y.		4.45		4.45	
	Paint	S.F.	.28	.60		.88	
	Minimum Charge	Job		193		193	
Fill Cracks							
	Install	S.F.	.44	3.09		3.53	Includes labor and material to fill-in
	Minimum Charge	Job		193		193	hairline cracks up to 1/8" with filler, including sand and fill per S.F.
Furring							
1" x 2"							
	Demolish	L.F.		.14		.14	Cost includes material and labor to
	Install	L.F.	.29	.87		1.16	install 1" x 2" furring on masonry wall.
	Demolish and Install	L.F.	.29	1.01		1.30	
	Minimum Charge	Job		216		216	
2" x 2"							
	Demolish	L.F.		.15		.15	Cost includes material and labor to
	Install	L.F.	.28	.96		1.24	install 2" x 2" furring on masonry wall.
	Demolish and Install	L.F.	.28	1.11		1.39	
	Minimum Charge	Job		216		216	
2" x 4"							
	Demolish	L.F.		.17		.17	Cost includes material and labor to
	Install	L.F.	.51	1.09		1.60	install 2" x 4" furring on masonry wall.
	Demolish and Install	L.F.	.51	1.26		1.77	
	Reinstall	L.F.		.87		.87	
	Minimum Charge	Job		216		216	
Maintenance / Cleaning							
Repoint							
	Install	S.F.	.56	5.30		5.86	Includes labor and material to cut and
	Minimum Charge	Hr.		53		53	repoint brick, hard mortar, running bond.
Acid Etch							
	Install	S.F.	.07	.76		.83	Includes labor and material to acid
	Minimum Charge	Job		160	46	206	wash smooth brick.
Pressure Wash							
	Clean	S.F.		.85	.20	1.05	Includes labor and material to high
	Minimum Charge	Job		160	46	206	pressure water wash masonry, average.
Waterproof							
	Install	S.F.	.36	.80		1.16	Includes labor and material to install
	Minimum Charge	Job		199		199	masory waterproofing.

Masonry

Chimney		Unit	Material	Labor	Equip.	Total	Specification
Demo & Haul Exterior							
	Demolish	C.F.		5.85		5.85	Includes minimum labor and
	Minimum Charge	Job		178		178	equipment to remove masonry and haul debris to truck or dumpster.
Demo & Haul Interior							
	Demolish	C.F.		8		8	Includes minimum labor and
	Minimum Charge	Job		178		178	equipment to remove masonry and haul debris to truck or dumpster.
Install New (w / flue)							
Brick							
	Install	V.L.F.	42.50	48		90.50	Includes material and labor to install
	Minimum Charge	Job		212		212	brick chimney with flue from ground level up. Foundation not included.
Natural Stone							
	Install	L.F.	97	77		174	Includes labor and material to install
	Minimum Charge	Job		212		212	natural stone chimney.
Install From Roof Up							
Brick							
	Install	V.L.F.	42.50	48		90.50	Includes material and labor to install
	Minimum Charge	Job		212		212	brick chimney with flue from ground level up. Foundation not included.
Natural Stone							
	Install	L.F.	97	64		161	Includes labor and material to install
	Minimum Charge	Job		212		212	natural stone chimney.
Install Base Pad							
	Install	Ea.	272	236	1.49	509.49	Includes labor and material to replace
	Minimum Charge	Job		1025	36	1061	spread footing, 5' square x 16" deep.
Metal Cap							
	Install	Ea.	58.50	26.50		85	Includes labor and materials to install
	Minimum Charge	Job		216		216	bird and squirrel screens in a chimney flue.

Fireplace		Unit	Material	Labor	Equip.	Total	Specification
Common Brick							
30"							
	Demolish	Ea.		1275		1275	Includes material and labor to install a
	Install	Ea.	2025	3850		5875	complete unit which includes common
	Demolish and Install	Ea.	2025	5125		7150	brick, foundation, damper, flue lining
	Minimum Charge	Job		212		212	stack to 15' high and a 30" fire box.
36"							
	Demolish	Ea.		1275		1275	Includes material and labor to install a
	Install	Ea.	2175	4275		6450	complete unit which includes common
	Demolish and Install	Ea.	2175	5550		7725	brick, foundation, damper, flue lining
	Minimum Charge	Job		212		212	stack to 15' high and a 36" fire box.
42"							
	Demolish	Ea.		1275		1275	Includes material and labor to install a
	Install	Ea.	2350	4800		7150	complete unit which includes common
	Demolish and Install	Ea.	2350	6075		8425	brick, foundation, damper, flue lining
	Minimum Charge	Job		212		212	stack to 15' high and a 42" fire box.

Fireplace		Unit	Material	Labor	Equip.	Total	Specification
48″							Includes material and labor to install
	Demolish	Ea.		1275		1275	a complete unit which includes common
	Install	Ea.	2475	5475		7950	brick, foundation, damper, flue lining
	Demolish and Install	Ea.	2475	6750		9225	stack to 15′ high and a 48″ fire box.
	Minimum Charge	Job		212		212	
Raised Hearth							
Brick Hearth							
	Demolish	S.F.		5.55		5.55	Includes material and labor to install a
	Install	S.F.	18.80	32		50.80	brick fireplace hearth based on 30″ x
	Demolish and Install	S.F.	18.80	37.55		56.35	29″ opening.
	Clean	S.F.	.11	.42		.53	
	Minimum Charge	Job		212		212	
Marble Hearth / Facing							
	Demolish	Ea.		35.50		35.50	Includes material and labor to install
	Install	Ea.	660	129		789	marble fireplace hearth.
	Demolish and Install	Ea.	660	164.50		824.50	
	Reinstall	Ea.		103.59		103.59	
	Clean	Ea.	40.50	6.40		46.90	
	Minimum Charge	Job		212		212	
Breast (face) Brick							
	Demolish	S.F.		5.55		5.55	Includes material and labor to install
	Install	S.F.	4.40	8.95		13.35	standard red brick, running bond.
	Demolish and Install	S.F.	4.40	14.50		18.90	
	Clean	S.F.		.85	.20	1.05	
	Minimum Charge	Hr.		53		53	
Fire Box							
	Demolish	Ea.		285		285	Includes material and labor to install
	Install	Ea.	173	385		558	fireplace box only (110 brick).
	Demolish and Install	Ea.	173	670		843	
	Clean	Ea.	.15	14.65		14.80	
	Minimum Charge	Hr.		53		53	
Natural Stone							
	Demolish	S.F.		5.55		5.55	Includes material and labor to install
	Install	S.F.	21	16.35		37.35	high priced stone, split or rock face.
	Demolish and Install	S.F.	21	21.90		42.90	
	Clean	S.F.	.09	.96		1.05	
	Minimum Charge	Job		385		385	
Slumpstone Veneer							
	Demolish	S.F.		2.09		2.09	Cost includes material and labor to
	Install	S.F.	8.20	5.15		13.35	install 8″ x 6″ x 16″ concrete slump
	Demolish and Install	S.F.	8.20	7.24		15.44	block.
	Clean	S.F.	.11	.49		.60	
	Paint	S.F.	.15	.84		.99	
	Minimum Charge	Job		212		212	
Prefabricated							
Firebox							
	Demolish	Ea.		51		51	Includes material and labor to install
	Install	Ea.	2275	395		2670	up to 43″ radiant heat, zero
	Demolish and Install	Ea.	2275	446		2721	clearance, prefabricated fireplace.
	Reinstall	Ea.		314.18		314.18	Flues, doors or blowers not included.
	Clean	Ea.	2.01	20		22.01	
	Minimum Charge	Job		216		216	

Masonry

Fireplace

		Unit	Material	Labor	Equip.	Total	Specification
Flue							
	Demolish	V.L.F.		5.95		5.95	Includes material and labor to install
	Install	V.L.F.	19.15	16.70		35.85	prefabricated chimney vent, 8"
	Demolish and Install	V.L.F.	19.15	22.65		41.80	exposed metal flue.
	Reinstall	V.L.F.		13.34		13.34	
	Clean	L.F.	.80	4.01		4.81	
	Minimum Charge	Job		315		315	
Blower							
	Demolish	Ea.		4.75		4.75	Includes material and labor to install
	Install	Ea.	165	30		195	blower for metal fireplace flue.
	Demolish and Install	Ea.	165	34.75		199.75	
	Reinstall	Ea.		24.08		24.08	
	Clean	Ea.	4.03	40		44.03	
	Minimum Charge	Job		315		315	
Accessories							
Wood Mantle							
	Demolish	L.F.		5.95		5.95	Includes material and labor to install
	Install	L.F.	12	12.35		24.35	wood fireplace mantel.
	Demolish and Install	L.F.	12	18.30		30.30	
	Reinstall	L.F.		12.34		12.34	
	Clean	Ea.	.03	.90		.93	
	Paint	L.F.	.11	10.05		10.16	
	Minimum Charge	Job		216		216	
Colonial Style							
	Demolish	Ea.		53.50		53.50	Includes material and labor to install
	Install	Opng.	1650	216		1866	wood fireplace mantel.
	Demolish and Install	Opng.	1650	269.50		1919.50	
	Reinstall	Opng.		216		216	
	Clean	Ea.		.65		.65	
	Paint	Ea.	19.35	138		157.35	
	Minimum Charge	Job		216		216	
Modern Design							
	Demolish	Ea.		53.50		53.50	Includes material and labor to install
	Install	Opng.	490	86.50		576.50	wood fireplace mantel.
	Demolish and Install	Opng.	490	140		630	
	Reinstall	Opng.		86.40		86.40	
	Clean	Ea.		.65		.65	
	Paint	Ea.	19.35	138		157.35	
	Minimum Charge	Job		216		216	
Glass Door Unit							
	Demolish	Ea.		7.40		7.40	Includes material and labor to install a
	Install	Ea.	335	8.85		343.85	fireplace glass door unit.
	Demolish and Install	Ea.	335	16.25		351.25	
	Reinstall	Ea.		8.85		8.85	
	Clean	Ea.	.48	12.30		12.78	
	Minimum Charge	Job		216		216	
Fire Screen							
	Demolish	Ea.		3.71		3.71	Includes material and labor to install a
	Install	Ea.	136	4.42		140.42	fireplace fire screen.
	Demolish and Install	Ea.	136	8.13		144.13	
	Reinstall	Ea.		4.42		4.42	
	Clean	Ea.	.24	10.70		10.94	
	Minimum Charge	Job		216		216	

Siding

Shingles

Board & Batten

Texture 1-11

Exterior Siding		Unit	Material	Labor	Equip.	Total	Specification
Trim							
1" x 2"							
	Demolish	L.F.		.30		.30	Cost includes material and labor to
	Install	L.F.	.28	1.31		1.59	install 1" x 2" pine trim.
	Demolish and Install	L.F.	.28	1.61		1.89	
	Clean	L.F.	.01	.21		.22	
	Paint	L.F.	.02	.58		.60	
	Minimum Charge	Job		216		216	
1" x 3"							
	Demolish	L.F.		.30		.30	Cost includes material and labor to
	Install	L.F.	.30	1.49		1.79	install 1" x 3" pine trim.
	Demolish and Install	L.F.	.30	1.79		2.09	
	Clean	L.F.	.01	.21		.22	
	Paint	L.F.	.02	.58		.60	
	Minimum Charge	Job		216		216	
1" x 4"							
	Demolish	L.F.		.30		.30	Cost includes material and labor to
	Install	L.F.	.54	1.73		2.27	install 1" x 4" pine trim.
	Demolish and Install	L.F.	.54	2.03		2.57	
	Clean	L.F.	.01	.21		.22	
	Paint	L.F.	.02	.58		.60	
	Minimum Charge	Job		216		216	
1" x 6"							
	Demolish	L.F.		.30		.30	Cost includes material and labor to
	Install	L.F.	.91	1.73		2.64	install 1" x 6" pine trim.
	Demolish and Install	L.F.	.91	2.03		2.94	
	Clean	L.F.	.02	.21		.23	
	Paint	L.F.	.09	.58		.67	
	Minimum Charge	Job		216		216	
1" x 8"							
	Demolish	L.F.		.32		.32	Cost includes material and labor to
	Install	L.F.	1.34	2.16		3.50	install 1" x 8" pine trim.
	Demolish and Install	L.F.	1.34	2.48		3.82	
	Clean	L.F.	.03	.23		.26	
	Paint	L.F.	.09	.58		.67	
	Minimum Charge	Job		216		216	
Aluminum							
8" Non-Insulated							
	Demolish	S.F.		.80		.80	Includes material and labor to install
	Install	S.F.	2.60	1.72		4.32	horizontal, colored clapboard, 8" to
	Demolish and Install	S.F.	2.60	2.52		5.12	10" wide, plain.
	Reinstall	S.F.		1.72		1.72	
	Clean	S.F.		.32		.32	
	Minimum Charge	Job		216		216	

Siding

Exterior Siding	Unit	Material	Labor	Equip.	Total	Specification
8″ Insulated						
Demolish	S.F.		.80		.80	Includes material and labor to install
Install	S.F.	2.83	1.72		4.55	horizontal, colored insulated
Demolish and Install	S.F.	2.83	2.52		5.35	clapboard, 8″ wide, plain.
Reinstall	S.F.		1.72		1.72	
Clean	S.F.		.32		.32	
Minimum Charge	Job		216		216	
12″ Non-Insulated						
Demolish	S.F.		.80		.80	Includes material and labor to install
Install	S.F.	2.65	1.48		4.13	horizontal, colored clapboard, plain.
Demolish and Install	S.F.	2.65	2.28		4.93	
Reinstall	S.F.		1.48		1.48	
Clean	S.F.		.32		.32	
Minimum Charge	Job		216		216	
12″ Insulated						
Demolish	S.F.		.80		.80	Includes material and labor to install
Install	S.F.	2.83	1.48		4.31	horizontal, colored insulated
Demolish and Install	S.F.	2.83	2.28		5.11	clapboard, plain.
Reinstall	S.F.		1.48		1.48	
Clean	S.F.		.32		.32	
Minimum Charge	Job		216		216	
Clapboard 8″ to 10″						
Demolish	S.F.		.80		.80	Includes material and labor to install
Install	S.F.	2.60	1.72		4.32	horizontal, colored clapboard, 8″ to
Demolish and Install	S.F.	2.60	2.52		5.12	10″ wide, plain.
Reinstall	S.F.		1.72		1.72	
Clean	S.F.		.32		.32	
Minimum Charge	Job		216		216	
Corner Strips						
Demolish	L.F.		.42		.42	Includes material and labor to install
Install	V.L.F.	3.55	1.72		5.27	corners for horizontal lapped
Demolish and Install	V.L.F.	3.55	2.14		5.69	aluminum siding.
Reinstall	V.L.F.		1.72		1.72	
Clean	L.F.		.21		.21	
Minimum Charge	Job		216		216	
Vinyl						
Non-Insulated						
Demolish	S.F.		.63		.63	Cost includes material and labor to
Install	S.F.	1.43	1.57		3	install 10″ non-insulated solid vinyl
Demolish and Install	S.F.	1.43	2.20		3.63	siding.
Reinstall	S.F.		1.26		1.26	
Clean	S.F.		.32		.32	
Minimum Charge	Job		216		216	
Insulated						
Demolish	S.F.		.63		.63	Cost includes material and labor to
Install	S.F.	3.16	2.16		5.32	install insulated solid vinyl siding
Demolish and Install	S.F.	3.16	2.79		5.95	panels.
Reinstall	S.F.		1.73		1.73	
Clean	S.F.		.32		.32	
Minimum Charge	Job		216		216	
Corner Strips						
Demolish	L.F.		.40		.40	Cost includes material and labor to
Install	L.F.	2	1.23		3.23	install corner posts for vinyl siding
Demolish and Install	L.F.	2	1.63		3.63	panels.
Reinstall	L.F.		.99		.99	
Clean	L.F.		.21		.21	
Minimum Charge	Job		216		216	

Siding

Exterior Siding		Unit	Material	Labor	Equip.	Total	Specification
Fiber Cement Siding							
4' x 8' Panel							
	Demolish	S.F.		.65		.65	Cost includes material and labor to
	Install	S.F.	1.17	.95		2.12	install 4' x 8' fiber cement 7/16"
	Demolish and Install	S.F.	1.17	1.60		2.77	thick.
	Clean	S.F.		.32		.32	
	Paint	S.F.	.32	1.24		1.56	
	Minimum Charge	Job		216		216	
Lap							
	Demolish	S.F.		.64		.64	Cost includes material and labor to
	Install	S.F.	1.08	1.71		2.79	install 8" or 12" fiber cement lap
	Demolish and Install	S.F.	1.08	2.35		3.43	siding 7/16" thick with wood grain
	Clean	S.F.		.32		.32	finish.
	Paint	S.F.	.32	1.24		1.56	
	Minimum Charge	Job		216		216	
Plywood Panel							
Douglas Fir (T-1-11)							
	Demolish	S.F.		.49		.49	Includes material and labor to install
	Install	S.F.	1.73	1.31		3.04	Douglas fir 4' x 8' plywood exterior
	Demolish and Install	S.F.	1.73	1.80		3.53	siding plain or patterns.
	Reinstall	S.F.		1.31		1.31	
	Clean	S.F.		.32		.32	
	Paint	S.F.	.32	1.24		1.56	
	Minimum Charge	Job		216		216	
Redwood							
	Demolish	S.F.		.49		.49	Includes material and labor to install
	Install	S.F.	2.11	1.31		3.42	redwood 4' x 8' plywood exterior
	Demolish and Install	S.F.	2.11	1.80		3.91	siding plain or patterns.
	Reinstall	S.F.		1.31		1.31	
	Clean	S.F.		.32		.32	
	Paint	S.F.	.32	1.24		1.56	
	Minimum Charge	Job		216		216	
Cedar							
	Demolish	S.F.		.49		.49	Cost includes material and labor to
	Install	S.F.	2.67	1.31		3.98	install 4' x 8' cedar plywood exterior
	Demolish and Install	S.F.	2.67	1.80		4.47	siding plain or patterns.
	Reinstall	S.F.		1.31		1.31	
	Clean	S.F.		.32		.32	
	Paint	S.F.	.32	1.24		1.56	
	Minimum Charge	Job		216		216	
Tongue and Groove							
Fir, Tongue and Groove							
	Demolish	S.F.		.89		.89	Includes material and labor to install
	Install	S.F.	5.35	1.31		6.66	fir tongue and groove exterior siding
	Demolish and Install	S.F.	5.35	2.20		7.55	1" x 8".
	Reinstall	S.F.		1.05		1.05	
	Clean	S.F.		.32		.32	
	Paint	S.F.	.32	1.24		1.56	
	Minimum Charge	Job		216		216	
Pine, Tongue and Groove							
	Demolish	S.F.		.89		.89	Includes labor and material to install
	Install	S.F.	2.41	1.31		3.72	Pine tongue and groove exterior
	Demolish and Install	S.F.	2.41	2.20		4.61	siding 1" x 8".
	Reinstall	S.F.		1.31		1.31	
	Clean	S.F.		.32		.32	
	Paint	S.F.	.32	1.24		1.56	
	Minimum Charge	Job		216		216	

Siding

Exterior Siding	Unit	Material	Labor	Equip.	Total	Specification
Cedar, Tongue and Groove						
Demolish	S.F.		.89		.89	Includes labor and material to install
Install	S.F.	7	1.96		8.96	cedar tongue and groove exterior
Demolish and Install	S.F.	7	2.85		9.85	siding 1" x 8".
Reinstall	S.F.		1.57		1.57	
Clean	S.F.		.32		.32	
Paint	S.F.	.32	1.24		1.56	
Minimum Charge	Job		216		216	
Redwood, Tongue and Groove						
Demolish	S.F.		.89		.89	Includes labor and material to install
Install	S.F.	2.79	1.96		4.75	redwood tongue and groove exterior
Demolish and Install	S.F.	2.79	2.85		5.64	siding 1" x 4".
Reinstall	S.F.		1.96		1.96	
Clean	S.F.		.32		.32	
Paint	S.F.	.32	1.24		1.56	
Minimum Charge	Job		216		216	
Board and Batten						
Fir						
Demolish	S.F.		.89		.89	Cost includes material and labor to
Install	S.F.	6.20	1.31		7.51	install 1" x 8" fir boards with 1" x 3"
Demolish and Install	S.F.	6.20	2.20		8.40	battens.
Reinstall	S.F.		1.05		1.05	
Clean	S.F.		.32		.32	
Paint	S.F.	.32	1.24		1.56	
Minimum Charge	Job		216		216	
Pine						
Demolish	S.F.		.89		.89	Cost includes material and labor to
Install	S.F.	3.50	1.15		4.65	install 1" x 10" pine boards with 1" x
Demolish and Install	S.F.	3.50	2.04		5.54	3" battens.
Reinstall	S.F.		.92		.92	
Clean	S.F.		.32		.32	
Paint	S.F.	.32	1.24		1.56	
Minimum Charge	Job		216		216	
Cedar						
Demolish	S.F.		.89		.89	Cost includes material and labor to
Install	S.F.	5.60	1.15		6.75	install 1" x 10" cedar boards with 1" x
Demolish and Install	S.F.	5.60	2.04		7.64	3" battens.
Reinstall	S.F.		.92		.92	
Clean	S.F.		.32		.32	
Paint	S.F.	.32	1.24		1.56	
Minimum Charge	Job		216		216	
Redwood						
Demolish	S.F.		.89		.89	Cost includes material and labor to
Install	S.F.	5.85	1.15		7	install 1" x 10" redwood boards with
Demolish and Install	S.F.	5.85	2.04		7.89	1" x 3" battens.
Reinstall	S.F.		.92		.92	
Clean	S.F.		.32		.32	
Paint	S.F.	.32	1.24		1.56	
Minimum Charge	Job		216		216	
Wood Shingle						
Demolish	Sq.		82.50		82.50	Includes material and labor to install
Install	Sq.	184	192		376	wood shingles/shakes.
Demolish and Install	Sq.	184	274.50		458.50	
Clean	Sq.		33.50		33.50	
Paint	Sq.	21	111		132	
Minimum Charge	Job		216		216	

Siding

Exterior Siding	Unit	Material	Labor	Equip.	Total	Specification
Synthetic Stucco System						
Demolish	S.F.		2.97		2.97	Cost includes material and labor to
Install	S.F.	2.92	6.90	.59	10.41	install 2 coats of adhesive mixture,
Demolish and Install	S.F.	2.92	9.87	.59	13.38	glass fiber mesh, 1" insulation board,
Clean	S.F.		.29		.29	and textured finish coat.
Paint	S.F.	.28	.60		.88	
Minimum Charge	Job		920	79	999	

Front-end Loader

Bulldozer

Grading

Grading		Unit	Material	Labor	Equip.	Total	Specification
Hand (fine)							Includes labor and material to install fine grade for slab on grade, hand grade.
	Install	S.F.		.64		.64	
	Minimum Charge	Job		160		160	
Machine (fine)							Includes labor and material to install fine grade for roadway, base or leveling course.
	Install	S.Y.		.56	.57	1.13	
	Minimum Charge	Job		385	390	775	

Asphalt Paving

Asphalt Paving		Unit	Material	Labor	Equip.	Total	Specification
Seal Coat							Includes labor and material to install sealcoat for a small area.
	Install	S.F.	.15	.12		.27	
	Minimum Charge	Job		160		160	
Wearing Course							Cost includes labor and material to install 1" thick wearing course.
	Install	S.F.	.18	.35	.29	.82	
	Minimum Charge	Job		160		160	

Masonry Pavers

Masonry Pavers		Unit	Material	Labor	Equip.	Total	Specification
Natural Concrete							
Sand Base							Includes material and labor to install concrete pavers on sand base.
	Demolish	S.F.		3.56		3.56	
	Install	S.F.	2.94	7.10		10.04	
	Demolish and Install	S.F.	2.94	10.66		13.60	
	Reinstall	S.F.		5.66		5.66	
	Clean	S.F.		1.28		1.28	
	Minimum Charge	Job		212		212	
Mortar Base							Includes material and labor to install concrete pavers on mortar base.
	Demolish	S.F.		5.95	2.23	8.18	
	Install	S.F.	3.84	5.90		9.74	
	Demolish and Install	S.F.	3.84	11.85	2.23	17.92	
	Reinstall	S.F.		4.72		4.72	
	Clean	S.F.		1.17		1.17	
	Minimum Charge	Job		212		212	

Site Work

Masonry Pavers	Unit	Material	Labor	Equip.	Total	Specification
Adobe						
Sand Base						
Demolish	S.F.		3.56		3.56	Includes material and labor to install
Install	S.F.	2.04	4.72		6.76	adobe pavers on sand base.
Demolish and Install	S.F.	2.04	8.28		10.32	
Reinstall	S.F.		3.78		3.78	
Clean	S.F.		1.28		1.28	
Minimum Charge	Job		212		212	
Mortar Base						
Demolish	S.F.		5.95	2.23	8.18	Includes material and labor to install
Install	S.F.	2.97	5.90		8.87	adobe pavers on mortar base.
Demolish and Install	S.F.	2.97	11.85	2.23	17.05	
Reinstall	S.F.		4.72		4.72	
Clean	S.F.		1.17		1.17	
Minimum Charge	Job		212		212	
Standard Brick						
Sand Base						
Demolish	S.F.		3.56		3.56	Includes material and labor to install
Install	S.F.	3.43	7.70		11.13	standard brick pavers on sand base.
Demolish and Install	S.F.	3.43	11.26		14.69	
Reinstall	S.F.		6.16		6.16	
Clean	S.F.		1.28		1.28	
Minimum Charge	Job		212		212	
Mortar Base						
Demolish	S.F.		5.95	2.23	8.18	Includes material and labor to install
Install	S.F.	3.47	10.60		14.07	standard brick pavers on mortar base.
Demolish and Install	S.F.	3.47	16.55	2.23	22.25	
Reinstall	S.F.		8.50		8.50	
Clean	S.F.		1.17		1.17	
Minimum Charge	Job		212		212	
Deluxe Brick						
Sand Base						
Demolish	S.F.		3.56		3.56	Includes material and labor to install
Install	S.F.	4.04	5.90		9.94	deluxe brick pavers on sand base.
Demolish and Install	S.F.	4.04	9.46		13.50	
Reinstall	S.F.		4.72		4.72	
Clean	S.F.		1.28		1.28	
Minimum Charge	Job		212		212	
Mortar Base						
Demolish	S.F.		5.95	2.23	8.18	Includes material and labor to install
Install	S.F.	4.16	10.60		14.76	deluxe brick pavers on mortar base.
Demolish and Install	S.F.	4.16	16.55	2.23	22.94	
Reinstall	S.F.		8.50		8.50	
Clean	S.F.		1.17		1.17	
Minimum Charge	Job		212		212	

Fencing	Unit	Material	Labor	Equip.	Total	Specification
Block w / Footing						
4″						
Demolish	S.F.		1.98		1.98	Cost includes material and labor to
Install	S.F.	1.74	4.57		6.31	install 4″ non-reinforced concrete
Demolish and Install	S.F.	1.74	6.55		8.29	block.
Clean	S.F.	.24	1.07	.25	1.56	
Paint	S.F.	.32	.70		1.02	
Minimum Charge	Job		212		212	

Fencing	Unit	Material	Labor	Equip.	Total	Specification
4" Reinforced						
Demolish	S.F.		1.98	1.19	3.17	Cost includes material and labor to
Install	S.F.	1.90	4.62		6.52	install 4" reinforced concrete block.
Demolish and Install	S.F.	1.90	6.60	1.19	9.69	
Clean	S.F.	.24	1.07	.25	1.56	
Paint	S.F.	.32	.70		1.02	
Minimum Charge	Job		212		212	
6"						
Demolish	S.F.		2.09		2.09	Cost includes material and labor to
Install	S.F.	2.31	4.91		7.22	install 6" non-reinforced concrete
Demolish and Install	S.F.	2.31	7		9.31	block.
Clean	S.F.	.24	1.07	.25	1.56	
Paint	S.F.	.32	.70		1.02	
Minimum Charge	Job		212		212	
6" Reinforced						
Demolish	S.F.		2.08	.60	2.68	Cost includes material and labor to
Install	S.F.	2.48	4.97		7.45	install 6" reinforced concrete block.
Demolish and Install	S.F.	2.48	7.05	.60	10.13	
Clean	S.F.	.24	1.07	.25	1.56	
Paint	S.F.	.32	.70		1.02	
Minimum Charge	Job		212		212	
Cap for Block Wall						
Demolish	L.F.		2.23		2.23	Includes labor and equipment to install
Install	L.F.	18.80	10.25		29.05	precast concrete coping.
Demolish and Install	L.F.	18.80	12.48		31.28	
Clean	L.F.	.03	3.34		3.37	
Paint	S.F.	.32	.70		1.02	
Minimum Charge	Job		212		212	
Block Pilaster						
Demolish	Ea.		153		153	Includes material and labor to install
Install	Ea.	61.50	154		215.50	block pilaster for fence.
Demolish and Install	Ea.	61.50	307		368.50	
Reinstall	Ea.		153.92		153.92	
Paint	Ea.	4.59	16.45		21.04	
Minimum Charge	Job		212		212	
Block w / o Footing						
4"						
Demolish	S.F.		1.98		1.98	Cost includes material and labor to
Install	S.F.	1.89	3.50		5.39	install 4" non-reinforced hollow
Demolish and Install	S.F.	1.89	5.48		7.37	lightweight block.
Clean	S.F.	.24	1.07	.25	1.56	
Paint	S.F.	.32	.70		1.02	
Minimum Charge	Job		212		212	
4" Reinforced						
Demolish	S.F.		1.98	1.19	3.17	Cost includes material and labor to
Install	S.F.	2.01	4.51		6.52	install 4" reinforced hollow lightweight
Demolish and Install	S.F.	2.01	6.49	1.19	9.69	block.
Clean	S.F.	.24	1.07	.25	1.56	
Paint	S.F.	.32	.70		1.02	
Minimum Charge	Job		212		212	
6"						
Demolish	S.F.		2.09		2.09	Cost includes material and labor to
Install	S.F.	2.70	3.85		6.55	install 6" non-reinforced hollow
Demolish and Install	S.F.	2.70	5.94		8.64	lightweight block.
Clean	S.F.	.24	1.07	.25	1.56	
Paint	S.F.	.32	.70		1.02	
Minimum Charge	Job		212		212	

Fencing	Unit	Material	Labor	Equip.	Total	Specification
6" Reinforced						
Demolish	S.F.		2.08	.60	2.68	Cost includes material and labor to
Install	S.F.	2.84	4.85		7.69	install 6" reinforced hollow lightweight
Demolish and Install	S.F.	2.84	6.93	.60	10.37	block.
Clean	S.F.	.24	1.07	.25	1.56	
Paint	S.F.	.32	.70		1.02	
Minimum Charge	Job		212		212	
Cap for Block Wall						
Demolish	L.F.		2.23		2.23	Includes labor and equipment to install
Install	L.F.	18.80	10.25		29.05	precast concrete coping.
Demolish and Install	L.F.	18.80	12.48		31.28	
Clean	L.F.	.03	3.34		3.37	
Paint	S.F.	.32	.70		1.02	
Minimum Charge	Job		212		212	
Block Pilaster						
Demolish	Ea.		153		153	Includes material and labor to install
Install	Ea.	61.50	154		215.50	block pilaster for fence.
Demolish and Install	Ea.	61.50	307		368.50	
Reinstall	Ea.		153.92		153.92	
Paint	Ea.	4.59	16.45		21.04	
Minimum Charge	Job		212		212	
Chain Link						
3' High w / o Top Rail						
Demolish	L.F.		2.80	1.05	3.85	Includes material and labor to install
Install	L.F.	5.85	1.88	.58	8.31	residential galvanized fence 3' high
Demolish and Install	L.F.	5.85	4.68	1.63	12.16	with 1-3/8" steel post 10' O.C. set
Reinstall	L.F.		1.50	.47	1.97	without concrete.
Clean	L.F.	.12	1.17		1.29	
Minimum Charge	Job		495		495	
4' High w / o Top Rail						
Demolish	L.F.		2.80	1.05	3.85	Includes material and labor to install
Install	L.F.	6.65	2.32	.72	9.69	residential galvanized fence 4' high
Demolish and Install	L.F.	6.65	5.12	1.77	13.54	with 1-3/8" steel post 10' O.C. set
Reinstall	L.F.		1.86	.58	2.44	without concrete.
Clean	L.F.	.17	1.28		1.45	
Minimum Charge	Job		495		495	
5' High w / o Top Rail						
Demolish	L.F.		2.80	1.05	3.85	Includes material and labor to install
Install	L.F.	8.90	3.03	.94	12.87	residential galvanized fence 5' high
Demolish and Install	L.F.	8.90	5.83	1.99	16.72	with 1-3/8" steel post 10' O.C. set
Reinstall	L.F.		2.43	.75	3.18	without concrete.
Clean	L.F.	.20	1.42		1.62	
Minimum Charge	Job		495		495	
3' High w / Top Rail						
Demolish	L.F.		2.97	1.12	4.09	Includes material and labor to install
Install	L.F.	2.20	1.97	.61	4.78	residential galvanized fence 3' high
Demolish and Install	L.F.	2.20	4.94	1.73	8.87	with 1-3/8" steel post 10' O.C. set
Reinstall	L.F.		1.58	.49	2.07	without concrete.
Clean	L.F.	.12	1.19		1.31	
Minimum Charge	Job		495		495	
4' High w / Top Rail						
Demolish	L.F.		2.97	1.12	4.09	Includes material and labor to install
Install	L.F.	7.75	2.46	.77	10.98	residential galvanized fence 4' high
Demolish and Install	L.F.	7.75	5.43	1.89	15.07	with 1-5/8" steel post 10' O.C. set
Reinstall	L.F.		1.97	.61	2.58	without concrete and 1-5/8" top rail
Clean	L.F.	.17	1.31		1.48	with sleeves.
Minimum Charge	Job		495		495	

Fencing	Unit	Material	Labor	Equip.	Total	Specification
5' High w / Top Rail						
Demolish	L.F.		2.97	1.12	4.09	Includes material and labor to install
Install	L.F.	8.85	3.29	1.02	13.16	residential galvanized fence 5' high
Demolish and Install	L.F.	8.85	6.26	2.14	17.25	with 1-5/8" steel post 10' O.C. set
Reinstall	L.F.		2.63	.82	3.45	without concrete and 1-5/8" top rail
Clean	L.F.	.20	1.46		1.66	with sleeves.
Minimum Charge	Job		495		495	
6' High w / Top Rail						
Demolish	L.F.		2.97	1.12	4.09	Includes material and labor to install
Install	L.F.	10.65	4.93	1.53	17.11	residential galvanized fence 6' high
Demolish and Install	L.F.	10.65	7.90	2.65	21.20	with 2" steel post 10' O.C. set without
Reinstall	L.F.		3.94	1.22	5.16	concrete and 1-3/8" top rail with
Clean	L.F.	.24	1.64		1.88	sleeves.
Minimum Charge	Job		495		495	
Barbed Wire						
Demolish	L.F.		1.66		1.66	Cost includes material and labor to
Install	L.F.	.40	.64	.24	1.28	install 3 strand galvanized barbed
Demolish and Install	L.F.	.40	2.30	.24	2.94	wire fence.
Reinstall	L.F.		.51	.20	.71	
Minimum Charge	Job		495	415	910	
6' Redwood						
Demolish	L.F.		11		11	Cost includes material and labor to
Install	L.F.	28.50	7.90	2.45	38.85	install 6' high redwood fencing.
Demolish and Install	L.F.	28.50	18.90	2.45	49.85	
Reinstall	L.F.		6.31	1.96	8.27	
Clean	L.F.	.24	1.49		1.73	
Paint	L.F.	.87	3.89		4.76	
Minimum Charge	Job		495		495	
6' Red Cedar						
Demolish	L.F.		11		11	Cost includes material and labor to
Install	L.F.	20.50	7.90	2.45	30.85	install 6' cedar fence.
Demolish and Install	L.F.	20.50	18.90	2.45	41.85	
Reinstall	L.F.		6.31	1.96	8.27	
Clean	L.F.	.24	1.49		1.73	
Paint	L.F.	.87	3.89		4.76	
Minimum Charge	Job		495		495	
6' Shadowbox						
Demolish	L.F.		11		11	Cost includes material and labor to
Install	L.F.	17.50	6.55	2.04	26.09	install 6' pressure treated pine fence.
Demolish and Install	L.F.	17.50	17.55	2.04	37.09	
Reinstall	L.F.		5.26	1.63	6.89	
Clean	L.F.	.24	1.49		1.73	
Paint	L.F.	.87	3.89		4.76	
Minimum Charge	Job		495		495	
3' Picket						
Demolish	L.F.		11		11	Includes material, labor and
Install	L.F.	7.45	7.05	2.19	16.69	equipment to install pressure treated
Demolish and Install	L.F.	7.45	18.05	2.19	27.69	pine picket fence.
Reinstall	L.F.		5.63	1.75	7.38	
Clean	L.F.	.12	1.28		1.40	
Paint	L.F.	.43	2.11		2.54	
Minimum Charge	Job		495		495	

Fencing	Unit	Material	Labor	Equip.	Total	Specification
Wrought Iron						
Demolish	L.F.		23.50		23.50	Cost includes material and labor to
Install	L.F.	42	13.15		55.15	install 5' high wrought iron fence with
Demolish and Install	L.F.	42	36.65		78.65	pickets at 4-1/2" O.C.
Reinstall	L.F.		10.54		10.54	
Clean	L.F.		1.28		1.28	
Paint	L.F.	4.15	4.35		8.50	
Minimum Charge	Job		495		495	
Post						
Dirt Based Wood						
Demolish	Ea.		27.50		27.50	Includes material and labor to install
Install	Ea.	33	124		157	wood post set in earth.
Demolish and Install	Ea.	33	151.50		184.50	
Reinstall	Ea.		98.81		98.81	
Clean	Ea.		4.01		4.01	
Paint	Ea.	.95	1.48		2.43	
Minimum Charge	Job		495		495	
Concrete Based Wood						
Demolish	Ea.		39.50	14.90	54.40	Includes material and labor to install
Install	Ea.	18.80	165		183.80	wood post set in concrete.
Demolish and Install	Ea.	18.80	204.50	14.90	238.20	
Clean	Ea.		4.01		4.01	
Paint	Ea.	.95	1.48		2.43	
Minimum Charge	Job		495		495	
Block Pilaster						
Demolish	Ea.		153		153	Includes material and labor to install
Install	Ea.	61.50	154		215.50	block pilaster for fence.
Demolish and Install	Ea.	61.50	307		368.50	
Reinstall	Ea.		153.92		153.92	
Paint	Ea.	4.59	16.45		21.04	
Minimum Charge	Job		212		212	
Gate						
Chain Link						
Demolish	Ea.		36.50		36.50	Cost includes material and labor to
Install	Ea.	110	55		165	install 3' wide chain link pass gate
Demolish and Install	Ea.	110	91.50		201.50	and hardware.
Reinstall	Ea.		43.91		43.91	
Clean	Ea.		4.45		4.45	
Minimum Charge	Job		495		495	
Redwood						
Demolish	Ea.		31.50		31.50	Includes material, labor and
Install	Ea.	245	55		300	equipment to install redwood pass
Demolish and Install	Ea.	245	86.50		331.50	gate and hardware. .
Reinstall	Ea.		43.91		43.91	
Clean	Ea.		4.45		4.45	
Paint	Ea.	1.43	7.40		8.83	
Minimum Charge	Job		495		495	
Red Cedar						
Demolish	Ea.		31.50		31.50	Cost includes material and labor to
Install	Ea.	101	55		156	install 3' wide red cedar pass gate
Demolish and Install	Ea.	101	86.50		187.50	and hardware.
Reinstall	Ea.		43.91		43.91	
Clean	Ea.		4.45		4.45	
Paint	Ea.	1.43	7.40		8.83	
Minimum Charge	Job		495		495	

Site Work

Fencing	Unit	Material	Labor	Equip.	Total	Specification
Wrought Iron						
Demolish	Ea.		23.50		23.50	Includes material, labor and
Install	Ea.	286	124		410	equipment to install wrought iron gate
Demolish and Install	Ea.	286	147.50	.	433.50	with hardware.
Reinstall	Ea.		98.81		98.81	
Clean	Ea.		4.45		4.45	
Paint	Ea.	8.30	7.40		15.70	
Minimum Charge	Job		495		495	

Fire-extinguishing System					Space Heater		Hot-air Furnace

Plumbing	Unit	Material	Labor	Equip.	Total	Specification
Components						
3/4″ Supply						
Demolish	L.F.		2.79		2.79	Includes material and labor to install
Install	L.F.	5.65	6.60		12.25	type L copper tubing including
Demolish and Install	L.F.	5.65	9.39		15.04	couplings and hangers at 10′ O.C.
Reinstall	L.F.		6.60		6.60	
Minimum Charge	Job		251		251	
1/2″ Fixture Supply						
Install	Ea.	77.50	167		244.50	Includes labor and materials to install supply pipe only to a plumbing fixture.
2″ Single Vent Stack						
Demolish	Ea.		46.50		46.50	Includes material and labor to install
Install	Ea.	33.50	251		284.50	PVC vent stack pipe with couplings at
Demolish and Install	Ea.	33.50	297.50		331	10′ O.C.
Reinstall	Ea.		250.80		250.80	
Minimum Charge	Job		251		251	
4″ Drain						
Demolish	L.F.		3.72		3.72	Includes material and labor to install
Install	L.F.	7.10	8.20		15.30	DVW type PVC pipe with couplings at
Demolish and Install	L.F.	7.10	11.92		19.02	10′ O.C. and 3 strap hangers per 10′
Reinstall	L.F.		8.21		8.21	run.
Minimum Charge	Job		251		251	
1-1/2″ Drain						
Demolish	L.F.		2.79		2.79	Includes material and labor to install
Install	L.F.	2.01	5.35		7.36	DVW type PVC pipe with couplings at
Demolish and Install	L.F.	2.01	8.14		10.15	10′ O.C. and 3 strap hangers per 10′
Reinstall	L.F.		5.34		5.34	run.
Minimum Charge	Job		251		251	
Maintenance						
Flush Out / Unclog						
Clean	Job		251		251	Includes 4 hour minimum labor charge
Minimum Charge	Job		251		251	for a plumber.
Vent Cap						
Large						
Demolish	Ea.		12.65		12.65	Includes labor and material to install a
Install	Ea.	43.50	23		66.50	PVC plumbing pipe vent cap.
Demolish and Install	Ea.	43.50	35.65		79.15	
Clean	Ea.	.56	7.30		7.86	
Paint	Ea.	.21	8.40		8.61	
Minimum Charge	Job		125		125	

Rough Mechanical

Plumbing

Plumbing	Unit	Material	Labor	Equip.	Total	Specification
Medium						
Demolish	Ea.		12.65		12.65	Includes labor and material to install a
Install	Ea.	37.50	22		59.50	PVC plumbing pipe vent cap.
Demolish and Install	Ea.	37.50	34.65		72.15	
Clean	Ea.	.56	7.30		7.86	
Paint	Ea.	.21	8.40		8.61	
Minimum Charge	Job		125		125	
Small						
Demolish	Ea.		12.65		12.65	Includes material and labor to install a
Install	Ea.	10.10	21		31.10	PVC plumbing pipe vent cap.
Demolish and Install	Ea.	10.10	33.65		43.75	
Clean	Ea.	.56	7.30		7.86	
Paint	Ea.	.21	8.40		8.61	
Minimum Charge	Job		125		125	

Plumbing

Plumbing	Unit	Material	Labor	Equip.	Total	Specification
Sump Pump						
1/4 HP						
Demolish	Ea.		50		50	Includes material and labor to install a
Install	Ea.	147	83.50		230.50	submersible sump pump.
Demolish and Install	Ea.	147	133.50		280.50	
Reinstall	Ea.		66.88		66.88	
Clean	Ea.	1.41	20		21.41	
Minimum Charge	Job		251		251	
1/3 HP						
Demolish	Ea.		50		50	Includes material and labor to install a
Install	Ea.	213	100		313	submersible sump pump.
Demolish and Install	Ea.	213	150		363	
Reinstall	Ea.		80.26		80.26	
Clean	Ea.	1.41	20		21.41	
Minimum Charge	Job		251		251	
1/2 HP						
Demolish	Ea.		50		50	Includes material and labor to install a
Install	Ea.	262	100		362	submersible sump pump.
Demolish and Install	Ea.	262	150		412	
Reinstall	Ea.		80.26		80.26	
Clean	Ea.	1.41	20		21.41	
Minimum Charge	Job		251		251	
Clean and Service						
Clean	Ea.		31.50		31.50	Includes labor to clean and service a
Minimum Charge	Job		251		251	sump pump.

Water Heater

Water Heater	Unit	Material	Labor	Equip.	Total	Specification
Electric						
30 Gallon						
Demolish	Ea.		157		157	Includes material and labor to install a
Install	Ea.	525	228		753	30 gallon electric water heater.
Demolish and Install	Ea.	525	385		910	
Reinstall	Ea.		182.40		182.40	
Clean	Ea.	1.41	20		21.41	
Minimum Charge	Job		251		251	

Rough Mechanical

Water Heater	Unit	Material	Labor	Equip.	Total	Specification
40 Gallon						
Demolish	Ea.		157		157	Includes material and labor to install a
Install	Ea.	880	251		1131	40 gallon electric water heater.
Demolish and Install	Ea.	880	408		1288	
Reinstall	Ea.		200.64		200.64	
Clean	Ea.	1.41	20		21.41	
Minimum Charge	Job		251		251	
52 Gallon						
Demolish	Ea.		157		157	Includes material and labor to install a
Install	Ea.	985	251		1236	52 gallon electric water heater.
Demolish and Install	Ea.	985	408		1393	
Reinstall	Ea.		200.64		200.64	
Clean	Ea.	1.41	20		21.41	
Minimum Charge	Job		251		251	
82 Gallon						
Demolish	Ea.		157		157	Includes material and labor to install
Install	Ea.	1475	315		1790	an 82 gallon electric water heater.
Demolish and Install	Ea.	1475	472		1947	
Reinstall	Ea.		250.80		250.80	
Clean	Ea.	1.41	20		21.41	
Minimum Charge	Job		251		251	
Gas-fired						
30 Gallon Gas-fired						
Demolish	Ea.		193		193	Includes material and labor to install a
Install	Ea.	985	251		1236	30 gallon gas water heater.
Demolish and Install	Ea.	985	444		1429	
Reinstall	Ea.		200.64		200.64	
Clean	Ea.	1.41	20		21.41	
Minimum Charge	Job		251		251	
30 Gallon Gas-fired, Flue						
Install	Ea.	65.50	71.50		137	Includes labor and materials to install
Minimum Charge	Job		251		251	a flue for a water heater (up to 50 gallon size).
40 Gallon Gas-fired						
Demolish	Ea.		193		193	Includes material and labor to install a
Install	Ea.	985	264		1249	40 gallon gas water heater.
Demolish and Install	Ea.	985	457		1442	
Reinstall	Ea.		211.20		211.20	
Clean	Ea.	1.41	20		21.41	
Minimum Charge	Job		251		251	
40 Gallon Gas-fired, Flue						
Install	Ea.	65.50	71.50		137	Includes labor and materials to install
Minimum Charge	Job		251		251	a flue for a water heater (up to 50 gallon size).
50 Gallon Gas-fired						
Demolish	Ea.		193		193	Includes material and labor to install a
Install	Ea.	1025	279		1304	50 gallon gas water heater.
Demolish and Install	Ea.	1025	472		1497	
Reinstall	Ea.		222.93		222.93	
Clean	Ea.	1.41	20		21.41	
Minimum Charge	Job		251		251	
50 Gallon Gas-fired, Flue						
Install	Ea.	65.50	71.50		137	Includes labor and materials to install
Minimum Charge	Job		251		251	a flue for a water heater (up to 50 gallon size).

Water Heater	Unit	Material	Labor	Equip.	Total	Specification
Solar Hot Water System						
Water Heater						
Demolish	Ea.		125		125	Includes material and labor to install a
Install	Ea.	1675	335		2010	solar hot water heat exchanger
Demolish and Install	Ea.	1675	460		2135	storage tank, 100 gallon.
Reinstall	Ea.		267.52		267.52	
Minimum Charge	Job		255		255	
Solar Panel						
Demolish	S.F.		1.83		1.83	Includes material and labor to install
Install	S.F.	34	3.30		37.30	solar panel.
Demolish and Install	S.F.	34	5.13		39.13	
Reinstall	S.F.		2.64		2.64	
Minimum Charge	Job		255		255	
Repair Plumbing						
Install	Job		255		255	Includes 4 hour minimum labor charge
Minimum Charge	Job		255		255	for a steamfitter or pipefitter.
Insulating Wrap						
Demolish	Ea.		5.80		5.80	Includes material and labor to install
Install	Ea.	19.90	15.70		35.60	insulating wrap around a 100 gallon
Demolish and Install	Ea.	19.90	21.50		41.40	solar hot water heat exchanger
Reinstall	Ea.		12.54		12.54	storage tank.
Minimum Charge	Job		251		251	
Water Softener						
Demolish	Ea.		93		93	Includes material and labor to install a
Install	Ea.	1800	226		2026	14 GPM water softener.
Demolish and Install	Ea.	1800	319		2119	
Reinstall	Ea.		180.58		180.58	
Clean	Ea.	1.41	20		21.41	
Minimum Charge	Ea.		251		251	

Ductwork	Unit	Material	Labor	Equip.	Total	Specification
Galvanized, Square or Rectangular						
6"						
Demolish	L.F.		2.23		2.23	Includes material and labor to install
Install	L.F.	1.68	10.70		12.38	rectangular ductwork with a greatest
Demolish and Install	L.F.	1.68	12.93		14.61	dimension of 6".
Reinstall	L.F.		8.56		8.56	
Clean	L.F.		2.57		2.57	
Minimum Charge	Job		241		241	
8"						
Demolish	L.F.		2.23		2.23	Includes material and labor to install
Install	L.F.	2.23	13.75		15.98	rectangular ductwork with a greatest
Demolish and Install	L.F.	2.23	15.98		18.21	dimension of 8".
Reinstall	L.F.		11.01		11.01	
Clean	L.F.		3.42		3.42	
Minimum Charge	Job		241		241	
10"						
Demolish	L.F.		2.23		2.23	Includes material and labor to install
Install	L.F.	2.79	17.85		20.64	rectangular ductwork with a greatest
Demolish and Install	L.F.	2.79	20.08		22.87	dimension of 10".
Reinstall	L.F.		14.27		14.27	
Clean	L.F.		4.28		4.28	
Minimum Charge	Job		241		241	

Rough Mechanical

Ductwork	Unit	Material	Labor	Equip.	Total	Specification
Galvanized, Spiral						
4"						
Demolish	L.F.		2.68		2.68	Cost includes material and labor to
Install	L.F.	1.87	2.41		4.28	install 4" diameter spiral pre-formed
Demolish and Install	L.F.	1.87	5.09		6.96	steel galvanized ductwork.
Reinstall	L.F.		1.93		1.93	
Clean	L.F.		1.34		1.34	
Minimum Charge	Job		241		241	
6"						
Demolish	L.F.		2.68		2.68	Cost includes material and labor to
Install	L.F.	2.09	3.10		5.19	install 6" diameter spiral pre-formed
Demolish and Install	L.F.	2.09	5.78		7.87	steel galvanized ductwork.
Reinstall	L.F.		2.48		2.48	
Clean	L.F.		2.02		2.02	
Minimum Charge	Job		241		241	
8"						
Demolish	L.F.		2.68		2.68	Cost includes material and labor to
Install	L.F.	2.66	4.34		7	install 8" diameter spiral pre-formed
Demolish and Install	L.F.	2.66	7.02		9.68	steel galvanized ductwork.
Reinstall	L.F.		3.47		3.47	
Clean	L.F.		2.69		2.69	
Minimum Charge	Job		241		241	
10"						
Demolish	L.F.		3.34		3.34	Cost includes material and labor to
Install	L.F.	3.32	5.40		8.72	install 10" diameter spiral pre-formed
Demolish and Install	L.F.	3.32	8.74		12.06	steel galvanized ductwork.
Reinstall	L.F.		4.34		4.34	
Clean	L.F.		3.36		3.36	
Minimum Charge	Job		241		241	
12"						
Demolish	L.F.		4.46		4.46	Cost includes material and labor to
Install	L.F.	3.99	7.25		11.24	install 12" diameter spiral pre-formed
Demolish and Install	L.F.	3.99	11.71		15.70	steel galvanized ductwork.
Reinstall	L.F.		5.78		5.78	
Clean	L.F.		4.03		4.03	
Minimum Charge	Job		241		241	
16"						
Demolish	L.F.		8.90		8.90	Cost includes material and labor to
Install	L.F.	6.20	14.45		20.65	install 16" diameter spiral pre-formed
Demolish and Install	L.F.	6.20	23.35		29.55	steel galvanized ductwork.
Reinstall	L.F.		11.56		11.56	
Clean	L.F.		5.40		5.40	
Minimum Charge	Job		241		241	
Flexible Fiberglass						
6" Non-insulated						
Demolish	L.F.		2.06		2.06	Cost includes material and labor to
Install	L.F.	1.65	3.10		4.75	install 6" diameter non-insulated
Demolish and Install	L.F.	1.65	5.16		6.81	flexible fiberglass fabric on corrosion
Reinstall	L.F.		2.48		2.48	resistant metal ductwork.
Clean	L.F.		2.02		2.02	
Minimum Charge	Job		241		241	
8" Non-insulated						
Demolish	L.F.		2.97		2.97	Cost includes material and labor to
Install	L.F.	2.10	4.34		6.44	install 8" diameter non-insulated
Demolish and Install	L.F.	2.10	7.31		9.41	flexible fiberglass fabric on corrosion
Reinstall	L.F.		3.47		3.47	resistant metal ductwork.
Clean	L.F.		2.69		2.69	
Minimum Charge	Job		241		241	

Rough Mechanical

Ductwork		Unit	Material	Labor	Equip.	Total	Specification
10″ Non-insulated							
	Demolish	L.F.		3.82		3.82	Cost includes material and labor to
	Install	L.F.	2.71	5.40		8.11	install 10″ diameter non-insulated
	Demolish and Install	L.F.	2.71	9.22		11.93	flexible fiberglass fabric on corrosion
	Reinstall	L.F.		4.34		4.34	resistant metal ductwork.
	Clean	L.F.		3.36		3.36	
	Minimum Charge	Job		241		241	
12″ Non-insulated							
	Demolish	L.F.		5.35		5.35	Cost includes material and labor to
	Install	L.F.	3.23	7.25		10.48	install 12″ diameter non-insulated
	Demolish and Install	L.F.	3.23	12.60		15.83	flexible fiberglass fabric on corrosion
	Reinstall	L.F.		5.78		5.78	resistant metal ductwork.
	Clean	L.F.		4.03		4.03	
	Minimum Charge	Job		241		241	
4″ Insulated							
	Demolish	L.F.		1.57		1.57	Cost includes material and labor to
	Install	L.F.	2.86	2.55		5.41	install 4″ diameter insulated flexible
	Demolish and Install	L.F.	2.86	4.12		6.98	fiberglass fabric on corrosion resistant
	Reinstall	L.F.		2.04		2.04	metal ductwork.
	Clean	L.F.		1.34		1.34	
	Minimum Charge	Job		241		241	
6″ Insulated							
	Demolish	L.F.		2.06		2.06	Cost includes material and labor to
	Install	L.F.	3.23	3.34		6.57	install 6″ diameter insulated flexible
	Demolish and Install	L.F.	3.23	5.40		8.63	fiberglass fabric on corrosion resistant
	Reinstall	L.F.		2.67		2.67	metal ductwork.
	Clean	L.F.		2.02		2.02	
	Minimum Charge	Job		241		241	
8″ Insulated							
	Demolish	L.F.		2.97		2.97	Cost includes material and labor to
	Install	L.F.	3.84	4.82		8.66	install 8″ diameter insulated flexible
	Demolish and Install	L.F.	3.84	7.79		11.63	fiberglass fabric on corrosion resistant
	Reinstall	L.F.		3.85		3.85	metal ductwork.
	Clean	L.F.		2.69		2.69	
	Minimum Charge	Job		241		241	
10″ Insulated							
	Demolish	L.F.		3.82		3.82	Cost includes material and labor to
	Install	L.F.	4.68	6.20		10.88	install 10″ diameter insulated flexible
	Demolish and Install	L.F.	4.68	10.02		14.70	fiberglass fabric on corrosion resistant
	Reinstall	L.F.		4.96		4.96	metal ductwork.
	Clean	L.F.		3.36		3.36	
	Minimum Charge	Job		241		241	
12″ Insulated							
	Demolish	L.F.		5.35		5.35	Cost includes material and labor to
	Install	L.F.	5.40	8.65		14.05	install 12″ diameter insulated flexible
	Demolish and Install	L.F.	5.40	14		19.40	fiberglass fabric on corrosion resistant
	Reinstall	L.F.		6.94		6.94	metal ductwork.
	Clean	L.F.		4.03		4.03	
	Minimum Charge	Job		241		241	

Rough Mechanical

Heating		Unit	Material	Labor	Equip.	Total	Specification
Hot Water Baseboard							
	Demolish	L.F.		8.70		8.70	Includes material and labor to install
	Install	L.F.	12.30	15.30		27.60	baseboard radiation.
	Demolish and Install	L.F.	12.30	24		36.30	
	Reinstall	L.F.		12.23		12.23	
	Clean	L.F.	1.41	5		6.41	
	Minimum Charge	Job		251		251	
3'							
	Demolish	Ea.		28		28	Includes material and labor to install
	Install	Ea.	24	51		75	fin tube baseboard radiation in 3'
	Demolish and Install	Ea.	24	79		103	sections.
	Reinstall	Ea.		40.78		40.78	
	Clean	Ea.	.41	15.25		15.66	
	Minimum Charge	Job		251		251	
4'							
	Demolish	Ea.		37		37	Includes material and labor to install
	Install	Ea.	32.50	57.50		90	fin tube baseboard radiation in 4'
	Demolish and Install	Ea.	32.50	94.50		127	sections.
	Reinstall	Ea.		45.88		45.88	
	Clean	Ea.	.80	20		20.80	
	Minimum Charge	Job		251		251	
5'							
	Demolish	Ea.		46.50		46.50	Includes material and labor to install
	Install	Ea.	40.50	65.50		106	fin tube baseboard radiation in 5'
	Demolish and Install	Ea.	40.50	112		152.50	sections.
	Reinstall	Ea.		52.43		52.43	
	Clean	Ea.	.80	24.50		25.30	
	Minimum Charge	Job		251		251	
6'							
	Demolish	Ea.		55.50		55.50	Includes material and labor to install
	Install	Ea.	48.50	76.50		125	fin tube baseboard radiation in 6'
	Demolish and Install	Ea.	48.50	132		180.50	sections.
	Reinstall	Ea.		61.17		61.17	
	Clean	Ea.	.80	29		29.80	
	Minimum Charge	Job		251		251	
7'							
	Demolish	Ea.		62		62	Includes material and labor to install
	Install	Ea.	56.50	100		156.50	fin tube baseboard radiation in 7'
	Demolish and Install	Ea.	56.50	162		218.50	sections.
	Reinstall	Ea.		80.26		80.26	
	Clean	Ea.	1.01	35.50		36.51	
	Minimum Charge	Job		251		251	
9'							
	Demolish	Ea.		93		93	Includes material and labor to install
	Install	Ea.	73	143		216	fin tube baseboard radiation in 9'
	Demolish and Install	Ea.	73	236		309	sections.
	Reinstall	Ea.		114.65		114.65	
	Clean	Ea.	1.62	46		47.62	
	Minimum Charge	Job		251		251	
Cabinet Unit Heater							
50 MBH							
	Demolish	Ea.		46		46	Includes material and labor to install a
	Install	Ea.	1350	131		1481	cabinet space heater with an output of
	Demolish and Install	Ea.	1350	177		1527	50 MBH.
	Reinstall	Ea.		104.87		104.87	
	Clean	Ea.	1.01	40		41.01	
	Minimum Charge	Job		255		255	

Rough Mechanical

Heating

Heating	Unit	Material	Labor	Equip.	Total	Specification
75 MBH						
Demolish	Ea.		46		46	Includes material and labor to install a
Install	Ea.	1525	153		1678	cabinet space heater with an output of
Demolish and Install	Ea.	1525	199		1724	75 MBH.
Reinstall	Ea.		122.35		122.35	
Clean	Ea.	1.01	40		41.01	
Minimum Charge	Job		255		255	
125 MBH						
Demolish	Ea.		55		55	Includes material and labor to install a
Install	Ea.	1900	184		2084	cabinet space heater with an output of
Demolish and Install	Ea.	1900	239		2139	125 MBH.
Reinstall	Ea.		146.82		146.82	
Clean	Ea.	1.01	40		41.01	
Minimum Charge	Job		255		255	
175 MBH						
Demolish	Ea.		69		69	Includes material and labor to install a
Install	Ea.	2250	262		2512	cabinet space heater with an output of
Demolish and Install	Ea.	2250	331		2581	175 MBH.
Reinstall	Ea.		209.74		209.74	
Clean	Ea.	1.01	40		41.01	
Minimum Charge	Job		255		255	

Furnace Unit

Wall (gas-fired)

Furnace Unit	Unit	Material	Labor	Equip.	Total	Specification
25 MBH w / Thermostat						
Demolish	Ea.		108		108	Includes material and labor to install a
Install	Ea.	670	173		843	gas fired hot air furnace rated at 25
Demolish and Install	Ea.	670	281		951	MBH.
Reinstall	Ea.		138.75		138.75	
Clean	Ea.	2.01	89		91.01	
Minimum Charge	Job		255		255	
35 MBH w / Thermostat						
Demolish	Ea.		108		108	Includes material and labor to install a
Install	Ea.	860	193		1053	gas fired hot air furnace rated at 35
Demolish and Install	Ea.	860	301		1161	MBH.
Reinstall	Ea.		154.17		154.17	
Clean	Ea.	2.01	89		91.01	
Minimum Charge	Job		255		255	
50 MBH w / Thermostat						
Demolish	Ea.		108		108	Includes material and labor to install a
Install	Ea.	1000	217		1217	gas fired hot air furnace rated at 50
Demolish and Install	Ea.	1000	325		1325	MBH.
Reinstall	Ea.		173.44		173.44	
Clean	Ea.	2.01	89		91.01	
Minimum Charge	Job		255		255	
60 MBH w / Thermostat						
Demolish	Ea.		108		108	Includes material and labor to install a
Install	Ea.	1125	241		1366	gas fired hot air furnace rated at 60
Demolish and Install	Ea.	1125	349		1474	MBH.
Reinstall	Ea.		192.71		192.71	
Clean	Ea.	2.01	89		91.01	
Minimum Charge	Job		255		255	

Furnace Unit	Unit	Material	Labor	Equip.	Total	Specification
Floor (gas-fired)						
30 MBH w / Thermostat						
Demolish	Ea.		108		108	Includes material and labor to install a
Install	Ea.	890	173		1063	gas fired hot air floor furnace rated at
Demolish and Install	Ea.	890	281		1171	30 MBH.
Reinstall	Ea.		138.75		138.75	
Clean	Ea.	2.01	89		91.01	
Minimum Charge	Job		255		255	
50 MBH w / Thermostat						
Demolish	Ea.		108		108	Includes material and labor to install a
Install	Ea.	965	217		1182	gas fired hot air floor furnace rated at
Demolish and Install	Ea.	965	325		1290	50 MBH.
Reinstall	Ea.		173.44		173.44	
Clean	Ea.	2.01	89		91.01	
Minimum Charge	Job		255		255	
Gas Forced Air						
50 MBH						
Demolish	Ea.		108		108	Includes material and labor to install
Install	Ea.	990	217		1207	an up flow gas fired hot air furnace
Demolish and Install	Ea.	990	325		1315	rated at 50 MBH.
Reinstall	Ea.		173.44		173.44	
Clean	Ea.	2.01	89		91.01	
Minimum Charge	Job		255		255	
80 MBH						
Demolish	Ea.		108		108	Includes material and labor to install
Install	Ea.	1075	241		1316	an up flow gas fired hot air furnace
Demolish and Install	Ea.	1075	349		1424	rated at 80 MBH.
Reinstall	Ea.		192.71		192.71	
Clean	Ea.	2.01	89		91.01	
Minimum Charge	Job		255		255	
100 MBH						
Demolish	Ea.		108		108	Includes material and labor to install
Install	Ea.	1200	271		1471	an up flow gas fired hot air furnace
Demolish and Install	Ea.	1200	379		1579	rated at 100 MBH.
Reinstall	Ea.		216.80		216.80	
Clean	Ea.	2.01	89		91.01	
Minimum Charge	Job		255		255	
120 MBH						
Demolish	Ea.		108		108	Includes material and labor to install
Install	Ea.	1200	289		1489	an up flow gas fired hot air furnace
Demolish and Install	Ea.	1200	397		1597	rated at 120 MBH.
Reinstall	Ea.		231.25		231.25	
Clean	Ea.	2.01	89		91.01	
Minimum Charge	Job		255		255	
Electric Forced Air						
31.4 MBH						
Demolish	Ea.		108		108	Includes material and labor to install
Install	Ea.	1625	245		1870	an electric hot air furnace rated at
Demolish and Install	Ea.	1625	353		1978	31.4 MBH.
Reinstall	Ea.		195.77		195.77	
Clean	Ea.	2.01	89		91.01	
Minimum Charge	Job		255		255	

Rough Mechanical

Furnace Unit		Unit	Material	Labor	Equip.	Total	Specification
47.1 MBH							
	Demolish	Ea.		108		108	Includes material and labor to install
	Install	Ea.	1850	256		2106	an electric hot air furnace rated at
	Demolish and Install	Ea.	1850	364		2214	47.1 MBH.
	Reinstall	Ea.		204.87		204.87	
	Clean	Ea.	2.01	89		91.01	
	Minimum Charge	Job		255		255	
62.9 MBH							
	Demolish	Ea.		108		108	Includes material and labor to install
	Install	Ea.	2025	275		2300	an electric hot air furnace rated at
	Demolish and Install	Ea.	2025	383		2408	62.9 MBH.
	Reinstall	Ea.		220.24		220.24	
	Clean	Ea.	2.01	89		91.01	
	Minimum Charge	Job		255		255	
78.5 MBH							
	Demolish	Ea.		108		108	Includes material and labor to install
	Install	Ea.	2450	282		2732	an electric hot air furnace rated at
	Demolish and Install	Ea.	2450	390		2840	78.5 MBH.
	Reinstall	Ea.		225.89		225.89	
	Clean	Ea.	2.01	89		91.01	
	Minimum Charge	Job		255		255	
110 MBH							
	Demolish	Ea.		108		108	Includes material and labor to install
	Install	Ea.	3225	298		3523	an electric hot air furnace rated at
	Demolish and Install	Ea.	3225	406		3631	110 MBH.
	Reinstall	Ea.		238.10		238.10	
	Clean	Ea.	2.01	89		91.01	
	Minimum Charge	Job		255		255	
A/C Junction Box							
	Install	Ea.	58	117		175	Includes labor and materials to install
	Minimum Charge	Job		255		255	a heating system emergency shut-off switch. Cost includes up to 40 feet of non-metallic cable.

Boiler		Unit	Material	Labor	Equip.	Total	Specification
Gas-Fired							
60 MBH							
	Demolish	Ea.		925		925	Includes material and labor to install a
	Install	Ea.	2900	1675		4575	gas fired cast iron boiler rated at 60
	Demolish and Install	Ea.	2900	2600		5500	MBH.
	Reinstall	Ea.		1334.69		1334.69	
	Clean	Ea.	4.03	53.50		57.53	
	Minimum Charge	Job		255		255	
Gas-Fired							
125 MBH							
	Demolish	Ea.		2550		2550	Includes material and labor to install a
	Install	Ea.	4600	2050		6650	gas fired cast iron boiler rated at 125
	Demolish and Install	Ea.	4600	4600		9200	MBH.
	Reinstall	Ea.		1631.29		1631.29	
	Clean	Ea.	4.03	53.50		57.53	
	Minimum Charge	Job		255		255	

Rough Mechanical

Boiler		Unit	Material	Labor	Equip.	Total	Specification
Gas-Fired							
400 MBH							
	Demolish	Ea.		2550		2550	Includes material and labor to install a
	Install	Ea.	5925	2875		8800	gas fired cast iron boiler rated at 400
	Demolish and Install	Ea.	5925	5425		11350	MBH.
	Reinstall	Ea.		2867.50		2867.50	
	Clean	Ea.	4.03	53.50		57.53	
	Minimum Charge	Job		255		255	

Heat Pump		Unit	Material	Labor	Equip.	Total	Specification
2 Ton							
	Demolish	Ea.		255		255	Includes material and labor to install a
	Install	Ea.	2525	460		2985	2 ton heat pump.
	Demolish and Install	Ea.	2525	715		3240	
	Reinstall	Ea.		367.04		367.04	
	Clean	Ea.	4.03	40		44.03	
	Minimum Charge	Job		255		255	
3 Ton							
	Demolish	Ea.		425		425	Includes material and labor to install a
	Install	Ea.	3075	765		3840	3 ton heat pump.
	Demolish and Install	Ea.	3075	1190		4265	
	Reinstall	Ea.		611.73		611.73	
	Clean	Ea.	4.03	40		44.03	
	Minimum Charge	Job		255		255	
4 Ton							
	Demolish	Ea.		635		635	Includes material and labor to install a
	Install	Ea.	3625	1150		4775	4 ton heat pump.
	Demolish and Install	Ea.	3625	1785		5410	
	Reinstall	Ea.		917.60		917.60	
	Clean	Ea.	4.03	40		44.03	
	Minimum Charge	Job		255		255	
5 Ton							
	Demolish	Ea.		1025		1025	Includes material and labor to install a
	Install	Ea.	4000	1825		5825	5 ton heat pump.
	Demolish and Install	Ea.	4000	2850		6850	
	Reinstall	Ea.		1468.16		1468.16	
	Clean	Ea.	4.03	40		44.03	
	Minimum Charge	Job		255		255	
Thermostat							
	Demolish	Ea.		14.15		14.15	Includes material and labor to install
	Install	Ea.	197	63.50		260.50	an electric thermostat, 2 set back.
	Demolish and Install	Ea.	197	77.65		274.65	
	Reinstall	Ea.		50.96		50.96	
	Clean	Ea.	.08	10		10.08	
	Minimum Charge	Job		255		255	
A/C Junction Box							
	Install	Ea.	580	360		940	Includes labor and materials to install
	Minimum Charge	Job		234		234	a heat pump circuit including up to 40 feet of non-metallic cable.

Heating		Unit	Material	Labor	Equip.	Total	Specification
Electric Baseboard							
	Demolish	L.F.		6.50		6.50	Includes material and labor to install
	Install	L.F.	11.20	15.60		26.80	electric baseboard heating elements.
	Demolish and Install	L.F.	11.20	22.10		33.30	
	Reinstall	L.F.		12.48		12.48	
	Clean	L.F.	1.41	5		6.41	
	Minimum Charge	Job		234		234	
2' 6"							
	Demolish	Ea.		21.50		21.50	Includes material and labor to install a
	Install	Ea.	33	58.50		91.50	2' 6" long section of electric
	Demolish and Install	Ea.	33	80		113	baseboard heating elements.
	Reinstall	Ea.		46.80		46.80	
	Clean	Ea.	.41	12.30		12.71	
	Minimum Charge	Job		234		234	
3'							
	Demolish	Ea.		23.50		23.50	Includes material and labor to install a
	Install	Ea.	38	58.50		96.50	3' long section of electric baseboard
	Demolish and Install	Ea.	38	82		120	heating elements.
	Reinstall	Ea.		46.80		46.80	
	Clean	Ea.	.41	15.25		15.66	
	Minimum Charge	Job		234		234	
4'							
	Demolish	Ea.		26		26	Includes material and labor to install a
	Install	Ea.	45	70		115	4' long section of electric baseboard
	Demolish and Install	Ea.	45	96		141	heating elements.
	Reinstall	Ea.		55.88		55.88	
	Clean	Ea.	.17	3.34		3.51	
	Minimum Charge	Job		234		234	
5'							
	Demolish	Ea.		29		29	Includes material and labor to install a
	Install	Ea.	56	82		138	5' long section of electric baseboard
	Demolish and Install	Ea.	56	111		167	heating elements.
	Reinstall	Ea.		65.68		65.68	
	Clean	Ea.	.80	24.50		25.30	
	Minimum Charge	Job		234		234	
6'							
	Demolish	Ea.		32.50		32.50	Includes material and labor to install a
	Install	Ea.	61.50	93.50		155	6' long section of electric baseboard
	Demolish and Install	Ea.	61.50	126		187.50	heating elements.
	Reinstall	Ea.		74.88		74.88	
	Clean	Ea.	.17	4.01		4.18	
	Minimum Charge	Job		234		234	
8'							
	Demolish	Ea.		43.50		43.50	Includes material and labor to install
	Install	Ea.	76.50	117		193.50	an 8' long section of electric
	Demolish and Install	Ea.	76.50	160.50		237	baseboard heating elements.
	Reinstall	Ea.		93.60		93.60	
	Clean	Ea.	.17	5		5.17	
	Minimum Charge	Job		234		234	
10'							
	Demolish	Ea.		52		52	Includes material and labor to install a
	Install	Ea.	212	142		354	10' long section of electric baseboard
	Demolish and Install	Ea.	212	194		406	heating elements.
	Reinstall	Ea.		113.45		113.45	
	Clean	Ea.	1.62	50		51.62	
	Minimum Charge	Job		234		234	

Rough Mechanical

Heating

	Unit	Material	Labor	Equip.	Total	Specification
Electric Radiant Wall Panel						
Demolish	Ea.		34.50		34.50	Includes material and labor to install
Install	Ea.	460	93.50		553.50	an 18" x 23" electric radiant heat wall
Demolish and Install	Ea.	460	128		588	panel.
Reinstall	Ea.		74.88		74.88	
Clean	Ea.	.20	10		10.20	
Minimum Charge	Job		234		234	

Heating Control

	Unit	Material	Labor	Equip.	Total	Specification
Thermostat						
Demolish	Ea.		14.15		14.15	Includes material and labor to install
Install	Ea.	197	63.50		260.50	an electric thermostat, 2 set back.
Demolish and Install	Ea.	197	77.65		274.65	
Reinstall	Ea.		50.96		50.96	
Clean	Ea.	.08	10		10.08	
Minimum Charge	Job		255		255	

Air Conditioning

	Unit	Material	Labor	Equip.	Total	Specification
Self-contained						
2 Ton						
Demolish	Ea.		465		465	Includes material and labor to install a
Install	Ea.	2300	790		3090	rooftop air conditioning unit, 2 ton.
Demolish and Install	Ea.	2300	1255		3555	No hoisting is included.
Reinstall	Ea.		791.72		791.72	
Clean	Ea.	4.03	40		44.03	
Minimum Charge	Job		255		255	
3 Ton						
Demolish	Ea.		465		465	Includes material and labor to install a
Install	Ea.	2775	1050		3825	rooftop air conditioning unit, 3 ton.
Demolish and Install	Ea.	2775	1515		4290	No hoisting is included.
Reinstall	Ea.		1043.91		1043.91	
Clean	Ea.	4.03	40		44.03	
Minimum Charge	Job		255		255	
4 Ton						
Demolish	Ea.		465		465	Includes material and labor to install a
Install	Ea.	3375	1200		4575	rooftop air conditioning unit, 4 ton.
Demolish and Install	Ea.	3375	1665		5040	No hoisting is included.
Reinstall	Ea.		1210.55		1210.55	
Clean	Ea.	4.03	40		44.03	
Minimum Charge	Job		255		255	
5 Ton						
Demolish	Ea.		465		465	Includes material and labor to install a
Install	Ea.	3450	1300		4750	rooftop air conditioning unit, 5 ton.
Demolish and Install	Ea.	3450	1765		5215	No hoisting is included.
Reinstall	Ea.		1307.12		1307.12	
Clean	Ea.	4.03	40		44.03	
Minimum Charge	Job		255		255	
Compressor						
2 Ton						
Demolish	Ea.		425		425	Includes material and labor to install a
Install	Ea.	293	255		548	refrigeration compressor.
Demolish and Install	Ea.	293	680		973	
Reinstall	Ea.		203.84		203.84	
Clean	Ea.	4.03	40		44.03	
Minimum Charge	Job		255		255	

Rough Mechanical

Air Conditioning		Unit	Material	Labor	Equip.	Total	Specification
2.5 Ton							
	Demolish	Ea.		425		425	Includes material and labor to install a
	Install	Ea.	345	276		621	refrigeration compressor.
	Demolish and Install	Ea.	345	701		1046	
	Reinstall	Ea.		220.85		220.85	
	Clean	Ea.	4.03	40		44.03	
	Minimum Charge	Job		255		255	
3 Ton							
	Demolish	Ea.		425		425	Includes material and labor to install a
	Install	Ea.	380	288		668	refrigeration compressor.
	Demolish and Install	Ea.	380	713		1093	
	Reinstall	Ea.		230.46		230.46	
	Clean	Ea.	4.03	40		44.03	
	Minimum Charge	Job		255		255	
4 Ton							
	Demolish	Ea.		425		425	Includes material and labor to install a
	Install	Ea.	485	232		717	refrigeration compressor.
	Demolish and Install	Ea.	485	657		1142	
	Reinstall	Ea.		185.31		185.31	
	Clean	Ea.	4.03	40		44.03	
	Minimum Charge	Job		255		255	
5 Ton							
	Demolish	Ea.		425		425	Includes material and labor to install a
	Install	Ea.	535	315		850	refrigeration compressor.
	Demolish and Install	Ea.	535	740		1275	
	Reinstall	Ea.		252.43		252.43	
	Clean	Ea.	4.03	40		44.03	
	Minimum Charge	Job		255		255	
Condensing Unit							
2 Ton Air-cooled							
	Demolish	Ea.		121		121	Includes material and labor to install a
	Install	Ea.	1600	435		2035	2 ton condensing unit.
	Demolish and Install	Ea.	1600	556		2156	
	Reinstall	Ea.		349.56		349.56	
	Clean	Ea.	4.03	40		44.03	
	Minimum Charge	Job		255		255	
2.5 Ton Air-cooled							
	Demolish	Ea.		142		142	Includes material and labor to install a
	Install	Ea.	1675	540		2215	2.5 ton condensing unit.
	Demolish and Install	Ea.	1675	682		2357	
	Reinstall	Ea.		431.81		431.81	
	Clean	Ea.	4.03	40		44.03	
	Minimum Charge	Job		255		255	
3 Ton Air-cooled							
	Demolish	Ea.		170		170	Includes material and labor to install a
	Install	Ea.	1675	705		2380	3 ton condensing unit.
	Demolish and Install	Ea.	1675	875		2550	
	Reinstall	Ea.		564.68		564.68	
	Clean	Ea.	4.03	40		44.03	
	Minimum Charge	Job		255		255	
4 Ton Air-cooled							
	Demolish	Ea.		255		255	Includes material and labor to install a
	Install	Ea.	2175	1025		3200	4 ton condensing unit.
	Demolish and Install	Ea.	2175	1280		3455	
	Reinstall	Ea.		815.64		815.64	
	Clean	Ea.	4.03	40		44.03	
	Minimum Charge	Job		255		255	

Air Conditioning		Unit	Material	Labor	Equip.	Total	Specification
5 Ton Air-cooled							
	Demolish	Ea.		380		380	Includes material and labor to install a
	Install	Ea.	2725	1525		4250	5 ton condensing unit.
	Demolish and Install	Ea.	2725	1905		4630	
	Reinstall	Ea.		1223.47		1223.47	
	Clean	Ea.	4.03	40		44.03	
	Minimum Charge	Job		255		255	
Air Handler							
1,200 CFM							
	Demolish	Ea.		305		305	Includes material and labor to install a
	Install	Ea.	2950	705		3655	1200 CFM capacity air handling unit.
	Demolish and Install	Ea.	2950	1010		3960	
	Reinstall	Ea.		564.68		564.68	
	Clean	Ea.	4.03	40		44.03	
	Minimum Charge	Job		255		255	
2,000 CFM							
	Demolish	Ea.		305		305	Includes material and labor to install a
	Install	Ea.	4900	835		5735	2000 CFM capacity air handling unit.
	Demolish and Install	Ea.	4900	1140		6040	
	Reinstall	Ea.		667.35		667.35	
	Clean	Ea.	4.03	40		44.03	
	Minimum Charge	Job		255		255	
3,000 CFM							
	Demolish	Ea.		340		340	Includes material and labor to install a
	Install	Ea.	6125	920		7045	3000 CFM capacity air handling unit.
	Demolish and Install	Ea.	6125	1260		7385	
	Reinstall	Ea.		734.08		734.08	
	Clean	Ea.	4.03	40		44.03	
	Minimum Charge	Job		255		255	
Evaporative Cooler							
4,300 CFM, 1/3 HP							
	Demolish	Ea.		124		124	Includes material and labor to install
	Install	Ea.	790	271		1061	an evaporative cooler.
	Demolish and Install	Ea.	790	395		1185	
	Reinstall	Ea.		216.80		216.80	
	Clean	Ea.	1.62	40		41.62	
	Minimum Charge	Job		255		255	
4,700 CFM, 1/2 HP							
	Demolish	Ea.		124		124	Includes material and labor to install
	Install	Ea.	790	280		1070	an evaporative cooler.
	Demolish and Install	Ea.	790	404		1194	
	Reinstall	Ea.		223.79		223.79	
	Clean	Ea.	1.62	40		41.62	
	Minimum Charge	Job		255		255	
5,600 CFM, 3/4 HP							
	Demolish	Ea.		124		124	Includes material and labor to install
	Install	Ea.	1400	289		1689	an evaporative cooler.
	Demolish and Install	Ea.	1400	413		1813	
	Reinstall	Ea.		231.25		231.25	
	Clean	Ea.	1.62	40		41.62	
	Minimum Charge	Job		255		255	
Master Cool Brand							
	Demolish	Ea.		124		124	Includes material and labor to install
	Install	Ea.	790	299		1089	an evaporative cooler.
	Demolish and Install	Ea.	790	423		1213	
	Reinstall	Ea.		239.23		239.23	
	Clean	Ea.	1.62	40		41.62	
	Minimum Charge	Job		255		255	

Rough Mechanical

Air Conditioning		Unit	Material	Labor	Equip.	Total	Specification
Motor							
	Demolish	Ea.		69.50		69.50	Includes material and labor to install
	Install	Ea.	205	211		416	an evaporative cooler motor.
	Demolish and Install	Ea.	205	280.50		485.50	
	Reinstall	Ea.		168.54		168.54	
	Clean	Ea.	1.62	40		41.62	
	Minimum Charge	Job		255		255	
Water Pump							
	Demolish	Ea.		69.50		69.50	Includes material and labor to install
	Install	Ea.	57	120		177	an evaporative cooler water pump.
	Demolish and Install	Ea.	57	189.50		246.50	
	Reinstall	Ea.		96.32		96.32	
	Clean	Ea.	1.62	40		41.62	
	Minimum Charge	Job		255		255	
Fan Belt							
	Demolish	Ea.		13.95		13.95	Includes material and labor to install
	Install	Ea.	41.50	24		65.50	an evaporative cooler fan belt.
	Demolish and Install	Ea.	41.50	37.95		79.45	
	Reinstall	Ea.		19.26		19.26	
	Minimum Charge	Job		255		255	
Pads (4 ea.)							
	Demolish	Ea.		13.95		13.95	Includes material and labor to install
	Install	Ea.	22.50	60		82.50	pre-fabricated roof pads for an
	Demolish and Install	Ea.	22.50	73.95		96.45	evaporative cooler.
	Reinstall	Ea.		48.16		48.16	
	Clean	Ea.	1.62	40		41.62	
	Minimum Charge	Job		255		255	
Service call							
	Install	Job		241		241	Includes 4 hour minimum labor charge for a sheetmetal worker.
Window Mounted							
Low Output BTU							
	Install	Ea.	360	54		414	Includes material and labor to install a
	Reinstall	Ea.		43.20		43.20	window air conditioning unit.
	Clean	Ea.	.61	10		10.61	
	Minimum Charge	Job		255		255	
Mid-range Output BTU							
	Demolish	Ea.		38		38	Includes material and labor to install a
	Install	Ea.	490	72		562	window air conditioning unit.
	Demolish and Install	Ea.	490	110		600	
	Reinstall	Ea.		57.60		57.60	
	Clean	Ea.	.61	10		10.61	
	Minimum Charge	Job		255		255	
High Output BTU							
	Demolish	Ea.		48		48	Includes material and labor to install a
	Install	Ea.	625	72		697	window air conditioning unit.
	Demolish and Install	Ea.	625	120		745	
	Reinstall	Ea.		57.60		57.60	
	Clean	Ea.	.61	10		10.61	
	Minimum Charge	Job		255		255	
Hotel-type Hot / Cold							
	Demolish	Ea.		80		80	Includes material and labor to install
	Install	Ea.	1275	305		1580	packaged air conditioning unit,
	Demolish and Install	Ea.	1275	385		1660	15000 BTU cooling, 13900 BTU
	Reinstall	Ea.		244.69		244.69	heating.
	Clean	Ea.	.80	20		20.80	
	Minimum Charge	Job		255		255	

Rough Mechanical

Air Conditioning

Air Conditioning	Unit	Material	Labor	Equip.	Total	Specification
Thermostat						
Demolish	Ea.		14.15		14.15	Includes material and labor to install
Install	Ea.	197	63.50		260.50	an electric thermostat, 2 set back.
Demolish and Install	Ea.	197	77.65		274.65	
Reinstall	Ea.		50.96		50.96	
Clean	Ea.	.08	10		10.08	
Minimum Charge	Job		255		255	
Concrete Pad						
Demolish	S.F.		2.23		2.23	Includes material and labor to install
Install	S.F.	2.52	4.99		7.51	air conditioner pad.
Demolish and Install	S.F.	2.52	7.22		9.74	
Reinstall	S.F.		3.99		3.99	
Clean	S.F.	.08	.64		.72	
Paint	S.F.	.17	.38		.55	
Minimum Charge	Job		255		255	
A/C Junction Box						
Install	Ea.	200	134		334	Includes labor and materials to install
Minimum Charge	Job		234		234	an air conditioning circuit including up to 40 feet of non-metallic cable.

Sprinkler System

Sprinkler System	Unit	Material	Labor	Equip.	Total	Specification
Exposed						
Wet Type						
Demolish	SF Flr.		.22		.22	Includes material and labor to install
Install	SF Flr.	2.39	2.12		4.51	an exposed wet pipe fire sprinkler
Demolish and Install	SF Flr.	2.39	2.34		4.73	system.
Reinstall	SF Flr.		2.12		2.12	
Minimum Charge	Job		251		251	
Dry Type						
Demolish	SF Flr.		.22		.22	Includes material and labor to install
Install	SF Flr.	2.75	2.12		4.87	an exposed dry pipe fire sprinkler
Demolish and Install	SF Flr.	2.75	2.34		5.09	system.
Reinstall	SF Flr.		2.12		2.12	
Minimum Charge	Job		251		251	
Concealed						
Wet Type						
Demolish	SF Flr.		.45		.45	Includes material and labor to install a
Install	SF Flr.	2.39	2.90		5.29	concealed wet pipe fire sprinkler
Demolish and Install	SF Flr.	2.39	3.35		5.74	system.
Reinstall	SF Flr.		2.90		2.90	
Minimum Charge	Job		251		251	
Dry Type						
Demolish	SF Flr.		.45		.45	Includes material and labor to install a
Install	SF Flr.	.02	2.90		2.92	concealed dry pipe fire sprinkler
Demolish and Install	SF Flr.	.02	3.35		3.37	system.
Reinstall	SF Flr.		2.90		2.90	
Minimum Charge	Job		251		251	

Rough Electrical

Junction Boxes

Cable

Switch Box

Electrical Per S.F.	Unit	Material	Labor	Equip.	Total	Specification
Residential						
Wiring, Lighting and Fixtures						
Install	S.F.	1.71	1.95		3.66	Includes labor and material to replace house wiring, lighting fixtures, and built-in appliances. Apply S.F. cost to floor area including garages but not basements.
Minimum Charge	Job		234		234	
Wiring Only						
Install	S.F.	.21	.77		.98	Includes labor and material to replace house wiring only. Apply S.F. cost to floor area including garages but not basements.

Main Service	Unit	Material	Labor	Equip.	Total	Specification
Complete Panel						
100 Amp.						
Demolish	Ea.		193		193	Cost includes material and labor to install 100 Amp. residential service panel including 12 breaker interior panel, 10 single pole breakers and hook-up. Wiring is not included.
Install	Ea.	595	395		990	
Demolish and Install	Ea.	595	588		1183	
Reinstall	Ea.		314.62		314.62	
Clean	Ea.	.41	80		80.41	
Minimum Charge	Job		234		234	
150 Amp.						
Demolish	Ea.		193		193	Cost includes material and labor to install 150 Amp. residential service, incl. 20 breaker exterior panel, main switch, 1 GFI and 14 single pole breakers, meter socket including hookup. Wiring is not included.
Install	Ea.	925	455		1380	
Demolish and Install	Ea.	925	648		1573	
Reinstall	Ea.		363.50		363.50	
Clean	Ea.	.41	80		80.41	
Minimum Charge	Job		234		234	
200 Amp.						
Demolish	Ea.		193		193	Cost includes material and labor to install 200 Amp. residential service, incl. 20 breaker exterior panel, main switch, 1 GFI and 18 single pole breakers, meter socket including hookup. Wiring is not included.
Install	Ea.	1250	520		1770	
Demolish and Install	Ea.	1250	713		1963	
Reinstall	Ea.		416		416	
Clean	Ea.	.41	80		80.41	
Minimum Charge	Job		234		234	

Rough Electrical

Main Service		Unit	Material	Labor	Equip.	Total	Specification
Masthead							
	Demolish	Ea.		32.50		32.50	Includes material and labor to install
	Install	Ea.	127	195		322	galvanized steel conduit including
	Demolish and Install	Ea.	127	227.50		354.50	masthead.
	Reinstall	Ea.		156		156	
	Minimum Charge	Job		234		234	
Allowance to Repair							
	Install	Job		234		234	Minimum labor charge for residential
	Minimum Charge	Job		234		234	wiring.

Wall Insulation

Floor Insulation	Unit	Material	Labor	Equip.	Total	Specification
Kraft Faced Batt						
3-1/2″ (R-13)						
Demolish	S.F.		.15		.15	Cost includes material and labor to
Install	S.F.	.41	.62		1.03	install 3-1/2″ (R-13) kraft paper or foil
Demolish and Install	S.F.	.41	.77		1.18	faced roll and batt fiberglass
Minimum Charge	Job		216		216	insulation, joists 16″ O.C.
6″ (R-19)						
Demolish	S.F.		.15		.15	Cost includes material and labor to
Install	S.F.	.53	.72		1.25	install 6″ (R-19) kraft paper or foil
Demolish and Install	S.F.	.53	.87		1.40	faced roll and batt fiberglass
Minimum Charge	Job		216		216	insulation, joists 16″ O.C.
10″ (R-30)						
Demolish	S.F.		.15		.15	Cost includes material and labor to
Install	S.F.	.77	.86		1.63	install 10″ (R-30) kraft paper-faced roll
Demolish and Install	S.F.	.77	1.01		1.78	and batt fiberglass insulation, joists
Minimum Charge	Job		216		216	16″ O.C.
12″ (R-38)						
Demolish	S.F.		.15		.15	Cost includes material and labor to
Install	S.F.	.98	.91		1.89	install 12″ (R-38) kraft paper-faced roll
Demolish and Install	S.F.	.98	1.06		2.04	and batt fiberglass insulation, joists
Minimum Charge	Job		216		216	16″ O.C.
Foil Faced Batt						
3-1/2″ (R-13)						
Demolish	S.F.		.15		.15	Cost includes material and labor to
Install	S.F.	.41	.62		1.03	install 3-1/2″ (R-13) kraft paper or foil
Demolish and Install	S.F.	.41	.77		1.18	faced roll and batt fiberglass
Minimum Charge	Job		216		216	insulation, joists 16″ O.C.
6″ (R-19)						
Demolish	S.F.		.15		.15	Cost includes material and labor to
Install	S.F.	.53	.72		1.25	install 6″ (R-19) kraft paper or foil
Demolish and Install	S.F.	.53	.87		1.40	faced roll and batt fiberglass
Minimum Charge	Job		216		216	insulation, joists 16″ O.C.
Unfaced Batt						
3-1/2″ (R-13)						
Demolish	S.F.		.15		.15	Cost includes material and labor to
Install	S.F.	.35	.72		1.07	install 3-1/2″ (R-13) unfaced roll and
Demolish and Install	S.F.	.35	.87		1.22	batt fiberglass insulation, joists 16″
Minimum Charge	Job		216		216	O.C.

Insulation

Floor Insulation

Floor Insulation		Unit	Material	Labor	Equip.	Total	Specification
6" (R-19)							
	Demolish	S.F.		.15		.15	Cost includes material and labor to
	Install	S.F.	.41	.86		1.27	install 6" (R-19) unfaced roll and batt
	Demolish and Install	S.F.	.41	1.01		1.42	fiberglass insulation, joists 16" O.C.
	Minimum Charge	Job		216		216	
10" (R-30)							
	Demolish	S.F.		.15		.15	Cost includes material and labor to
	Install	S.F.	.66	.96		1.62	install 10" (R-30) unfaced roll and batt
	Demolish and Install	S.F.	.66	1.11		1.77	fiberglass insulation, joists 16" O.C.
	Minimum Charge	Job		216		216	
12" (R-38)							
	Demolish	S.F.		.15		.15	Cost includes material and labor to
	Install	S.F.	.83	1.02		1.85	install 12" (R-38) unfaced roll and batt
	Demolish and Install	S.F.	.83	1.17		2	fiberglass insulation, joists 16" O.C.
	Minimum Charge	Job		216		216	

Rigid Board

		Unit	Material	Labor	Equip.	Total	Specification
1/2"							
	Demolish	S.F.		.15		.15	Includes material and labor to install
	Install	S.F.	.32	.54		.86	rigid foam insulation board foil faced
	Demolish and Install	S.F.	.32	.69		1.01	two sides.
	Minimum Charge	Job		216		216	
3/4"							
	Demolish	S.F.		.15		.15	Includes material and labor to install
	Install	S.F.	.36	.54		.90	rigid foam insulation board foil faced
	Demolish and Install	S.F.	.36	.69		1.05	two sides.
	Minimum Charge	Job		216		216	
1-1/2"							
	Demolish	S.F.		.15		.15	Includes material and labor to install
	Install	S.F.	.69	.58		1.27	rigid foam insulation board foil faced
	Demolish and Install	S.F.	.69	.73		1.42	two sides.
	Minimum Charge	Job		216		216	

Support Wire

		Unit	Material	Labor	Equip.	Total	Specification
	Demolish	S.F.		.06		.06	Includes material and labor to install
	Install	S.F.	.02	.12		.14	friction fit support wire.
	Demolish and Install	S.F.	.02	.18		.20	
	Minimum Charge	Job		216		216	

Vapor Barrier

		Unit	Material	Labor	Equip.	Total	Specification
	Demolish	S.F.		.08		.08	Cost includes material and labor to
	Install	S.F.	.03	.12		.15	install 4 mil polyethylene vapor barrier
	Demolish and Install	S.F.	.03	.20		.23	10' wide sheets with 6" overlaps.
	Minimum Charge	Job		216		216	

Wall Insulation

Wall Insulation		Unit	Material	Labor	Equip.	Total	Specification
Kraft Faced Batt							
3-1/2" (R-13)							
	Demolish	S.F.		.14		.14	Cost includes material and labor to
	Install	S.F.	.34	.32		.66	install 3-1/2" (R-13) kraft paper-faced
	Demolish and Install	S.F.	.34	.46		.80	roll and batt fiberglass insulation, joist
	Minimum Charge	Job		216		216	or studs 16" O.C.
6" (R-19)							
	Demolish	S.F.		.14		.14	Cost includes material and labor to
	Install	S.F.	.46	.32		.78	install 6" (R-19) kraft paper-faced roll
	Demolish and Install	S.F.	.46	.46		.92	and batt fiberglass insulation, joist or
	Minimum Charge	Job		216		216	studs 16" O.C.

Insulation

Wall Insulation		Unit	Material	Labor	Equip.	Total	Specification
10″ (R-30)							
	Demolish	S.F.		.14		.14	Cost includes material and labor to
	Install	S.F.	.77	.38		1.15	install 10″ (R-30) kraft paper-faced roll
	Demolish and Install	S.F.	.77	.52		1.29	and batt fiberglass insulation, joist or
	Minimum Charge	Job		216		216	studs 16″ O.C.
12″ (R-38)							
	Demolish	S.F.		.14		.14	Cost includes material and labor to
	Install	S.F.	.98	.38		1.36	install 12″ (R-38) kraft paper-faced roll
	Demolish and Install	S.F.	.98	.52		1.50	and batt fiberglass insulation, joist or
	Minimum Charge	Job		216		216	studs 16″ O.C.
Foil Faced Batt							
3-1/2″ (R-13)							
	Demolish	S.F.		.14		.14	Cost includes material and labor to
	Install	S.F.	.48	.32		.80	install 3-1/2″ (R-13) foil faced roll and
	Demolish and Install	S.F.	.48	.46		.94	batt fiberglass insulation, joist or studs
	Minimum Charge	Job		216		216	16″ O.C.
6″ (R-19)							
	Demolish	S.F.		.14		.14	Cost includes material and labor to
	Install	S.F.	.63	.32		.95	install 6″ (R-19) foil faced roll and batt
	Demolish and Install	S.F.	.63	.46		1.09	fiberglass insulation, joist or studs 16″
	Minimum Charge	Job		216		216	O.C.
Unfaced Batt							
3-1/2″ (R-13)							
	Demolish	S.F.		.14		.14	Cost includes material and labor to
	Install	S.F.	.35	.32		.67	install 3-1/2″ (R-13) unfaced roll and
	Demolish and Install	S.F.	.35	.46		.81	batt fiberglass insulation, joist or studs
	Minimum Charge	Job		216		216	16″ O.C.
6″ (R-19)							
	Demolish	S.F.		.14		.14	Cost includes material and labor to
	Install	S.F.	.41	.38		.79	install 6″ (R-19) unfaced roll and batt
	Demolish and Install	S.F.	.41	.52		.93	fiberglass insulation, joist or studs 16″
	Minimum Charge	Job		216		216	O.C.
10″ (R-30)							
	Demolish	S.F.		.14		.14	Cost includes material and labor to
	Install	S.F.	.66	.38		1.04	install 10″ (R-30) unfaced roll and batt
	Demolish and Install	S.F.	.66	.52		1.18	fiberglass insulation, joist or studs 16″
	Minimum Charge	Job		216		216	O.C.
12″ (R-38)							
	Demolish	S.F.		.14		.14	Cost includes material and labor to
	Install	S.F.	.83	.43		1.26	install 12″ (R-38) unfaced roll and batt
	Demolish and Install	S.F.	.83	.57		1.40	fiberglass insulation, joist or studs 16″
	Minimum Charge	Job		216		216	O.C.
Blown							
R-13							
	Demolish	S.F.		.14		.14	Includes material and labor to install
	Install	S.F.	.26	1.43	.68	2.37	fiberglass blown-in insulation in wall
	Demolish and Install	S.F.	.26	1.57	.68	2.51	with wood siding.
	Minimum Charge	Job		495	235	730	
R-19							
	Demolish	S.F.		.14		.14	Includes material and labor to install
	Install	S.F.	.42	1.65	.78	2.85	fiberglass blown-in insulation in wall
	Demolish and Install	S.F.	.42	1.79	.78	2.99	with wood siding.
	Minimum Charge	Job		495	235	730	

Insulation

Wall Insulation

Wall Insulation	Unit	Material	Labor	Equip.	Total	Specification
Rigid Board						
1/2″						
Demolish	S.F.		.18		.18	Includes material and labor to install
Install	S.F.	.32	.54		.86	rigid foam insulation board, foil faced,
Demolish and Install	S.F.	.32	.72		1.04	two sides.
Minimum Charge	Job		216		216	
3/4″						
Demolish	S.F.		.18		.18	Includes material and labor to install
Install	S.F.	.36	.54		.90	rigid foam insulation board, foil faced,
Demolish and Install	S.F.	.36	.72		1.08	two sides.
Minimum Charge	Job		216		216	
1-1/2″						
Demolish	S.F.		.18		.18	Includes material and labor to install
Install	S.F.	.69	.59		1.28	rigid foam insulation board, foil faced,
Demolish and Install	S.F.	.69	.77		1.46	two sides.
Minimum Charge	Job		216		216	
Vapor Barrier						
Demolish	S.F.		.05		.05	Cost includes material and labor to
Install	S.F.	.03	.12		.15	install 4 mil polyethylene vapor barrier
Demolish and Install	S.F.	.03	.17		.20	10′ wide sheets with 6″ overlaps.
Minimum Charge	Job		216		216	

Ceiling Insulation

Ceiling Insulation	Unit	Material	Labor	Equip.	Total	Specification
Kraft Faced Batt						
3-1/2″ (R-13)						
Demolish	S.F.		.15		.15	Cost includes material and labor to
Install	S.F.	.34	.32		.66	install 3-1/2″ (R-13) kraft paper-faced
Demolish and Install	S.F.	.34	.47		.81	roll and batt fiberglass insulation, joist
Minimum Charge	Job		216		216	or studs 16″ O.C.
6″ (R-19)						
Demolish	S.F.		.15		.15	Cost includes material and labor to
Install	S.F.	.46	.32		.78	install 6″ (R-19) kraft paper-faced roll
Demolish and Install	S.F.	.46	.47		.93	and batt fiberglass insulation, joist or
Minimum Charge	Job		216		216	studs 16″ O.C.
10″ (R-30)						
Demolish	S.F.		.15		.15	Cost includes material and labor to
Install	S.F.	.77	.38		1.15	install 10″ (R-30) kraft paper-faced roll
Demolish and Install	S.F.	.77	.53		1.30	and batt fiberglass insulation, joist or
Minimum Charge	Job		216		216	studs 16″ O.C.
12″ (R-38)						
Demolish	S.F.		.15		.15	Cost includes material and labor to
Install	S.F.	.98	.38		1.36	install 12″ (R-38) kraft paper-faced roll
Demolish and Install	S.F.	.98	.53		1.51	and batt fiberglass insulation, joist or
Minimum Charge	Job		216		216	studs 16″ O.C.
Foil Faced Batt						
3-1/2″ (R-13)						
Demolish	S.F.		.15		.15	Cost includes material and labor to
Install	S.F.	.48	.32		.80	install 3-1/2″ (R-13) foil faced roll and
Demolish and Install	S.F.	.48	.47		.95	batt fiberglass insulation, joist or studs
Minimum Charge	Job		216		216	16″ O.C.

Insulation

Ceiling Insulation		Unit	Material	Labor	Equip.	Total	Specification
6" (R-19)							
	Demolish	S.F.		.15		.15	Cost includes material and labor to
	Install	S.F.	.63	.32		.95	install 6" (R-19) foil faced roll and batt
	Demolish and Install	S.F.	.63	.47		1.10	fiberglass insulation, joist or studs 16"
	Minimum Charge	Job		216		216	O.C.
Unfaced Batt							
3-1/2" (R-13)							
	Demolish	S.F.		.15		.15	Cost includes material and labor to
	Install	S.F.	.35	.32		.67	install 3-1/2" (R-13) unfaced roll and
	Demolish and Install	S.F.	.35	.47		.82	batt fiberglass insulation, joist or studs
	Minimum Charge	Job		216		216	16" O.C.
6" (R-19)							
	Demolish	S.F.		.15		.15	Cost includes material and labor to
	Install	S.F.	.41	.38		.79	install 6" (R-19) unfaced roll and batt
	Demolish and Install	S.F.	.41	.53		.94	fiberglass insulation, joist or studs 16"
	Minimum Charge	Job		216		216	O.C.
10" (R-30)							
	Demolish	S.F.		.15		.15	Cost includes material and labor to
	Install	S.F.	.66	.38		1.04	install 10" (R-30) unfaced roll and batt
	Demolish and Install	S.F.	.66	.53		1.19	fiberglass insulation, joist or studs 16"
	Minimum Charge	Job		216		216	O.C.
12" (R-38)							
	Demolish	S.F.		.15		.15	Cost includes material and labor to
	Install	S.F.	.83	.43		1.26	install 12" (R-38) unfaced roll and batt
	Demolish and Install	S.F.	.83	.58		1.41	fiberglass insulation, joist or studs 16"
	Minimum Charge	Job		216		216	O.C.
Blown							
5"							
	Demolish	S.F.		.44		.44	Includes material and labor to install
	Install	S.F.	.20	.26	.12	.58	fiberglass blown-in insulation.
	Demolish and Install	S.F.	.20	.70	.12	1.02	
	Minimum Charge	Job		495	235	730	
6"							
	Demolish	S.F.		.44		.44	Includes material and labor to install
	Install	S.F.	.29	.33	.16	.78	fiberglass blown-in insulation.
	Demolish and Install	S.F.	.29	.77	.16	1.22	
	Minimum Charge	Job		495	235	730	
9"							
	Demolish	S.F.		.44		.44	Includes material and labor to install
	Install	S.F.	.35	.45	.21	1.01	fiberglass blown-in insulation.
	Demolish and Install	S.F.	.35	.89	.21	1.45	
	Minimum Charge	Job		495	235	730	
12"							
	Demolish	S.F.		.44		.44	Includes material and labor to install
	Install	S.F.	.48	.66	.31	1.45	fiberglass blown-in insulation.
	Demolish and Install	S.F.	.48	1.10	.31	1.89	
	Minimum Charge	Job		495	235	730	
Rigid Board							
1/2"							
	Demolish	S.F.		.25		.25	Includes material and labor to install
	Install	S.F.	.32	.54		.86	rigid foam insulation board, foil faced,
	Demolish and Install	S.F.	.32	.79		1.11	two sides.
	Minimum Charge	Job		216		216	

Insulation

Ceiling Insulation

	Unit	Material	Labor	Equip.	Total	Specification
3/4"						
Demolish	S.F.		.25		.25	Includes material and labor to install
Install	S.F.	.36	.54		.90	rigid foam insulation board, foil faced,
Demolish and Install	S.F.	.36	.79		1.15	two sides.
Minimum Charge	Job		216		216	
1-1/2"						
Demolish	S.F.		.25		.25	Includes material and labor to install
Install	S.F.	.69	.59		1.28	rigid foam insulation board, foil faced,
Demolish and Install	S.F.	.69	.84		1.53	two sides.
Minimum Charge	Job		216		216	

Exterior Insulation

	Unit	Material	Labor	Equip.	Total	Specification
Rigid Board						
1/2"						
Demolish	S.F.		.14		.14	Includes material and labor to install
Install	S.F.	.32	.54		.86	rigid foam insulation board foil faced
Demolish and Install	S.F.	.32	.68		1	two sides.
Minimum Charge	Job		216		216	
3/4"						
Demolish	S.F.		.14		.14	Includes material and labor to install
Install	S.F.	.36	.54		.90	rigid foam insulation board foil faced
Demolish and Install	S.F.	.36	.68		1.04	two sides.
Minimum Charge	Job		216		216	
1-1/2"						
Demolish	S.F.		.14		.14	Includes material and labor to install
Install	S.F.	.69	.58		1.27	rigid foam insulation board foil faced
Demolish and Install	S.F.	.69	.72		1.41	two sides.
Minimum Charge	Job		216		216	
Vapor Barrier						
Demolish	S.F.		.08		.08	Cost includes material and labor to
Install	S.F.	.03	.12		.15	install 4 mil polyethylene vapor barrier
Demolish and Install	S.F.	.03	.20		.23	10' wide sheets with 6" overlaps.
Minimum Charge	Job		216		216	

Roof Insulation Board

	Unit	Material	Labor	Equip.	Total	Specification
Fiberglass						
3/4" Fiberglass						
Demolish	Sq.		46.50		46.50	Includes material and labor to install
Install	Sq.	67	24.50		91.50	fiberglass board insulation 3/4" thick,
Demolish and Install	Sq.	67	71		138	R-2.80 and C-0.36 values.
Minimum Charge	Job		216		216	
1" Fiberglass						
Demolish	Sq.		46.50		46.50	Includes material and labor to install
Install	Sq.	95	27.50		122.50	fiberglass board insulation 1" thick,
Demolish and Install	Sq.	95	74		169	R-4.20 and C-0.24 values.
Minimum Charge	Job		216		216	
1-3/8" Fiberglass						
Demolish	Sq.		46.50		46.50	Includes material and labor to install
Install	Sq.	151	30		181	fiberglass board insulation 1-3/8"
Demolish and Install	Sq.	151	76.50		227.50	thick, R-5.30 and C-0.19 values.
Minimum Charge	Job		216		216	

Insulation

Roof Insulation Board		Unit	Material	Labor	Equip.	Total	Specification
1-5/8" Fiberglass							
	Demolish	Sq.		46.50		46.50	Includes material and labor to install
	Install	Sq.	156	31.50		187.50	fiberglass board insulation 1-5/8"
	Demolish and Install	Sq.	156	78		234	thick, R-6.70 and C-0.15 values.
	Minimum Charge	Job		216		216	
2-1/4" Fiberglass							
	Demolish	Sq.		46.50		46.50	Includes material and labor to install
	Install	Sq.	185	35		220	fiberglass board insulation 2-1/4"
	Demolish and Install	Sq.	185	81.50		266.50	thick, R-8.30 and C-0.12 values.
	Minimum Charge	Job		216		216	
Perlite							
1" Perlite							
	Demolish	Sq.		46.50		46.50	Includes material and labor to install
	Install	Sq.	54	27.50		81.50	perlite board insulation 1" thick,
	Demolish and Install	Sq.	54	74		128	R-2.80 and C-0.36 values,
	Minimum Charge	Job		216		216	
4" Perlite							
	Demolish	Sq.		46.50		46.50	Includes material and labor to install
	Install	Sq.	216	53		269	perlite board insulation 4" thick,
	Demolish and Install	Sq.	216	99.50		315.50	R-10.0 and C-0.10 values.
	Minimum Charge	Job		216		216	
1-1/2" Perlite							
	Demolish	Sq.		46.50		46.50	Includes material and labor to install
	Install	Sq.	79	30		109	perlite board insulation 1-1/2" thick,
	Demolish and Install	Sq.	79	76.50		155.50	R-4.20 and C-0.24 values.
	Minimum Charge	Job		216		216	
2" Perlite							
	Demolish	Sq.		46.50		46.50	Includes material and labor to install
	Install	Sq.	109	37		146	perlite board insulation 2" thick,
	Demolish and Install	Sq.	109	83.50		192.50	R-5.30 and C-0.19 values.
	Minimum Charge	Job		216		216	
2-1/2" Perlite							
	Demolish	Sq.		46.50		46.50	Includes material and labor to install
	Install	Sq.	143	41.50		184.50	perlite board insulation 2-1/2" thick,
	Demolish and Install	Sq.	143	88		231	R-6.70 and C-0.15 values.
	Minimum Charge	Job		216		216	
3" Perlite							
	Demolish	Sq.		46.50		46.50	Includes material and labor to install
	Install	Sq.	162	44.50		206.50	perlite board insulation 3" thick,
	Demolish and Install	Sq.	162	91		253	R-8.30 and C-0.12 values.
	Minimum Charge	Job		216		216	
Polystyrene							
2" Polystyrene							
	Demolish	Sq.		46.50		46.50	Includes material and labor to install
	Install	Sq.	53	35		88	extruded polystyrene board, R5.0/ 2"
	Demolish and Install	Sq.	53	81.50		134.50	in thickness @25PSI compressive
	Minimum Charge	Job		216		216	strength.
1" Polystyrene							
	Demolish	Sq.		46.50		46.50	Includes material and labor to install
	Install	Sq.	26.50	23.50		50	extruded polystyrene board, R5.0/ 1"
	Demolish and Install	Sq.	26.50	70		96.50	in thickness @25PSI compressive
	Minimum Charge	Job		216		216	strength.
1-1/2" Polystyrene							
	Demolish	Sq.		46.50		46.50	Includes material and labor to install
	Install	Sq.	39.50	27.50		67	extruded polystyrene board, R5.0/
	Demolish and Install	Sq.	39.50	74		113.50	1-1/2" in thickness @25PSI
	Minimum Charge	Job		216		216	compressive strength.

Insulation

Roof Insulation Board	Unit	Material	Labor	Equip.	Total	Specification
Urethane						
3/4" Urethane						
Demolish	Sq.		46.50		46.50	Includes material and labor to install
Install	Sq.	48.50	21		69.50	urethane board insulation 3/4" thick,
Demolish and Install	Sq.	48.50	67.50		116	R-5.30 and C-0.19 values.
Minimum Charge	Job		216		216	
1" Urethane						
Demolish	Sq.		46.50		46.50	Includes material and labor to install
Install	Sq.	55	22		77	urethane board insulation 1" thick,
Demolish and Install	Sq.	55	68.50		123.50	R-6.70 and C-0.15 values.
Minimum Charge	Job		216		216	
1-1/2" Urethane						
Demolish	Sq.		46.50		46.50	Includes material and labor to install
Install	Sq.	71.50	25.50		97	urethane board insulation 1-1/2"
Demolish and Install	Sq.	71.50	72		143.50	thick, R-10.1 and C-0.09 values.
Minimum Charge	Job		216		216	
2" Urethane						
Demolish	Sq.		46.50		46.50	Includes material and labor to install
Install	Sq.	87	30		117	urethane board insulation 2" thick,
Demolish and Install	Sq.	87	76.50		163.50	R-13.4 and C-0.06 values.
Minimum Charge	Job		216		216	

Gypsum Wallboard | **Tile Ceiling** | **Gypsum Wallboard Ceiling**

Wall Plaster	Unit	Material	Labor	Equip.	Total	Specification
Interior						
Cement						
Demolish	S.Y.		5.95		5.95	Includes material and labor to install
Install	S.Y.	14.65	25	2.14	41.79	cement plaster on interior wood
Demolish and Install	S.Y.	14.65	30.95	2.14	47.74	framing with metal lath.
Clean	S.Y.		2.91		2.91	
Paint	S.Y.	2.05	4.93		6.98	
Minimum Charge	Job		193		193	
Acoustic						
Demolish	S.Y.		5.95		5.95	Includes material and labor to install
Install	S.Y.	11.60	30	2.13	43.73	acoustical cement plaster on interior
Demolish and Install	S.Y.	11.60	35.95	2.13	49.68	wood framing with metal lath.
Clean	S.Y.		2.91		2.91	
Paint	S.Y.	2.05	4.93		6.98	
Minimum Charge	Job		193		193	
Gypsum						
Demolish	S.Y.		5.95		5.95	Includes material and labor to install
Install	S.Y.	9.95	25.50	1.82	37.27	gypsum wall or ceiling plaster on
Demolish and Install	S.Y.	9.95	31.45	1.82	43.22	interior wood framing with metal lath.
Clean	S.Y.		2.91		2.91	
Paint	S.Y.	2.05	4.93		6.98	
Minimum Charge	Job		193		193	
Stucco						
Demolish	S.Y.		14.25		14.25	Includes material and labor to install
Install	S.Y.	7.20	35	2.51	44.71	stucco on wire mesh over wood
Demolish and Install	S.Y.	7.20	49.25	2.51	58.96	framing.
Clean	S.Y.		2.91		2.91	
Paint	S.Y.	2.05	4.93		6.98	
Minimum Charge	Job		193		193	
Thin Coat						
Veneer						
Demolish	S.Y.		5.95		5.95	Includes materials and labor to install
Install	S.Y.	.90	4.61	.40	5.91	thin coat veneer plaster.
Demolish and Install	S.Y.	.90	10.56	.40	11.86	
Clean	S.Y.		2.91		2.91	
Paint	S.Y.	2.05	4.93		6.98	
Minimum Charge	Job		193		193	

Walls / Ceilings

Wall Plaster		Unit	Material	Labor	Equip.	Total	Specification
Lath							
Metal							
	Demolish	S.Y.		1.40		1.40	Includes material and labor to install
	Install	S.Y.	4.71	4.87		9.58	wire lath on steel framed walls.
	Demolish and Install	S.Y.	4.71	6.27		10.98	
	Clean	S.Y.		2.91		2.91	
	Minimum Charge	Job		86		86	
Gypsum							
	Demolish	S.Y.		1.40		1.40	Includes material and labor to install
	Install	S.Y.	2.67	4.57		7.24	gypsum lath on walls.
	Demolish and Install	S.Y.	2.67	5.97		8.64	
	Clean	S.Y.		2.91		2.91	
	Minimum Charge	Job		193		193	
Repairs							
Fill in Small Cracks							
	Install	L.F.	.08	3.09		3.17	Includes labor and material to fill-in
	Minimum Charge	Job		193		193	hairline cracks up to 1/8" with filler, sand and prep for paint.
Repair up to 1" Crack							
	Install	L.F.	.31	3.86		4.17	Includes labor and material to fill-in
	Minimum Charge	Job		193		193	hairline cracks up to 1" with filler, sand and prep for paint.
Patch Small Hole (2")							
	Install	Ea.	.08	4.07		4.15	Includes labor and material to patch
	Minimum Charge	Job		193		193	up to a 2" diameter hole in plaster.
Patch Large Hole							
	Install	Ea.	9.25	129		138.25	Includes labor and material to patch
	Minimum Charge	Job		193		193	up to a 20" diameter hole in plaster.
Patch Plaster Section							
	Install	Ea.	2.19	3.86		6.05	Includes labor and material to repair
	Minimum Charge	Job		193		193	section of plaster wall, area less than 20 S.F.
Repair Inside Corner							
	Install	L.F.	3.69	9.65		13.34	Includes material and labor to patch
	Minimum Charge	Job		193		193	plaster corners.

Ceiling Plaster		Unit	Material	Labor	Equip.	Total	Specification
Interior							
Cement							
	Demolish	S.Y.		5.95		5.95	Includes material and labor to install
	Install	S.Y.	14.65	25	2.14	41.79	cement plaster on interior wood
	Demolish and Install	S.Y.	14.65	30.95	2.14	47.74	framing with metal lath.
	Clean	S.Y.		3.05		3.05	
	Paint	S.Y.	2.05	4.93		6.98	
	Minimum Charge	Job		193		193	
Acoustic							
	Demolish	S.Y.		5.95		5.95	Includes material and labor to install
	Install	S.Y.	11.60	30	2.13	43.73	acoustical cement plaster on interior
	Demolish and Install	S.Y.	11.60	35.95	2.13	49.68	wood framing with metal lath.
	Clean	S.Y.		3.05		3.05	
	Paint	S.Y.	2.05	4.93		6.98	
	Minimum Charge	Job		193		193	

Walls / Ceilings

Ceiling Plaster

Ceiling Plaster		Unit	Material	Labor	Equip.	Total	Specification
Gypsum							
	Demolish	S.Y.		5.95		5.95	Includes material and labor to install
	Install	S.Y.	9.95	25.50	1.82	37.27	gypsum wall or ceiling plaster on
	Demolish and Install	S.Y.	9.95	31.45	1.82	43.22	interior wood framing with metal lath.
	Clean	S.Y.		3.05		3.05	
	Paint	S.Y.	2.05	4.93		6.98	
	Minimum Charge	Job		193		193	
Stucco							
	Demolish	S.Y.		14.25		14.25	Includes material and labor to install
	Install	S.Y.	7.20	35	2.51	44.71	stucco on wire mesh over wood
	Demolish and Install	S.Y.	7.20	49.25	2.51	58.96	framing.
	Clean	S.Y.		3.05		3.05	
	Paint	S.Y.	2.05	4.93		6.98	
	Minimum Charge	Job		193		193	

Thin Coat

		Unit	Material	Labor	Equip.	Total	Specification
Veneer							
	Demolish	S.Y.		5.95		5.95	Includes materials and labor to install
	Install	S.Y.	.90	4.61	.40	5.91	thin coat veneer plaster.
	Demolish and Install	S.Y.	.90	10.56	.40	11.86	
	Clean	S.Y.		3.05		3.05	
	Paint	S.Y.	2.05	4.93		6.98	
	Minimum Charge	Job		193		193	

Lath

		Unit	Material	Labor	Equip.	Total	Specification
Metal							
	Demolish	S.Y.		1.40		1.40	Includes material and labor to install
	Install	S.Y.	4.71	6.10		10.81	wire lath on steel framed ceilings.
	Demolish and Install	S.Y.	4.71	7.50		12.21	
	Minimum Charge	Job		193		193	
Gypsum							
	Demolish	S.Y.		1.40		1.40	Includes material and labor to install
	Install	S.Y.	2.67	3.81		6.48	gypsum lath on ceilings.
	Demolish and Install	S.Y.	2.67	5.21		7.88	
	Minimum Charge	Job		193		193	

Repairs

		Unit	Material	Labor	Equip.	Total	Specification
Fill in Small Cracks							
	Install	S.F.	.08	.70		.78	Includes labor and material to fill in
	Minimum Charge	Job		385		385	hairline cracks up to 1/8" with filler, sand and prep for paint.

Gypsum Wallboard

Gypsum Wallboard		Unit	Material	Labor	Equip.	Total	Specification
Finished							
1/4"							
	Demolish	S.F.		.36		.36	Cost includes material and labor to
	Install	S.F.	.30	1.31		1.61	install 1/4" drywall, including joint
	Demolish and Install	S.F.	.30	1.67		1.97	taping, premixed compound and
	Clean	S.F.		.29		.29	screws.
	Paint	S.F.	.26	.32		.58	
	Minimum Charge	Job		216		216	
3/8"							
	Demolish	S.F.		.36		.36	Cost includes material and labor to
	Install	S.F.	.30	1.33		1.63	install 3/8" drywall including joint
	Demolish and Install	S.F.	.30	1.69		1.99	tape, premixed compound and
	Clean	S.F.		.29		.29	screws.
	Paint	S.F.	.26	.32		.58	
	Minimum Charge	Job		216		216	

Walls / Ceilings

Gypsum Wallboard		Unit	Material	Labor	Equip.	Total	Specification
1/2"							
	Demolish	S.F.		.36		.36	Cost includes material and labor to
	Install	S.F.	.29	1.34		1.63	install 1/2" drywall including joint
	Demolish and Install	S.F.	.29	1.70		1.99	tape, premixed compound and
	Clean	S.F.		.29		.29	screws.
	Paint	S.F.	.26	.32		.58	
	Minimum Charge	Job		216		216	
1/2" Water Resistant							
	Demolish	S.F.		.36		.36	Cost includes material and labor to
	Install	S.F.	.32	1.34		1.66	install 1/2" WR drywall including joint
	Demolish and Install	S.F.	.32	1.70		2.02	tape, premixed compound and
	Clean	S.F.		.29		.29	screws.
	Paint	S.F.	.26	.32		.58	
	Minimum Charge	Job		216		216	
1/2" Fire-rated							
	Demolish	S.F.		.36		.36	Cost includes material and labor to
	Install	S.F.	.31	1.34		1.65	install 1/2" FR drywall including
	Demolish and Install	S.F.	.31	1.70		2.01	screws. Taping and finishing not
	Clean	S.F.		.29		.29	included.
	Paint	S.F.	.26	.32		.58	
	Minimum Charge	Job		216		216	
5/8"							
	Demolish	S.F.		.36		.36	Cost includes material and labor to
	Install	S.F.	.34	1.29		1.63	install 5/8" drywall including joint
	Demolish and Install	S.F.	.34	1.65		1.99	tape, premixed compound and
	Clean	S.F.		.29		.29	screws.
	Paint	S.F.	.26	.32		.58	
	Minimum Charge	Job		216		216	
5/8" Fire-rated							
	Demolish	S.F.		.36		.36	Cost includes material and labor to
	Install	S.F.	.36	1.52		1.88	install 5/8" FR drywall, including joint
	Demolish and Install	S.F.	.36	1.88		2.24	taping, premixed compound and
	Clean	S.F.		.29		.29	screws.
	Paint	S.F.	.26	.32		.58	
	Minimum Charge	Job		216		216	
2-hour fire-rated							
	Demolish	S.F.		.89		.89	Cost includes material and labor to
	Install	S.F.	.76	3.02		3.78	install 2 layers of 5/8" type X drywall
	Demolish and Install	S.F.	.76	3.91		4.67	including joint taping, premixed
	Clean	S.F.		.29		.29	compound and screws.
	Paint	S.F.	.26	.32		.58	
	Minimum Charge	Job		216		216	
Unfinished							
1/4"							
	Demolish	S.F.		.36		.36	Cost includes material and labor to
	Install	S.F.	.26	.45		.71	install 1/4" drywall including screws.
	Demolish and Install	S.F.	.26	.81		1.07	Taping and finishing not included.
	Clean	S.F.		.29		.29	
	Minimum Charge	Job		216		216	
3/8"							
	Demolish	S.F.		.36		.36	Cost includes material and labor to
	Install	S.F.	.26	.46		.72	install 3/8" drywall including screws.
	Demolish and Install	S.F.	.26	.82		1.08	Tape, finish or texture is not included.
	Clean	S.F.		.29		.29	
	Minimum Charge	Job		216		216	

Walls / Ceilings

Gypsum Wallboard		Unit	Material	Labor	Equip.	Total	Specification
1/2″							
	Demolish	S.F.		.36		.36	Cost includes material and labor to
	Install	S.F.	.25	.46		.71	install 1/2″ drywall including screws.
	Demolish and Install	S.F.	.25	.82		1.07	Taping and finishing not included.
	Clean	S.F.		.29		.29	
	Minimum Charge	Job		216		216	
1/2″ Water Resistant							
	Demolish	S.F.		.36		.36	Cost includes material and labor to
	Install	S.F.	.28	.46		.74	install 1/2″ WR drywall including
	Demolish and Install	S.F.	.28	.82		1.10	screws. Taping and finishing is not
	Clean	S.F.		.29		.29	included.
	Minimum Charge	Job		216		216	
1/2″ Fire-rated							
	Demolish	S.F.		.36		.36	Cost includes labor and material to
	Install	S.F.	.25	.31		.56	install 1/2″ FR drywall including
	Demolish and Install	S.F.	.25	.67		.92	screws. Tape, finish or texture is not
	Clean	S.F.		.29		.29	included.
	Minimum Charge	Job		216		216	
5/8″							
	Demolish	S.F.		.36		.36	Cost includes material and labor to
	Install	S.F.	.29	.52		.81	install 5/8″ drywall including screws.
	Demolish and Install	S.F.	.29	.88		1.17	Taping and finishing not included.
	Clean	S.F.		.29		.29	
	Minimum Charge	Job		216		216	
5/8″ Fire-rated							
	Demolish	S.F.		.36		.36	Cost includes material and labor to
	Install	S.F.	.31	.52		.83	install 5/8″ FR drywall including
	Demolish and Install	S.F.	.31	.88		1.19	screws. Taping and finishing not
	Clean	S.F.		.29		.29	included.
	Minimum Charge	Job		216		216	
2-hour Fire-rated							
	Demolish	S.F.		.89		.89	Cost includes material and labor to
	Install	S.F.	.76	3.02		3.78	install 2 layers of 5/8″ type X drywall
	Demolish and Install	S.F.	.76	3.91		4.67	including joint taping, premixed
	Clean	S.F.		.29		.29	compound and screws.
	Minimum Charge	Job		216		216	
Accessories							
Tape & Finish							
	Install	S.F.	.06	.43		.49	Includes labor and material for taping,
	Minimum Charge	Job		216		216	sanding and finish.
Texture							
Sprayed							
	Install	S.F.	.04	.46		.50	Includes labor and material to install
	Minimum Charge	Job		216		216	by spray, texture finish.
Trowel							
	Install	S.F.		.25		.25	Includes labor and material to apply
	Minimum Charge	Job		216		216	hand troweled texture.
Patch Hole in Gypsum Wallboard							
	Install	S.F.	.50	58		58.50	Includes labor and material to patch a
	Minimum Charge	Job		216		216	one square foot area of damaged
							drywall.
Furring Strips							
	Demolish	S.F.		.09		.09	Cost includes material and labor to
	Install	S.F.	.20	.96		1.16	install 1″ x 2″ furring strips, 16″ O.C.
	Demolish and Install	S.F.	.20	1.05		1.25	per S.F. of surface area to be covered.
	Minimum Charge	Job		108		108	

Walls / Ceilings

Ceramic Wall Tile	Unit	Material	Labor	Equip.	Total	Specification
Thin Set						
2″ x 2″						
Demolish	S.F.		1.19		1.19	Cost includes material and labor to
Install	S.F.	6.55	6.30		12.85	install 2″ x 2″ ceramic tile in organic
Demolish and Install	S.F.	6.55	7.49		14.04	adhesive including cutting and grout.
Clean	S.F.		.61		.61	
Minimum Charge	Job		189		189	
4-1/4″ x 4-1/4″						
Demolish	S.F.		1.19		1.19	Cost includes material and labor to
Install	S.F.	2.49	3.58		6.07	install 4-1/4″ x 4-1/4″ ceramic tile in
Demolish and Install	S.F.	2.49	4.77		7.26	organic adhesive including grout.
Clean	S.F.		.61		.61	
Minimum Charge	Job		189		189	
6″ x 6″						
Demolish	S.F.		1.19		1.19	Cost includes material and labor to
Install	S.F.	3.43	3.88		7.31	install 6″ x 6″ ceramic tile in organic
Demolish and Install	S.F.	3.43	5.07		8.50	adhesive including and grout.
Clean	S.F.		.61		.61	
Minimum Charge	Job		189		189	
8″ x 8″						
Demolish	S.F.		1.19		1.19	Cost includes material and labor to
Install	S.F.	4.70	4		8.70	install 8″ x 8″ ceramic tile in organic
Demolish and Install	S.F.	4.70	5.19		9.89	adhesive including cutting and grout.
Clean	S.F.		.61		.61	
Minimum Charge	Job		189		189	
Thick Set						
2″ x 2″						
Demolish	S.F.		1.42		1.42	Cost includes material and labor to
Install	S.F.	6.95	7.60		14.55	install 2″ x 2″ ceramic tile in mortar
Demolish and Install	S.F.	6.95	9.02		15.97	bed including cutting and grout.
Clean	S.F.		.61		.61	
Minimum Charge	Job		189		189	
4-1/4″ x 4-1/4″						
Demolish	S.F.		1.42		1.42	Cost includes material and labor to
Install	S.F.	10.35	7.60		17.95	install 4-1/4″ x 4-1/4″ ceramic tile in
Demolish and Install	S.F.	10.35	9.02		19.37	mortar bed including cutting and
Clean	S.F.		.61		.61	grout.
Minimum Charge	Job		189		189	
6″ x 6″						
Demolish	S.F.		1.42		1.42	Cost includes material and labor to
Install	S.F.	10.55	6.90		17.45	install 6″ x 6″ ceramic tile in mortar
Demolish and Install	S.F.	10.55	8.32		18.87	bed including cutting and grout.
Clean	S.F.		.61		.61	
Minimum Charge	Job		189		189	
8″ x 8″						
Demolish	S.F.		1.42		1.42	Cost includes material and labor to
Install	S.F.	12.10	6.30		18.40	install 8″ x 8″ ceramic tile in mortar
Demolish and Install	S.F.	12.10	7.72		19.82	bed including cutting and grout.
Clean	S.F.		.61		.61	
Minimum Charge	Job		189		189	
Re-grout						
Install	S.F.	.15	3.79		3.94	Includes material and labor to regrout
Minimum Charge	Job		189		189	wall tiles.

Walls / Ceilings

Wall Tile	Unit	Material	Labor	Equip.	Total	Specification
Mirror						
Custom Cut Wall						
Demolish	S.F.		.68		.68	Includes material and labor to install
Install	S.F.	2.44	4.27		6.71	distortion-free float glass mirror, 1/8"
Demolish and Install	S.F.	2.44	4.95		7.39	to 3/16" thick with cut and polished
Clean	S.F.	.03	.19		.22	edges.
Minimum Charge	Job		208		208	
Beveled Wall						
Demolish	S.F.		.68		.68	Includes material and labor to install
Install	S.F.	6.65	7.55		14.20	distortion-free float glass mirror, 1/8"
Demolish and Install	S.F.	6.65	8.23		14.88	to 3/16" thick with beveled edges.
Clean	S.F.	.03	.19		.22	
Minimum Charge	Job		208		208	
Smoked Wall						
Demolish	S.F.		.68		.68	Includes material and labor to install
Install	S.F.	8.90	7.55		16.45	distortion-free smoked float glass
Demolish and Install	S.F.	8.90	8.23		17.13	mirror, 1/8" to 3/16" thick with cut
Clean	S.F.	.03	.19		.22	and polished edges.
Minimum Charge	Job		208		208	
Marble						
Good Grade						
Demolish	S.F.		2.23		2.23	Cost includes material and labor to
Install	S.F.	9.90	16.45		26.35	install 3/8" x 12" x 12" marble tile in
Demolish and Install	S.F.	9.90	18.68		28.58	mortar bed with grout.
Clean	S.F.		.61		.61	
Minimum Charge	Job		189		189	
Better Grade						
Demolish	S.F.		2.23		2.23	Cost includes material and labor to
Install	S.F.	11	16.45		27.45	install 3/8" x 12" x 12" marble, in
Demolish and Install	S.F.	11	18.68		29.68	mortar bed with grout.
Clean	S.F.		.61		.61	
Minimum Charge	Job		189		189	
Premium Grade						
Demolish	S.F.		2.23		2.23	Cost includes material and labor to
Install	S.F.	21	16.45		37.45	install 3/8" x 12" x 12" marble, in
Demolish and Install	S.F.	21	18.68		39.68	mortar bed with grout.
Clean	S.F.		.61		.61	
Minimum Charge	Job		189		189	
Glass Block						
Demolish	S.F.		1.78		1.78	Cost includes material and labor to
Install	S.F.	32	17.10		49.10	install 3-7/8" thick, 6" x 6" smooth
Demolish and Install	S.F.	32	18.88		50.88	face glass block including mortar and
Clean	S.F.		.61		.61	cleaning.
Minimum Charge	Job		385		385	
Cork						
Demolish	S.F.		.28		.28	Cost includes material and labor to
Install	S.F.	5.55	1.55		7.10	install 3/16" thick cork tile and
Demolish and Install	S.F.	5.55	1.83		7.38	installation.
Clean	S.F.		.61		.61	
Minimum Charge	Job		186		186	
Re-grout						
Install	S.F.	.15	3.79		3.94	Includes material and labor to regrout
Minimum Charge	Job		189		189	wall tiles.

Walls / Ceilings

Wall Paneling	Unit	Material	Labor	Equip.	Total	Specification
Plywood						
Good Grade						
Demolish	S.F.		.36		.36	Cost includes material and labor to
Install	S.F.	.45	1.73		2.18	install 4' x 8' x 1/4" paneling,
Demolish and Install	S.F.	.45	2.09		2.54	including nails and adhesive.
Clean	S.F.		.29		.29	
Paint	S.F.	.32	.70		1.02	
Minimum Charge	Job		216		216	
Better Grade						
Demolish	S.F.		.36		.36	Cost includes material and labor to
Install	S.F.	.91	2.06		2.97	install 4' x 8' x 1/4" plywood wall
Demolish and Install	S.F.	.91	2.42		3.33	panel, including nails and adhesive.
Clean	S.F.		.29		.29	
Paint	S.F.	.32	.70		1.02	
Minimum Charge	Job		216		216	
Premium Grade						
Demolish	S.F.		.36		.36	Cost includes material and labor to
Install	S.F.	1.38	2.47		3.85	install 4' x 8' x 1/4" plywood wall
Demolish and Install	S.F.	1.38	2.83		4.21	panel, including nails and adhesive.
Clean	S.F.		.29		.29	
Paint	S.F.	.32	.70		1.02	
Minimum Charge	Job		216		216	
Hardboard						
Embossed Paneling						
Demolish	S.F.		.36		.36	Includes material and labor to install
Install	S.F.	.69	1.73		2.42	hardboard embossed paneling
Demolish and Install	S.F.	.69	2.09		2.78	including adhesives.
Clean	S.F.		.29		.29	
Minimum Charge	Job		216		216	
Plastic Molding						
Demolish	L.F.		.36		.36	Includes material and labor to install
Install	L.F.	.81	1.08		1.89	plastic trim for paneling.
Demolish and Install	L.F.	.81	1.44		2.25	
Clean	L.F.	.03	.19		.22	
Minimum Charge	Job		216		216	
Hardboard						
Embossed Brick						
Demolish	S.F.		.36		.36	Cost includes material and labor to
Install	S.F.	.91	1.92		2.83	install 4' x 8' non-ceramic mineral
Demolish and Install	S.F.	.91	2.28		3.19	brick-like veneer wall panels including
Clean	S.F.		.29		.29	adhesive.
Paint	S.F.	.23	.56		.79	
Minimum Charge	Job		216		216	
Embossed Ceramic Tile						
Demolish	S.F.		.36		.36	Includes material and labor to install
Install	S.F.	.69	1.73		2.42	hardboard embossed paneling
Demolish and Install	S.F.	.69	2.09		2.78	including adhesives.
Clean	S.F.		.29		.29	
Paint	S.F.	.23	.56		.79	
Minimum Charge	Job		216		216	
Pegboard						
Demolish	S.F.		.36		.36	Cost includes material and labor to
Install	S.F.	.51	1.73		2.24	install 4' x 8' x 1/4" pegboard panel,
Demolish and Install	S.F.	.51	2.09		2.60	including adhesive.
Clean	S.F.		.29		.29	
Paint	S.F.	.23	.56		.79	
Minimum Charge	Job		216		216	

Walls / Ceilings

Wall Paneling		Unit	Material	Labor	Equip.	Total	Specification
Furring Strips							
	Demolish	S.F.		.09		.09	Cost includes material and labor to
	Install	S.F.	.20	.96		1.16	install 1" x 2" furring strips, 16" O.C.
	Demolish and Install	S.F.	.20	1.05		1.25	per S.F. of surface area to be covered.
	Minimum Charge	Job		216		216	
Molding							
Unfinished Base							
	Demolish	L.F.		.59		.59	Cost includes material and labor to
	Install	L.F.	.69	1.30		1.99	install 1/2" x 2-1/2" pine or birch
	Demolish and Install	L.F.	.69	1.89		2.58	base molding.
	Reinstall	L.F.		1.04		1.04	
	Clean	L.F.	.03	.19		.22	
	Paint	L.F.	.06	.40		.46	
	Minimum Charge	Job		216		216	
Unfinished Corner							
	Demolish	L.F.		.59		.59	Includes material and labor to install
	Install	L.F.	2.35	1.80		4.15	unfinished pine corner molding.
	Demolish and Install	L.F.	2.35	2.39		4.74	
	Reinstall	L.F.		1.44		1.44	
	Clean	L.F.	.03	.19		.22	
	Paint	L.F.	.14	.59		.73	
	Minimum Charge	Job		216		216	
Unfinished Cove							
	Demolish	L.F.		.59		.59	Cost includes material and labor to
	Install	L.F.	2.43	1.63		4.06	install 11/16" x 2-3/4" pine cove
	Demolish and Install	L.F.	2.43	2.22		4.65	molding.
	Reinstall	L.F.		1.30		1.30	
	Clean	L.F.	.03	.19		.22	
	Paint	L.F.	.14	.59		.73	
	Minimum Charge	Job		216		216	
Unfinished Crown							
	Demolish	L.F.		.71		.71	Includes material and labor to install
	Install	L.F.	2.97	1.73		4.70	unfinished pine crown molding.
	Demolish and Install	L.F.	2.97	2.44		5.41	
	Reinstall	L.F.		1.38		1.38	
	Clean	L.F.	.04	.25		.29	
	Paint	L.F.	.10	.40		.50	
	Minimum Charge	Job		216		216	
Prefinished Base							
	Demolish	L.F.		.59		.59	Cost includes material and labor to
	Install	L.F.	1.49	1.38		2.87	install 9/16" x 3-5/16" prefinished
	Demolish and Install	L.F.	1.49	1.97		3.46	base molding.
	Reinstall	L.F.		1.11		1.11	
	Clean	L.F.	.03	.19		.22	
	Paint	L.F.	.06	.40		.46	
	Minimum Charge	Job		216		216	
Prefinished Corner							
	Demolish	L.F.		.59		.59	Includes material and labor to install
	Install	L.F.	2.64	1.80		4.44	inside or outside prefinished corner
	Demolish and Install	L.F.	2.64	2.39		5.03	molding.
	Reinstall	L.F.		1.44		1.44	
	Clean	L.F.	.03	.19		.22	
	Paint	L.F.	.14	.59		.73	
	Minimum Charge	Job		216		216	

Walls / Ceilings

Wall Paneling

Wall Paneling	Unit	Material	Labor	Equip.	Total	Specification
Prefinished Crown						
Demolish	L.F.		.71		.71	Cost includes material and labor to
Install	L.F.	1.67	1.73		3.40	install 3/4" x 3-13/16" prefinished
Demolish and Install	L.F.	1.67	2.44		4.11	crown molding.
Reinstall	L.F.		1.38		1.38	
Clean	L.F.	.04	.25		.29	
Paint	L.F.	.10	.40		.50	
Minimum Charge	Job		216		216	

Wallcovering

Wallcovering	Unit	Material	Labor	Equip.	Total	Specification
Surface Prep						
Patch Walls						
Install	S.F.	.11	3.86		3.97	Includes labor and material to repair
Minimum Charge	Job		186		186	section of plaster wall, area less than
Sizing						20 S.F.
Install	S.F.	.09	.19		.28	Includes labor and materials to apply
Minimum Charge	Job		186		186	wall sizing.
Good Grade						
Walls						
Demolish	S.F.		.69		.69	Includes material and labor to install
Install	S.F.	1.03	.77		1.80	pre-pasted, vinyl-coated wallcovering.
Demolish and Install	S.F.	1.03	1.46		2.49	
Clean	S.F.	.01	.07		.08	
Minimum Charge	Job		186		186	
Ceiling						
Demolish	S.F.		.69		.69	Includes material and labor to install
Install	S.F.	1.03	.77		1.80	pre-pasted, vinyl-coated wallcovering.
Demolish and Install	S.F.	1.03	1.46		2.49	
Clean	S.F.	.03	.19		.22	
Minimum Charge	Job		186		186	
Better Grade						
Walls						
Demolish	S.F.		.69		.69	Includes material and labor to install
Install	S.F.	1.16	.77		1.93	pre-pasted, vinyl-coated wallcovering.
Demolish and Install	S.F.	1.16	1.46		2.62	
Clean	S.F.	.01	.07		.08	
Minimum Charge	Job		186		186	
Ceiling						
Demolish	S.F.		.69		.69	Includes material and labor to install
Install	S.F.	1.16	.77		1.93	pre-pasted, vinyl-coated wallcovering.
Demolish and Install	S.F.	1.16	1.46		2.62	
Clean	S.F.	.03	.19		.22	
Minimum Charge	Job		186		186	
Premium Grade						
Walls						
Demolish	S.F.		.86		.86	Includes material and labor to install
Install	S.F.	1.24	.77		2.01	pre-pasted, vinyl-coated wallcovering.
Demolish and Install	S.F.	1.24	1.63		2.87	
Clean	S.F.	.01	.07		.08	
Minimum Charge	Job		186		186	
Ceiling						
Demolish	S.F.		.86		.86	Includes material and labor to install
Install	S.F.	1.24	.77		2.01	pre-pasted, vinyl-coated wallcovering.
Demolish and Install	S.F.	1.24	1.63		2.87	
Clean	S.F.	.03	.19		.22	
Minimum Charge	Job		186		186	

Wallcovering	Unit	Material	Labor	Equip.	Total	Specification
Mural						
Pre-printed						
Demolish	Ea.		111		111	Includes material and labor to install
Install	Ea.	276	279		555	wallcovering with a pre-printed mural.
Demolish and Install	Ea.	276	390		666	
Clean	Ea.		8		8	
Minimum Charge	Job		186		186	
Hand-painted						
Demolish	Ea.		111		111	Includes material and labor to install
Install	Ea.	535	565		1100	wallcovering with a hand-painted
Demolish and Install	Ea.	535	676		1211	mural.
Clean	Ea.		8		8	
Minimum Charge	Job		186		186	
Vinyl-coated						
Good Grade						
Demolish	Ea.		19.80		19.80	Includes material and labor to install
Install	Ea.	16.95	26		42.95	pre-pasted, vinyl-coated wallcovering.
Demolish and Install	Ea.	16.95	45.80		62.75	Based upon 30 S.F. rolls.
Clean	Ea.		8		8	
Minimum Charge	Job		186		186	
Better Grade						
Demolish	Ea.		19.80		19.80	Includes material and labor to install
Install	Ea.	26.50	26		52.50	pre-pasted, vinyl-coated wallcovering.
Demolish and Install	Ea.	26.50	45.80		72.30	Based upon 30 S.F. rolls.
Clean	Ea.		8		8	
Minimum Charge	Job		186		186	
Premium Grade						
Demolish	Ea.		19.80		19.80	Includes material and labor to install
Install	Ea.	31.50	26		57.50	pre-pasted, vinyl-coated wallcovering.
Demolish and Install	Ea.	31.50	45.80		77.30	Based upon 30 S.F. rolls.
Clean	Ea.		8		8	
Minimum Charge	Job		186		186	
Blank Underliner						
Demolish	Ea.		19.80		19.80	Includes material and labor to install
Install	Ea.	9.90	26.50		36.40	blank stock liner paper or bridging
Demolish and Install	Ea.	9.90	46.30		56.20	paper. Based upon 30 S.F. rolls.
Clean	Ea.		8		8	
Minimum Charge	Job		186		186	
Solid Vinyl						
Good Grade						
Demolish	Roll		23		23	Includes material and labor to install
Install	Ea.	24	26		50	pre-pasted, vinyl wallcovering. Based
Demolish and Install	Ea.	24	49		73	upon 30 S.F. rolls.
Clean	Ea.		8		8	
Minimum Charge	Job		186		186	
Better Grade						
Demolish	Roll		23		23	Includes material and labor to install
Install	Ea.	31.50	26		57.50	pre-pasted, vinyl wallcovering. Based
Demolish and Install	Ea.	31.50	49		80.50	upon 30 S.F. rolls.
Clean	Ea.		8		8	
Minimum Charge	Job		186		186	
Premium Grade						
Demolish	Roll		23		23	Includes material and labor to install
Install	Ea.	50.50	26		76.50	pre-pasted, vinyl wallcovering. Based
Demolish and Install	Ea.	50.50	49		99.50	upon 30 S.F. rolls.
Clean	Ea.		8		8	
Minimum Charge	Job		186		186	

Walls / Ceilings

Wallcovering		Unit	Material	Labor	Equip.	Total	Specification
Blank Underliner							
	Demolish	Ea.		19.80		19.80	Includes material and labor to install
	Install	Ea.	9.90	26.50		36.40	blank stock liner paper or bridging
	Demolish and Install	Ea.	9.90	46.30		56.20	paper. Based upon 30 S.F. rolls.
	Clean	Ea.		8		8	
	Minimum Charge	Job		186		186	
Grasscloth / String							
Good Grade							
	Demolish	Ea.		19.80		19.80	Includes material and labor to install
	Install	Ea.	53.50	34		87.50	grasscloth or string wallcovering.
	Demolish and Install	Ea.	53.50	53.80		107.30	Based upon 30 S.F. rolls.
	Clean	Ea.		10.70		10.70	
	Minimum Charge	Job		186		186	
Better Grade							
	Demolish	Ea.		19.80		19.80	Includes material and labor to install
	Install	Ea.	60.50	34		94.50	grasscloth or string wallcovering.
	Demolish and Install	Ea.	60.50	53.80		114.30	Based upon 30 S.F. rolls.
	Clean	Ea.		10.70		10.70	
	Minimum Charge	Job		186		186	
Premium Grade							
	Demolish	Ea.		19.80		19.80	Includes material and labor to install
	Install	Ea.	67.50	34		101.50	grasscloth or string wallcovering.
	Demolish and Install	Ea.	67.50	53.80		121.30	Based upon 30 S.F. rolls.
	Clean	Ea.		10.70		10.70	
	Minimum Charge	Job		186		186	
Blank Underliner							
	Demolish	Ea.		19.80		19.80	Includes material and labor to install
	Install	Ea.	9.90	26.50		36.40	blank stock liner paper or bridging
	Demolish and Install	Ea.	9.90	46.30		56.20	paper. Based upon 30 S.F. rolls.
	Clean	Ea.		8		8	
	Minimum Charge	Job		186		186	
Designer							
Premium Grade							
	Demolish	S.F.		.86		.86	Includes material and labor to install
	Install	Ea.	113	39		152	paperback vinyl, untrimmed and
	Demolish and Install	Ea.	113	39.86		152.86	hand-painted. Based upon 30 S.F.
	Clean	Ea.		8		8	rolls.
	Minimum Charge	Job		186		186	
Blank Underliner							
	Demolish	Ea.		19.80		19.80	Includes material and labor to install
	Install	Ea.	9.90	26.50		36.40	blank stock liner paper or bridging
	Demolish and Install	Ea.	9.90	46.30		56.20	paper. Based upon 30 S.F. rolls.
	Clean	Ea.		8		8	
	Minimum Charge	Job		186		186	
Foil							
	Demolish	Ea.		19.80		19.80	Includes material and labor to install
	Install	Ea.	28.50	34		62.50	foil coated wallcovering. Based upon
	Demolish and Install	Ea.	28.50	53.80		82.30	30 S.F. rolls.
	Clean	Ea.		8		8	
	Minimum Charge	Job		186		186	
Wallcovering Border							
Good Grade							
	Demolish	L.F.		1.29		1.29	Includes material and labor install
	Install	L.F.	1.65	1.43		3.08	vinyl-coated border 4" to 6" wide.
	Demolish and Install	L.F.	1.65	2.72		4.37	
	Clean	L.F.		.12		.12	
	Minimum Charge	Job		186		186	

Walls / Ceilings

Wallcovering

Wallcovering	Unit	Material	Labor	Equip.	Total	Specification
Better Grade						
Demolish	L.F.		1.29		1.29	Includes material and labor install
Install	L.F.	2.97	1.43		4.40	vinyl-coated border 4" to 6" wide.
Demolish and Install	L.F.	2.97	2.72		5.69	
Clean	L.F.		.12		.12	
Minimum Charge	Job		186		186	
Premium Grade						
Demolish	L.F.		1.29		1.29	Includes material and labor install
Install	L.F.	3.69	1.43		5.12	vinyl-coated border 4" to 6" wide.
Demolish and Install	L.F.	3.69	2.72		6.41	
Clean	L.F.		.12		.12	
Minimum Charge	Job		186		186	

Acoustical Ceiling

Acoustical Ceiling	Unit	Material	Labor	Equip.	Total	Specification
Complete System						
2' x 2' Square Edge						
Demolish	S.F.		.59		.59	Includes material and labor to install
Install	S.F.	2.52	1.33		3.85	T-bar grid acoustical ceiling system,
Demolish and Install	S.F.	2.52	1.92		4.44	random pinhole 5/8" thick square
Reinstall	S.F.		1.06		1.06	edge tile.
Clean	S.F.	.04	.24		.28	
Minimum Charge	Job		216		216	
2' x 2' Reveal Edge						
Demolish	S.F.		.59		.59	Includes material and labor to install
Install	S.F.	3.43	1.73		5.16	T-bar grid acoustical ceiling system,
Demolish and Install	S.F.	3.43	2.32		5.75	random pinhole 5/8" thick reveal
Reinstall	S.F.		1.38		1.38	edge tile.
Clean	S.F.	.04	.24		.28	
Minimum Charge	Job		216		216	
2' x 2' Fire-rated						
Demolish	S.F.		.59		.59	Includes material and labor to install
Install	S.F.	3.32	1.33		4.65	T-bar grid FR acoustical ceiling system,
Demolish and Install	S.F.	3.32	1.92		5.24	random pinhole 5/8" thick square
Reinstall	S.F.		1.06		1.06	edge tile.
Clean	S.F.	.04	.24		.28	
Minimum Charge	Job		216		216	
2' x 4' Square Edge						
Demolish	S.F.		.59		.59	Cost includes material and labor to
Install	S.F.	2.92	1.14		4.06	install 2' x 4' T-bar grid acoustical
Demolish and Install	S.F.	2.92	1.73		4.65	ceiling system, random pinhole 5/8"
Reinstall	S.F.		.91		.91	thick square edge tile.
Clean	S.F.	.04	.24		.28	
Minimum Charge	Job		216		216	
2' x 4' Reveal Edge						
Demolish	S.F.		.59		.59	Includes material and labor to install
Install	S.F.	2.98	1.57		4.55	T-bar grid acoustical ceiling system,
Demolish and Install	S.F.	2.98	2.16		5.14	random pinhole 5/8" thick reveal
Reinstall	S.F.		1.26		1.26	edge tile.
Clean	S.F.	.04	.24		.28	
Minimum Charge	Job		216		216	
2' x 4' Fire-rated						
Demolish	S.F.		.59		.59	Includes material and labor to install
Install	S.F.	3.32	1.33		4.65	T-bar grid FR acoustical ceiling system,
Demolish and Install	S.F.	3.32	1.92		5.24	random pinhole 5/8" thick square
Reinstall	S.F.		1.06		1.06	edge tile.
Clean	S.F.	.04	.24		.28	
Minimum Charge	Job		216		216	

Walls / Ceilings

Acoustical Ceiling	Unit	Material	Labor	Equip.	Total	Specification
T-bar Grid						
2′ x 2′						
Demolish	S.F.		.70		.70	Includes material and labor to install
Install	S.F.	1	.66		1.66	T-bar grid acoustical ceiling
Demolish and Install	S.F.	1	1.36		2.36	suspension system.
Reinstall	S.F.		.53		.53	
Clean	S.F.	.04	.24		.28	
Minimum Charge	Job		193		193	
2′ x 4′						
Demolish	S.F.		.70		.70	Includes material and labor to install
Install	S.F.	.77	.54		1.31	T-bar grid acoustical ceiling
Demolish and Install	S.F.	.77	1.24		2.01	suspension system.
Reinstall	S.F.		.43		.43	
Clean	S.F.	.04	.24		.28	
Minimum Charge	Job		193		193	
Tile Panels						
2′ x 2′ Square Edge						
Demolish	S.F.		.20		.20	Includes material and labor to install
Install	S.F.	1.38	.69		2.07	square edge panels 5/8″ thick with
Demolish and Install	S.F.	1.38	.89		2.27	pinhole pattern. T-bar grid not
Reinstall	S.F.		.55		.55	included.
Clean	S.F.	.04	.24		.28	
Minimum Charge	Job		216		216	
2′ x 2′ Reveal Edge						
Demolish	S.F.		.20		.20	Includes material and labor to install
Install	S.F.	1.80	.92		2.72	reveal edge panels 5/8″ thick with
Demolish and Install	S.F.	1.80	1.12		2.92	pinhole pattern. T-bar grid not
Reinstall	S.F.		.74		.74	included.
Clean	S.F.	.04	.24		.28	
Minimum Charge	Job		216		216	
2′ x 2′ Fire-rated						
Demolish	S.F.		.20		.20	Includes material and labor to install
Install	S.F.	1.05	.64		1.69	FR square edge panels 5/8″ thick with
Demolish and Install	S.F.	1.05	.84		1.89	pinhole pattern. T-bar grid not
Reinstall	S.F.		.51		.51	included.
Clean	S.F.	.04	.24		.28	
Minimum Charge	Job		216		216	
2′ x 4′ Square Edge						
Demolish	S.F.		.20		.20	Includes material and labor to install
Install	S.F.	1.38	.69		2.07	square edge panels 5/8″ thick with
Demolish and Install	S.F.	1.38	.89		2.27	pinhole pattern. T-bar grid not
Reinstall	S.F.		.55		.55	included.
Clean	S.F.	.04	.24		.28	
Minimum Charge	Job		216		216	
2′ x 4′ Reveal Edge						
Demolish	S.F.		.20		.20	Includes material and labor to install
Install	S.F.	1.80	.92		2.72	reveal edge panels 5/8″ thick with
Demolish and Install	S.F.	1.80	1.12		2.92	pinhole pattern. T-bar grid not
Reinstall	S.F.		.74		.74	included.
Clean	S.F.	.04	.24		.28	
Minimum Charge	Job		216		216	
2′ x 4′ Fire-rated						
Demolish	S.F.		.20		.20	Includes material and labor to install
Install	S.F.	1.05	.64		1.69	FR square edge panels 5/8″ thick with
Demolish and Install	S.F.	1.05	.84		1.89	pinhole pattern. T-bar grid not
Reinstall	S.F.		.51		.51	included.
Clean	S.F.	.04	.24		.28	
Minimum Charge	Job		216		216	

Walls / Ceilings

Acoustical Ceiling		Unit	Material	Labor	Equip.	Total	Specification
Bleach Out Stains							
	Install	S.F.	.15	.32		.47	Includes labor and material to apply
	Minimum Charge	Job		216		216	laundry type chlorine bleach to
							remove light staining of acoustic tile
							material.
Adhesive Tile							
Good Grade							
	Demolish	S.F.		.79		.79	Cost includes material and labor to
	Install	S.F.	1.23	1.44		2.67	install 12" x 12" tile with embossed
	Demolish and Install	S.F.	1.23	2.23		3.46	texture pattern. Furring strips not
	Clean	S.F.	.03	.19		.22	included.
	Minimum Charge	Job		216		216	
Better Grade							
	Demolish	S.F.		.79		.79	Cost includes material and labor to
	Install	S.F.	1.51	1.44		2.95	install 12" x 12" tile with embossed
	Demolish and Install	S.F.	1.51	2.23		3.74	texture pattern. Furring strips not
	Clean	S.F.	.03	.19		.22	included.
	Minimum Charge	Job		216		216	
Premium Grade							
	Demolish	S.F.		.79		.79	Cost includes material and labor to
	Install	S.F.	5.45	1.44		6.89	install 12" x 12" tile with embossed
	Demolish and Install	S.F.	5.45	2.23		7.68	texture pattern. Furring strips not
	Clean	S.F.	.03	.19		.22	included.
	Minimum Charge	Job		216		216	
Bleach Out Stains							
	Install	S.F.	.15	.32		.47	Includes labor and material to apply
	Minimum Charge	Job		216		216	laundry type chlorine bleach to
							remove light staining of acoustic tile
							material.
Stapled Tile							
Good Grade							
	Demolish	S.F.		.47		.47	Cost includes material and labor to
	Install	S.F.	1.23	1.44		2.67	install 12" x 12" tile with embossed
	Demolish and Install	S.F.	1.23	1.91		3.14	texture pattern. Furring strips not
	Clean	S.F.	.03	.19		.22	included.
	Minimum Charge	Job		216		216	
Better Grade							
	Demolish	S.F.		.47		.47	Cost includes material and labor to
	Install	S.F.	1.51	1.44		2.95	install 12" x 12" tile with embossed
	Demolish and Install	S.F.	1.51	1.91		3.42	texture pattern. Furring strips not
	Clean	S.F.	.03	.19		.22	included.
	Minimum Charge	Job		216		216	
Premium Grade							
	Demolish	S.F.		.47		.47	Cost includes material and labor to
	Install	S.F.	5.45	1.44		6.89	install 12" x 12" tile with embossed
	Demolish and Install	S.F.	5.45	1.91		7.36	texture pattern. Furring strips not
	Clean	S.F.	.03	.19		.22	included.
	Minimum Charge	Job		216		216	
Bleach Out Stains							
	Install	S.F.	.15	.32		.47	Includes labor and material to apply
	Minimum Charge	Job		216		216	laundry type chlorine bleach to
							remove light staining of acoustic tile
							material.

Walls / Ceilings

Acoustical Ceiling		Unit	Material	Labor	Equip.	Total	Specification
Blown							
Scrape Off Existing							
	Install	S.F.		.66		.66	Includes labor and material to remove
	Minimum Charge	Job		216		216	existing blown acoustical ceiling material.
Seal Ceiling Gypsum Wallboard							
	Install	S.F.	.07	.32		.39	Includes labor and material to seal
	Minimum Charge	Job		185		185	existing drywall with shellac-based material.
Reblow Existing							
	Install	S.F.	.04	.46		.50	Includes labor and material to install
	Minimum Charge	Job		525	74	599	by spray, texture finish.
Bleach Out Stains							
	Install	S.F.	.15	.32		.47	Includes labor and material to apply
	Minimum Charge	Job		216		216	laundry type chlorine bleach to remove light staining of acoustic tile material.
New Blown							
	Install	S.F.	.04	.46		.50	Includes labor and material to install
	Minimum Charge	Job		185		185	by spray, texture finish.
Apply Glitter To							
	Install	S.F.	.22	.17		.39	Includes labor and material to apply
	Minimum Charge	Job		185		185	glitter material to existing or new drywall.
Furring Strips							
	Demolish	S.F.		.09		.09	Cost includes material and labor to
	Install	S.F.	.20	.96		1.16	install 1" x 2" furring strips, 16" O.C.
	Demolish and Install	S.F.	.20	1.05		1.25	per S.F. of surface area to be covered.
	Minimum Charge	Job		108		108	

Finish Carpentry

Finished Stair

Bi-Fold Door

Raised Panel Door

Hollow Core Door	Unit	Material	Labor	Equip.	Total	Specification
Pre-hung Wood						
1' 6" x 6' 8"						
Demolish	Ea.		40		40	Cost includes material and labor to
Install	Ea.	151	24		175	install 1' 6" x 6' 8" pre-hung 1-3/8"
Demolish and Install	Ea.	151	64		215	lauan door with split pine jamb
Reinstall	Ea.		24		24	including casing, stops, and hinges.
Clean	Ea.	4.03	13.35		17.38	
Paint	Ea.	10.30	53		63.30	
Minimum Charge	Job		216		216	
2' x 6' 8"						
Demolish	Ea.		40		40	Cost includes material and labor to
Install	Ea.	165	25.50		190.50	install 2' x 6' 8" pre-hung 1-3/8"
Demolish and Install	Ea.	165	65.50		230.50	lauan door with split pine jamb
Reinstall	Ea.		25.41		25.41	including casing, stops, and hinges.
Clean	Ea.	4.03	13.35		17.38	
Paint	Ea.	10.30	53		63.30	
Minimum Charge	Job		216		216	
2' 4" x 6' 8"						
Demolish	Ea.		40		40	Cost includes material and labor to
Install	Ea.	169	25.50		194.50	install 2' 4" x 6' 8" pre-hung 1-3/8"
Demolish and Install	Ea.	169	65.50		234.50	lauan door with split pine jamb
Reinstall	Ea.		25.41		25.41	including casing, stops, and hinges.
Clean	Ea.	4.03	13.35		17.38	
Paint	Ea.	10.30	53		63.30	
Minimum Charge	Job		216		216	
2' 6" x 6' 8"						
Demolish	Ea.		40		40	Cost includes material and labor to
Install	Ea.	174	25.50		199.50	install 2' 6" x 6' 8" pre-hung 1-3/8"
Demolish and Install	Ea.	174	65.50		239.50	lauan door with split pine jamb
Reinstall	Ea.		25.41		25.41	including casing, stops, and hinges.
Clean	Ea.	4.03	13.35		17.38	
Paint	Ea.	10.30	53		63.30	
Minimum Charge	Job		216		216	
2' 8" x 6' 8"						
Demolish	Ea.		40		40	Cost includes material and labor to
Install	Ea.	169	25.50		194.50	install 2' 8" x 6' 8" pre-hung 1-3/8"
Demolish and Install	Ea.	169	65.50		234.50	lauan door with split pine jamb,
Reinstall	Ea.		25.41		25.41	including casing, stop and hinges.
Clean	Ea.	4.03	13.35		17.38	
Paint	Ea.	10.30	53		63.30	
Minimum Charge	Job		216		216	

Finish Carpentry

Hollow Core Door	Unit	Material	Labor	Equip.	Total	Specification
3′ x 6′ 8″						
Demolish	Ea.		40		40	Cost includes material and labor to
Install	Ea.	175	27		202	install 3′ x 6′ 8″ pre-hung 1-3/8″
Demolish and Install	Ea.	175	67		242	lauan door with split pine jamb
Reinstall	Ea.		27		27	including casing, stops, and hinges.
Clean	Ea.	4.03	13.35		17.38	
Paint	Ea.	10.30	53		63.30	
Minimum Charge	Job		216		216	
Pocket Type						
Demolish	Ea.		60		60	Cost includes material and labor to
Install	Ea.	44	48		92	install 2′ 8″ x 6′ 8″ lauan door.
Demolish and Install	Ea.	44	108		152	
Reinstall	Ea.		48		48	
Clean	Ea.	4.03	13.35		17.38	
Paint	Ea.	10.30	53		63.30	
Minimum Charge	Job		216		216	
Stain						
Install	Ea.	6.80	31		37.80	Includes labor and material to stain
Minimum Charge	Job		185		185	single door and trim on both sides.
Pre-hung Masonite						
1′ 6″ x 6′ 8″						
Demolish	Ea.		40		40	Cost includes material and labor to
Install	Ea.	211	24		235	install 1′ 6″ x 6′ 8″ pre-hung 1-3/8″
Demolish and Install	Ea.	211	64		275	masonite door with split pine jamb
Reinstall	Ea.		24		24	including casing, stops, and hinges.
Clean	Ea.	4.03	13.35		17.38	
Paint	Ea.	10.30	53		63.30	
Minimum Charge	Job		216		216	
2′ x 6′ 8″						
Demolish	Ea.		40		40	Cost includes material and labor to
Install	Ea.	220	25.50		245.50	install 2′ x 6′ 8″ pre-hung 1-3/8″
Demolish and Install	Ea.	220	65.50		285.50	masonite door with split pine jamb
Reinstall	Ea.		25.41		25.41	including casing, stops, and hinges.
Clean	Ea.	4.03	13.35		17.38	
Paint	Ea.	10.30	53		63.30	
Minimum Charge	Job		216		216	
2′ 4″ x 6′ 8″						
Demolish	Ea.		40		40	Cost includes material and labor to
Install	Ea.	222	25.50		247.50	install 2′ 4″ x 6′ 8″ pre-hung 1-3/8″
Demolish and Install	Ea.	222	65.50		287.50	masonite door with split pine jamb
Reinstall	Ea.		25.41		25.41	including casing, stops, and hinges.
Clean	Ea.	4.03	13.35		17.38	
Paint	Ea.	10.30	53		63.30	
Minimum Charge	Job		216		216	
2′ 8″ x 6′ 8″						
Demolish	Ea.		40		40	Cost includes material and labor to
Install	Ea.	226	25.50		251.50	install 2′ 8″ x 6′ 8″ pre-hung 1-3/8″
Demolish and Install	Ea.	226	65.50		291.50	masonite door with split pine jamb
Reinstall	Ea.		25.41		25.41	including casing, stops, and hinges.
Clean	Ea.	4.03	13.35		17.38	
Paint	Ea.	10.30	53		63.30	
Minimum Charge	Job		216		216	
3′ x 6′ 8″						
Demolish	Ea.		40		40	Cost includes material and labor to
Install	Ea.	230	27		257	install 3′ x 6′ 8″ pre-hung 1-3/8″
Demolish and Install	Ea.	230	67		297	masonite door with split pine jamb
Reinstall	Ea.		27		27	including casing, stops, and hinges.
Clean	Ea.	4.03	13.35		17.38	
Paint	Ea.	10.30	53		63.30	
Minimum Charge	Job		216		216	

Finish Carpentry

Hollow Core Door		Unit	Material	Labor	Equip.	Total	Specification
Pocket Type							
	Demolish	Ea.		60		60	Cost includes material and labor to
	Install	Ea.	44	48		92	install 2' 8" x 6' 8" lauan door.
	Demolish and Install	Ea.	44	108		152	
	Reinstall	Ea.		48		48	
	Clean	Ea.	4.03	13.35		17.38	
	Paint	Ea.	10.30	53		63.30	
	Minimum Charge	Job		216		216	
Stain							
	Install	Ea.	6.80	31		37.80	Includes labor and material to stain
	Minimum Charge	Job		185		185	single door and trim on both sides.
Hollow Core Door Only							
1' 6" x 6' 8'							
	Demolish	Ea.		8.55		8.55	Cost includes material and labor to
	Install	Ea.	54	22.50		76.50	install 1' 6" x 6' 8" lauan hollow core
	Demolish and Install	Ea.	54	31.05		85.05	door slab.
	Reinstall	Ea.		22.74		22.74	
	Clean	Ea.	1.68	10		11.68	
	Paint	Ea.	4.86	46		50.86	
	Minimum Charge	Job		216		216	
2' x 6' 8'							
	Demolish	Ea.		8.55		8.55	Cost includes material and labor to
	Install	Ea.	54.50	24		78.50	install 2' x 6' 8" lauan hollow core
	Demolish and Install	Ea.	54.50	32.55		87.05	door slab.
	Reinstall	Ea.		24		24	
	Clean	Ea.	1.68	10		11.68	
	Paint	Ea.	4.86	46		50.86	
	Minimum Charge	Job		216		216	
2' 4" x 6' 8'							
	Demolish	Ea.		8.55		8.55	Cost includes material and labor to
	Install	Ea.	59	24		83	install 2' 4" x 6' 8" lauan hollow core
	Demolish and Install	Ea.	59	32.55		91.55	door slab.
	Reinstall	Ea.		24		24	
	Clean	Ea.	1.68	10		11.68	
	Paint	Ea.	4.86	46		50.86	
	Minimum Charge	Job		216		216	
2' 8" x 6' 8'							
	Demolish	Ea.		8.55		8.55	Cost includes material and labor to
	Install	Ea.	60.50	24		84.50	install 2' 8" x 6' 8" lauan hollow core
	Demolish and Install	Ea.	60.50	32.55		93.05	door slab.
	Reinstall	Ea.		24		24	
	Clean	Ea.	1.68	10		11.68	
	Paint	Ea.	4.86	46		50.86	
	Minimum Charge	Job		216		216	
3' x 6' 8'							
	Demolish	Ea.		8.55		8.55	Cost includes material and labor to
	Install	Ea.	62.50	25.50		88	install 3' x 6' 8" lauan hollow core
	Demolish and Install	Ea.	62.50	34.05		96.55	door slab.
	Reinstall	Ea.		25.41		25.41	
	Clean	Ea.	1.68	10		11.68	
	Paint	Ea.	4.86	46		50.86	
	Minimum Charge	Job		216		216	
Pocket Type							
	Demolish	Ea.		8.55		8.55	Cost includes material and labor to
	Install	Ea.	44	48		92	install 2' 8" x 6' 8" lauan door.
	Demolish and Install	Ea.	44	56.55		100.55	
	Reinstall	Ea.		48		48	
	Clean	Ea.	1.68	10		11.68	
	Paint	Ea.	4.86	46		50.86	
	Minimum Charge	Job		216		216	

Finish Carpentry

Hollow Core Door	Unit	Material	Labor	Equip.	Total	Specification
Stain						
Install	Ea.	3.76	41		44.76	Includes labor and materials to stain a
Minimum Charge	Job		185		185	flush style door on both sides by brush.
Casing Trim						
Single Width						
Demolish	Ea.		7.60		7.60	Cost includes material and labor to
Install	Opng.	28	36		64	install 11/16" x 2-1/2" pine ranch
Demolish and Install	Opng.	28	43.60		71.60	style casing for one side of a standard
Reinstall	Opng.		28.80		28.80	door opening.
Clean	Opng.	.57	3.20		3.77	
Paint	Ea.	5.20	7.40		12.60	
Minimum Charge	Job		216		216	
Double Width						
Demolish	Ea.		9.05		9.05	Cost includes material and labor to
Install	Opng.	33	43		76	install 11/16" x 2-1/2" pine ranch
Demolish and Install	Opng.	33	52.05		85.05	style door casing for one side of a
Reinstall	Opng.		34.56		34.56	double door opening.
Clean	Opng.	.67	6.40		7.07	
Paint	Ea.	5.20	8.40		13.60	
Minimum Charge	Job		216		216	
Hardware						
Doorknob w / Lock						
Demolish	Ea.		17.15		17.15	Includes material and labor to install
Install	Ea.	39	27		66	privacy lockset.
Demolish and Install	Ea.	39	44.15		83.15	
Reinstall	Ea.		21.60		21.60	
Clean	Ea.	.41	10		10.41	
Minimum Charge	Job		216		216	
Doorknob						
Demolish	Ea.		17.15		17.15	Includes material and labor to install
Install	Ea.	38	27		65	residential passage lockset, keyless
Demolish and Install	Ea.	38	44.15		82.15	bored type.
Reinstall	Ea.		21.60		21.60	
Clean	Ea.	.41	10		10.41	
Minimum Charge	Job		216		216	
Deadbolt						
Demolish	Ea.		15		15	Includes material and labor to install a
Install	Ea.	70	31		101	deadbolt.
Demolish and Install	Ea.	70	46		116	
Reinstall	Ea.		24.69		24.69	
Clean	Ea.	.41	10		10.41	
Minimum Charge	Job		216		216	
Lever Handle						
Demolish	Ea.		17.15		17.15	Includes material and labor to install
Install	Ea.	36.50	43		79.50	residential passage lockset, keyless
Demolish and Install	Ea.	36.50	60.15		96.65	bored type with lever handle.
Reinstall	Ea.		34.56		34.56	
Clean	Ea.	.41	10		10.41	
Minimum Charge	Job		216		216	
Closer						
Demolish	Ea.		9		9	Includes material and labor to install
Install	Ea.	138	66.50		204.50	pneumatic light duty closer for interior
Demolish and Install	Ea.	138	75.50		213.50	type doors.
Reinstall	Ea.		53.17		53.17	
Clean	Ea.	.20	13.35		13.55	
Minimum Charge	Job		216		216	

Finish Carpentry

Hollow Core Door

Hollow Core Door		Unit	Material	Labor	Equip.	Total	Specification
Push Plate							
	Demolish	Ea.		13.35		13.35	Includes material and labor to install
	Install	Ea.	27.50	36		63.50	bronze push-pull plate.
	Demolish and Install	Ea.	27.50	49.35		76.85	
	Reinstall	Ea.		28.80		28.80	
	Clean	Ea.	.41	10		10.41	
	Minimum Charge	Job		216		216	
Kickplate							
	Demolish	Ea.		13.35		13.35	Includes material and labor to install
	Install	Ea.	24	29		53	aluminum kickplate, 10" x 28".
	Demolish and Install	Ea.	24	42.35		66.35	
	Reinstall	Ea.		23.04		23.04	
	Clean	Ea.	.41	10		10.41	
	Minimum Charge	Job		216		216	
Exit Sign							
	Demolish	Ea.		23.50		23.50	Includes material and labor to install a
	Install	Ea.	113	58.50		171.50	wall mounted interior electric exit sign.
	Demolish and Install	Ea.	113	82		195	
	Reinstall	Ea.		46.80		46.80	
	Clean	Ea.	.03	7.35		7.38	
	Minimum Charge	Job		216		216	
Jamb							
	Demolish	Ea.		30		30	Includes material and labor to install
	Install	Ea.	146	11.70		157.70	flat pine jamb with square cut heads
	Demolish and Install	Ea.	146	41.70		187.70	and rabbeted sides for 6' 8" high and
	Clean	Ea.	.13	8		8.13	3-9/16" door including trim sets for
	Paint	Ea.	7.55	24.50		32.05	both sides.
	Minimum Charge	Job		216		216	
Shave & Refit							
	Install	Ea.		36		36	Includes labor to shave and rework
	Minimum Charge	Job		216		216	door to fit opening at the job site.

Solid Core Door

Solid Core Door		Unit	Material	Labor	Equip.	Total	Specification
Pre-hung Wood							
2' 4" x 6' 8"							
	Demolish	Ea.		40		40	Cost includes material and labor to
	Install	Ea.	252	25.50		277.50	install 2' 4" x 6' 8" pre-hung 1-3/4"
	Demolish and Install	Ea.	252	65.50		317.50	door, 4-1/2" split jamb, including
	Reinstall	Ea.		25.41		25.41	casing and stop, hinges, aluminum sill,
	Clean	Ea.	4.03	13.35		17.38	weatherstripping.
	Paint	Ea.	11.60	53		64.60	
	Minimum Charge	Job		216		216	
2' 6" x 6' 8"							
	Demolish	Ea.		40		40	Cost includes material and labor to
	Install	Ea.	250	25.50		275.50	install 2' 6" x 6' 8" pre-hung 1-3/4"
	Demolish and Install	Ea.	250	65.50		315.50	door, 4-1/2" split jamb, including
	Reinstall	Ea.		25.41		25.41	casing and stop, hinges, aluminum sill,
	Clean	Ea.	4.03	13.35		17.38	weatherstripping.
	Paint	Ea.	11.60	53		64.60	
	Minimum Charge	Job		216		216	

Finish Carpentry

Solid Core Door

	Unit	Material	Labor	Equip.	Total	Specification
2' 8" x 6' 8"						
Demolish	Ea.		40		40	Cost includes material and labor to
Install	Ea.	243	25.50		268.50	install 2' 8" x 6' 8" pre-hung 1-3/4"
Demolish and Install	Ea.	243	65.50		308.50	door, 4-1/2" split jamb, including
Reinstall	Ea.		25.41		25.41	casing and stop, hinges, aluminum sill,
Clean	Ea.	4.03	13.35		17.38	weatherstripping.
Paint	Ea.	11.60	53		64.60	
Minimum Charge	Job		216		216	
3' x 6' 8"						
Demolish	Ea.		40		40	Cost includes material and labor to
Install	Ea.	252	27		279	install 3' x 6' 8" pre-hung 1-3/4"
Demolish and Install	Ea.	252	67		319	door, including casing and stop,
Reinstall	Ea.		27		27	hinges, jamb, aluminum sill,
Clean	Ea.	4.03	13.35		17.38	weatherstripped.
Paint	Ea.	11.60	53		64.60	
Minimum Charge	Job		216		216	
3' 6" x 6' 8"						
Demolish	Ea.		40		40	Cost includes material and labor to
Install	Ea.	395	29		424	install 3' 6" x 6' 8" pre-hung 1-3/4"
Demolish and Install	Ea.	395	69		464	door, 4-1/2" split jamb, including
Reinstall	Ea.		28.80		28.80	casing and stop, hinges, aluminum sill,
Clean	Ea.	4.03	13.35		17.38	weatherstripping.
Paint	Ea.	11.60	53		64.60	
Minimum Charge	Job		216		216	
Raised Panel						
Demolish	Ea.		40		40	Cost includes material and labor to
Install	Ea.	485	24		509	install 3' x 6' 8" pre-hung 1-3/4"
Demolish and Install	Ea.	485	64		549	door, jamb, including casing and
Reinstall	Ea.		24		24	stop, hinges, aluminum sill,
Clean	Ea.	4.03	13.35		17.38	weatherstripping.
Paint	Ea.	11.60	123		134.60	
Minimum Charge	Job		216		216	
Stain						
Install	Ea.	6.80	31		37.80	Includes labor and material to stain
Minimum Charge	Job		185		185	single door and trim on both sides.

Bifold Door

	Unit	Material	Labor	Equip.	Total	Specification
Wood, Single						
3'						
Demolish	Ea.		30		30	Cost includes material and labor to
Install	Ea.	78.50	66.50		145	install 3' wide solid wood bi-fold door
Demolish and Install	Ea.	78.50	96.50		175	not including jamb, trim, track, and
Reinstall	Ea.		66.46		66.46	hardware.
Clean	Ea.	4.03	13.35		17.38	
Paint	Ea.	10.30	53		63.30	
Minimum Charge	Job		216		216	
5'						
Demolish	Ea.		30		30	Includes material and labor to install
Install	Ea.	116	78.50		194.50	pair of 2' 6" wide solid wood bi-fold
Demolish and Install	Ea.	116	108.50		224.50	doors not including jamb, trim, track,
Reinstall	Ea.		78.55		78.55	and hardware.
Clean	Ea.	1.76	23		24.76	
Paint	Ea.	33.50	92.50		126	
Minimum Charge	Job		216		216	

Finish Carpentry

Bifold Door		Unit	Material	Labor	Equip.	Total	Specification
6'							
	Demolish	Ea.		30		30	Includes material and labor to install
	Install	Ea.	141	86.50		227.50	pair of 3' wide solid wood bi-fold
	Demolish and Install	Ea.	141	116.50		257.50	doors not including jamb, trim, track,
	Reinstall	Ea.		86.40		86.40	and hardware.
	Clean	Ea.	2.01	26.50		28.51	
	Paint	Ea.	33.50	92.50		126	
	Minimum Charge	Job		216		216	
8'							
	Demolish	Ea.		30		30	Includes material and labor to install
	Install	Ea.	215	96		311	pair of 4' wide solid wood bi-fold
	Demolish and Install	Ea.	215	126		341	doors not including jamb, trim, track,
	Reinstall	Ea.		96		96	and hardware.
	Clean	Ea.	2.77	32		34.77	
	Paint	Ea.	17.60	92.50		110.10	
	Minimum Charge	Job		216		216	
Mirrored							
6'							
	Demolish	Ea.		30		30	Includes material and labor to install
	Install	Ea.	450	48		498	pair of 3' wide mirrored bi-fold doors
	Demolish and Install	Ea.	450	78		528	including jamb, trim, track, and
	Reinstall	Ea.		48		48	hardware.
	Clean	Ea.	2.01	13.35		15.36	
	Minimum Charge	Job		216		216	
8'							
	Demolish	Ea.		30		30	Includes material and labor to install
	Install	Ea.	710	72		782	pair of 4' wide mirrored bi-fold doors
	Demolish and Install	Ea.	710	102		812	including jamb, trim, track, and
	Reinstall	Ea.		72		72	hardware.
	Clean	Ea.	2.77	16		18.77	
	Minimum Charge	Job		216		216	
Louvered							
3'							
	Demolish	Ea.		30		30	Cost includes material and labor to
	Install	Ea.	229	66.50		295.50	install 3' wide louvered bi-fold door
	Demolish and Install	Ea.	229	96.50		325.50	not including jamb, trim, track, and
	Reinstall	Ea.		66.46		66.46	hardware.
	Clean	Ea.	4.03	13.35		17.38	
	Paint	Ea.	10.30	53		63.30	
	Minimum Charge	Job		216		216	
5'							
	Demolish	Ea.		30		30	Includes material and labor to install
	Install	Ea.	288	78.50		366.50	pair of 2' 6" wide louvered wood
	Demolish and Install	Ea.	288	108.50		396.50	bi-fold doors not including jamb, trim,
	Reinstall	Ea.		78.55		78.55	track, and hardware.
	Clean	Ea.	1.76	23		24.76	
	Paint	Ea.	33.50	92.50		126	
	Minimum Charge	Job		216		216	
6'							
	Demolish	Ea.		30		30	Includes material and labor to install
	Install	Ea.	320	86.50		406.50	pair of 3' wide louvered wood bi-fold
	Demolish and Install	Ea.	320	116.50		436.50	doors not including jamb, trim, track,
	Reinstall	Ea.		86.40		86.40	and hardware.
	Clean	Ea.	2.01	26.50		28.51	
	Paint	Ea.	33.50	92.50		126	
	Minimum Charge	Job		216		216	

Bifold Door		Unit	Material	Labor	Equip.	Total	Specification
8'							
	Demolish	Ea.		30		30	Includes material and labor to install
	Install	Ea.	490	86.50		576.50	pair of 4' wide solid wood bi-fold
	Demolish and Install	Ea.	490	116.50		606.50	doors not including jamb, trim, track,
	Reinstall	Ea.		86.40		86.40	and hardware.
	Clean	Ea.	9.55	23		32.55	
	Paint	Ea.	17.60	92.50		110.10	
	Minimum Charge	Job		216		216	
Accordion Type							
	Demolish	S.F.		1.05		1.05	Includes material and labor to install
	Install	Ea.	45	86.50		131.50	vinyl folding accordion closet doors,
	Demolish and Install	Ea.	45	87.55		132.55	including track and frame.
	Reinstall	Ea.		86.40		86.40	
	Clean	S.F.		.39		.39	
	Minimum Charge	Job		216		216	
Casing Trim							
Single Width							
	Demolish	Ea.		7.60		7.60	Cost includes material and labor to
	Install	Opng.	28	36		64	install 11/16" x 2-1/2" pine ranch
	Demolish and Install	Opng.	28	43.60		71.60	style casing for one side of a standard
	Reinstall	Opng.		28.80		28.80	door opening.
	Clean	Opng.	.57	3.20		3.77	
	Paint	Ea.	5.20	7.40		12.60	
	Minimum Charge	Job		216		216	
Double Width							
	Demolish	Ea.		9.05		9.05	Cost includes material and labor to
	Install	Opng.	33	43		76	install 11/16" x 2-1/2" pine ranch
	Demolish and Install	Opng.	33	52.05		85.05	style door casing for one side of a
	Reinstall	Opng.		34.56		34.56	double door opening.
	Clean	Opng.	.67	6.40		7.07	
	Paint	Ea.	5.20	8.40		13.60	
	Minimum Charge	Job		216		216	
Jamb							
	Demolish	Ea.		30		30	Includes material and labor to install
	Install	Ea.	146	11.70		157.70	flat pine jamb with square cut heads
	Demolish and Install	Ea.	146	41.70		187.70	and rabbeted sides for 6' 8" high and
	Clean	Ea.	.13	8		8.13	3-9/16" door including trim sets for
	Paint	Ea.	7.55	24.50		32.05	both sides.
	Minimum Charge	Job		108		108	
Stain							
	Install	Ea.	6.80	31		37.80	Includes labor and material to stain
	Minimum Charge	Job		185		185	single door and trim on both sides.
Shave & Refit							
	Install	Ea.		36		36	Includes labor to shave and rework
	Minimum Charge	Job		108		108	door to fit opening at the job site.

Finish Carpentry

Louver Door		Unit	Material	Labor	Equip.	Total	Specification
Full							
2' x 6' 8"							
	Demolish	Ea.		8.55		8.55	Cost includes material and labor to
	Install	Ea.	266	43		309	install 2' x 6' 8" pine full louver door,
	Demolish and Install	Ea.	266	51.55		317.55	jamb, hinges.
	Reinstall	Ea.		43.20		43.20	
	Clean	Ea.	7.50	40		47.50	
	Paint	Ea.	10.30	53		63.30	
	Minimum Charge	Job		216		216	
2' 8" x 6' 8"							
	Demolish	Ea.		8.55		8.55	Cost includes material and labor to
	Install	Ea.	299	43		342	install 2' 8" x 6' 8" pine full louver
	Demolish and Install	Ea.	299	51.55		350.55	door, jamb, hinges.
	Reinstall	Ea.		43.20		43.20	
	Clean	Ea.	7.50	40		47.50	
	Paint	Ea.	10.30	53		63.30	
	Minimum Charge	Job		216		216	
3' x 6' 8"							
	Demolish	Ea.		8.55		8.55	Cost includes material and labor to
	Install	Ea.	315	45.50		360.50	install 3' x 6' 8" pine full louver door,
	Demolish and Install	Ea.	315	54.05		369.05	jamb, hinges.
	Reinstall	Ea.		45.47		45.47	
	Clean	Ea.	7.50	40		47.50	
	Paint	Ea.	10.30	53		63.30	
	Minimum Charge	Job		216		216	
Half							
2' x 6' 8"							
	Demolish	Ea.		8.55		8.55	Cost includes material and labor to
	Install	Ea.	390	43		433	install 2' x 6' 8" pine half louver door,
	Demolish and Install	Ea.	390	51.55		441.55	jamb, hinges.
	Reinstall	Ea.		43.20		43.20	
	Clean	Ea.	7.50	40		47.50	
	Paint	Ea.	10.30	53		63.30	
	Minimum Charge	Job		216		216	
2' 8" x 6' 8"							
	Demolish	Ea.		8.55		8.55	Cost includes material and labor to
	Install	Ea.	415	43		458	install 2' 8" x 6' 8" pine half louver
	Demolish and Install	Ea.	415	51.55		466.55	door, jamb, hinges.
	Reinstall	Ea.		43.20		43.20	
	Clean	Ea.	7.50	40		47.50	
	Paint	Ea.	10.30	53		63.30	
	Minimum Charge	Job		216		216	
3' x 6' 8"							
	Demolish	Ea.		8.55		8.55	Cost includes material and labor to
	Install	Ea.	425	45.50		470.50	install 3' x 6' 8" pine half louver door,
	Demolish and Install	Ea.	425	54.05		479.05	jamb, hinges.
	Reinstall	Ea.		45.47		45.47	
	Clean	Ea.	7.50	40		47.50	
	Paint	Ea.	10.30	53		63.30	
	Minimum Charge	Job		216		216	
Jamb							
	Demolish	Ea.		30		30	Includes material and labor to install
	Install	Ea.	146	11.70		157.70	flat pine jamb with square cut heads
	Demolish and Install	Ea.	146	41.70		187.70	and rabbeted sides for 6' 8" high and
	Clean	Ea.	.13	8		8.13	3-9/16" door including trim sets for
	Paint	Ea.	7.55	24.50		32.05	both sides.
	Minimum Charge	Job		108		108	

Finish Carpentry

Louver Door

Louver Door		Unit	Material	Labor	Equip.	Total	Specification
Stain							
	Install	Ea.	6.80	31		37.80	Includes labor and material to stain
	Minimum Charge	Job		185		185	single door and trim on both sides.
Shave & Refit							
	Install	Ea.		36		36	Includes labor to shave and rework
	Minimum Charge	Job		185		185	door to fit opening at the job site.

Bypass Sliding Door

Bypass Sliding Door		Unit	Material	Labor	Equip.	Total	Specification
Wood							
5'							
	Demolish	Ea.		40		40	Includes material and labor to install
	Install	Opng.	206	78.50		284.50	pair of 2' 6" wide lauan hollow core
	Demolish and Install	Opng.	206	118.50		324.50	wood bi-pass doors with jamb, track
	Reinstall	Opng.		78.55		78.55	hardware.
	Clean	Ea.	1.76	23		24.76	
	Paint	Ea.	33.50	92.50		126	
	Minimum Charge	Job		216		216	
6'							
	Demolish	Ea.		40		40	Includes material and labor to install
	Install	Opng.	230	86.50		316.50	pair of 3' wide lauan hollow core
	Demolish and Install	Opng.	230	126.50		356.50	wood bi-pass doors with jamb, track
	Reinstall	Opng.		86.40		86.40	and hardware.
	Clean	Ea.	2.01	26.50		28.51	
	Paint	Ea.	33.50	92.50		126	
	Minimum Charge	Job		216		216	
8'							
	Demolish	Ea.		40		40	Includes material and labor to install
	Install	Opng.	345	108		453	pair of 4' wide lauan hollow core
	Demolish and Install	Opng.	345	148		493	wood bi-pass doors with jamb, track
	Reinstall	Opng.		108		108	and hardware.
	Clean	Ea.	2.77	32		34.77	
	Paint	Ea.	17.60	92.50		110.10	
	Minimum Charge	Job		216		216	
Mirrored							
6'							
	Demolish	Ea.		40		40	Includes material and labor to install
	Install	Opng.	299	86.50		385.50	pair of 3' wide mirrored bi-pass doors
	Demolish and Install	Opng.	299	126.50		425.50	with jamb, trim, track hardware.
	Reinstall	Opng.		86.40		86.40	
	Clean	Ea.	2.01	13.35		15.36	
	Minimum Charge	Job		216		216	
8'							
	Demolish	Ea.		40		40	Includes material and labor to install
	Install	Opng.	485	96		581	pair of 4' wide mirrored bi-pass doors
	Demolish and Install	Opng.	485	136		621	with jamb, trim, track hardware.
	Reinstall	Opng.		96		96	
	Clean	Ea.	2.77	16		18.77	
	Minimum Charge	Job		216		216	

Finish Carpentry

Bypass Sliding Door

Bypass Sliding Door	Unit	Material	Labor	Equip.	Total	Specification
Casing Trim						
Single Width						
Demolish	Ea.		7.60		7.60	Cost includes material and labor to
Install	Opng.	28	36		64	install 11/16" x 2-1/2" pine ranch
Demolish and Install	Opng.	28	43.60		71.60	style casing for one side of a standard
Reinstall	Opng.		28.80		28.80	door opening.
Clean	Opng.	.57	3.20		3.77	
Paint	Ea.	5.20	7.40		12.60	
Minimum Charge	Job		216		216	
Double Width						
Demolish	Ea.		9.05		9.05	Cost includes material and labor to
Install	Opng.	33	43		76	install 11/16" x 2-1/2" pine ranch
Demolish and Install	Opng.	33	52.05		85.05	style door casing for one side of a
Reinstall	Opng.		34.56		34.56	double door opening.
Clean	Opng.	.67	6.40		7.07	
Paint	Ea.	5.20	8.40		13.60	
Minimum Charge	Job		216		216	
Jamb						
Demolish	Ea.		30		30	Includes material and labor to install
Install	Ea.	146	11.70		157.70	flat pine jamb with square cut heads
Demolish and Install	Ea.	146	41.70		187.70	and rabbeted sides for 6' 8" high and
Clean	Ea.	.13	8		8.13	3-9/16" door including trim sets for
Paint	Ea.	7.55	24.50		32.05	both sides.
Minimum Charge	Job		108		108	
Stain						
Install	Ea.	6.80	31		37.80	Includes labor and material to stain
Minimum Charge	Job		185		185	single door and trim on both sides.
Shave & Refit						
Install	Ea.		36		36	Includes labor to shave and rework
Minimum Charge	Job		108		108	door to fit opening at the job site.

Base Molding

Base Molding	Unit	Material	Labor	Equip.	Total	Specification
One Piece						
1-5/8"						
Demolish	L.F.		.59		.59	Includes material and labor to install
Install	L.F.	.48	1.28		1.76	pine or birch base molding.
Demolish and Install	L.F.	.48	1.87		2.35	
Reinstall	L.F.		1.02		1.02	
Clean	L.F.	.03	.19		.22	
Paint	L.F.	.06	.40		.46	
Minimum Charge	Job		216		216	
2-1/2"						
Demolish	L.F.		.59		.59	Cost includes material and labor to
Install	L.F.	.69	1.30		1.99	install 1/2" x 2-1/2" pine or birch
Demolish and Install	L.F.	.69	1.89		2.58	base molding.
Reinstall	L.F.		1.04		1.04	
Clean	L.F.	.03	.19		.22	
Paint	L.F.	.06	.40		.46	
Minimum Charge	Job		216		216	

Finish Carpentry

Base Molding		Unit	Material	Labor	Equip.	Total	Specification
3-1/2″							
	Demolish	L.F.		.59		.59	Cost includes material and labor to
	Install	L.F.	1.11	1.38		2.49	install 9/16″ x 3-1/2″ pine or birch
	Demolish and Install	L.F.	1.11	1.97		3.08	base molding.
	Reinstall	L.F.		1.11		1.11	
	Clean	L.F.	.03	.19		.22	
	Paint	L.F.	.09	.44		.53	
	Minimum Charge	Job		216		216	
6″							
	Demolish	L.F.		.59		.59	Cost includes material and labor to
	Install	L.F.	.68	1.38		2.06	install 1″ x 6″ pine or birch base
	Demolish and Install	L.F.	.68	1.97		2.65	molding.
	Reinstall	L.F.		1.11		1.11	
	Clean	L.F.	.03	.27		.30	
	Paint	L.F.	.10	.56		.66	
	Minimum Charge	Job		216		216	
8″							
	Demolish	L.F.		.71		.71	Cost includes material and labor to
	Install	L.F.	.91	1.38		2.29	install 1″ x 8″ pine or birch base
	Demolish and Install	L.F.	.91	2.09		3	molding.
	Reinstall	L.F.		1.11		1.11	
	Clean	L.F.	.04	.32		.36	
	Paint	L.F.	.11	.62		.73	
	Minimum Charge	Job		216		216	
Premium / Custom Grade							
	Demolish	L.F.		.71		.71	Includes material and labor to install
	Install	L.F.	4	4.15		8.15	custom 2 or 3 piece oak or other
	Demolish and Install	L.F.	4	4.86		8.86	hardwood, stain grade trim.
	Reinstall	L.F.		3.32		3.32	
	Clean	L.F.	.04	.32		.36	
	Paint	L.F.	.12	.62		.74	
	Minimum Charge	Job		216		216	
One Piece Oak							
1-5/8″							
	Demolish	L.F.		.59		.59	Cost includes material and labor to
	Install	L.F.	.96	1.28		2.24	install 1/2″ x 1-5/8″ oak base
	Demolish and Install	L.F.	.96	1.87		2.83	molding.
	Reinstall	L.F.		1.02		1.02	
	Clean	L.F.	.03	.19		.22	
	Paint	L.F.	.12	.55		.67	
	Minimum Charge	Job		216		216	
2-1/2″							
	Demolish	L.F.		.59		.59	Cost includes material and labor to
	Install	L.F.	1.47	1.30		2.77	install 1/2″ x 2-1/2″ oak base
	Demolish and Install	L.F.	1.47	1.89		3.36	molding.
	Reinstall	L.F.		1.04		1.04	
	Clean	L.F.	.03	.19		.22	
	Paint	L.F.	.12	.56		.68	
	Minimum Charge	Job		216		216	
3-1/2″							
	Demolish	L.F.		.59		.59	Cost includes material and labor to
	Install	L.F.	1.78	1.33		3.11	install 1/2″ x 3-1/2″ oak base
	Demolish and Install	L.F.	1.78	1.92		3.70	molding.
	Reinstall	L.F.		1.06		1.06	
	Clean	L.F.	.03	.19		.22	
	Paint	L.F.	.12	.57		.69	
	Minimum Charge	Job		216		216	

Finish Carpentry

Base Molding

	Unit	Material	Labor	Equip.	Total	Specification
6"						
Demolish	L.F.		.59		.59	Cost includes material and labor to
Install	L.F.	2.80	1.38		4.18	install 1" x 6" oak base molding.
Demolish and Install	L.F.	2.80	1.97		4.77	
Reinstall	L.F.		1.11		1.11	
Clean	L.F.	.04	.32		.36	
Paint	L.F.	.13	.59		.72	
Minimum Charge	Job		216		216	
8"						
Demolish	L.F.		.71		.71	Cost includes material and labor to
Install	L.F.	3.93	1.38		5.31	install 1" x 8" oak base molding.
Demolish and Install	L.F.	3.93	2.09		6.02	
Reinstall	L.F.		1.11		1.11	
Clean	L.F.	.04	.32		.36	
Paint	L.F.	.13	.62		.75	
Minimum Charge	Job		216		216	

Vinyl Base Molding
2-1/2"

	Unit	Material	Labor	Equip.	Total	Specification
Demolish	L.F.		.59		.59	Cost includes material and labor to
Install	L.F.	1.39	1.20		2.59	install 2-1/2" vinyl or rubber cove
Demolish and Install	L.F.	1.39	1.79		3.18	base including adhesive.
Reinstall	L.F.		1.20		1.20	
Clean	L.F.		.29		.29	
Minimum Charge	Job		195		195	

4"

	Unit	Material	Labor	Equip.	Total	Specification
Demolish	L.F.		.59		.59	Cost includes material and labor to
Install	Ea.	1.87	1.20		3.07	install 4" vinyl or rubber cove base
Demolish and Install	Ea.	1.87	1.79		3.66	including adhesive.
Reinstall	Ea.		1.20		1.20	
Clean	L.F.		.29		.29	
Minimum Charge	Job		195		195	

6"

	Unit	Material	Labor	Equip.	Total	Specification
Demolish	L.F.		.59		.59	Cost includes material and labor to
Install	L.F.	1.39	1.20		2.59	install 6" vinyl or rubber cove base
Demolish and Install	L.F.	1.39	1.79		3.18	including adhesive.
Reinstall	L.F.		1.20		1.20	
Clean	L.F.		.29		.29	
Minimum Charge	Job		195		195	

Prefinished

	Unit	Material	Labor	Equip.	Total	Specification
Demolish	L.F.		.59		.59	Cost includes material and labor to
Install	L.F.	1.49	1.38		2.87	install 9/16" x 3-5/16" prefinished
Demolish and Install	L.F.	1.49	1.97		3.46	base molding.
Reinstall	L.F.		1.11		1.11	
Clean	L.F.	.03	.19		.22	
Paint	L.F.	.09	.44		.53	
Minimum Charge	Job		216		216	

Shoe

	Unit	Material	Labor	Equip.	Total	Specification
Demolish	L.F.		.59		.59	Includes material and labor to install
Install	L.F.	.48	1.28		1.76	pine or birch base molding.
Demolish and Install	L.F.	.48	1.87		2.35	
Reinstall	L.F.		1.02		1.02	
Clean	L.F.	.03	.19		.22	
Paint	L.F.	.14	.59		.73	
Minimum Charge	Job		216		216	

Base Molding

Base Molding	Unit	Material	Labor	Equip.	Total	Specification
Carpeted						
Demolish	L.F.		.24		.24	Includes material and labor to install
Install	L.F.	1.52	2.30		3.82	carpet baseboard with adhesive.
Demolish and Install	L.F.	1.52	2.54		4.06	
Reinstall	L.F.		1.84		1.84	
Clean	L.F.		.12		.12	
Minimum Charge	Job		189		189	
Ceramic Tile						
Demolish	L.F.		1.29		1.29	Includes material and labor to install
Install	L.F.	4.35	5.30		9.65	thin set ceramic tile cove base
Demolish and Install	L.F.	4.35	6.59		10.94	including grout.
Clean	L.F.		.61		.61	
Minimum Charge	Job		189		189	
Quarry Tile						
Demolish	L.F.		1.29		1.29	Includes material and labor to install
Install	L.F.	5.90	6.20		12.10	quarry tile base including grout.
Demolish and Install	L.F.	5.90	7.49		13.39	
Clean	L.F.		.61		.61	
Minimum Charge	Job		189		189	
Caulk and Renail						
Install	L.F.	.01	.68		.69	Includes labor and material to renail
Minimum Charge	Job		216		216	base and caulk where necessary.

Molding

Molding	Unit	Material	Labor	Equip.	Total	Specification
Oak Base						
Demolish	L.F.		.59		.59	Cost includes material and labor to
Install	L.F.	1.47	1.30		2.77	install 1/2" x 2-1/2" oak base
Demolish and Install	L.F.	1.47	1.89		3.36	molding.
Reinstall	L.F.		1.04		1.04	
Clean	L.F.	.03	.19		.22	
Paint	L.F.	.12	.56		.68	
Minimum Charge	Job		216		216	
Shoe						
Demolish	L.F.		.59		.59	Includes material and labor to install
Install	L.F.	.48	1.28		1.76	pine or birch base molding.
Demolish and Install	L.F.	.48	1.87		2.35	
Reinstall	L.F.		1.02		1.02	
Clean	L.F.	.03	.19		.22	
Paint	L.F.	.14	.59		.73	
Minimum Charge	Job		216		216	
Quarter Round						
Demolish	L.F.		.59		.59	Includes material and labor to install
Install	L.F.	.78	1.69		2.47	pine base quarter round molding.
Demolish and Install	L.F.	.78	2.28		3.06	
Reinstall	L.F.		1.36		1.36	
Clean	L.F.	.03	.19		.22	
Paint	L.F.	.12	.92		1.04	
Minimum Charge	Job		216		216	
Chair Rail						
Demolish	L.F.		.59		.59	Cost includes material and labor to
Install	L.F.	1.85	1.60		3.45	install 5/8" x 2-1/2" oak chair rail
Demolish and Install	L.F.	1.85	2.19		4.04	molding.
Reinstall	L.F.		1.28		1.28	
Clean	L.F.	.03	.19		.22	
Paint	L.F.	.12	.92		1.04	
Minimum Charge	Job		216		216	

Finish Carpentry

Molding

Molding	Unit	Material	Labor	Equip.	Total	Specification
Crown						
Demolish	L.F.		.59		.59	Includes material and labor to install
Install	L.F.	2.97	1.73		4.70	unfinished pine crown molding.
Demolish and Install	L.F.	2.97	2.32		5.29	
Reinstall	L.F.		1.38		1.38	
Clean	L.F.	.04	.25		.29	
Paint	L.F.	.12	.92		1.04	
Minimum Charge	Job		216		216	
Cove						
Demolish	L.F.		.59		.59	Cost includes material and labor to
Install	L.F.	2.43	1.63		4.06	install 11/16" x 2-3/4" pine cove
Demolish and Install	L.F.	2.43	2.22		4.65	molding.
Reinstall	L.F.		1.30		1.30	
Clean	L.F.	.03	.19		.22	
Paint	L.F.	.12	.92		1.04	
Minimum Charge	Job		216		216	
Corner						
Demolish	L.F.		.59		.59	Includes material and labor to install
Install	L.F.	1.89	.68		2.57	inside or outside pine corner molding.
Demolish and Install	L.F.	1.89	1.27		3.16	
Reinstall	L.F.		.54		.54	
Clean	L.F.	.03	.19		.22	
Paint	L.F.	.12	.92		1.04	
Minimum Charge	Job		216		216	
Picture						
Demolish	L.F.		.59		.59	Cost includes material and labor to
Install	L.F.	1.66	1.80		3.46	install 9/16" x 2-1/2" pine casing.
Demolish and Install	L.F.	1.66	2.39		4.05	
Reinstall	L.F.		1.44		1.44	
Clean	L.F.	.03	.19		.22	
Paint	L.F.	.12	.92		1.04	
Minimum Charge	Job		216		216	
Single Cased Opening						
Demolish	Ea.		30		30	Includes material and labor to install
Install	Ea.	27	27		54	flat pine jamb with square cut heads
Demolish and Install	Ea.	27	57		84	and rabbeted sides for 6' 8" high
Clean	Ea.	.28	6.70		6.98	opening including trim sets for both
Paint	Ea.	1.50	9.25		10.75	sides.
Minimum Charge	Job		216		216	
Double Cased Opening						
Demolish	Ea.		30		30	Includes material and labor to install
Install	Ea.	54	31		85	flat pine jamb with square cut heads
Demolish and Install	Ea.	54	61		115	and rabbeted sides for 6' 8" high
Clean	Ea.	.33	7.80		8.13	opening including trim sets for both
Paint	Ea.	1.74	10.85		12.59	sides.
Minimum Charge	Job		216		216	

Window Trim Set

Window Trim Set	Unit	Material	Labor	Equip.	Total	Specification
Single						
Demolish	Ea.		7.90		7.90	Cost includes material and labor to
Install	Opng.	48	43		91	install 11/16" x 2-1/2" pine ranch
Demolish and Install	Opng.	48	50.90		98.90	style window casing.
Reinstall	Opng.		34.56		34.56	
Clean	Ea.	.41	4.58		4.99	
Paint	Ea.	1.41	8.80		10.21	
Minimum Charge	Job		216		216	

Finish Carpentry

Window Trim Set

Window Trim Set	Unit	Material	Labor	Equip.	Total	Specification
Double						
Demolish	Ea.		8.90		8.90	Cost includes material and labor to
Install	Ea.	62	54		116	install 11/16" x 2-1/2" pine ranch
Demolish and Install	Ea.	62	62.90		124.90	style trim for casing one side of a
Reinstall	Ea.		43.20		43.20	double window opening.
Clean	Ea.	.72	5.35		6.07	
Paint	Ea.	2.35	14.80		17.15	
Minimum Charge	Job		216		216	
Triple						
Demolish	Ea.		10.15		10.15	Cost includes material and labor to
Install	Opng.	69	72		141	install 11/16" x 2-1/2" pine ranch
Demolish and Install	Opng.	69	82.15		151.15	style trim for casing one side of a
Reinstall	Opng.		57.60		57.60	triple window opening.
Clean	Ea.	1.01	6.40		7.41	
Paint	Ea.	3.30	20.50		23.80	
Minimum Charge	Job		216		216	
Window Casing Per L.F.						
Demolish	L.F.		.59		.59	Cost includes material and labor to
Install	L.F.	1.67	1.73		3.40	install 11/16" x 2-1/2" pine ranch
Demolish and Install	L.F.	1.67	2.32		3.99	style trim for casing.
Reinstall	L.F.		1.38		1.38	
Clean	L.F.	.03	.19		.22	
Paint	L.F.	.12	.92		1.04	
Minimum Charge	Job		216		216	

Window Sill

Window Sill	Unit	Material	Labor	Equip.	Total	Specification
Wood						
Demolish	L.F.		.59		.59	Includes material and labor to install
Install	L.F.	2.92	2.16		5.08	flat, wood window stool.
Demolish and Install	L.F.	2.92	2.75		5.67	
Reinstall	L.F.		1.73		1.73	
Clean	L.F.	.03	.19		.22	
Paint	L.F.	.12	.92		1.04	
Minimum Charge	Job		216		216	
Marble						
Demolish	L.F.		.89		.89	Includes material and labor to install
Install	L.F.	11.50	9.05		20.55	marble window sills, 6" x 3/4" thick.
Demolish and Install	L.F.	11.50	9.94		21.44	
Reinstall	L.F.		7.24		7.24	
Clean	L.F.	.03	.19		.22	
Minimum Charge	Job		189		189	

Shelving

Shelving	Unit	Material	Labor	Equip.	Total	Specification
Pine						
18"						
Demolish	L.F.		1.02		1.02	Cost includes material and labor to
Install	L.F.	7.55	4.55		12.10	install 1" thick custom shelving board
Demolish and Install	L.F.	7.55	5.57		13.12	18" wide.
Reinstall	L.F.		3.64		3.64	
Clean	L.F.	.07	.53		.60	
Paint	L.F.	1.49	.58		2.07	
Minimum Charge	Job		216		216	

Finish Carpentry

Shelving

Shelving	Unit	Material	Labor	Equip.	Total	Specification
24"						
Demolish	L.F.		1.02		1.02	Cost includes material and labor to
Install	L.F.	10	5.10		15.10	install 1" thick custom shelving board.
Demolish and Install	L.F.	10	6.12		16.12	
Reinstall	L.F.		4.07		4.07	
Clean	L.F.	.08	.80		.88	
Paint	L.F.	2.02	.78		2.80	
Minimum Charge	Job		216		216	
Particle Board						
Demolish	L.F.		.94		.94	Cost includes material and labor to
Install	L.F.	1.30	2.27		3.57	install 3/4" thick particle shelving
Demolish and Install	L.F.	1.30	3.21		4.51	board 18" wide.
Reinstall	L.F.		1.82		1.82	
Clean	L.F.	.07	.53		.60	
Paint	S.F.	.14	.86		1	
Minimum Charge	Job		216		216	
Plywood						
Demolish	L.F.		.94		.94	Cost includes material and labor to
Install	L.F.	.95	6.65		7.60	install 3/4" thick plywood shelving
Demolish and Install	L.F.	.95	7.59		8.54	board.
Reinstall	L.F.		5.32		5.32	
Clean	L.F.	.07	.53		.60	
Paint	S.F.	.14	.86		1	
Minimum Charge	Job		216		216	
Hardwood (oak)						
Demolish	L.F.		.94		.94	Includes material and labor to install
Install	L.F.	5.15	2.98		8.13	oak shelving, 1" x 12", incl. cleats and
Demolish and Install	L.F.	5.15	3.92		9.07	bracing.
Reinstall	L.F.		2.38		2.38	
Clean	L.F.	.07	.53		.60	
Paint	S.F.	.14	.86		1	
Minimum Charge	Job		216		216	
Custom Bookcase						
Demolish	L.F.		11.85		11.85	Includes material and labor to install
Install	L.F.	38.50	43		81.50	custom modular bookcase unit with
Demolish and Install	L.F.	38.50	54.85		93.35	clear pine faced frames, shelves 12"
Reinstall	L.F.		34.56		34.56	O.C., 7' high, 8" deep.
Clean	L.F.	1.62	11.45		13.07	
Paint	L.F.	1.60	28.50		30.10	
Minimum Charge	Job		216		216	
Glass						
Demolish	L.F.		.94		.94	Includes material and labor to install
Install	L.F.	34.50	2.98		37.48	glass shelving, 1" x 12", incl. cleats
Demolish and Install	L.F.	34.50	3.92		38.42	and bracing.
Reinstall	L.F.		2.38		2.38	
Clean	L.F.	.08	.49		.57	
Minimum Charge	Job		208		208	

Closet Shelving

Closet Shelving	Unit	Material	Labor	Equip.	Total	Specification
Closet Shelf and Rod						
Demolish	L.F.		.94		.94	Cost includes material and labor to
Install	L.F.	3.04	7.20		10.24	install 1" thick custom shelving board
Demolish and Install	L.F.	3.04	8.14		11.18	18" wide and 1" diameter clothes pole
Reinstall	L.F.		5.76		5.76	with brackets 3' O.C.
Clean	L.F.	.04	.40		.44	
Paint	L.F.	.23	.92		1.15	
Minimum Charge	Job		216		216	

Finish Carpentry

Closet Shelving

Closet Shelving		Unit	Material	Labor	Equip.	Total	Specification
Clothing Rod							Includes material and labor to install
	Demolish	L.F.		.62		.62	fir closet pole, 1-5/8" diameter.
	Install	L.F.	2.60	2.16		4.76	
	Demolish and Install	L.F.	2.60	2.78		5.38	
	Reinstall	L.F.		1.73		1.73	
	Clean	L.F.	.04	.55		.59	
	Paint	L.F.	.21	1.01		1.22	
	Minimum Charge	Job		216		216	

Stair Assemblies

Stair Assemblies		Unit	Material	Labor	Equip.	Total	Specification
Straight Hardwood							Includes material and labor to install
	Demolish	Ea.		420		420	factory cut and assembled straight
	Install	Flight	1250	288		1538	closed box stairs with oak treads and
	Demolish and Install	Flight	1250	708		1958	prefinished stair rail with balusters.
	Clean	Flight	4.03	27.50		31.53	
	Paint	Flight	21	49.50		70.50	
	Minimum Charge	Job		216		216	
Clear Oak Tread							Includes material and labor to install
	Demolish	Ea.		10.90		10.90	1-1/4" thick clear oak treads per riser.
	Install	Ea.	89	24		113	
	Demolish and Install	Ea.	89	34.90		123.90	
	Clean	Ea.	.12	2.74		2.86	
	Paint	Ea.	.69	2.74		3.43	
	Minimum Charge	Job		216		216	
Landing							Includes material and labor to install
	Demolish	S.F.		3.71		3.71	clear oak landing.
	Install	S.F.	11	24		35	
	Demolish and Install	S.F.	11	27.71		38.71	
	Clean	S.F.		.40		.40	
	Paint	S.F.	.44	.91		1.35	
	Minimum Charge	Job		216		216	
Refinish / Stain							Includes labor and material to sand
	Install	S.F.	1.44	2.46		3.90	and finish (3 passes) with two coats of
	Minimum Charge	Job		185		185	urethane on a new floor.
Spiral Hardwood							Cost includes material and labor to
	Demolish	Ea.		420		420	install 4' - 6' diameter spiral stairs with
	Install	Flight	4000	575		4575	oak treads, factory cut and assembled
	Demolish and Install	Flight	4000	995		4995	with double handrails.
	Clean	Flight	4.03	27.50		31.53	
	Paint	Flight	21	49.50		70.50	
	Minimum Charge	Job		216		216	

Stairs

Stairs		Unit	Material	Labor	Equip.	Total	Specification
Disappearing							Includes material and labor to install a
	Demolish	Ea.		22.50		22.50	folding staircase.
	Install	Ea.	275	123		398	
	Demolish and Install	Ea.	275	145.50		420.50	
	Reinstall	Ea.		98.74		98.74	
	Clean	Ea.	.61	20		20.61	
	Minimum Charge	Job		216		216	

Finish Carpentry

Stair Components	Unit	Material	Labor	Equip.	Total	Specification
Handrail w / Balusters						
Demolish	L.F.		2.97		2.97	Includes material and labor to install
Install	L.F.	45	9		54	prefinished assembled stair rail with
Demolish and Install	L.F.	45	11.97		56.97	brackets, turned balusters and newel.
Clean	L.F.	.80	2.21		3.01	
Paint	L.F.	2.29	4.35		6.64	
Minimum Charge	Job		216		216	
Bannister						
Demolish	L.F.		2.97		2.97	Includes material and labor to install
Install	L.F.	38	7.20		45.20	built-up oak railings.
Demolish and Install	L.F.	38	10.17		48.17	
Clean	L.F.	.80	2		2.80	
Paint	L.F.	2.29	3.36		5.65	
Minimum Charge	Job		216		216	

Cabinets and Countertops

Wall and Base Cabinets

Countertop

Wall Cabinets	Unit	Material	Labor	Equip.	Total	Specification
Good Grade Laminated						
12″ Wide, 1 Door						
Demolish	Ea.		8.90		8.90	Includes material and labor to install
Install	Ea.	171	39.50		210.50	good modular unit with melamine
Demolish and Install	Ea.	171	48.40		219.40	laminated to particle board, in
Reinstall	Ea.		31.42		31.42	textured colors or wood grain print
Clean	Ea.	.61	6.15		6.76	finish, hinges and pulls.
Paint	Ea.	.68	13.20		13.88	
Minimum Charge	Job		216		216	
15″ Wide, 1 Door						
Demolish	Ea.		11.15		11.15	Includes material and labor to install
Install	Ea.	190	40.50		230.50	good modular unit with melamine
Demolish and Install	Ea.	190	51.65		241.65	laminated to particle board, in
Reinstall	Ea.		32.30		32.30	textured colors or wood grain print
Clean	Ea.	.76	7.65		8.41	finish, hinges and pulls.
Paint	Ea.	.86	16.80		17.66	
Minimum Charge	Job		216		216	
18″ Wide, 1 Door						
Demolish	Ea.		13.45		13.45	Includes material and labor to install
Install	Ea.	210	41.50		251.50	good modular unit with melamine
Demolish and Install	Ea.	210	54.95		264.95	laminated to particle board, in
Reinstall	Ea.		33.07		33.07	textured colors or wood grain print
Clean	Ea.	.90	9.15		10.05	finish, hinges and pulls.
Paint	Ea.	1.02	19.45		20.47	
Minimum Charge	Job		216		216	
21″ Wide, 1 Door						
Demolish	Ea.		15.50		15.50	Includes material and labor to install
Install	Ea.	220	42		262	good modular unit with melamine
Demolish and Install	Ea.	220	57.50		277.50	laminated to particle board, in
Reinstall	Ea.		33.55		33.55	textured colors or wood grain print
Clean	Ea.	1.06	10.70		11.76	finish, hinges and pulls.
Paint	Ea.	1.20	23		24.20	
Minimum Charge	Job		216		216	
24″ w / Blind Corner						
Demolish	Ea.		17.80		17.80	Includes material and labor to install
Install	Ea.	244	42.50		286.50	good modular unit with melamine
Demolish and Install	Ea.	244	60.30		304.30	laminated to particle board, in
Reinstall	Ea.		34.05		34.05	textured colors or wood grain print
Clean	Ea.	1.21	12.30		13.51	finish, hinges and pulls.
Paint	Ea.	1.36	26.50		27.86	
Minimum Charge	Job		216		216	

Cabinets and Countertops

Wall Cabinets	Unit	Material	Labor	Equip.	Total	Specification
27″ Wide, 2 Door						
Demolish	Ea.		19.80		19.80	Includes material and labor to install
Install	Ea.	272	43.50		315.50	good modular unit with melamine
Demolish and Install	Ea.	272	63.30		335.30	laminated to particle board, in
Reinstall	Ea.		34.91		34.91	textured colors or wood grain print
Clean	Ea.	1.36	13.95		15.31	finish, hinges and pulls.
Paint	Ea.	1.55	31		32.55	
Minimum Charge	Job		216		216	
30″ Wide, 2 Door						
Demolish	Ea.		22.50		22.50	Includes material and labor to install
Install	Ea.	285	45		330	good modular unit with melamine
Demolish and Install	Ea.	285	67.50		352.50	laminated to particle board, in
Reinstall	Ea.		35.81		35.81	textured colors or wood grain print
Clean	Ea.	1.51	15.25		16.76	finish, hinges and pulls.
Paint	Ea.	1.72	33.50		35.22	
Minimum Charge	Job		216		216	
36″ Wide, 2 Door						
Demolish	Ea.		26.50		26.50	Includes material and labor to install
Install	Ea.	325	46		371	good modular unit with melamine
Demolish and Install	Ea.	325	72.50		397.50	laminated to particle board, in
Reinstall	Ea.		36.77		36.77	textured colors or wood grain print
Clean	Ea.	1.82	18.85		20.67	finish, hinges and pulls.
Paint	Ea.	2.08	41		43.08	
Minimum Charge	Job		216		216	
48″ Wide, 2 Door						
Demolish	Ea.		35.50		35.50	Includes material and labor to install
Install	Ea.	395	47		442	good modular unit with melamine
Demolish and Install	Ea.	395	82.50		477.50	laminated to particle board, in
Reinstall	Ea.		37.57		37.57	textured colors or wood grain print
Clean	Ea.	2.42	24.50		26.92	finish, hinges and pulls.
Paint	Ea.	2.75	53		55.75	
Minimum Charge	Job		216		216	
Above-Appliance						
Demolish	Ea.		22.50		22.50	Includes material and labor to install
Install	Ea.	188	35		223	good modular unit with melamine
Demolish and Install	Ea.	188	57.50		245.50	laminated to particle board, in
Reinstall	Ea.		27.87		27.87	textured colors or wood grain print
Clean	Ea.	1.51	15.25		16.76	finish, hinges and pulls.
Paint	Ea.	1.72	33.50		35.22	
Minimum Charge	Job		216		216	
Better Grade Wood						
12″ Wide, 1 Door						
Demolish	Ea.		8.90		8.90	Includes material and labor to install
Install	Ea.	228	39.50		267.50	custom modular unit with solid
Demolish and Install	Ea.	228	48.40		276.40	hardwood faced frames, hardwood
Reinstall	Ea.		31.42		31.42	door frames and drawer fronts,
Clean	Ea.	.61	6.15		6.76	hardwood veneer on raised door
Paint	Ea.	.68	14.20		14.88	panels, hinges and pulls.
Minimum Charge	Job		216		216	
15″ Wide, 1 Door						
Demolish	Ea.		11.15		11.15	Includes material and labor to install
Install	Ea.	254	40.50		294.50	custom modular unit with solid
Demolish and Install	Ea.	254	51.65		305.65	hardwood faced frames, hardwood
Reinstall	Ea.		32.30		32.30	door frames and drawer fronts,
Clean	Ea.	.76	7.65		8.41	hardwood veneer on raised door
Paint	Ea.	.86	17.60		18.46	panels, hinges and pulls.
Minimum Charge	Job		216		216	

Cabinets and Countertops

Wall Cabinets	Unit	Material	Labor	Equip.	Total	Specification
18″ Wide, 1 Door						
Demolish	Ea.		13.45		13.45	Includes material and labor to install
Install	Ea.	279	41.50		320.50	custom modular unit with solid
Demolish and Install	Ea.	279	54.95		333.95	hardwood faced frames, hardwood
Reinstall	Ea.		33.07		33.07	door frames and drawer fronts,
Clean	Ea.	.90	9.15		10.05	hardwood veneer on raised door
Paint	Ea.	1.02	21.50		22.52	panels, hinges and pulls.
Minimum Charge	Job		216		216	
21″ Wide, 1 Door						
Demolish	Ea.		15.50		15.50	Includes material and labor to install
Install	Ea.	294	42		336	custom modular unit with solid
Demolish and Install	Ea.	294	57.50		351.50	hardwood faced frames, hardwood
Reinstall	Ea.		33.55		33.55	door frames and drawer fronts,
Clean	Ea.	1.06	10.70		11.76	hardwood veneer on raised door
Paint	Ea.	1.20	24.50		25.70	panels, hinges and pulls.
Minimum Charge	Job		216		216	
24″ w / Blind Corner						
Demolish	Ea.		17.80		17.80	Includes material and labor to install
Install	Ea.	325	42.50		367.50	custom modular unit with solid
Demolish and Install	Ea.	325	60.30		385.30	hardwood faced frames, hardwood
Reinstall	Ea.		34.05		34.05	door frames and drawer fronts,
Clean	Ea.	1.21	12.30		13.51	hardwood veneer on raised door
Paint	Ea.	1.36	28.50		29.86	panels, hinges and pulls.
Minimum Charge	Job		216		216	
27″ Wide, 2 Door						
Demolish	Ea.		19.80		19.80	Includes material and labor to install
Install	Ea.	365	43.50		408.50	custom modular unit with solid
Demolish and Install	Ea.	365	63.30		428.30	hardwood faced frames, hardwood
Reinstall	Ea.		34.91		34.91	door frames and drawer fronts,
Clean	Ea.	1.36	13.95		15.31	hardwood veneer on raised door
Paint	Ea.	1.55	31		32.55	panels, hinges and pulls.
Minimum Charge	Job		216		216	
30″ Wide, 2 Door						
Demolish	Ea.		22.50		22.50	Includes material and labor to install
Install	Ea.	380	45		425	custom modular unit with solid
Demolish and Install	Ea.	380	67.50		447.50	hardwood faced frames, hardwood
Reinstall	Ea.		35.81		35.81	door frames and drawer fronts,
Clean	Ea.	1.51	15.25		16.76	hardwood veneer on raised door
Paint	Ea.	1.72	37		38.72	panels, hinges and pulls.
Minimum Charge	Job		216		216	
36″ Wide, 2 Door						
Demolish	Ea.		26.50		26.50	Includes material and labor to install
Install	Ea.	435	46		481	custom modular unit with solid
Demolish and Install	Ea.	435	72.50		507.50	hardwood faced frames, hardwood
Reinstall	Ea.		36.77		36.77	door frames and drawer fronts,
Clean	Ea.	1.82	18.85		20.67	hardwood veneer on raised door
Paint	Ea.	2.08	41		43.08	panels, hinges and pulls.
Minimum Charge	Job		216		216	
48″ Wide, 2 Door						
Demolish	Ea.		35.50		35.50	Includes material and labor to install
Install	Ea.	530	47		577	custom modular unit with solid
Demolish and Install	Ea.	530	82.50		612.50	hardwood faced frames, hardwood
Reinstall	Ea.		37.57		37.57	door frames and drawer fronts,
Clean	Ea.	2.42	24.50		26.92	hardwood veneer on raised door
Paint	Ea.	2.75	53		55.75	panels, hinges and pulls.
Minimum Charge	Job		216		216	

Cabinets and Countertops

Wall Cabinets	Unit	Material	Labor	Equip.	Total	Specification
Above-appliance						
Demolish	Ea.		22.50		22.50	Includes material and labor to install
Install	Ea.	250	35		285	custom modular unit with solid
Demolish and Install	Ea.	250	57.50		307.50	hardwood faced frames, hardwood
Reinstall	Ea.		27.87		27.87	door frames and drawer fronts,
Clean	Ea.	1.51	15.25		16.76	hardwood veneer on raised door
Paint	Ea.	1.72	37		38.72	panels, hinges and pulls.
Minimum Charge	Job		216		216	
Premium Grade Wood						
12" Wide, 1 Door						
Demolish	Ea.		8.90		8.90	Includes material and labor to install
Install	Ea.	273	39.50		312.50	premium modular unit with solid
Demolish and Install	Ea.	273	48.40		321.40	hardwood faced frames, hardwood
Reinstall	Ea.		31.42		31.42	door frames and drawer fronts,
Clean	Ea.	.61	6.15		6.76	hardwood veneer on raised door
Paint	Ea.	.68	15.40		16.08	panels, hinges and pulls.
Minimum Charge	Job		216		216	
15" Wide, 1 Door						
Demolish	Ea.		11.15		11.15	Includes material and labor to install
Install	Ea.	335	40.50		375.50	premium modular unit with solid
Demolish and Install	Ea.	335	51.65		386.65	hardwood faced frames, hardwood
Reinstall	Ea.		32.30		32.30	door frames and drawer fronts,
Clean	Ea.	.76	7.65		8.41	hardwood veneer on raised door
Paint	Ea.	.86	19.45		20.31	panels, hinges and pulls.
Minimum Charge	Job		216		216	
18" Wide, 1 Door						
Demolish	Ea.		13.45		13.45	Includes material and labor to install
Install	Ea.	335	41.50		376.50	premium modular unit with solid
Demolish and Install	Ea.	335	54.95		389.95	hardwood faced frames, hardwood
Reinstall	Ea.		33.07		33.07	door frames and drawer fronts,
Clean	Ea.	.90	9.15		10.05	hardwood veneer on raised door
Paint	Ea.	1.02	23		24.02	panels, hinges and pulls.
Minimum Charge	Job		216		216	
21" Wide, 1 Door						
Demolish	Ea.		15.50		15.50	Includes material and labor to install
Install	Ea.	350	42		392	premium modular unit with solid
Demolish and Install	Ea.	350	57.50		407.50	hardwood faced frames, hardwood
Reinstall	Ea.		33.55		33.55	door frames and drawer fronts,
Clean	Ea.	1.06	10.70		11.76	hardwood veneer on raised door
Paint	Ea.	1.20	26.50		27.70	panels, hinges and pulls.
Minimum Charge	Job		216		216	
24" w / Blind Corner						
Demolish	Ea.		17.80		17.80	Includes material and labor to install
Install	Ea.	390	42.50		432.50	premium modular unit with solid
Demolish and Install	Ea.	390	60.30		450.30	hardwood faced frames, hardwood
Reinstall	Ea.		34.05		34.05	door frames and drawer fronts,
Clean	Ea.	1.21	12.30		13.51	hardwood veneer on raised door
Paint	Ea.	1.36	31		32.36	panels, hinges and pulls.
Minimum Charge	Job		216		216	
27" Wide, 2 Door						
Demolish	Ea.		19.80		19.80	Includes material and labor to install
Install	Ea.	360	43.50		403.50	premium modular unit with solid
Demolish and Install	Ea.	360	63.30		423.30	hardwood faced frames, hardwood
Reinstall	Ea.		34.91		34.91	door frames and drawer fronts,
Clean	Ea.	1.36	13.95		15.31	hardwood veneer on raised door
Paint	Ea.	1.55	33.50		35.05	panels, hinges and pulls.
Minimum Charge	Job		216		216	

Cabinets and Countertops

Wall Cabinets	Unit	Material	Labor	Equip.	Total	Specification
30" Wide, 2 Door						
Demolish	Ea.		22.50		22.50	Includes material and labor to install
Install	Ea.	455	45		500	premium modular unit with solid
Demolish and Install	Ea.	455	67.50		522.50	hardwood faced frames, hardwood
Reinstall	Ea.		35.81		35.81	door frames and drawer fronts,
Clean	Ea.	1.51	15.25		16.76	hardwood veneer on raised door
Paint	Ea.	1.72	37		38.72	panels, hinges and pulls.
Minimum Charge	Job		216		216	
36" Wide, 2 Door						
Demolish	Ea.		26.50		26.50	Includes material and labor to install
Install	Ea.	515	46		561	premium modular unit with solid
Demolish and Install	Ea.	515	72.50		587.50	hardwood faced frames, hardwood
Reinstall	Ea.		36.77		36.77	door frames and drawer fronts,
Clean	Ea.	1.82	18.85		20.67	hardwood veneer on raised door
Paint	Ea.	2.08	46		48.08	panels, hinges and pulls.
Minimum Charge	Job		216		216	
48" Wide, 2 Door						
Demolish	Ea.		35.50		35.50	Includes material and labor to install
Install	Ea.	635	47		682	premium modular unit with solid
Demolish and Install	Ea.	635	82.50		717.50	hardwood faced frames, hardwood
Reinstall	Ea.		37.57		37.57	door frames and drawer fronts,
Clean	Ea.	2.42	24.50		26.92	hardwood veneer on raised door
Paint	Ea.	2.75	61.50		64.25	panels, hinges and pulls.
Minimum Charge	Job		216		216	
Above-appliance						
Demolish	Ea.		22.50		22.50	Includes material and labor to install
Install	Ea.	300	35		335	premium modular unit with solid
Demolish and Install	Ea.	300	57.50		357.50	hardwood faced frames, hardwood
Reinstall	Ea.		27.87		27.87	door frames and drawer fronts,
Clean	Ea.	1.51	15.25		16.76	hardwood veneer on raised door
Paint	Ea.	1.72	37		38.72	panels, hinges, pulls.
Minimum Charge	Job		216		216	
Premium Hardwood						
12" Wide, 1 Door						
Demolish	Ea.		8.90		8.90	Includes material and labor to install
Install	Ea.	298	39.50		337.50	premium hardwood modular unit with
Demolish and Install	Ea.	298	48.40		346.40	solid hardwood faced frames, drawer
Reinstall	Ea.		31.42		31.42	fronts, and door panels, steel drawer
Clean	Ea.	.61	6.15		6.76	guides, hinges, pulls, laminated
Paint	Ea.	.68	16.80		17.48	interior.
Minimum Charge	Job		216		216	
15" Wide, 1 Door						
Demolish	Ea.		11.15		11.15	Includes material and labor to install
Install	Ea.	445	40.50		485.50	premium hardwood modular unit with
Demolish and Install	Ea.	445	51.65		496.65	solid hardwood faced frames, drawer
Reinstall	Ea.		32.30		32.30	fronts, and door panels, steel drawer
Clean	Ea.	.76	7.65		8.41	guides, hinges, pulls, laminated
Paint	Ea.	.86	20.50		21.36	interior.
Minimum Charge	Job		216		216	
18" Wide, 1 Door						
Demolish	Ea.		13.45		13.45	Includes material and labor to install
Install	Ea.	370	41.50		411.50	premium hardwood modular unit with
Demolish and Install	Ea.	370	54.95		424.95	solid hardwood faced frames, drawer
Reinstall	Ea.		33.07		33.07	fronts, and door panels, steel drawer
Clean	Ea.	.90	9.15		10.05	guides, hinges, pulls, laminated
Paint	Ea.	1.02	24.50		25.52	interior.
Minimum Charge	Job		216		216	

Cabinets and Countertops

Wall Cabinets	Unit	Material	Labor	Equip.	Total	Specification
21" Wide, 1 Door						
Demolish	Ea.		15.50		15.50	Includes material and labor to install
Install	Ea.	385	42		427	premium hardwood modular unit with
Demolish and Install	Ea.	385	57.50		442.50	solid hardwood faced frames, drawer
Reinstall	Ea.		33.55		33.55	fronts, and door panels, steel drawer
Clean	Ea.	1.06	10.70		11.76	guides, hinges, pulls, laminated
Paint	Ea.	1.20	28.50		29.70	interior.
Minimum Charge	Job		216		216	
24" w / Blind Corner						
Demolish	Ea.		17.80		17.80	Includes material and labor to install
Install	Ea.	430	42.50		472.50	premium hardwood modular unit with
Demolish and Install	Ea.	430	60.30		490.30	solid hardwood faced frames, drawer
Reinstall	Ea.		34.05		34.05	fronts, and door panels, steel drawer
Clean	Ea.	1.21	12.30		13.51	guides, hinges, pulls, laminated
Paint	Ea.	1.36	33.50		34.86	interior.
Minimum Charge	Job		216		216	
27" Wide, 2 Door						
Demolish	Ea.		19.80		19.80	Includes material and labor to install
Install	Ea.	475	43.50		518.50	premium hardwood modular unit with
Demolish and Install	Ea.	475	63.30		538.30	solid hardwood faced frames, drawer
Reinstall	Ea.		34.91		34.91	fronts, and door panels, steel drawer
Clean	Ea.	1.36	13.95		15.31	guides, hinges, pulls, laminated
Paint	Ea.	1.55	37		38.55	interior.
Minimum Charge	Job		216		216	
30" Wide, 2 Door						
Demolish	Ea.		22.50		22.50	Includes material and labor to install
Install	Ea.	495	45		540	premium hardwood modular unit with
Demolish and Install	Ea.	495	67.50		562.50	solid hardwood faced frames, drawer
Reinstall	Ea.		35.81		35.81	fronts, and door panels, steel drawer
Clean	Ea.	1.51	15.25		16.76	guides, hinges, pulls, laminated
Paint	Ea.	1.72	41		42.72	interior.
Minimum Charge	Job		216		216	
36" Wide, 2 Door						
Demolish	Ea.		26.50		26.50	Includes material and labor to install
Install	Ea.	565	46		611	premium hardwood modular unit with
Demolish and Install	Ea.	565	72.50		637.50	solid hardwood faced frames, drawer
Reinstall	Ea.		36.77		36.77	fronts, and door panels, steel drawer
Clean	Ea.	1.82	18.85		20.67	guides, hinges, pulls, laminated
Paint	Ea.	2.08	53		55.08	interior.
Minimum Charge	Job		216		216	
48" Wide, 2 Door						
Demolish	Ea.		35.50		35.50	Includes material and labor to install
Install	Ea.	695	47		742	premium hardwood modular unit with
Demolish and Install	Ea.	695	82.50		777.50	solid hardwood faced frames, drawer
Reinstall	Ea.		37.57		37.57	fronts, and door panels, steel drawer
Clean	Ea.	2.42	24.50		26.92	guides, hinges, pulls, laminated
Paint	Ea.	2.75	61.50		64.25	interior.
Minimum Charge	Job		216		216	
Above-appliance						
Demolish	Ea.		22.50		22.50	Includes material and labor to install
Install	Ea.	330	35		365	premium hardwood modular unit with
Demolish and Install	Ea.	330	57.50		387.50	solid hardwood faced frames, drawer
Reinstall	Ea.		27.87		27.87	fronts, and door panels, steel drawer
Clean	Ea.	1.51	15.25		16.76	guides, hinges, pulls, laminated
Paint	Ea.	1.72	41		42.72	interior.
Minimum Charge	Job		216		216	

Cabinets and Countertops

Wall Cabinets	Unit	Material	Labor	Equip.	Total	Specification
Medicine Cabinet						
Good Grade						
Demolish	Ea.		14.85		14.85	Cost includes material and labor to
Install	Ea.	165	31		196	install 14" x 18" recessed medicine
Demolish and Install	Ea.	165	45.85		210.85	cabinet with stainless steel frame,
Reinstall	Ea.		24.69		24.69	mirror. Light not included.
Clean	Ea.	.03	14.65		14.68	
Paint	Ea.	2.02	23		25.02	
Minimum Charge	Job		216		216	
Good Grade Lighted						
Demolish	Ea.		14.85		14.85	Cost includes material and labor to
Install	Ea.	420	36		456	install 14" x 18" recessed medicine
Demolish and Install	Ea.	420	50.85		470.85	cabinet with stainless steel frame,
Reinstall	Ea.		28.80		28.80	mirror and light.
Clean	Ea.	.03	14.65		14.68	
Paint	Ea.	2.02	23		25.02	
Minimum Charge	Job		216		216	
Better Grade						
Demolish	Ea.		14.85		14.85	Includes material and labor to install
Install	Ea.	275	31		306	recessed medicine cabinet with
Demolish and Install	Ea.	275	45.85		320.85	polished chrome frame and mirror.
Reinstall	Ea.		24.69		24.69	Light not included.
Clean	Ea.	.03	14.65		14.68	
Paint	Ea.	2.02	23		25.02	
Minimum Charge	Job		216		216	
Better Grade Lighted						
Demolish	Ea.		14.85		14.85	Includes material and labor to install
Install	Ea.	530	36		566	recessed medicine cabinet with
Demolish and Install	Ea.	530	50.85		580.85	polished chrome frame, mirror and
Reinstall	Ea.		28.80		28.80	light.
Clean	Ea.	.03	14.65		14.68	
Paint	Ea.	2.02	23		25.02	
Minimum Charge	Job		216		216	
Premium Grade						
Demolish	Ea.		14.85		14.85	Cost includes material and labor to
Install	Ea.	330	31		361	install 14" x 24" recessed medicine
Demolish and Install	Ea.	330	45.85		375.85	cabinet with beveled mirror, frameless
Reinstall	Ea.		24.69		24.69	swing door. Light not included.
Clean	Ea.	.03	14.65		14.68	
Paint	Ea.	2.02	23		25.02	
Minimum Charge	Job		216		216	
Premium Grade Light						
Demolish	Ea.		14.85		14.85	Cost includes material and labor to
Install	Ea.	580	36		616	install 36" x 30" surface mounted
Demolish and Install	Ea.	580	50.85		630.85	medicine cabinet with beveled tri-view
Reinstall	Ea.		28.80		28.80	mirror, frameless swing door and light.
Clean	Ea.	.03	14.65		14.68	
Paint	Ea.	2.02	23		25.02	
Minimum Charge	Job		216		216	
Bath Mirror						
Demolish	Ea.		11.15		11.15	Cost includes material and labor to
Install	Ea.	51.50	21.50		73	install 18" x 24" surface mount mirror
Demolish and Install	Ea.	51.50	32.65		84.15	with stainless steel frame.
Reinstall	Ea.		17.28		17.28	
Clean	Ea.	.03	.98		1.01	
Minimum Charge	Job		216		216	

Cabinets and Countertops

Wall Cabinets	Unit	Material	Labor	Equip.	Total	Specification
Garage						Includes material and labor to install
Demolish	L.F.		8.90		8.90	good modular unit with melamine
Install	L.F.	92	21.50		113.50	laminated to particle board, in
Demolish and Install	L.F.	92	30.40		122.40	textured colors or wood grain print
Reinstall	L.F.		17.28		17.28	finish, hinges and pulls.
Clean	L.F.	.61	6.15		6.76	
Paint	L.F.	.68	13.20		13.88	
Minimum Charge	Job		216		216	
Strip and Refinish						
Install	L.F.	4.61	46		50.61	Includes labor and material to strip,
Minimum Charge	Job		185		185	prep and refinish exterior of cabinets.

Tall Cabinets	Unit	Material	Labor	Equip.	Total	Specification
Good Grade Laminated						Includes material and labor to install
Demolish	L.F.		15.80		15.80	custom modular unit with solid
Install	L.F.	229	48		277	hardwood faced frames, hardwood
Demolish and Install	L.F.	229	63.80		292.80	door frames and drawer fronts,
Reinstall	L.F.		38.40		38.40	hardwood veneer on raised door
Clean	L.F.	1.62	11.45		13.07	panels, hinges and pulls.
Paint	L.F.	1.60	26.50		28.10	
Minimum Charge	Job		216		216	
Better Grade Wood						Includes material and labor to install
Demolish	L.F.		15.80		15.80	custom modular unit with solid
Install	L.F.	330	48		378	hardwood faced frames, hardwood
Demolish and Install	L.F.	330	63.80		393.80	door frames and drawer fronts,
Reinstall	L.F.		38.40		38.40	hardwood veneer on raised door
Clean	L.F.	1.62	11.45		13.07	panels, hinges and pulls.
Paint	L.F.	1.60	28.50		30.10	
Minimum Charge	Job		216		216	
Premium Grade Wood						Includes material and labor to install
Demolish	L.F.		15.80		15.80	premium modular unit with solid
Install	L.F.	470	48		518	hardwood faced frames, hardwood
Demolish and Install	L.F.	470	63.80		533.80	door frames and drawer fronts,
Reinstall	L.F.		38.40		38.40	hardwood veneer on raised door
Clean	L.F.	1.62	11.45		13.07	panels, hinges and pulls.
Paint	L.F.	1.60	31		32.60	
Minimum Charge	Job		216		216	
Premium Hardwood						Includes material and labor to install
Demolish	L.F.		15.80		15.80	premium hardwood modular unit with
Install	L.F.	655	48		703	solid hardwood faced frames, drawer
Demolish and Install	L.F.	655	63.80		718.80	fronts, and door panels, steel drawer
Reinstall	L.F.		38.40		38.40	guides, hinges and pulls, laminated
Clean	L.F.	1.62	11.45		13.07	interior.
Paint	L.F.	1.60	33.50		35.10	
Minimum Charge	Job		216		216	

Cabinets and Countertops

Tall Cabinets	Unit	Material	Labor	Equip.	Total	Specification
Single Oven, 27″ Wide						
Good Grade Laminated						
Demolish	Ea.		35.50		35.50	Includes material and labor to install
Install	Ea.	790	108		898	good modular unit with melamine
Demolish and Install	Ea.	790	143.50		933.50	laminated to particle board, in
Reinstall	Ea.		86.40		86.40	textured colors or wood grain print
Clean	Ea.	5.05	20		25.05	finish, hinges and pulls.
Paint	Ea.	2.70	59		61.70	
Minimum Charge	Job		216		216	
Better Grade Veneer						
Demolish	Ea.		35.50		35.50	Includes material and labor to install
Install	Ea.	1400	108		1508	custom modular unit with solid
Demolish and Install	Ea.	1400	143.50		1543.50	hardwood faced frames, hardwood
Reinstall	Ea.		86.40		86.40	door frames and drawer fronts,
Clean	Ea.	5.05	20		25.05	hardwood veneer on raised door
Paint	Ea.	2.70	63.50		66.20	panels, hinges and pulls.
Minimum Charge	Job		216		216	
Premium Grade Veneer						
Demolish	Ea.		35.50		35.50	Includes material and labor to install
Install	Ea.	1275	108		1383	premium modular unit with solid
Demolish and Install	Ea.	1275	143.50		1418.50	hardwood faced frames, hardwood
Reinstall	Ea.		86.40		86.40	door frames and drawer fronts,
Clean	Ea.	5.05	20		25.05	hardwood veneer on raised door
Paint	Ea.	2.70	69.50		72.20	panels, hinges and pulls.
Minimum Charge	Job		216		216	
Premium Hardwood						
Demolish	Ea.		35.50		35.50	Includes material and labor to install
Install	Ea.	1375	108		1483	premium hardwood modular unit with
Demolish and Install	Ea.	1375	143.50		1518.50	solid hardwood faced frames, drawer
Reinstall	Ea.		86.40		86.40	fronts, and door panels, steel drawer
Clean	Ea.	5.05	20		25.05	guides, hinges and pulls, laminated
Paint	Ea.	2.70	75.50		78.20	interior.
Minimum Charge	Job		216		216	
Single Oven, 30″ Wide						
Good Grade Laminated						
Demolish	Ea.		35.50		35.50	Includes material and labor to install
Install	Ea.	910	108		1018	good modular unit with melamine
Demolish and Install	Ea.	910	143.50		1053.50	laminated to particle board, in
Reinstall	Ea.		86.40		86.40	textured colors or wood grain print
Clean	Ea.	5.05	20		25.05	finish, hinges and pulls.
Paint	Ea.	2.70	59		61.70	
Minimum Charge	Job		216		216	
Better Grade Veneer						
Demolish	Ea.		35.50		35.50	Includes material and labor to install
Install	Ea.	1025	108		1133	custom modular unit with solid
Demolish and Install	Ea.	1025	143.50		1168.50	hardwood faced frames, hardwood
Reinstall	Ea.		86.40		86.40	door frames and drawer fronts,
Clean	Ea.	5.05	20		25.05	hardwood veneer on raised door
Paint	Ea.	2.70	59		61.70	panels, hinges and pulls.
Minimum Charge	Job		216		216	

Cabinets and Countertops

Tall Cabinets	Unit	Material	Labor	Equip.	Total	Specification
Premium Grade Veneer						
Demolish	Ea.		35.50		35.50	Includes material and labor to install
Install	Ea.	1150	108		1258	premium modular unit with solid
Demolish and Install	Ea.	1150	143.50		1293.50	hardwood faced frames, hardwood
Reinstall	Ea.		86.40		86.40	door frames and drawer fronts,
Clean	Ea.	5.05	20		25.05	hardwood veneer on raised door
Paint	Ea.	2.70	59		61.70	panels, hinges and pulls.
Minimum Charge	Job		216		216	
Premium Hardwood						
Demolish	Ea.		35.50		35.50	Includes material and labor to install
Install	Ea.	1250	108		1358	premium hardwood modular unit with
Demolish and Install	Ea.	1250	143.50		1393.50	solid hardwood faced frames, drawer
Reinstall	Ea.		86.40		86.40	fronts, and door panels, steel drawer
Clean	Ea.	5.05	20		25.05	guides, hinges and pulls, laminated
Paint	Ea.	2.70	59		61.70	interior.
Minimum Charge	Job		216		216	

Utility 18″ W x 12″ D

	Unit	Material	Labor	Equip.	Total	Specification
Good Grade Laminated						
Demolish	Ea.		35.50		35.50	Includes material and labor to install
Install	Ea.	555	86.50		641.50	good modular unit with melamine
Demolish and Install	Ea.	555	122		677	laminated to particle board, in
Reinstall	Ea.		69.12		69.12	textured colors or wood grain print
Clean	Ea.	1.19	9.70		10.89	finish, hinges and pulls.
Paint	Ea.	1.02	23		24.02	
Minimum Charge	Job		216		216	
Better Grade Veneer						
Demolish	Ea.		35.50		35.50	Includes material and labor to install
Install	Ea.	745	86.50		831.50	custom modular unit with solid
Demolish and Install	Ea.	745	122		867	hardwood faced frames, hardwood
Reinstall	Ea.		69.12		69.12	door frames and drawer fronts,
Clean	Ea.	1.19	9.70		10.89	hardwood veneer on raised door
Paint	Ea.	1.02	24.50		25.52	panels, hinges and pulls.
Minimum Charge	Job		216		216	
Premium Grade Veneer						
Demolish	Ea.		35.50		35.50	Includes material and labor to install
Install	Ea.	890	86.50		976.50	premium modular unit with solid
Demolish and Install	Ea.	890	122		1012	hardwood faced frames, hardwood
Reinstall	Ea.		69.12		69.12	door frames and drawer fronts,
Clean	Ea.	1.19	9.70		10.89	hardwood veneer on raised door
Paint	Ea.	1.02	28.50		29.52	panels, hinges and pulls.
Minimum Charge	Job		216		216	
Premium Hardwood						
Demolish	Ea.		35.50		35.50	Includes material and labor to install
Install	Ea.	975	86.50		1061.50	premium hardwood modular unit with
Demolish and Install	Ea.	975	122		1097	solid hardwood faced frames, drawer
Reinstall	Ea.		69.12		69.12	fronts, and door panels, steel drawer
Clean	Ea.	1.19	9.70		10.89	guides, hinges and pulls, laminated
Paint	Ea.	1.02	31		32.02	interior.
Minimum Charge	Job		216		216	

Cabinets and Countertops

Tall Cabinets	Unit	Material	Labor	Equip.	Total	Specification
Utility 24″ W x 24″ D						
Good Grade Laminated						
Demolish	Ea.		35.50		35.50	Includes material and labor to install
Install	Ea.	665	108		773	good modular unit with melamine
Demolish and Install	Ea.	665	143.50		808.50	laminated to particle board, in
Reinstall	Ea.		86.40		86.40	textured colors or wood grain print
Clean	Ea.	1.55	12.80		14.35	finish, hinges and pulls.
Paint	Ea.	1.36	31		32.36	
Minimum Charge	Job		216		216	
Better Grade Veneer						
Demolish	Ea.		35.50		35.50	Includes material and labor to install
Install	Ea.	885	108		993	custom modular unit with solid
Demolish and Install	Ea.	885	143.50		1028.50	hardwood faced frames, hardwood
Reinstall	Ea.		86.40		86.40	door frames and drawer fronts,
Clean	Ea.	1.55	12.80		14.35	hardwood veneer on raised door
Paint	Ea.	1.36	33.50		34.86	panels, hinges and pulls.
Minimum Charge	Job		216		216	
Premium Grade Veneer						
Demolish	Ea.		35.50		35.50	Includes material and labor to install
Install	Ea.	1075	108		1183	premium modular unit with solid
Demolish and Install	Ea.	1075	143.50		1218.50	hardwood faced frames, hardwood
Reinstall	Ea.		86.40		86.40	door frames and drawer fronts,
Clean	Ea.	1.55	12.80		14.35	hardwood veneer on raised door
Paint	Ea.	1.36	37		38.36	panels, hinges and pulls.
Minimum Charge	Job		216		216	
Premium Hardwood						
Demolish	Ea.		35.50		35.50	Includes material and labor to install
Install	Ea.	1150	108		1258	premium hardwood modular unit with
Demolish and Install	Ea.	1150	143.50		1293.50	solid hardwood faced frames, drawer
Reinstall	Ea.		86.40		86.40	fronts, and door panels, steel drawer
Clean	Ea.	1.55	12.80		14.35	guides, hinges and pulls, laminated
Paint	Ea.	1.36	41		42.36	interior.
Minimum Charge	Job		216		216	
Plain Shelves						
Install	Ea.	31.50	24		55.50	Includes labor and material to install
Rotating Shelves						tall cabinet shelving, per set.
Install	Ea.	90	21.50		111.50	Includes labor and material to install
Strip and Refinish						lazy susan shelving for wall cabinet.
Install	L.F.	9.20	74		83.20	Includes labor and material to strip,
Minimum Charge	Job		185		185	prep and refinish exterior of cabinets.
Stain						
Install	L.F.	.26	3.36		3.62	Includes labor and material to replace
Minimum Charge	Job		185		185	normal prep and stain on doors and
						exterior cabinets.

Cabinets and Countertops

Base Cabinets	Unit	Material	Labor	Equip.	Total	Specification
Good Grade Laminated						
12" w, 1 Door, 1 Drawer						
Demolish	Ea.		8.90		8.90	Includes material and labor to install
Install	Ea.	210	35		245	good modular unit with melamine
Demolish and Install	Ea.	210	43.90		253.90	laminate, textured colors or wood
Reinstall	Ea.		27.87		27.87	grain print finish including hinges and
Clean	Ea.	.80	6.40		7.20	pulls.
Paint	Ea.	.68	15.40		16.08	
Minimum Charge	Job		216		216	
15" w, 1 Door, 1 Drawer						
Demolish	Ea.		11.15		11.15	Includes material and labor to install
Install	Ea.	218	36		254	good modular unit with melamine
Demolish and Install	Ea.	218	47.15		265.15	laminate, textured colors or wood
Reinstall	Ea.		28.80		28.80	grain print finish including hinges and
Clean	Ea.	1.01	8		9.01	pulls.
Paint	Ea.	.86	19.45		20.31	
Minimum Charge	Job		216		216	
18" w, 1 Door, 1 Drawer						
Demolish	Ea.		13.20		13.20	Includes material and labor to install
Install	Ea.	238	37		275	good modular unit with melamine
Demolish and Install	Ea.	238	50.20		288.20	laminate, textured colors or wood
Reinstall	Ea.		29.67		29.67	grain print finish including hinges and
Clean	Ea.	1.19	9.70		10.89	pulls.
Paint	Ea.	1.02	23		24.02	
Minimum Charge	Job		216		216	
21" w, 1 Door, 1 Drawer						
Demolish	Ea.		15.50		15.50	Includes material and labor to install
Install	Ea.	243	38		281	good modular unit with melamine
Demolish and Install	Ea.	243	53.50		296.50	laminate, textured colors or wood
Reinstall	Ea.		30.45		30.45	grain print finish including hinges and
Clean	Ea.	1.44	11.45		12.89	pulls.
Paint	Ea.	1.20	26.50		27.70	
Minimum Charge	Job		216		216	
24" w, 1 Door, 1 Drawer						
Demolish	Ea.		17.80		17.80	Includes material and labor to install
Install	Ea.	287	38.50		325.50	good modular unit with melamine
Demolish and Install	Ea.	287	56.30		343.30	laminate, textured colors or wood
Reinstall	Ea.		31		31	grain print finish including hinges and
Clean	Ea.	1.55	12.80		14.35	pulls.
Paint	Ea.	1.36	31		32.36	
Minimum Charge	Job		216		216	
30" Wide Sink Base						
Demolish	Ea.		22.50		22.50	Includes material and labor to install
Install	Ea.	278	40.50		318.50	good modular unit with melamine
Demolish and Install	Ea.	278	63		341	laminate, textured colors or wood
Reinstall	Ea.		32.30		32.30	grain print finish including hinges and
Clean	Ea.	2.01	16		18.01	pulls.
Paint	Ea.	1.72	37		38.72	
Minimum Charge	Job		216		216	
36" Wide Sink Base						
Demolish	Ea.		27.50		27.50	Includes material and labor to install
Install	Ea.	310	42.50		352.50	good modular unit with melamine
Demolish and Install	Ea.	310	70		380	laminate, textured colors or wood
Reinstall	Ea.		34.05		34.05	grain print finish including hinges and
Clean	Ea.	2.24	18.85		21.09	pulls.
Paint	Ea.	2.08	46		48.08	
Minimum Charge	Job		216		216	

Base Cabinets		Unit	Material	Labor	Equip.	Total	Specification
36" Blind Corner							
	Demolish	Ea.		27.50		27.50	Includes material and labor to install
	Install	Ea.	495	48		543	good modular unit with melamine
	Demolish and Install	Ea.	495	75.50		570.50	laminate, textured colors or wood
	Reinstall	Ea.		38.40		38.40	grain print finish including hinges and
	Clean	Ea.	2.24	18.85		21.09	pulls.
	Paint	Ea.	2.08	46		48.08	
	Minimum Charge	Job		216		216	
42" w, 2 Door, 2 Drawer							
	Demolish	Ea.		32.50		32.50	Includes material and labor to install
	Install	Ea.	380	43.50		423.50	good modular unit with melamine
	Demolish and Install	Ea.	380	76		456	laminate, textured colors or wood
	Reinstall	Ea.		34.91		34.91	grain print finish including hinges and
	Clean	Ea.	2.88	23		25.88	pulls.
	Paint	Ea.	2.38	53		55.38	
	Minimum Charge	Job		216		216	
Clean Interior							
	Clean	L.F.	.80	4.85		5.65	Includes labor and materials to clean
	Minimum Charge	Job		160		160	the interior of a 27" cabinet.
Better Grade Wood							
12" w, 1 Door, 1 Drawer							
	Demolish	Ea.		8.90		8.90	Includes material and labor to install
	Install	Ea.	279	35		314	custom modular unit including solid
	Demolish and Install	Ea.	279	43.90		322.90	hardwood faced frames, hardwood
	Reinstall	Ea.		27.87		27.87	door frames and drawer fronts,
	Clean	Ea.	.80	6.40		7.20	hardwood veneer on raised door
	Paint	Ea.	.68	16.80		17.48	panels, hinges and pulls.
	Minimum Charge	Job		216		216	
15" w, 1 Door, 1 Drawer							
	Demolish	Ea.		11.15		11.15	Includes material and labor to install
	Install	Ea.	290	36		326	custom modular unit including solid
	Demolish and Install	Ea.	290	47.15		337.15	hardwood faced frames, hardwood
	Reinstall	Ea.		28.80		28.80	door frames and drawer fronts,
	Clean	Ea.	1.01	8		9.01	hardwood veneer on raised door
	Paint	Ea.	.86	21.50		22.36	panels, hinges and pulls.
	Minimum Charge	Job		216		216	
18" w, 1 Door, 1 Drawer							
	Demolish	Ea.		13.20		13.20	Includes material and labor to install
	Install	Ea.	315	37		352	custom modular unit including solid
	Demolish and Install	Ea.	315	50.20		365.20	hardwood faced frames, hardwood
	Reinstall	Ea.		29.67		29.67	door frames and drawer fronts,
	Clean	Ea.	1.19	9.70		10.89	hardwood veneer on raised door
	Paint	Ea.	1.02	24.50		25.52	panels, hinges and pulls.
	Minimum Charge	Job		216		216	
21" w, 1 Door, 1 Drawer							
	Demolish	Ea.		15.50		15.50	Includes material and labor to install
	Install	Ea.	325	38		363	custom modular unit including solid
	Demolish and Install	Ea.	325	53.50		378.50	hardwood faced frames, hardwood
	Reinstall	Ea.		30.45		30.45	door frames and drawer fronts,
	Clean	Ea.	1.44	11.45		12.89	hardwood veneer on raised door
	Paint	Ea.	1.20	28.50		29.70	panels, hinges and pulls.
	Minimum Charge	Job		216		216	

Cabinets and Countertops

Base Cabinets	Unit	Material	Labor	Equip.	Total	Specification
24" w, 1 Door, 1 Drawer						
Demolish	Ea.		17.80		17.80	Includes material and labor to install
Install	Ea.	385	38.50		423.50	custom modular unit including solid
Demolish and Install	Ea.	385	56.30		441.30	hardwood faced frames, hardwood
Reinstall	Ea.		31		31	door frames and drawer fronts,
Clean	Ea.	1.55	12.80		14.35	hardwood veneer on raised door
Paint	Ea.	1.36	33.50		34.86	panels, hinges and pulls.
Minimum Charge	Job		216		216	
30" Wide Sink Base						
Demolish	Ea.		22.50		22.50	Includes material and labor to install
Install	Ea.	370	40.50		410.50	custom modular unit including solid
Demolish and Install	Ea.	370	63		433	hardwood faced frames, hardwood
Reinstall	Ea.		32.30		32.30	door frames and drawer fronts,
Clean	Ea.	2.01	16		18.01	hardwood veneer on raised door
Paint	Ea.	1.72	41		42.72	panels, hinges and pulls.
Minimum Charge	Job		216		216	
36" Wide Sink Base						
Demolish	Ea.		27.50		27.50	Includes material and labor to install
Install	Ea.	420	42.50		462.50	custom modular unit including solid
Demolish and Install	Ea.	420	70		490	hardwood faced frames, hardwood
Reinstall	Ea.		34.05		34.05	door frames and drawer fronts,
Clean	Ea.	2.24	18.85		21.09	hardwood veneer on raised door
Paint	Ea.	2.08	53		55.08	panels, hinges and pulls.
Minimum Charge	Job		216		216	
36" Blind Corner						
Demolish	Ea.		27.50		27.50	Includes material and labor to install
Install	Ea.	660	48		708	custom modular unit including solid
Demolish and Install	Ea.	660	75.50		735.50	hardwood faced frames, hardwood
Reinstall	Ea.		38.40		38.40	door frames and drawer fronts,
Clean	Ea.	2.24	18.85		21.09	hardwood veneer on raised door
Paint	Ea.	2.08	53		55.08	panels, hinges and pulls.
Minimum Charge	Job		216		216	
42" w, 2 Door, 2 Drawer						
Demolish	Ea.		32.50		32.50	Includes material and labor to install
Install	Ea.	505	43.50		548.50	modular unit including solid hardwood
Demolish and Install	Ea.	505	76		581	faced frames, hardwood door frames
Reinstall	Ea.		34.91		34.91	and drawer fronts, hardwood veneer
Clean	Ea.	2.88	23		25.88	on raised door panels, hinges and
Paint	Ea.	2.38	61.50		63.88	pulls.
Minimum Charge	Job		216		216	
Clean Interior						
Clean	L.F.	.80	4.85		5.65	Includes labor and materials to clean
Minimum Charge	Job		160		160	the interior of a 27" cabinet.
Premium Grade Wood						
12" w, 1 Door, 1 Drawer						
Demolish	Ea.		8.90		8.90	Includes material and labor to install
Install	Ea.	335	17.40		352.40	premium hardwood modular unit with
Demolish and Install	Ea.	335	26.30		361.30	solid hardwood faced frames, drawer
Reinstall	Ea.		13.94		13.94	fronts, and door panels, steel drawer
Clean	Ea.	.80	6.40		7.20	guides, hinges, pulls and laminated
Paint	Ea.	.68	18.50		19.18	interior.
Minimum Charge	Job		216		216	

Base Cabinets	Unit	Material	Labor	Equip.	Total	Specification
15″ w, 1 Door, 1 Drawer						
Demolish	Ea.		11.15		11.15	Includes material and labor to install
Install	Ea.	345	36		381	premium modular unit including solid
Demolish and Install	Ea.	345	47.15		392.15	hardwood faced frames, hardwood
Reinstall	Ea.		28.80		28.80	door frames and drawer fronts,
Clean	Ea.	1.01	8		9.01	hardwood veneer on raised door
Paint	Ea.	.86	23		23.86	panels, hinges and pulls.
Minimum Charge	Job		216		216	
18″ w, 1 Door, 1 Drawer						
Demolish	Ea.		13.20		13.20	Includes material and labor to install
Install	Ea.	380	37		417	premium modular unit including solid
Demolish and Install	Ea.	380	50.20		430.20	hardwood faced frames, hardwood
Reinstall	Ea.		29.67		29.67	door frames and drawer fronts,
Clean	Ea.	1.19	9.70		10.89	hardwood veneer on raised door
Paint	Ea.	1.02	28.50		29.52	panels, hinges and pulls.
Minimum Charge	Job		216		216	
21″ w, 1 Door, 1 Drawer						
Demolish	Ea.		15.50		15.50	Includes material and labor to install
Install	Ea.	390	38		428	premium modular unit including solid
Demolish and Install	Ea.	390	53.50		443.50	hardwood faced frames, hardwood
Reinstall	Ea.		30.45		30.45	door frames and drawer fronts,
Clean	Ea.	1.44	11.45		12.89	hardwood veneer on raised door
Paint	Ea.	1.20	31		32.20	panels, hinges and pulls.
Minimum Charge	Job		216		216	
24″ w, 1 Door, 1 Drawer						
Demolish	Ea.		17.80		17.80	Includes material and labor to install
Install	Ea.	455	38.50		493.50	premium modular unit including solid
Demolish and Install	Ea.	455	56.30		511.30	hardwood faced frames, hardwood
Reinstall	Ea.		31		31	door frames and drawer fronts,
Clean	Ea.	1.55	12.80		14.35	hardwood veneer on raised door
Paint	Ea.	1.36	37		38.36	panels, hinges and pulls.
Minimum Charge	Job		216		216	
30″ Wide Sink Base						
Demolish	Ea.		22.50		22.50	Includes material and labor to install
Install	Ea.	445	40.50		485.50	premium modular unit including solid
Demolish and Install	Ea.	445	63		508	hardwood faced frames, hardwood
Reinstall	Ea.		32.30		32.30	door frames and drawer fronts,
Clean	Ea.	2.01	16		18.01	hardwood veneer on raised door
Paint	Ea.	1.72	46		47.72	panels, hinges and pulls.
Minimum Charge	Job		216		216	
36″ Wide Sink Base						
Demolish	Ea.		27.50		27.50	Includes material and labor to install
Install	Ea.	500	42.50		542.50	premium modular unit including solid
Demolish and Install	Ea.	500	70		570	hardwood faced frames, hardwood
Reinstall	Ea.		34.05		34.05	door frames and drawer fronts,
Clean	Ea.	2.24	18.85		21.09	hardwood veneer on raised door
Paint	Ea.	2.08	53		55.08	panels, hinges and pulls.
Minimum Charge	Job		216		216	
36″ Blind Corner						
Demolish	Ea.		27.50		27.50	Includes material and labor to install
Install	Ea.	790	48		838	premium modular unit including solid
Demolish and Install	Ea.	790	75.50		865.50	hardwood faced frames, hardwood
Reinstall	Ea.		38.40		38.40	door frames and drawer fronts,
Clean	Ea.	2.24	18.85		21.09	hardwood veneer on raised door
Paint	Ea.	2.08	53		55.08	panels, hinges and pulls.
Minimum Charge	Job		216		216	

Cabinets and Countertops

Base Cabinets	Unit	Material	Labor	Equip.	Total	Specification
42" w, 2 Door, 2 Drawer						
Demolish	Ea.		32.50		32.50	Includes material and labor to install
Install	Ea.	675	43.50		718.50	premium modular unit including solid
Demolish and Install	Ea.	675	76		751	hardwood faced frames, hardwood
Reinstall	Ea.		34.91		34.91	door frames and drawer fronts,
Clean	Ea.	2.88	23		25.88	hardwood veneer on raised door
Paint	Ea.	2.38	61.50		63.88	panels, hinges and pulls.
Minimum Charge	Job		216		216	
Clean Interior						
Clean	L.F.	.80	4.85		5.65	Includes labor and materials to clean
Minimum Charge	Job		160		160	the interior of a 27" cabinet.
Premium Hardwood						
12" w, 1 Door, 1 Drawer						
Demolish	Ea.		8.90		8.90	Includes material and labor to install
Install	Ea.	370	35		405	premium hardwood modular unit with
Demolish and Install	Ea.	370	43.90		413.90	solid hardwood faced frames, drawer
Reinstall	Ea.		27.87		27.87	fronts, and door panels, steel drawer
Clean	Ea.	.80	6.40		7.20	guides, hinges, pulls and laminated
Paint	Ea.	.68	20.50		21.18	interior.
Minimum Charge	Job		216		216	
15" w, 1 Door, 1 Drawer						
Demolish	Ea.		11.15		11.15	Includes material and labor to install
Install	Ea.	380	36		416	premium hardwood modular unit with
Demolish and Install	Ea.	380	47.15		427.15	solid hardwood faced frames, drawer
Reinstall	Ea.		28.80		28.80	fronts, and door panels, steel drawer
Clean	Ea.	1.01	8		9.01	guides, hinges, pulls and laminated
Paint	Ea.	.86	26.50		27.36	interior.
Minimum Charge	Job		216		216	
18" w, 1 Door, 1 Drawer						
Demolish	Ea.		13.20		13.20	Includes material and labor to install
Install	Ea.	415	37		452	premium hardwood modular unit with
Demolish and Install	Ea.	415	50.20		465.20	solid hardwood faced frames, drawer
Reinstall	Ea.		29.67		29.67	fronts, and door panels, steel drawer
Clean	Ea.	1.19	9.70		10.89	guides, hinges, pulls and laminated
Paint	Ea.	1.02	31		32.02	interior.
Minimum Charge	Job		216		216	
21" w, 1 Door, 1 Drawer						
Demolish	Ea.		15.50		15.50	Includes material and labor to install
Install	Ea.	425	38		463	premium hardwood modular unit with
Demolish and Install	Ea.	425	53.50		478.50	solid hardwood faced frames, drawer
Reinstall	Ea.		30.45		30.45	fronts, and door panels, steel drawer
Clean	Ea.	1.44	11.45		12.89	guides, hinges, pulls and laminated
Paint	Ea.	1.20	33.50		34.70	interior.
Minimum Charge	Job		216		216	
24" w, 1 Door, 1 Drawer						
Demolish	Ea.		17.80		17.80	Includes material and labor to install
Install	Ea.	500	38.50		538.50	premium hardwood modular unit with
Demolish and Install	Ea.	500	56.30		556.30	solid hardwood faced frames, drawer
Reinstall	Ea.		31		31	fronts, and door panels, steel drawer
Clean	Ea.	1.55	12.80		14.35	guides, hinges and pulls, laminated
Paint	Ea.	1.36	41		42.36	interior.
Minimum Charge	Job		216		216	

Cabinets and Countertops

Base Cabinets		Unit	Material	Labor	Equip.	Total	Specification
30″ Wide Sink Base							
	Demolish	Ea.		22.50		22.50	Includes material and labor to install
	Install	Ea.	485	40.50		525.50	premium hardwood modular unit with
	Demolish and Install	Ea.	485	63		548	solid hardwood faced frames, drawer
	Reinstall	Ea.		32.30		32.30	fronts, and door panels, steel drawer
	Clean	Ea.	2.01	16		18.01	guides, hinges, pulls and laminated
	Paint	Ea.	1.72	46		47.72	interior.
	Minimum Charge	Job		216		216	
36″ Wide Sink Base							
	Demolish	Ea.		27.50		27.50	Includes material and labor to install
	Install	Ea.	545	42.50		587.50	premium hardwood modular unit with
	Demolish and Install	Ea.	545	70		615	solid hardwood faced frames, drawer
	Reinstall	Ea.		34.05		34.05	fronts, and door panels, steel drawer
	Clean	Ea.	2.24	18.85		21.09	guides, hinges, pulls and laminated
	Paint	Ea.	2.08	61.50		63.58	interior.
	Minimum Charge	Job		216		216	
36″ Blind Corner							
	Demolish	Ea.		27.50		27.50	Includes material and labor to install
	Install	Ea.	865	48		913	premium hardwood modular unit with
	Demolish and Install	Ea.	865	75.50		940.50	solid hardwood faced frames, drawer
	Reinstall	Ea.		38.40		38.40	fronts, and door panels, steel drawer
	Clean	Ea.	2.24	18.85		21.09	guides, hinges, pulls and laminated
	Paint	Ea.	2.08	61.50		63.58	interior.
	Minimum Charge	Job		216		216	
42″ w, 2 Door, 2 Drawer							
	Demolish	Ea.		32.50		32.50	Includes material and labor to install
	Install	Ea.	890	43.50		933.50	premium hardwood modular unit with
	Demolish and Install	Ea.	890	76		966	solid hardwood faced frames, drawer
	Reinstall	Ea.		34.91		34.91	fronts, and door panels, steel drawer
	Clean	Ea.	2.88	23		25.88	guides, hinges, pulls and laminated
	Paint	Ea.	2.38	74		76.38	interior.
	Minimum Charge	Job		216		216	
Clean Interior							
	Clean	L.F.	.80	4.85		5.65	Includes labor and materials to clean
	Minimum Charge	Job		160		160	the interior of a 27″ cabinet.
Island							
24″ Wide							
	Demolish	Ea.		17.80		17.80	Includes material and labor to install
	Install	Ea.	590	36		626	custom modular unit with solid
	Demolish and Install	Ea.	590	53.80		643.80	hardwood faced frames, hardwood
	Reinstall	Ea.		28.80		28.80	door frames and drawer fronts,
	Clean	Ea.	2.24	18.85		21.09	hardwood veneer on raised door
	Paint	Ea.	2.06	53		55.06	panels, hinges and pulls.
	Minimum Charge	Job		216		216	
30″ Wide							
	Demolish	Ea.		22.50		22.50	Includes material and labor to install
	Install	Ea.	655	45		700	custom modular unit with solid
	Demolish and Install	Ea.	655	67.50		722.50	hardwood faced frames, hardwood
	Reinstall	Ea.		36		36	door frames and drawer fronts,
	Clean	Ea.	2.88	23		25.88	hardwood veneer on raised door
	Paint	Ea.	2.57	61.50		64.07	panels, hinges and pulls.
	Minimum Charge	Job		216		216	

Cabinets and Countertops

Base Cabinets		Unit	Material	Labor	Equip.	Total	Specification
36″ Wide							
	Demolish	Ea.		27.50		27.50	Includes material and labor to install
	Install	Ea.	755	54		809	custom modular unit with solid
	Demolish and Install	Ea.	755	81.50		836.50	hardwood faced frames, hardwood
	Reinstall	Ea.		43.20		43.20	door frames and drawer fronts,
	Clean	Ea.	3.36	29		32.36	hardwood veneer on raised door
	Paint	Ea.	3.11	74		77.11	panels, hinges and pulls.
	Minimum Charge	Job		216		216	
48″ Wide							
	Demolish	Ea.		35.50		35.50	Includes material and labor to install
	Install	Ea.	1175	72		1247	custom modular unit with solid
	Demolish and Install	Ea.	1175	107.50		1282.50	hardwood faced frames, hardwood
	Reinstall	Ea.		57.60		57.60	door frames and drawer fronts,
	Clean	Ea.	4.03	35.50		39.53	hardwood veneer on raised door
	Paint	Ea.	3.58	92.50		96.08	panels, hinges and pulls.
	Minimum Charge	Job		216		216	
60″ Wide							
	Demolish	Ea.		39.50		39.50	Includes material and labor to install
	Install	Ea.	1325	90		1415	custom modular unit with solid
	Demolish and Install	Ea.	1325	129.50		1454.50	hardwood faced frames, hardwood
	Reinstall	Ea.		72		72	door frames and drawer fronts,
	Clean	Ea.	5.05	46		51.05	hardwood veneer on raised door
	Paint	Ea.	3.58	123		126.58	panels, hinges and pulls.
	Minimum Charge	Job		216		216	
Clean Interior							
	Clean	L.F.	.80	4.85		5.65	Includes labor and materials to clean
	Minimum Charge	Job		160		160	the interior of a 27″ cabinet.
Liquor Bar							
	Demolish	L.F.		8.90		8.90	Includes material and labor to install
	Install	L.F.	179	43		222	custom modular unit with solid
	Demolish and Install	L.F.	179	51.90		230.90	hardwood faced frames, hardwood
	Reinstall	L.F.		34.56		34.56	door frames and drawer fronts,
	Clean	L.F.	.80	6.70		7.50	hardwood veneer on raised door
	Paint	L.F.	5.50	16.80		22.30	panels, hinges and pulls.
	Minimum Charge	Job		216		216	
Clean Interior							
	Clean	L.F.	.80	4.85		5.65	Includes labor and materials to clean
	Minimum Charge	Job		160		160	the interior of a 27″ cabinet.
Seal Interior							
	Install	L.F.	.51	6.05		6.56	Includes labor and materials to seal a
	Minimum Charge	Job		185		185	cabinet interior.
Back Bar							
	Demolish	L.F.		8.90		8.90	Includes material and labor to install
	Install	L.F.	179	43		222	custom modular unit with solid
	Demolish and Install	L.F.	179	51.90		230.90	hardwood faced frames, hardwood
	Reinstall	L.F.		34.56		34.56	door frames and drawer fronts,
	Clean	L.F.	.80	6.70		7.50	hardwood veneer on raised door
	Paint	L.F.	5.50	16.80		22.30	panels, hinges and pulls.
	Minimum Charge	Job		216		216	
Clean Interior							
	Clean	L.F.	.80	4.85		5.65	Includes labor and materials to clean
	Minimum Charge	Job		160		160	the interior of a 27″ cabinet.

Cabinets and Countertops

Base Cabinets		Unit	Material	Labor	Equip.	Total	Specification
Seal Interior							
	Install	L.F.	.51	6.05		6.56	Includes labor and materials to seal a
	Minimum Charge	Job		185		185	cabinet interior.
Storage (garage)							
	Demolish	L.F.		8.90		8.90	Includes material and labor to install
	Install	L.F.	134	43		177	good modular unit with melamine
	Demolish and Install	L.F.	134	51.90		185.90	laminate, textured colors or wood
	Reinstall	L.F.		34.56		34.56	grain print finish including hinges and
	Clean	L.F.	.80	6.70		7.50	pulls.
	Paint	L.F.	5.50	16.80		22.30	
	Minimum Charge	Job		216		216	
Clean Interior							
	Clean	L.F.	.80	4.85		5.65	Includes labor and materials to clean
	Minimum Charge	Job		160		160	the interior of a 27″ cabinet.
Seal Interior							
	Install	L.F.	.51	6.05		6.56	Includes labor and materials to seal a
	Minimum Charge	Job		185		185	cabinet interior.
Built-in Desk							
	Demolish	L.F.		8.90		8.90	Includes material and labor to install
	Install	L.F.	179	43		222	custom modular unit with solid
	Demolish and Install	L.F.	179	51.90		230.90	hardwood faced frames, hardwood
	Reinstall	L.F.		34.56		34.56	door frames and drawer fronts,
	Clean	L.F.	.80	6.70		7.50	hardwood veneer on raised door
	Paint	L.F.	5.50	16.80		22.30	panels, hinges and pulls.
	Minimum Charge	Job		216		216	
Built-in Bookcase							
	Demolish	L.F.		11.85		11.85	Includes material and labor to install
	Install	L.F.	38.50	43		81.50	custom modular bookcase unit with
	Demolish and Install	L.F.	38.50	54.85		93.35	clear pine faced frames, shelves 12″
	Reinstall	L.F.		34.56		34.56	O.C., 7′ high, 8″ deep.
	Clean	L.F.	1.62	11.45		13.07	
	Paint	L.F.	1.60	28.50		30.10	
	Minimum Charge	Job		216		216	
Strip and Refinish							
	Install	L.F.	4.61	46		50.61	Includes labor and material to strip,
	Minimum Charge	Job		185		185	prep and refinish exterior of cabinets.
Stain							
	Install	L.F.	.59	1.72		2.31	Includes labor and material to stain
	Minimum Charge	Job		216		216	door and exterior of cabinets.

Countertop		Unit	Material	Labor	Equip.	Total	Specification
Laminated							
With Splash							
	Demolish	L.F.		5.95		5.95	Includes material and labor to install
	Install	L.F.	45.50	15.45		60.95	one piece laminated top with 4″
	Demolish and Install	L.F.	45.50	21.40		66.90	backsplash.
	Reinstall	L.F.		12.34		12.34	
	Clean	L.F.	.10	.80		.90	
	Minimum Charge	Job		216		216	

Cabinets and Countertops

Countertop	Unit	Material	Labor	Equip.	Total	Specification
Roll Top						
Demolish	L.F.		5.95		5.95	Includes material and labor to install
Install	L.F.	11	14.40		25.40	one piece laminated top with rolled
Demolish and Install	L.F.	11	20.35		31.35	drip edge (post formed) and
Reinstall	L.F.		11.52		11.52	backsplash.
Clean	L.F.	.14	1.21		1.35	
Minimum Charge	Job		216		216	
Ceramic Tile						
Demolish	S.F.		2.97		2.97	Cost includes material and labor to
Install	S.F.	18.15	8.65		26.80	install 4-1/4" x 4-1/4" to 6" x 6"
Demolish and Install	S.F.	18.15	11.62		29.77	glazed tile set in mortar bed and grout
Clean	S.F.	.08	.61		.69	on particle board substrate.
Minimum Charge	Job		189		189	
Cultured Marble						
Demolish	L.F.		5.95		5.95	Includes material and labor to install
Install	L.F.	49.50	42.50		92	marble countertop, 24" wide, no
Demolish and Install	L.F.	49.50	48.45		97.95	backsplash.
Reinstall	L.F.		33.98		33.98	
Clean	L.F.	.14	1.21		1.35	
Minimum Charge	Job		189		189	
With Splash						
Demolish	L.F.		5.95		5.95	Includes material and labor to install
Install	L.F.	57	42.50		99.50	marble countertop, 24" wide, with
Demolish and Install	L.F.	57	48.45		105.45	backsplash.
Reinstall	L.F.		33.98		33.98	
Clean	L.F.	.14	1.21		1.35	
Minimum Charge	Job		189		189	
Quarry Tile						
Demolish	S.F.		2.97		2.97	Includes material and labor to install
Install	S.F.	9.35	8.65		18	quarry tile countertop with no
Demolish and Install	S.F.	9.35	11.62		20.97	backsplash.
Clean	S.F.	.08	.61		.69	
Minimum Charge	Job		189		189	
With Splash						
Demolish	S.F.		2.97		2.97	Includes material and labor to install
Install	S.F.	12.20	9.60		21.80	quarry tile countertop with backsplash.
Demolish and Install	S.F.	12.20	12.57		24.77	
Clean	S.F.	.08	.61		.69	
Minimum Charge	Job		189		189	
Butcher Block						
Demolish	S.F.		2.97		2.97	Includes material and labor to install
Install	S.F.	40.50	7.70		48.20	solid laminated maple countertop with
Demolish and Install	S.F.	40.50	10.67		51.17	no backsplash.
Reinstall	S.F.		6.17		6.17	
Clean	S.F.	.03	.25		.28	
Minimum Charge	Job		216		216	
Solid Surface						
Demolish	L.F.		5.95		5.95	Includes material and labor to install
Install	L.F.	59	31		90	solid surface counter top 22" deep.
Demolish and Install	L.F.	59	36.95		95.95	
Reinstall	L.F.		24.69		24.69	
Clean	L.F.	.14	1.21		1.35	
Minimum Charge	Job		216		216	

Vanity Cabinets

Vanity Cabinets	Unit	Material	Labor	Equip.	Total	Specification
Good Grade Laminated						
24" Wide, 2 Door						
Demolish	Ea.		17.80		17.80	Includes material and labor to install
Install	Ea.	245	43		288	modular unit with melamine laminated
Demolish and Install	Ea.	245	60.80		305.80	to particle board, textured colors or
Reinstall	Ea.		34.56		34.56	wood grain print finish, hinges and
Clean	Ea.	1.55	12.80		14.35	pulls.
Paint	Ea.	1.36	31		32.36	
Minimum Charge	Job		216		216	
30" Wide, 2 Door						
Demolish	Ea.		22.50		22.50	Includes material and labor to install
Install	Ea.	293	54		347	modular unit with melamine laminated
Demolish and Install	Ea.	293	76.50		369.50	to particle board, textured colors or
Reinstall	Ea.		43.20		43.20	wood grain print finish, hinges and
Clean	Ea.	2.01	16		18.01	pulls.
Paint	Ea.	1.72	37		38.72	
Minimum Charge	Job		216		216	
36" Wide, 2 Door						
Demolish	Ea.		27.50		27.50	Includes material and labor to install
Install	Ea.	284	65		349	modular unit with melamine laminated
Demolish and Install	Ea.	284	92.50		376.50	to particle board, textured colors or
Reinstall	Ea.		51.85		51.85	wood grain print finish, hinges and
Clean	Ea.	2.24	18.85		21.09	pulls.
Paint	Ea.	2.08	46		48.08	
Minimum Charge	Job		216		216	
42" w, 3 Doors / Drawer						
Demolish	Ea.		32.50		32.50	Includes material and labor to install
Install	Ea.	470	70		540	modular unit with melamine laminated
Demolish and Install	Ea.	470	102.50		572.50	to particle board, textured colors or
Reinstall	Ea.		55.83		55.83	wood grain print finish, hinges and
Clean	Ea.	2.88	23		25.88	pulls.
Paint	Ea.	2.38	53		55.38	
Minimum Charge	Job		216		216	
48" w, 3 Doors / Drawer						
Demolish	Ea.		35.50		35.50	Includes material and labor to install
Install	Ea.	375	75.50		450.50	modular unit with melamine laminated
Demolish and Install	Ea.	375	111		486	to particle board, textured colors or
Reinstall	Ea.		60.47		60.47	wood grain print finish, hinges and
Clean	Ea.	4.03	35.50		39.53	pulls.
Paint	Ea.	3.58	92.50		96.08	
Minimum Charge	Job		216		216	
Clean Interior						
Install	L.F.	.80	6.70		7.50	Includes labor and materials to clean
Minimum Charge	Job		160		160	base cabinetry.
Better Grade Wood						
24" Wide, 2 Door						
Demolish	Ea.		17.80		17.80	Includes material and labor to install
Install	Ea.	325	43		368	custom modular unit with solid
Demolish and Install	Ea.	325	60.80		385.80	hardwood faced frames, hardwood
Reinstall	Ea.		34.56		34.56	door frames and drawer fronts,
Clean	Ea.	1.55	12.80		14.35	hardwood veneer on raised door
Paint	Ea.	1.36	33.50		34.86	panels, hinges and pulls.
Minimum Charge	Job		216		216	

Cabinets and Countertops

Vanity Cabinets	Unit	Material	Labor	Equip.	Total	Specification
30″ Wide, 2 Door						
Demolish	Ea.		22.50		22.50	Includes material and labor to install
Install	Ea.	390	54		444	custom modular unit with solid
Demolish and Install	Ea.	390	76.50		466.50	hardwood faced frames, hardwood
Reinstall	Ea.		43.20		43.20	door frames and drawer fronts,
Clean	Ea.	2.01	16		18.01	hardwood veneer on raised door
Paint	Ea.	1.72	41		42.72	panels, hinges and pulls.
Minimum Charge	Job		216		216	
36″ Wide, 2 Door						
Demolish	Ea.		27.50		27.50	Includes material and labor to install
Install	Ea.	380	65		445	custom modular unit with solid
Demolish and Install	Ea.	380	92.50		472.50	hardwood faced frames, hardwood
Reinstall	Ea.		51.85		51.85	door frames and drawer fronts,
Clean	Ea.	2.24	18.85		21.09	hardwood veneer on raised door
Paint	Ea.	2.08	53		55.08	panels, hinges and pulls.
Minimum Charge	Job		216		216	
42″ w, 3 Doors / Drawer						
Demolish	Ea.		32.50		32.50	Includes material and labor to install
Install	Ea.	470	70		540	custom modular unit with solid
Demolish and Install	Ea.	470	102.50		572.50	hardwood faced frames, hardwood
Reinstall	Ea.		55.83		55.83	door frames and drawer fronts,
Clean	Ea.	2.88	23		25.88	hardwood veneer on raised door
Paint	Ea.	2.38	61.50		63.88	panels, hinges and pulls.
Minimum Charge	Job		216		216	
48″ w, 3 Doors / Drawer						
Demolish	Ea.		35.50		35.50	Includes material and labor to install
Install	Ea.	495	75.50		570.50	custom modular unit with solid
Demolish and Install	Ea.	495	111		606	hardwood faced frames, hardwood
Reinstall	Ea.		60.47		60.47	door frames and drawer fronts,
Clean	Ea.	4.03	35.50		39.53	hardwood veneer on raised door
Paint	Ea.	3.58	92.50		96.08	panels, hinges and pulls.
Minimum Charge	Job		216		216	
Clean Interior						
Install	L.F.	.80	6.70		7.50	Includes labor and materials to clean
Minimum Charge	Job		160		160	base cabinetry.
Premium Grade Wood						
24″ Wide, 2 Door						
Demolish	Ea.		17.80		17.80	Includes material and labor to install
Install	Ea.	345	43		388	premium modular unit with solid
Demolish and Install	Ea.	345	60.80		405.80	hardwood faced frames, hardwood
Reinstall	Ea.		34.56		34.56	door frames and drawer fronts,
Clean	Ea.	1.55	12.80		14.35	hardwood veneer on raised door
Paint	Ea.	1.36	37		38.36	panels, hinges and pulls.
Minimum Charge	Job		216		216	
30″ Wide, 2 Door						
Demolish	Ea.		22.50		22.50	Includes material and labor to install
Install	Ea.	485	54		539	premium modular unit with solid
Demolish and Install	Ea.	485	76.50		561.50	hardwood faced frames, hardwood
Reinstall	Ea.		43.20		43.20	door frames and drawer fronts,
Clean	Ea.	2.01	16		18.01	hardwood veneer on raised door
Paint	Ea.	1.72	46		47.72	panels, hinges and pulls.
Minimum Charge	Job		216		216	

Cabinets and Countertops

Vanity Cabinets	Unit	Material	Labor	Equip.	Total	Specification
36" Wide, 2 Door						
Demolish	Ea.		27.50		27.50	Includes material and labor to install
Install	Ea.	470	65		535	premium modular unit with solid
Demolish and Install	Ea.	470	92.50		562.50	hardwood faced frames, hardwood
Reinstall	Ea.		51.85		51.85	door frames and drawer fronts,
Clean	Ea.	2.24	18.85		21.09	hardwood veneer on raised door
Paint	Ea.	2.08	53		55.08	panels, hinges and pulls.
Minimum Charge	Job		216		216	
42" w, 3 Doors / Drawer						
Demolish	Ea.		32.50		32.50	Includes material and labor to install
Install	Ea.	545	70		615	premium modular unit with solid
Demolish and Install	Ea.	545	102.50		647.50	hardwood faced frames, hardwood
Reinstall	Ea.		55.83		55.83	door frames and drawer fronts,
Clean	Ea.	2.88	23		25.88	hardwood veneer on raised door
Paint	Ea.	2.38	61.50		63.88	panels, hinges and pulls.
Minimum Charge	Job		216		216	
48" w, 3 Doors / Drawer						
Demolish	Ea.		35.50		35.50	Includes material and labor to install
Install	Ea.	565	75.50		640.50	premium modular unit with solid
Demolish and Install	Ea.	565	111		676	hardwood faced frames, hardwood
Reinstall	Ea.		60.47		60.47	door frames and drawer fronts,
Clean	Ea.	4.03	35.50		39.53	hardwood veneer on raised door
Paint	Ea.	3.58	92.50		96.08	panels, hinges and pulls.
Minimum Charge	Job		216		216	
Clean Interior						
Install	L.F.	.80	6.70		7.50	Includes labor and materials to clean
Minimum Charge	Job		160		160	base cabinetry.
Premium Hardwood						
24" Wide, 2 Door						
Demolish	Ea.		17.80		17.80	Includes material and labor to install
Install	Ea.	405	43		448	premium modular unit with solid
Demolish and Install	Ea.	405	60.80		465.80	hardwood faced frames, hardwood
Reinstall	Ea.		34.56		34.56	door frames and drawer fronts,
Clean	Ea.	1.55	12.80		14.35	hardwood veneer on raised door
Paint	Ea.	1.36	41		42.36	panels, hinges and pulls.
Minimum Charge	Job		216		216	
30" Wide, 2 Door						
Demolish	Ea.		22.50		22.50	Includes material and labor to install
Install	Ea.	610	54		664	premium modular unit with solid
Demolish and Install	Ea.	610	76.50		686.50	hardwood faced frames, hardwood
Reinstall	Ea.		43.20		43.20	door frames and drawer fronts,
Clean	Ea.	2.01	16		18.01	hardwood veneer on raised door
Paint	Ea.	1.72	46		47.72	panels, hinges and pulls.
Minimum Charge	Job		216		216	
36" Wide, 2 Door						
Demolish	Ea.		27.50		27.50	Includes material and labor to install
Install	Ea.	855	65		920	premium modular unit with solid
Demolish and Install	Ea.	855	92.50		947.50	hardwood faced frames, hardwood
Reinstall	Ea.		51.85		51.85	door frames and drawer fronts,
Clean	Ea.	2.24	18.85		21.09	hardwood veneer on raised door
Paint	Ea.	2.08	61.50		63.58	panels, hinges and pulls.
Minimum Charge	Job		216		216	

Cabinets and Countertops

Vanity Cabinets

	Unit	Material	Labor	Equip.	Total	Specification
42" w, 3 Doors / Drawer						Includes material and labor to install
Demolish	Ea.		32.50		32.50	premium modular unit with solid
Install	Ea.	550	70		620	hardwood faced frames, hardwood
Demolish and Install	Ea.	550	102.50		652.50	door frames and drawer fronts,
Reinstall	Ea.		55.83		55.83	hardwood veneer on raised door
Clean	Ea.	2.88	23		25.88	panels, hinges and pulls.
Paint	Ea.	2.38	74		76.38	
Minimum Charge	Job		216		216	
48" w, 3 Doors / Drawer						Includes material and labor to install
Demolish	Ea.		35.50		35.50	premium modular unit with solid
Install	Ea.	615	75.50		690.50	hardwood faced frames, hardwood
Demolish and Install	Ea.	615	111		726	door frames and drawer fronts,
Reinstall	Ea.		60.47		60.47	hardwood veneer on raised door
Clean	Ea.	4.03	35.50		39.53	panels, hinges and pulls.
Paint	Ea.	3.58	92.50		96.08	
Minimum Charge	Job		216		216	
Clean Interior						
Install	L.F.	.80	6.70		7.50	Includes labor and materials to clean
Minimum Charge	Job		160		160	base cabinetry.
Strip and Refinish						
Install	L.F.	4.61	46		50.61	Includes labor and material to strip,
Minimum Charge	Job		185		185	prep and refinish exterior of cabinets.

Vanity Cabinet Tops

	Unit	Material	Labor	Equip.	Total	Specification
Cultured Marble Top						
Demolish	L.F.		5.95		5.95	Includes material and labor to install
Install	L.F.	45	25		70	cultured marble vanity top with
Demolish and Install	L.F.	45	30.95		75.95	integral sink, 22" deep.
Reinstall	L.F.		19.99		19.99	
Clean	L.F.	.14	1.21		1.35	
Minimum Charge	Job		189		189	
Laminated Top						
Demolish	L.F.		3.56		3.56	Includes material and labor to install
Install	L.F.	45.50	15.45		60.95	one piece laminated top with 4"
Demolish and Install	L.F.	45.50	19.01		64.51	backsplash.
Reinstall	L.F.		12.34		12.34	
Clean	L.F.	.10	.80		.90	
Minimum Charge	Job		216		216	
Solid Surface						
Demolish	L.F.		5.95		5.95	Includes material and labor to install
Install	L.F.	82	32		114	solid surface vanity top with integral
Demolish and Install	L.F.	82	37.95		119.95	sink installed, 22" deep.
Reinstall	L.F.		25.60		25.60	
Clean	L.F.	.14	1.21		1.35	
Minimum Charge	Job		216		216	

Painting

Roller Handle

Paint Brush

Paint Preparation, Walls		Unit	Material	Labor	Equip.	Total	Specification
Cover / Protect Floors							
	Install	S.F.	.03	.14		.17	Includes material and labor to install
	Minimum Charge	Job		186		186	plastic masking sheet on large uninterrupted areas.
Cover / Protect Walls							
	Install	S.F.	.03	.14		.17	Includes material and labor to install
	Minimum Charge	Job		186		186	plastic masking sheet on walls.
Clean Walls							
Light							
	Clean	S.F.		.12		.12	Includes labor to wash gypsum
	Minimum Charge	Job		186		186	drywall or plaster wall surfaces.
Heavy							
	Clean	S.F.		.15		.15	Includes labor and material for heavy
	Minimum Charge	Job		186		186	cleaning (multiple applications) with detergent and solvent.
Prep Walls							
	Paint	S.F.	.04	.18		.22	Includes labor and material to prepare
	Minimum Charge	Job		186		186	for painting including scraping, patching and puttying.
Sand Walls							
	Paint	S.F.		.12		.12	Includes labor to sand gypsum drywall
	Minimum Charge	Job		186		186	wall surfaces.
Seal Walls							
Large Area							
	Paint	S.F.	.07	.27		.34	Includes labor and material to paint
	Minimum Charge	Job		186		186	with primer / sealer by roller.
Spot							
	Paint	S.F.	.07	.32		.39	Includes labor and material to seal
	Minimum Charge	Job		186		186	existing drywall with shellac-based material.

Paint Preparation, Ceilings		Unit	Material	Labor	Equip.	Total	Specification
Cover / Protect Floors							
	Install	S.F.	.03	.14		.17	Includes material and labor to install
	Minimum Charge	Job		186		186	plastic masking sheet on large uninterrupted areas.

Painting

Paint Preparation, Ceilings

Paint Preparation, Ceilings		Unit	Material	Labor	Equip.	Total	Specification
Cover / Protect Walls							
	Install	S.F.	.03	.14		.17	Includes material and labor to install
	Minimum Charge	Job		186		186	plastic masking sheet on walls.
Prep Ceiling							
	Paint	S.F.	.08	.70		.78	Includes labor and material to fill in
	Minimum Charge	Job		186		186	hairline cracks up to 1/8" with filler,
							sand and prep for paint.
Sand Ceiling							
	Paint	S.F.		.17		.17	Includes labor to sand gypsum drywall
	Minimum Charge	Job		186		186	ceiling surfaces.
Seal Ceiling							
Large Area							
	Paint	S.F.	.07	.28		.35	Includes labor and material to paint
	Minimum Charge	Job		185		185	ceiling, one coat flat latex.
Spot							
	Paint	S.F.	.07	.32		.39	Includes labor and material to seal
	Minimum Charge	Job		185		185	existing drywall with shellac-based
							material.

Paint / Texture, Walls

Paint / Texture, Walls		Unit	Material	Labor	Equip.	Total	Specification
Texture Walls							
Spray							
	Install	S.F.	.04	.46		.50	Includes labor and material to install
	Minimum Charge	Job		185		185	by spray, texture finish.
Trowel							
	Install	S.F.		.25		.25	Includes labor and material to apply
	Minimum Charge	Job		185		185	hand troweled texture.
Paint Walls 1 Coat							
	Paint	S.F.	.07	.28		.35	Includes labor and material to paint,
	Minimum Charge	Job		185		185	one coat flat latex.
Paint Walls 2 Coats							
	Paint	S.F.	.14	.46		.60	Includes labor and material to paint,
	Minimum Charge	Job		185		185	two coats flat latex.
Paint Walls 3 Coats							
	Paint	S.F.	.21	.57		.78	Includes labor and material to paint,
	Minimum Charge	Job		185		185	three coats flat latex.
Clean and Seal							
	Paint	S.F.	.51	.99		1.50	Includes labor and material to do light
	Minimum Charge	Job		185		185	cleaning, sealing with 2 coats of latex
							paint.

Paint / Texture, Ceilings

Paint / Texture, Ceilings		Unit	Material	Labor	Equip.	Total	Specification
Texture Ceiling							
Spray							
	Install	S.F.	.04	.46		.50	Includes labor and material to install
	Minimum Charge	Job		185		185	by spray, texture finish.
Trowel							
	Install	S.F.		.25		.25	Includes labor and material to apply
	Minimum Charge	Job		185		185	hand troweled texture.

Painting

Paint / Texture, Ceilings		Unit	Material	Labor	Equip.	Total	Specification
Paint Ceiling, 1 Coat							
	Paint	S.F.	.07	.28		.35	Includes labor and material to paint
	Minimum Charge	Job		185		185	ceiling, one coat flat latex.
Paint Ceiling, 2 Coats							
	Paint	S.F.	.29	.46		.75	Includes labor and material to paint
	Minimum Charge	Job		185		185	two coats flat latex paint.
Paint Ceiling, 3 Coats							
	Paint	S.F.	.43	.54		.97	Includes labor and material to paint
	Minimum Charge	Job		185		185	ceiling, three coats flat latex.
Clean and Seal							
	Paint	S.F.	.43	.78		1.21	Includes labor and material for light
	Minimum Charge	Job		185		185	cleaning, sealing and paint 3 coats of
							flat latex paint.

237

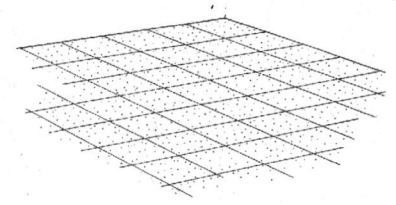

Plank Flooring　　　　　**Wood Strip Flooring**　　　　　**Tile Flooring**

Wood Plank Flooring	Unit	Material	Labor	Equip.	Total	Specification
Maple						
2-1/4″						
Demolish	S.F.		1.42		1.42	Includes material and labor to install
Install	S.F.	5.20	2.15		7.35	unfinished T&G maple flooring,
Demolish and Install	S.F.	5.20	3.57		8.77	25/32″ thick, 2-1/4″ wide, random
Reinstall	S.F.		1.72		1.72	3′ to 16′ lengths including felt
Clean	S.F.		.40		.40	underlayment, nailed in place over
Paint	S.F.	1.44	2.46		3.90	prepared subfloor.
Minimum Charge	Job		216		216	
3-1/4″						
Demolish	S.F.		1.42		1.42	Includes material and labor to install
Install	S.F.	4.05	2.15		6.20	unfinished T&G maple flooring,
Demolish and Install	S.F.	4.05	3.57		7.62	33/32″ thick, 3-1/4″ wide, random
Reinstall	S.F.		1.72		1.72	3′ to 16′ lengths including felt
Clean	S.F.		.40		.40	underlayment, nailed in place over
Paint	S.F.	1.44	2.46		3.90	prepared subfloor.
Minimum Charge	Job		216		216	
Sand and Finish						
Install	S.F.	.97	.80		1.77	Includes labor and material to sand (3
Minimum Charge	Job		216		216	passes) and finish and two coats of
						urethane existing floor.
Oak						
2-1/4″						
Demolish	S.F.		1.42		1.42	Includes material and labor to install
Install	S.F.	4.24	2.15		6.39	unfinished T&G oak flooring, 25/32″
Demolish and Install	S.F.	4.24	3.57		7.81	thick, 2-1/4″ wide, random 3′ to 16′
Reinstall	S.F.		1.72		1.72	lengths including felt underlayment,
Clean	S.F.		.40		.40	nailed in place over prepared
Paint	S.F.	1.44	2.46		3.90	subfloor.
Minimum Charge	Job		216		216	
3-1/4″						
Demolish	S.F.		1.42		1.42	Includes material and labor to install
Install	S.F.	4.23	1.53		5.76	unfinished T&G oak flooring, 25/32″
Demolish and Install	S.F.	4.23	2.95		7.18	thick, 3-1/4″ wide, random 3′ to 16′
Reinstall	S.F.		1.22		1.22	lengths including felt underlayment,
Clean	S.F.		.40		.40	nailed in place over prepared
Paint	S.F.	1.44	2.46		3.90	subfloor.
Minimum Charge	Job		216		216	

Flooring

Wood Plank Flooring	Unit	Material	Labor	Equip.	Total	Specification
Sand and Finish						
Install	S.F.	1.44	2.46		3.90	Includes labor and material to sand
Minimum Charge	Job		216		216	and finish (3 passes) with two coats of urethane on a new floor.
Walnut						
3″ to 7″						
Demolish	S.F.		1.42		1.42	Includes material and labor to install
Install	S.F.	18.05	1.53		19.58	unfinished T&G walnut flooring,
Demolish and Install	S.F.	18.05	2.95		21	25/32″ thick, random 3′ to 16′
Reinstall	S.F.		1.22		1.22	lengths including felt underlayment,
Clean	S.F.		.40		.40	nailed in place over prepared
Paint	S.F.	1.44	2.46		3.90	subfloor.
Minimum Charge	Job		216		216	
Sand and Finish						
Install	S.F.	1.44	2.46		3.90	Includes labor and material to sand
Minimum Charge	Job		216		216	and finish (3 passes) with two coats of urethane on a new floor.
Pine						
2-1/4″						
Demolish	S.F.		1.42		1.42	Includes material and labor to install
Install	S.F.	7.80	1.63		9.43	unfinished T&G pine flooring, 25/32″
Demolish and Install	S.F.	7.80	3.05		10.85	thick, 2-1/4″ wide, random 3′ to 16′
Reinstall	S.F.		1.30		1.30	lengths including felt underlayment,
Clean	S.F.		.40		.40	nailed in place over prepared
Paint	S.F.	.97	.80		1.77	subfloor.
Minimum Charge	Job		216		216	
Sand and Finish						
Install	S.F.	1.44	2.46		3.90	Includes labor and material to sand
Minimum Charge	Job		216		216	and finish (3 passes) with two coats of urethane on a new floor.
Prefinished Oak						
2-1/4″						
Demolish	S.F.		1.42		1.42	Includes material and labor to install
Install	S.F.	4.23	2.15		6.38	prefinished T&G oak flooring, 2-1/4″
Demolish and Install	S.F.	4.23	3.57		7.80	wide, random 3′ to 16′ lengths
Reinstall	S.F.		1.72		1.72	including felt underlayment, nailed in
Clean	S.F.		.40		.40	place over prepared subfloor.
Minimum Charge	Job		216		216	
3-1/4″						
Demolish	S.F.		1.42		1.42	Includes material and labor to install
Install	S.F.	4.60	1.98		6.58	prefinished T&G oak flooring, 25/32″
Demolish and Install	S.F.	4.60	3.40		8	thick, 3″ to 7″ wide, random 3′ to 16′
Reinstall	S.F.		1.58		1.58	lengths including felt underlayment,
Clean	S.F.		.40		.40	nailed in place over prepared
Minimum Charge	Job		216		216	subfloor.
Sand and Finish New						
Install	S.F.	.97	1.09		2.06	Includes labor and material to sand (3
Minimum Charge	Job		216		216	passes) and finish, two coats of urethane, new floor.
Refinish Existing						
Install	S.F.	.97	.80		1.77	Includes labor and material to sand (3
Minimum Charge	Job		216		216	passes) and finish and two coats of urethane existing floor.

Flooring

Wood Plank Flooring

Wood Plank Flooring	Unit	Material	Labor	Equip.	Total	Specification
Urethane Coat						
Install	S.F.	.17	.20		.37	Includes labor and material to install
Minimum Charge	Job		216		216	two coats of urethane, on existing floor.
Clean and Wax						
Clean	S.F.	.03	.25		.28	Includes labor and material to wash
Minimum Charge	Job		216		216	and wax a hardwood floor.
Underlayment Per S.F.						
Demolish	S.F.		.63		.63	Cost includes material and labor to
Install	S.F.	.92	.58		1.50	install 1/4" lauan subfloor, standard
Demolish and Install	S.F.	.92	1.21		2.13	interior grade, nailed every 6".
Clean	S.F.		.31		.31	
Minimum Charge	Job		216		216	

Wood Parquet Tile Floor

Wood Parquet Tile Floor	Unit	Material	Labor	Equip.	Total	Specification
Oak						
9" x 9"						
Demolish	S.F.		1.07		1.07	Includes material and labor to install
Install	S.F.	5.10	3.46		8.56	prefinished oak 9" x 9" parquet block
Demolish and Install	S.F.	5.10	4.53		9.63	flooring, 5/16" thick, installed in
Reinstall	S.F.		2.76		2.76	mastic.
Clean	S.F.		.40		.40	
Paint	S.F.	1.44	2.46		3.90	
Minimum Charge	Job		216		216	
13" x 13"						
Demolish	S.F.		1.07		1.07	Includes material and labor to install
Install	S.F.	9.35	2.70		12.05	prefinished oak 13" x 13" parquet
Demolish and Install	S.F.	9.35	3.77		13.12	block flooring, 5/16" thick, installed in
Reinstall	S.F.		2.16		2.16	mastic.
Clean	S.F.		.40		.40	
Paint	S.F.	1.44	2.46		3.90	
Minimum Charge	Job		216		216	
Cherry						
9" x 9"						
Demolish	S.F.		1.07		1.07	Includes material and labor to install
Install	S.F.	22	3.46		25.46	prefinished cherry 9" x 9" parquet
Demolish and Install	S.F.	22	4.53		26.53	block flooring, 5/16" thick, installed in
Reinstall	S.F.		3.46		3.46	mastic.
Clean	S.F.		.40		.40	
Paint	S.F.	1.44	2.46		3.90	
Minimum Charge	Job		216		216	
13" x 13"						
Demolish	S.F.		1.07		1.07	Includes material and labor to install
Install	S.F.	22	2.70		24.70	prefinished cherry 13" x 13" parquet
Demolish and Install	S.F.	22	3.77		25.77	block flooring, 5/16" thick, installed in
Reinstall	S.F.		2.70		2.70	mastic.
Clean	S.F.		.40		.40	
Paint	S.F.	1.44	2.46		3.90	
Minimum Charge	Job		216		216	

Flooring

Wood Parquet Tile Floor	Unit	Material	Labor	Equip.	Total	Specification
Walnut						
9" x 9"						
Demolish	S.F.		1.07		1.07	Includes material and labor to install
Install	S.F.	5.45	3.46		8.91	prefinished walnut 9" x 9" parquet
Demolish and Install	S.F.	5.45	4.53		9.98	flooring in mastic.
Reinstall	S.F.		2.76		2.76	
Clean	S.F.		.40		.40	
Paint	S.F.	1.44	2.46		3.90	
Minimum Charge	Job		216		216	
13" x 13"						
Demolish	S.F.		1.07		1.07	Includes material and labor to install
Install	S.F.	10.10	2.70		12.80	prefinished walnut 13" x 13" parquet
Demolish and Install	S.F.	10.10	3.77		13.87	block flooring, 5/16" thick, installed in
Reinstall	S.F.		2.70		2.70	mastic.
Clean	S.F.		.40		.40	
Paint	S.F.	1.44	2.46		3.90	
Minimum Charge	Job		216		216	
Acrylic Impregnated						
Oak 12" x 12"						
Demolish	S.F.		1.07		1.07	Includes material and labor to install
Install	S.F.	8.40	3.09		11.49	red oak 12" x 12" acrylic
Demolish and Install	S.F.	8.40	4.16		12.56	impregnated parquet block flooring,
Reinstall	S.F.		3.09		3.09	5/16" thick, installed in mastic.
Clean	S.F.		.40		.40	
Minimum Charge	Job		216		216	
Cherry 12" x 12"						
Demolish	S.F.		1.07		1.07	Includes material and labor to install
Install	S.F.	22	3.09		25.09	prefinished cherry 12" x 12" acrylic
Demolish and Install	S.F.	22	4.16		26.16	impregnated parquet block flooring,
Reinstall	S.F.		3.09		3.09	5/16" thick, installed in mastic.
Clean	S.F.		.40		.40	
Minimum Charge	Job		216		216	
Ash 12" x 12"						
Demolish	S.F.		1.07		1.07	Includes material and labor to install
Install	S.F.	16.50	3.09		19.59	ash 12" x 12" acrylic impregnated
Demolish and Install	S.F.	16.50	4.16		20.66	parquet block flooring, 5/16" thick in
Reinstall	S.F.		3.09		3.09	mastic.
Clean	S.F.		.40		.40	
Minimum Charge	Job		216		216	
Teak						
Demolish	S.F.		1.07		1.07	Includes material and labor to install
Install	S.F.	7.55	2.70		10.25	prefinished teak parquet block
Demolish and Install	S.F.	7.55	3.77		11.32	flooring, 5/16" thick, and installed in
Reinstall	S.F.		2.70		2.70	mastic.
Clean	S.F.		.40		.40	
Paint	S.F.	1.44	2.46		3.90	
Minimum Charge	Job		216		216	
Clean and Wax						
Clean	S.F.	.03	.25		.28	Includes labor and material to wash
Minimum Charge	Job		216		216	and wax a hardwood floor.

Flooring

Ceramic Tile Flooring	Unit	Material	Labor	Equip.	Total	Specification
Economy Grade						
Demolish	S.F.		1.05		1.05	Cost includes material and labor to
Install	S.F.	8.70	7.45		16.15	install 4-1/4″ x 4-1/4″ ceramic tile in
Demolish and Install	S.F.	8.70	8.50		17.20	mortar bed including grout.
Clean	S.F.		.61		.61	
Minimum Charge	Job		189		189	
Average Grade						
Demolish	S.F.		1.05		1.05	Cost includes material and labor to
Install	S.F.	11.05	7.60		18.65	install 4-1/4″ x 4-1/4″ ceramic tile in
Demolish and Install	S.F.	11.05	8.65		19.70	mortar bed including grout.
Clean	S.F.		.61		.61	
Minimum Charge	Job		189		189	
Premium Grade						
Demolish	S.F.		1.05		1.05	Cost includes material and labor to
Install	S.F.	13.25	7.60		20.85	install 4-1/4″ x 4-1/4″ ceramic tile in
Demolish and Install	S.F.	13.25	8.65		21.90	mortar bed including grout.
Clean	S.F.		.61		.61	
Minimum Charge	Job		189		189	
Re-grout						
Install	S.F.	.15	3.03		3.18	Includes material and labor to regrout
Minimum Charge	Job		189		189	tile floors.

Hard Tile Flooring	Unit	Material	Labor	Equip.	Total	Specification
Thick Set Paver						
Brick						
Demolish	S.F.		2.23		2.23	Cost includes material and labor to
Install	S.F.	1.52	18.30		19.82	install 6″ x 12″ adobe brick paver with
Demolish and Install	S.F.	1.52	20.53		22.05	1/2″ mortar joints.
Clean	S.F.		.61		.61	
Minimum Charge	Job		189		189	
Mexican Red						
Demolish	S.F.		2.23		2.23	Cost includes material and labor to
Install	S.F.	1.83	7.90		9.73	install 12″ x 12″ red Mexican paver
Demolish and Install	S.F.	1.83	10.13		11.96	tile in mortar bed with grout.
Clean	S.F.		.61		.61	
Minimum Charge	Job		189		189	
Saltillo						
Demolish	S.F.		1.05		1.05	Cost includes material and labor to
Install	S.F.	1.54	7.90		9.44	install 12″ x 12″ saltillo tile in mortar
Demolish and Install	S.F.	1.54	8.95		10.49	bed with grout.
Clean	S.F.		.61		.61	
Minimum Charge	Job		189		189	
Marble						
Premium Grade						
Demolish	S.F.		1.05		1.05	Cost includes material and labor to
Install	S.F.	21	16.45		37.45	install 3/8″ x 12″ x 12″ marble, in
Demolish and Install	S.F.	21	17.50		38.50	mortar bed with grout.
Clean	S.F.		.61		.61	
Minimum Charge	Job		189		189	

Flooring

Hard Tile Flooring	Unit	Material	Labor	Equip.	Total	Specification
Terrazzo						
Gray Cement						
Demolish	S.F.		1.41		1.41	Cost includes material and labor to
Install	S.F.	3.61	9.20	4.26	17.07	install 1-3/4" terrazzo , #1 and #2
Demolish and Install	S.F.	3.61	10.61	4.26	18.48	chips in gray Portland cement.
Clean	S.F.		.61		.61	
Minimum Charge	Job		345	160	505	
White Cement						
Demolish	S.F.		1.41		1.41	Cost includes material and labor to
Install	S.F.	4.02	9.20	4.26	17.48	install 1-3/4" terrazzo, #1 and #2
Demolish and Install	S.F.	4.02	10.61	4.26	18.89	chips in white Portland cement.
Clean	S.F.		.61		.61	
Minimum Charge	Job		345	160	505	
Non-skid Gray						
Demolish	S.F.		1.41		1.41	Cost includes material and labor to
Install	S.F.	6.65	11.50	5.35	23.50	install 1-3/4" terrazzo, #1 and #2
Demolish and Install	S.F.	6.65	12.91	5.35	24.91	chips in gray Portland cement with
Clean	S.F.		.61		.61	light non-skid abrasive.
Minimum Charge	Job		345	160	505	
Non-skid White						
Demolish	S.F.		1.41		1.41	Cost includes material and labor to
Install	S.F.	7	11.50	5.35	23.85	install 1-3/4" terrazzo, #1 and #2
Demolish and Install	S.F.	7	12.91	5.35	25.26	chips in white Portland cement with
Clean	S.F.		.61		.61	light non-skid abrasive.
Minimum Charge	Job		345	160	505	
Gray w / Brass Divider						
Demolish	S.F.		1.42		1.42	Cost includes material and labor to
Install	S.F.	10.10	12.55	5.80	28.45	install 1-3/4" terrazzo, #1 and #2
Demolish and Install	S.F.	10.10	13.97	5.80	29.87	chips in gray Portland cement with
Clean	S.F.		.61		.61	brass strips 2' O.C. each way.
Minimum Charge	Job		345	160	505	
Clean						
Clean	S.F.	.18	.41		.59	Includes labor and material to clean
Minimum Charge	Job		345	160	505	terrazzo flooring.
Slate						
Demolish	S.F.		1.27		1.27	Includes material and labor to install
Install	S.F.	7.70	3.78		11.48	slate tile flooring in thin set with grout.
Demolish and Install	S.F.	7.70	5.05		12.75	
Clean	S.F.		.61		.61	
Minimum Charge	Job		189		189	
Granite						
Demolish	S.F.		1.05		1.05	Includes material and labor to install
Install	S.F.	25	3.79		28.79	granite tile flooring in thin set with
Demolish and Install	S.F.	25	4.84		29.84	grout.
Reinstall	S.F.		3.79		3.79	
Clean	S.F.		.61		.61	
Minimum Charge	Job		189		189	
Re-grout						
Install	S.F.	.15	3.03		3.18	Includes material and labor to regrout
Minimum Charge	Job		189		189	tile floors.

Flooring

Sheet Vinyl Per S.F.

Sheet Vinyl Per S.F.	Unit	Material	Labor	Equip.	Total	Specification
Economy Grade						
Demolish	S.F.		.51		.51	Includes material and labor to install
Install	S.F.	2.35	1.18		3.53	resilient sheet vinyl flooring.
Demolish and Install	S.F.	2.35	1.69		4.04	
Clean	S.F.		.40		.40	
Minimum Charge	Job		189		189	
Average Grade						
Demolish	S.F.		.51		.51	Includes material and labor to install
Install	S.F.	3.76	1.18		4.94	resilient sheet vinyl flooring.
Demolish and Install	S.F.	3.76	1.69		5.45	
Clean	S.F.		.40		.40	
Minimum Charge	Job		189		189	
Premium Grade						
Demolish	S.F.		.51		.51	Includes material and labor to install
Install	S.F.	6.15	1.18		7.33	resilient sheet vinyl flooring.
Demolish and Install	S.F.	6.15	1.69		7.84	
Clean	S.F.		.40		.40	
Minimum Charge	Job		189		189	
Clean and Wax						
Clean	S.F.	.03	.20		.23	Includes labor and material to wash
Minimum Charge	Job		189		189	and wax a vinyl tile floor.

Sheet Vinyl

Sheet Vinyl	Unit	Material	Labor	Equip.	Total	Specification
Economy Grade						
Demolish	S.Y.		4.59		4.59	Includes material and labor to install
Install	S.Y.	21	10.65		31.65	no wax sheet vinyl flooring.
Demolish and Install	S.Y.	21	15.24		36.24	
Clean	S.Y.		2.79		2.79	
Minimum Charge	Job		189		189	
Average Grade						
Demolish	S.Y.		4.59		4.59	Includes material and labor to install
Install	S.Y.	34	10.65		44.65	no wax sheet vinyl flooring.
Demolish and Install	S.Y.	34	15.24		49.24	
Clean	S.Y.		2.79		2.79	
Minimum Charge	Job		189		189	
Premium Grade						
Demolish	S.Y.		4.59		4.59	Includes material and labor to install
Install	S.Y.	55	10.65		65.65	no wax sheet vinyl flooring.
Demolish and Install	S.Y.	55	15.24		70.24	
Clean	S.Y.		2.79		2.79	
Minimum Charge	Job		189		189	
Clean and Wax						
Clean	S.F.	.03	.20		.23	Includes labor and material to wash
Minimum Charge	Job		189		189	and wax a vinyl tile floor.

Vinyl Tile

Vinyl Tile	Unit	Material	Labor	Equip.	Total	Specification
Economy Grade						
Demolish	S.F.		.71		.71	Includes material and labor to install
Install	S.F.	3.76	.76		4.52	no wax 12" x 12" vinyl tile.
Demolish and Install	S.F.	3.76	1.47		5.23	
Clean	S.F.		.40		.40	
Minimum Charge	Job		189		189	

Flooring

Vinyl Tile		Unit	Material	Labor	Equip.	Total	Specification
Average Grade							
	Demolish	S.F.		.71		.71	Includes material and labor to install
	Install	S.F.	4.02	.76		4.78	no wax 12" x 12" vinyl tile.
	Demolish and Install	S.F.	4.02	1.47		5.49	
	Clean	S.F.		.40		.40	
	Minimum Charge	Job		189		189	
Premium Grade							
	Demolish	S.F.		.71		.71	Includes material and labor to install
	Install	S.F.	14.30	.76		15.06	no wax 12" x 12" vinyl tile.
	Demolish and Install	S.F.	14.30	1.47		15.77	
	Clean	S.F.		.40		.40	
	Minimum Charge	Job		189		189	
Clean and Wax							
	Clean	S.F.	.03	.20		.23	Includes labor and material to wash
	Minimum Charge	Job		189		189	and wax a vinyl tile floor.

Carpeting Per S.F.		Unit	Material	Labor	Equip.	Total	Specification
Economy Grade							
	Demolish	S.F.		.08		.08	Includes material and labor to install
	Install	S.F.	1.38	.74		2.12	carpet including tack strips and hot
	Demolish and Install	S.F.	1.38	.82		2.20	melt tape on seams.
	Clean	S.F.		.56		.56	
	Minimum Charge	Job		189		189	
Average Grade							
	Demolish	S.F.		.08		.08	Includes material and labor to install
	Install	S.F.	1.64	.74		2.38	carpet including tack strips and hot
	Demolish and Install	S.F.	1.64	.82		2.46	melt tape on seams.
	Clean	S.F.		.56		.56	
	Minimum Charge	Job		189		189	
Premium Grade							
	Demolish	S.F.		.08		.08	Includes material and labor to install
	Install	S.F.	2.56	.74		3.30	carpet including tack strips and hot
	Demolish and Install	S.F.	2.56	.82		3.38	melt tape on seams.
	Clean	S.F.		.56		.56	
	Minimum Charge	Job		189		189	
Indoor/Outdoor							
	Demolish	S.F.		.08		.08	Includes material and labor to install
	Install	S.F.	1.18	.90		2.08	indoor-outdoor carpet.
	Demolish and Install	S.F.	1.18	.98		2.16	
	Clean	S.F.		.56		.56	
	Minimum Charge	Job		189		189	
100% Wool							
Average Grade							
	Demolish	S.F.		.08		.08	Includes material and labor to install
	Install	S.F.	11.50	.75		12.25	carpet including tack strips and hot
	Demolish and Install	S.F.	11.50	.83		12.33	melt tape on seams.
	Clean	S.F.		.56		.56	
	Minimum Charge	Job		189		189	
Premium Grade							
	Demolish	S.F.		.08		.08	Includes material and labor to install
	Install	S.F.	12.80	.75		13.55	carpet including tack strips and hot
	Demolish and Install	S.F.	12.80	.83		13.63	melt tape on seams.
	Clean	S.F.		.56		.56	
	Minimum Charge	Job		189		189	

Flooring

Carpeting Per S.F.		Unit	Material	Labor	Equip.	Total	Specification
Luxury Grade							
	Demolish	S.F.		.08		.08	Includes material and labor to install
	Install	S.F.	18.30	.75		19.05	carpet including tack strips and hot
	Demolish and Install	S.F.	18.30	.83		19.13	melt tape on seams.
	Clean	S.F.		.56		.56	
	Minimum Charge	Job		189		189	
Berber							
Average Grade							
	Demolish	S.F.		.08		.08	Includes material and labor to install
	Install	S.F.	4.20	.90		5.10	carpet including tack strips and hot
	Demolish and Install	S.F.	4.20	.98		5.18	melt tape on seams.
	Clean	S.F.		.56		.56	
	Minimum Charge	Job		189		189	
Premium Grade							
	Demolish	S.F.		.08		.08	Includes material and labor to install
	Install	S.F.	8.05	.90		8.95	carpet including tack strips and hot
	Demolish and Install	S.F.	8.05	.98		9.03	melt tape on seams.
	Clean	S.F.		.56		.56	
	Minimum Charge	Job		189		189	

Carpeting		Unit	Material	Labor	Equip.	Total	Specification
Indoor/Outdoor							
	Demolish	S.Y.		1.19		1.19	Includes material and labor to install
	Install	S.Y.	10.60	8.05		18.65	indoor-outdoor carpet.
	Demolish and Install	S.Y.	10.60	9.24		19.84	
	Reinstall	S.Y.		6.45		6.45	
	Clean	S.Y.		5		5	
	Minimum Charge	Job		189		189	
Economy Grade							
	Demolish	S.Y.		1.19		1.19	Includes material and labor to install
	Install	S.Y.	12.40	6.65		19.05	carpet including tack strips and hot
	Demolish and Install	S.Y.	12.40	7.84		20.24	melt tape on seams.
	Reinstall	S.Y.		5.32		5.32	
	Clean	S.Y.		5		5	
	Minimum Charge	Job		189		189	
Average Grade							
	Demolish	S.Y.		1.19		1.19	Includes material and labor to install
	Install	S.Y.	14.75	6.65		21.40	carpet including tack strips and hot
	Demolish and Install	S.Y.	14.75	7.84		22.59	melt tape on seams.
	Reinstall	S.Y.		5.32		5.32	
	Clean	S.Y.		5		5	
	Minimum Charge	Job		189		189	
Premium Grade							
	Demolish	S.Y.		1.19		1.19	Includes material and labor to install
	Install	S.Y.	23	6.65		29.65	carpet including tack strips and hot
	Demolish and Install	S.Y.	23	7.84		30.84	melt tape on seams.
	Reinstall	S.Y.		5.32		5.32	
	Clean	S.Y.		5		5	
	Minimum Charge	Job		189		189	

Flooring

Carpeting

Carpeting		Unit	Material	Labor	Equip.	Total	Specification
100% Wool							
Average Grade							
	Demolish	S.Y.		1.19		1.19	Includes material and labor to install
	Install	S.Y.	103	6.75		109.75	wool carpet including tack strips and
	Demolish and Install	S.Y.	103	7.94		110.94	hot melt tape on seams.
	Reinstall	S.Y.		5.41		5.41	
	Clean	S.Y.		5		5	
	Minimum Charge	Job		189		189	
Premium Grade							
	Demolish	S.Y.		1.19		1.19	Includes material and labor to install
	Install	S.Y.	116	6.75		122.75	carpet including tack strips and hot
	Demolish and Install	S.Y.	116	7.94		123.94	melt tape on seams.
	Reinstall	S.Y.		5.41		5.41	
	Clean	S.Y.		5		5	
	Minimum Charge	Job		189		189	
Luxury Grade							
	Demolish	S.Y.		1.19		1.19	Includes material and labor to install
	Install	S.Y.	165	6.75		171.75	carpet including tack strips and hot
	Demolish and Install	S.Y.	165	7.94		172.94	melt tape on seams.
	Reinstall	S.Y.		5.41		5.41	
	Clean	S.Y.		5		5	
	Minimum Charge	Job		189		189	
Berber							
Average Grade							
	Demolish	S.Y.		1.19		1.19	Includes material and labor to install
	Install	S.Y.	38	8.05		46.05	berber carpet including tack strips and
	Demolish and Install	S.Y.	38	9.24		47.24	hot melt tape on seams.
	Reinstall	S.Y.		6.45		6.45	
	Clean	S.Y.		5		5	
	Minimum Charge	Job		189		189	
Premium Grade							
	Demolish	S.Y.		1.19		1.19	Includes material and labor to install
	Install	S.Y.	72.50	8.05		80.55	carpet including tack strips and hot
	Demolish and Install	S.Y.	72.50	9.24		81.74	melt tape on seams.
	Reinstall	S.Y.		6.45		6.45	
	Clean	S.Y.		5		5	
	Minimum Charge	Job		189		189	

Carpet Pad Per S.F.		Unit	Material	Labor	Equip.	Total	Specification
Urethane							
	Demolish	S.F.		.02		.02	Includes material and labor to install
	Install	S.F.	.72	.28		1	urethane carpet pad.
	Demolish and Install	S.F.	.72	.30		1.02	
	Minimum Charge	Job		189		189	
Foam Rubber Slab							
	Demolish	S.F.		.02		.02	Includes material and labor to install
	Install	S.F.	.64	.28		.92	carpet pad, 3/8" thick foam rubber.
	Demolish and Install	S.F.	.64	.30		.94	
	Minimum Charge	Job		189		189	
Waffle							
	Demolish	S.F.		.02		.02	Includes material and labor to install
	Install	S.F.	.42	.03		.45	rubber waffle carpet pad.
	Demolish and Install	S.F.	.42	.05		.47	
	Minimum Charge	Job		189		189	

Flooring

Carpet Pad Per S.F.

Carpet Pad Per S.F.	Unit	Material	Labor	Equip.	Total	Specification
Jute						
Demolish	S.F.		.02		.02	Includes material and labor to install
Install	S.F.	.81	.25		1.06	jute hair carpet pad.
Demolish and Install	S.F.	.81	.27		1.08	
Minimum Charge	Job		189		189	
Rebound						
Demolish	S.F.		.02		.02	Includes material and labor to install
Install	S.F.	.37	.21		.58	rebound carpet pad.
Demolish and Install	S.F.	.37	.23		.60	
Minimum Charge	Job		189		189	

Carpet Pad

Carpet Pad	Unit	Material	Labor	Equip.	Total	Specification
Urethane						
Demolish	S.Y.		.20		.20	Includes material and labor to install
Install	S.Y.	6.40	2.53		8.93	urethane carpet pad.
Demolish and Install	S.Y.	6.40	2.73		9.13	
Reinstall	S.Y.		2.02		2.02	
Minimum Charge	Job		189		189	
Foam Rubber Slab						
Demolish	S.Y.		.20		.20	Includes material and labor to install
Install	S.Y.	5.70	2.53		8.23	rubber slab carpet pad.
Demolish and Install	S.Y.	5.70	2.73		8.43	
Reinstall	S.Y.		2.02		2.02	
Minimum Charge	Job		189		189	
Waffle						
Demolish	S.Y.		.20		.20	Includes material and labor to install
Install	S.Y.	3.76	.28		4.04	rubber waffle carpet pad.
Demolish and Install	S.Y.	3.76	.48		4.24	
Reinstall	S.Y.		.22		.22	
Minimum Charge	Job		189		189	
Jute						
Demolish	S.Y.		.20		.20	Includes material and labor to install
Install	S.Y.	7.30	2.23		9.53	jute hair carpet pad.
Demolish and Install	S.Y.	7.30	2.43		9.73	
Reinstall	S.Y.		1.78		1.78	
Minimum Charge	Job		189		189	
Rebound						
Demolish	S.Y.		.20		.20	Includes material and labor to install
Install	S.Y.	3.30	1.89		5.19	rebound carpet pad.
Demolish and Install	S.Y.	3.30	2.09		5.39	
Reinstall	S.Y.		1.51		1.51	
Minimum Charge	Job		189		189	

Stair Components

Stair Components	Unit	Material	Labor	Equip.	Total	Specification
Carpeting						
Demolish	Ea.		2.16		2.16	Includes material and labor to install
Install	Riser	56.50	9.95		66.45	carpet and pad on stairs.
Demolish and Install	Riser	56.50	12.11		68.61	
Reinstall	Riser		7.97		7.97	
Clean	Ea.		5		5	
Minimum Charge	Job		189		189	

Finish Mechanical

Tub/Shower

Stainless Steel Double Sink

Water Closet

Commode	Unit	Material	Labor	Equip.	Total	Specification
Floor Mounted w / Tank						
Demolish	Ea.		50		50	Includes material and labor to install a
Install	Ea.	256	170		426	toilet with valve, seat and cover.
Demolish and Install	Ea.	256	220		476	
Reinstall	Ea.		136.28		136.28	
Clean	Ea.	.41	16		16.41	
Minimum Charge	Job		251		251	
Wall w / Flush Valve						
Demolish	Ea.		50		50	Includes material and labor to install a
Install	Ea.	830	156		986	wall hung toilet with flush valve, seat
Demolish and Install	Ea.	830	206		1036	and cover.
Reinstall	Ea.		124.54		124.54	
Clean	Ea.	.41	16		16.41	
Minimum Charge	Job		251		251	
Designer Floor Mount						
Demolish	Ea.		50		50	Includes material and labor to install a
Install	Ea.	1175	170		1345	toilet with valve, seat and cover.
Demolish and Install	Ea.	1175	220		1395	
Reinstall	Ea.		136.28		136.28	
Clean	Ea.	.41	16		16.41	
Minimum Charge	Job		251		251	
Urinal						
Demolish	Ea.		50		50	Includes material and labor to install a
Install	Ea.	345	300		645	wall hung urinal with flush valve.
Demolish and Install	Ea.	345	350		695	
Reinstall	Ea.		240.77		240.77	
Clean	Ea.	.41	16		16.41	
Minimum Charge	Job		251		251	
Bidet						
Vitreous China						
Demolish	Ea.		50		50	Includes material and labor to install a
Install	Ea.	655	181		836	vitreous china bidet complete with
Demolish and Install	Ea.	655	231		886	trim.
Reinstall	Ea.		144.46		144.46	
Clean	Ea.	.41	16		16.41	
Minimum Charge	Job		251		251	

Finish Mechanical

Commode		Unit	Material	Labor	Equip.	Total	Specification
Chrome Fittings							
	Install	Ea.	227	62.50		289.50	Includes labor and materials to install chrome fittings for a bidet.
Brass Fittings							
	Install	Ea.	250	62.50		312.50	Includes labor and materials to install brass fittings for a bidet.
Seat							
	Demolish	Ea.		21		21	Includes material and labor to install a toilet seat and cover.
	Install	Ea.	32	21		53	
	Demolish and Install	Ea.	32	42		74	
	Reinstall	Ea.		16.72		16.72	
	Clean	Ea.	.20	6.70		6.90	
	Minimum Charge	Job		251		251	
Rough-in							
	Install	Ea.	450	320		770	Includes labor and materials to install water supply pipe with valves and drain, waste and vent pipe with all couplings, hangers and fasteners necessary.

Sink (assembly)		Unit	Material	Labor	Equip.	Total	Specification
Single							
Porcelain							
	Demolish	Ea.		31.50		31.50	Includes material and labor to install a single bowl enamel finished cast iron kitchen sink with faucet and drain.
	Install	Ea.	635	161		796	
	Demolish and Install	Ea.	635	192.50		827.50	
	Reinstall	Ea.		128.98		128.98	
	Clean	Ea.	.26	11.45		11.71	
	Minimum Charge	Job		251		251	
Stainless Steel							
	Demolish	Ea.		31.50		31.50	Includes material and labor to install a single bowl stainless steel kitchen sink with faucet and drain.
	Install	Ea.	725	161		886	
	Demolish and Install	Ea.	725	192.50		917.50	
	Reinstall	Ea.		128.98		128.98	
	Clean	Ea.	.26	11.45		11.71	
	Minimum Charge	Job		251		251	
Double							
Porcelain							
	Demolish	Ea.		36		36	Includes material and labor to install a double bowl enamel finished cast iron kitchen sink with faucet and drain.
	Install	Ea.	375	188		563	
	Demolish and Install	Ea.	375	224		599	
	Reinstall	Ea.		150.48		150.48	
	Clean	Ea.	.41	16		16.41	
	Minimum Charge	Job		251		251	
Stainless Steel							
	Demolish	Ea.		36		36	Includes material and labor to install a double bowl stainless steel kitchen sink with faucet and drain.
	Install	Ea.	465	188		653	
	Demolish and Install	Ea.	465	224		689	
	Reinstall	Ea.		150.48		150.48	
	Clean	Ea.	.41	16		16.41	
	Minimum Charge	Job		251		251	
Bar							
	Demolish	Ea.		31.50		31.50	Includes material and labor to install a small single bowl stainless steel bar / vegetable / kitchen sink with faucet and drain.
	Install	Ea.	186	125		311	
	Demolish and Install	Ea.	186	156.50		342.50	
	Reinstall	Ea.		100.32		100.32	
	Clean	Ea.	.26	11.45		11.71	
	Minimum Charge	Job		251		251	

Finish Mechanical

Sink (assembly)

Sink (assembly)	Unit	Material	Labor	Equip.	Total	Specification
Floor						
Demolish	Ea.		100		100	Includes material and labor to install
Install	Ea.	1100	205		1305	an enameled cast iron floor mounted
Demolish and Install	Ea.	1100	305		1405	corner service sink with faucet and
Reinstall	Ea.		164.16		164.16	drain.
Clean	Ea.	.41	8		8.41	
Minimum Charge	Job		251		251	
Pedestal						
Demolish	Ea.		31.50		31.50	Includes material and labor to install a
Install	Ea.	470	141		611	vitreous china pedestal lavatory with
Demolish and Install	Ea.	470	172.50		642.50	faucet set and pop-up drain.
Reinstall	Ea.		112.86		112.86	
Clean	Ea.	.26	11.45		11.71	
Minimum Charge	Job		251		251	
Vanity Lavatory						
Demolish	Ea.		31.50		31.50	Includes material and labor to install a
Install	Ea.	294	167		461	vitreous china lavatory with faucet set
Demolish and Install	Ea.	294	198.50		492.50	and pop-up drain.
Reinstall	Ea.		133.76		133.76	
Clean	Ea.	.26	11.45		11.71	
Minimum Charge	Job		251		251	
Rough-in						
Install	Ea.	505	420		925	Includes labor and materials to install copper supply pipe with valves and drain, waste and vent pipe with all couplings, hangers and fasteners necessary.
Laundry						
Demolish	Ea.		32		32	Includes material and labor to install a
Install	Ea.	149	139		288	laundry sink (wall mounted or with
Demolish and Install	Ea.	149	171		320	legs) including faucet and pop up
Clean	Ea.	.26	11.45		11.71	drain.
Minimum Charge	Job		251		251	

Sink Only

Sink Only	Unit	Material	Labor	Equip.	Total	Specification
Single						
Porcelain						
Demolish	Ea.		31.50		31.50	Includes material and labor to install a
Install	Ea.	550	179		729	single bowl enamel finished cast iron
Demolish and Install	Ea.	550	210.50		760.50	kitchen sink.
Reinstall	Ea.		143.31		143.31	
Clean	Ea.	.26	11.45		11.71	
Minimum Charge	Job		251		251	
Stainless Steel						
Demolish	Ea.		31.50		31.50	Includes material and labor to install a
Install	Ea.	640	125		765	single bowl stainless steel kitchen sink.
Demolish and Install	Ea.	640	156.50		796.50	
Reinstall	Ea.		100.32		100.32	
Clean	Ea.	.26	11.45		11.71	
Minimum Charge	Job		251		251	

Finish Mechanical

Sink Only		Unit	Material	Labor	Equip.	Total	Specification
Double							
Porcelain							
	Demolish	Ea.		36		36	Includes material and labor to install a
	Install	Ea.	274	209		483	double bowl enamel finished cast iron
	Demolish and Install	Ea.	274	245		519	kitchen sink.
	Reinstall	Ea.		167.20		167.20	
	Clean	Ea.	.41	16		16.41	
	Minimum Charge	Job		251		251	
Stainless Steel							
	Demolish	Ea.		36		36	Includes material and labor to install a
	Install	Ea.	955	162		1117	double bowl stainless steel kitchen
	Demolish and Install	Ea.	955	198		1153	sink.
	Reinstall	Ea.		129.45		129.45	
	Clean	Ea.	.41	16		16.41	
	Minimum Charge	Job		251		251	
Bar							
	Demolish	Ea.		31.50		31.50	Includes material and labor to install a
	Install	Ea.	77.50	125		202.50	small single bowl stainless steel bar /
	Demolish and Install	Ea.	77.50	156.50		234	vegetable / kitchen sink.
	Reinstall	Ea.		100.32		100.32	
	Clean	Ea.	.26	11.45		11.71	
	Minimum Charge	Job		251		251	
Floor							
	Demolish	Ea.		100		100	Includes material and labor to install
	Install	Ea.	945	228		1173	an enameled cast iron floor mounted
	Demolish and Install	Ea.	945	328		1273	corner service sink.
	Reinstall	Ea.		182.40		182.40	
	Clean	Ea.	.41	8		8.41	
	Minimum Charge	Job		251		251	
Pedestal							
	Demolish	Ea.		31.50		31.50	Includes material and labor to install a
	Install	Ea.	350	157		507	vitreous china pedestal lavatory.
	Demolish and Install	Ea.	350	188.50		538.50	
	Reinstall	Ea.		125.40		125.40	
	Clean	Ea.	.26	11.45		11.71	
	Minimum Charge	Job		251		251	
Vanity Lavatory							
	Demolish	Ea.		31.50		31.50	Includes material and labor to install a
	Install	Ea.	168	157		325	vitreous china lavatory.
	Demolish and Install	Ea.	168	188.50		356.50	
	Reinstall	Ea.		125.40		125.40	
	Clean	Ea.	.26	11.45		11.71	
	Minimum Charge	Job		251		251	
Rough-in							
	Install	Ea.	455	395		850	Includes labor and materials to install copper supply pipe with valves and drain, waste and vent pipe with all couplings, hangers and fasteners necessary.
Faucet Sink							
Good Grade							
	Demolish	Ea.		25		25	Includes material and labor to install a
	Install	Ea.	67.50	34.50		102	sink faucet and fittings.
	Demolish and Install	Ea.	67.50	59.50		127	
	Reinstall	Ea.		27.69		27.69	
	Clean	Ea.	.17	10		10.17	
	Minimum Charge	Job		251		251	

Finish Mechanical

Sink Only

Sink Only		Unit	Material	Labor	Equip.	Total	Specification
Better Grade							
	Demolish	Ea.		25		25	Includes material and labor to install a
	Install	Ea.	114	34.50		148.50	sink faucet and fittings.
	Demolish and Install	Ea.	114	59.50		173.50	
	Reinstall	Ea.		27.69		27.69	
	Clean	Ea.	.17	10		10.17	
	Minimum Charge	Job		251		251	
Premium Grade							
	Demolish	Ea.		25		25	Includes material and labor to install a
	Install	Ea.	222	43		265	sink faucet and fittings.
	Demolish and Install	Ea.	222	68		290	
	Reinstall	Ea.		34.53		34.53	
	Clean	Ea.	.17	10		10.17	
	Minimum Charge	Job		251		251	
Drain & Basket							
	Demolish	Ea.		15.70		15.70	Includes material and labor to install a
	Install	Ea.	16.35	31.50		47.85	sink drain and basket.
	Demolish and Install	Ea.	16.35	47.20		63.55	
	Reinstall	Ea.		25.08		25.08	
	Clean	Ea.	.17	10		10.17	
	Minimum Charge	Job		251		251	

Bathtub

Bathtub		Unit	Material	Labor	Equip.	Total	Specification
Enameled							
Steel							
	Demolish	Ea.		90.50		90.50	Includes labor and material to install a
	Install	Ea.	570	164		734	formed steel bath tub with spout,
	Demolish and Install	Ea.	570	254.50		824.50	mixing valve, shower head and
	Reinstall	Ea.		131.33		131.33	pop-up drain.
	Clean	Ea.	.80	26.50		27.30	
	Minimum Charge	Job		251		251	
Cast Iron							
	Demolish	Ea.		90.50		90.50	Includes material and labor to install a
	Install	Ea.	1200	205		1405	cast iron bath tub with spout, mixing
	Demolish and Install	Ea.	1200	295.50		1495.50	valve, shower head and pop-up drain.
	Reinstall	Ea.		164.16		164.16	
	Clean	Ea.	.80	26.50		27.30	
	Minimum Charge	Job		251		251	
Fiberglass							
	Demolish	Ea.		90.50		90.50	Includes material and labor to install
	Install	Ea.	2000	164		2164	an acrylic soaking tub with spout,
	Demolish and Install	Ea.	2000	254.50		2254.50	mixing valve, shower head and
	Reinstall	Ea.		131.33		131.33	pop-up drain.
	Clean	Ea.	.80	26.50		27.30	
	Minimum Charge	Job		251		251	
Institutional							
	Demolish	Ea.		90.50		90.50	Includes material and labor to install a
	Install	Ea.	1375	300		1675	hospital / institutional type bathtub
	Demolish and Install	Ea.	1375	390.50		1765.50	with spout, mixing valve, shower head
	Reinstall	Ea.		240.77		240.77	and pop-up drain.
	Clean	Ea.	.80	26.50		27.30	
	Minimum Charge	Job		251		251	

Bathtub	Unit	Material	Labor	Equip.	Total	Specification
Whirlpool (Acrylic)						
Demolish	Ea.		279		279	Includes material and labor to install a
Install	Ea.	1875	905		2780	molded fiberglass whirlpool tub.
Demolish and Install	Ea.	1875	1184		3059	
Reinstall	Ea.		722.30		722.30	
Clean	Ea.	.80	26.50		27.30	
Minimum Charge	Job		251		251	
Pump / Motor						
Demolish	Ea.		69.50		69.50	Includes material and labor to install a
Install	Ea.	283	151		434	whirlpool tub pump / motor.
Demolish and Install	Ea.	283	220.50		503.50	
Reinstall	Ea.		120.50		120.50	
Clean	Ea.	.20	20		20.20	
Minimum Charge	Job		251		251	
Heater / Motor						
Demolish	Ea.		69.50		69.50	Includes material and labor to install a
Install	Ea.	218	223		441	whirlpool tub heater.
Demolish and Install	Ea.	218	292.50		510.50	
Reinstall	Ea.		178.35		178.35	
Clean	Ea.	.20	20		20.20	
Minimum Charge	Job		251		251	
Thermal Cover						
Demolish	Ea.		11.15		11.15	Includes material and labor to install a
Install	Ea.	395	31.50		426.50	whirlpool tub thermal cover.
Demolish and Install	Ea.	395	42.65		437.65	
Reinstall	Ea.		25.08		25.08	
Clean	Ea.	2.01	20		22.01	
Minimum Charge	Job		251		251	
Tub / Shower Combination						
Demolish	Ea.		79.50		79.50	Includes material and labor to install a
Install	Ea.	895	226		1121	fiberglass module tub with shower
Demolish and Install	Ea.	895	305.50		1200.50	surround with spout, mixing valve,
Reinstall	Ea.		180.58		180.58	shower head and pop-up drain.
Clean	Ea.	1.01	40		41.01	
Minimum Charge	Job		251		251	
Accessories						
Sliding Door						
Demolish	Ea.		22.50		22.50	Includes material and labor to install a
Install	Ea.	595	101		696	48" aluminum framed tempered glass
Demolish and Install	Ea.	595	123.50		718.50	shower door.
Reinstall	Ea.		81.11		81.11	
Clean	Ea.	1.68	13.35		15.03	
Minimum Charge	Job		251		251	
Shower Head						
Demolish	Ea.		6.25		6.25	Includes material and labor to install a
Install	Ea.	47.50	21		68.50	water saving shower head.
Demolish and Install	Ea.	47.50	27.25		74.75	
Reinstall	Ea.		16.72		16.72	
Clean	Ea.	.02	4.01		4.03	
Minimum Charge	Job		251		251	
Faucet Set						
Demolish	Ea.		31.50		31.50	Includes material and labor to install a
Install	Ea.	95	62.50		157.50	combination spout / diverter for a
Demolish and Install	Ea.	95	94		189	bathtub.
Reinstall	Ea.		50.16		50.16	
Clean	Ea.	.17	10		10.17	
Minimum Charge	Job		251		251	

Finish Mechanical

Bathtub

Bathtub		Unit	Material	Labor	Equip.	Total	Specification
Shower Rod							
	Demolish	Ea.		3.71		3.71	Includes material and labor to install a
	Install	Ea.	36	33		69	chrome plated shower rod.
	Demolish and Install	Ea.	36	36.71		72.71	
	Reinstall	Ea.		26.58		26.58	
	Clean	Ea.		4.01		4.01	
	Minimum Charge	Job		251		251	
Rough-in							
	Install	Ea.	535	435		970	Includes labor and materials to install copper supply pipe with valves and drain, waste and vent pipe with all couplings, hangers and fasteners necessary.

Shower

Shower		Unit	Material	Labor	Equip.	Total	Specification
Fiberglass							
32" x 32"							
	Demolish	Ea.		188		188	Includes material and labor to install a
	Install	Ea.	540	164		704	fiberglass shower stall with door,
	Demolish and Install	Ea.	540	352		892	mixing valve and shower head and
	Reinstall	Ea.		131.33		131.33	drain fitting.
	Clean	Ea.	.80	26.50		27.30	
	Minimum Charge	Job		251		251	
36" x 36"							
	Demolish	Ea.		188		188	Includes material and labor to install a
	Install	Ea.	555	164		719	fiberglass shower stall with door,
	Demolish and Install	Ea.	555	352		907	mixing valve and shower head and
	Reinstall	Ea.		131.33		131.33	drain fitting.
	Clean	Ea.	.80	26.50		27.30	
	Minimum Charge	Job		251		251	
35" x 60"							
	Demolish	Ea.		188		188	Includes material and labor to install a
	Install	Ea.	790	226		1016	handicap fiberglass shower stall with
	Demolish and Install	Ea.	790	414		1204	door & seat, mixing valve and shower
	Reinstall	Ea.		180.58		180.58	head and drain fitting.
	Clean	Ea.	.80	26.50		27.30	
	Minimum Charge	Job		251		251	
Accessories							
Single Door							
	Demolish	Ea.		22.50		22.50	Includes material and labor to install a
	Install	Ea.	158	53.50		211.50	shower door.
	Demolish and Install	Ea.	158	76		234	
	Reinstall	Ea.		42.81		42.81	
	Clean	Ea.	1.68	13.35		15.03	
	Minimum Charge	Job		251		251	
Shower Head							
	Demolish	Ea.		6.25		6.25	Includes material and labor to install a
	Install	Ea.	47.50	21		68.50	water saving shower head.
	Demolish and Install	Ea.	47.50	27.25		74.75	
	Reinstall	Ea.		16.72		16.72	
	Clean	Ea.	.02	4.01		4.03	
	Minimum Charge	Job		251		251	

Finish Mechanical

Shower

	Unit	Material	Labor	Equip.	Total	Specification
Faucet Set						
Demolish	Ea.		31.50		31.50	Includes material and labor to install a combination spout / diverter for a bathtub.
Install	Ea.	95	62.50		157.50	
Demolish and Install	Ea.	95	94		189	
Reinstall	Ea.		50.16		50.16	
Clean	Ea.	.17	10		10.17	
Minimum Charge	Job		251		251	
Shower Pan						
Demolish	Ea.		28		28	Includes material and labor to install the base portion of a fiberglass shower unit.
Install	Ea.	118	62.50		180.50	
Demolish and Install	Ea.	118	90.50		208.50	
Reinstall	Ea.		50.16		50.16	
Clean	Ea.	.80	26.50		27.30	
Minimum Charge	Job		251		251	
Rough-in						
Install	Ea.	595	440		1035	Includes labor and materials to install copper supply pipe with valves and drain, waste and vent pipe with all couplings, hangers and fasteners necessary.

Ductwork

	Unit	Material	Labor	Equip.	Total	Specification
Return Grill						
Under 10″ Wide						
Demolish	Ea.		10.70		10.70	Includes material and labor to install a 10″ x 10″ air return register.
Install	Ea.	18.25	27		45.25	
Demolish and Install	Ea.	18.25	37.70		55.95	
Reinstall	Ea.		21.40		21.40	
Clean	Ea.	.20	8.90		9.10	
Minimum Charge	Job		241		241	
12″ to 20″ Wide						
Demolish	Ea.		10.70		10.70	Includes material and labor to install a 16″ x 16″ air return register.
Install	Ea.	35	28.50		63.50	
Demolish and Install	Ea.	35	39.20		74.20	
Reinstall	Ea.		22.66		22.66	
Clean	Ea.	.20	8.90		9.10	
Minimum Charge	Job		241		241	
Over 20″ Wide						
Demolish	Ea.		16.20		16.20	Includes material and labor to install a 24″ x 24″ air return register.
Install	Ea.	71.50	44		115.50	
Demolish and Install	Ea.	71.50	60.20		131.70	
Reinstall	Ea.		35.03		35.03	
Clean	Ea.	.20	10		10.20	
Minimum Charge	Job		241		241	
Supply Grill						
Baseboard Type						
Demolish	Ea.		7.65		7.65	Includes material and labor to install a 14″ x 6″ baseboard air supply register.
Install	Ea.	6.80	24		30.80	
Demolish and Install	Ea.	6.80	31.65		38.45	
Reinstall	Ea.		19.26		19.26	
Clean	Ea.	.20	8.90		9.10	
Minimum Charge	Job		241		241	

Finish Mechanical

Ductwork		Unit	Material	Labor	Equip.	Total	Specification
10″ Wide							
	Demolish	Ea.		8.90		8.90	Includes material and labor to install a
	Install	Ea.	14.65	24		38.65	10″ x 6″ air supply register.
	Demolish and Install	Ea.	14.65	32.90		47.55	
	Reinstall	Ea.		19.26		19.26	
	Clean	Ea.	.20	8.90		9.10	
	Minimum Charge	Job		241		241	
12″ to 15″ Wide							
	Demolish	Ea.		8.90		8.90	Includes material and labor to install a
	Install	Ea.	20	28.50		48.50	14″ x 8″ air supply register.
	Demolish and Install	Ea.	20	37.40		57.40	
	Reinstall	Ea.		22.66		22.66	
	Clean	Ea.	.20	8.90		9.10	
	Minimum Charge	Job		241		241	
18″ to 24″ Wide							
	Demolish	Ea.		10.70		10.70	Includes material and labor to install a
	Install	Ea.	28	37		65	24″ x 8″ air supply register.
	Demolish and Install	Ea.	28	47.70		75.70	
	Reinstall	Ea.		29.64		29.64	
	Clean	Ea.	.20	10		10.20	
	Minimum Charge	Job		241		241	
30″ to 36″ Wide							
	Demolish	Ea.		13.40		13.40	Includes material and labor to install a
	Install	Ea.	37	34.50		71.50	30″ x 8″ air supply register.
	Demolish and Install	Ea.	37	47.90		84.90	
	Reinstall	Ea.		27.52		27.52	
	Clean	Ea.	.20	20		20.20	
	Minimum Charge	Job		241		241	
Diffuser							
12″ x 12″							
	Demolish	Ea.		10.70		10.70	Includes material and labor to install a
	Install	Ea.	93	40		133	12″ x 12″ aluminum diffuser.
	Demolish and Install	Ea.	93	50.70		143.70	
	Reinstall	Ea.		32.11		32.11	
	Clean	Ea.	.20	8.90		9.10	
	Minimum Charge	Job		241		241	
14″ x 14″							
	Demolish	Ea.		10.70		10.70	Includes material and labor to install a
	Install	Ea.	141	40		181	14″ x 14″ aluminum diffuser.
	Demolish and Install	Ea.	141	50.70		191.70	
	Reinstall	Ea.		32.11		32.11	
	Clean	Ea.	.20	10		10.20	
	Minimum Charge	Job		241		241	
18″ x 18″							
	Demolish	Ea.		16.20		16.20	Includes material and labor to install a
	Install	Ea.	152	53.50		205.50	18″ x 18″ aluminum diffuser.
	Demolish and Install	Ea.	152	69.70		221.70	
	Reinstall	Ea.		42.81		42.81	
	Clean	Ea.	.20	13.35		13.55	
	Minimum Charge	Job		241		241	
12″ Round							
	Demolish	Ea.		14.85		14.85	Includes material and labor to install a
	Install	Ea.	17.20	40		57.20	12″ diameter aluminum diffuser with a
	Demolish and Install	Ea.	17.20	54.85		72.05	butterfly damper.
	Reinstall	Ea.		32.11		32.11	
	Clean	Ea.	.20	8.90		9.10	
	Minimum Charge	Job		241		241	

Finish Mechanical

Ductwork	Unit	Material	Labor	Equip.	Total	Specification
14" to 20" Round						
Demolish	Ea.		19.80		19.80	Includes material and labor to install a
Install	Ea.	158	53.50		211.50	20" diameter aluminum diffuser with a
Demolish and Install	Ea.	158	73.30		231.30	butterfly damper.
Reinstall	Ea.		42.81		42.81	
Clean	Ea.	.20	10		10.20	
Minimum Charge	Job		241		241	
Flush-out / Sanitize						
Install	L.F.	.80	4.01		4.81	Includes labor and material costs to
Minimum Charge	Job		241		241	clean ductwork or flue.

Finish Electrical

Lighting Fixture

Duplex Receptacle

Electrical Per S.F.	Unit	Material	Labor	Equip.	Total	Specification
Residential						
Light Fixtures						
Install	S.F.	.29	.23		.52	Includes labor and material to replace house light fixtures. Apply S.F. cost to floor area including garages but not basements.

Circuits	Unit	Material	Labor	Equip.	Total	Specification
120V						
Outlet with Wiring						
Demolish	Ea.		26		26	Includes material and labor to install
Install	Ea.	12.10	32		44.10	general purpose outlet with cover, up
Demolish and Install	Ea.	12.10	58		70.10	to 20 feet of #12/2 wire.
Reinstall	Ea.		25.73		25.73	
Clean	Ea.		2		2	
Minimum Charge	Job		234		234	
GFCI Outlet w / Wiring						
Demolish	Ea.		26		26	Cost includes material and labor to
Install	Ea.	52.50	38		90.50	install 120V GFCI receptacle and wall
Demolish and Install	Ea.	52.50	64		116.50	plate, with up to 20 feet of #12/2
Reinstall	Ea.		30.41		30.41	wire.
Clean	Ea.		2		2	
Minimum Charge	Job		234		234	
Exterior Outlet w / Wiring						
Demolish	Ea.		26		26	Cost includes material and labor to
Install	Ea.	37	39		76	install 110V waterproof external
Demolish and Install	Ea.	37	65		102	receptacle and cover plate with up to
Reinstall	Ea.		31.20		31.20	20' of #12/2 wire.
Clean	Ea.		2		2	
Minimum Charge	Job		234		234	
240V Outlet w / Wiring						
Demolish	Ea.		26		26	Cost includes material and labor to
Install	Ea.	70.50	73		143.50	install 240V receptacle and cover
Demolish and Install	Ea.	70.50	99		169.50	plate with up to 20' of #12/2 wire.
Reinstall	Ea.		58.41		58.41	
Clean	Ea.		2		2	
Minimum Charge	Job		234		234	

Finish Electrical

Circuits

	Unit	Material	Labor	Equip.	Total	Specification
TV / Cable Jack w / Wiring						Includes material and labor to install
Demolish	Ea.		26		26	TV/cable outlet box and cover plate
Install	Ea.	21	29.50		50.50	including 20' of wiring.
Demolish and Install	Ea.	21	55.50		76.50	
Reinstall	Ea.		23.40		23.40	
Clean	Ea.		2		2	
Minimum Charge	Job		234		234	
Phone Jack with Wiring						Includes material and labor to install
Demolish	Ea.		26		26	phone jack and cover plate including
Install	Ea.	12.05	18		30.05	up to 20' of telephone cable.
Demolish and Install	Ea.	12.05	44		56.05	
Reinstall	Ea.		14.40		14.40	
Clean	Ea.		1.25		1.25	
Minimum Charge	Job		234		234	

Light Switch

	Unit	Material	Labor	Equip.	Total	Specification
Single						
Switch						
Demolish	Ea.		5.20		5.20	Includes material and labor to install
Install	Ea.	8	22.50		30.50	single switch and wall plate. Wiring is
Demolish and Install	Ea.	8	27.70		35.70	not included.
Reinstall	Ea.		17.83		17.83	
Clean	Ea.		2		2	
Minimum Charge	Job		234		234	
Plate						
Demolish	Ea.		2.60		2.60	Includes material and labor to install a
Install	Ea.	.42	5.85		6.27	one gang brown wall switch plate.
Demolish and Install	Ea.	.42	8.45		8.87	
Reinstall	Ea.		4.68		4.68	
Clean	Ea.	.08	.40		.48	
Minimum Charge	Job		234		234	
Double						
Switch						
Demolish	Ea.		10.40		10.40	Includes material and labor to install
Install	Ea.	7.65	33.50		41.15	double switch and wall plate. Wiring
Demolish and Install	Ea.	7.65	43.90		51.55	is not included.
Reinstall	Ea.		26.74		26.74	
Clean	Ea.	.08	6.40		6.48	
Minimum Charge	Job		234		234	
Plate						
Demolish	Ea.		2.60		2.60	Includes material and labor to install a
Install	Ea.	.83	8.85		9.68	two gang brown wall switch plate.
Demolish and Install	Ea.	.83	11.45		12.28	
Reinstall	Ea.		7.06		7.06	
Clean	Ea.	.08	.40		.48	
Minimum Charge	Job		234		234	
Triple						
Switch						
Demolish	Ea.		15.75		15.75	Includes material and labor to install
Install	Ea.	26.50	39		65.50	triple switch and wall plate. Wiring is
Demolish and Install	Ea.	26.50	54.75		81.25	not included.
Reinstall	Ea.		31.20		31.20	
Clean	Ea.	.08	9.60		9.68	
Minimum Charge	Job		234		234	

Finish Electrical

Light Switch		Unit	Material	Labor	Equip.	Total	Specification
Plate							
	Demolish	Ea.		2.60		2.60	Includes material and labor to install
	Install	Ea.	1.22	14.65		15.87	a three gang brown wall switch plate.
	Demolish and Install	Ea.	1.22	17.25		18.47	
	Reinstall	Ea.		11.70		11.70	
	Clean	Ea.	.08	.40		.48	
	Minimum Charge	Job		234		234	
Dimmer							
Switch							
	Demolish	Ea.		5.20		5.20	Includes material and labor to install
	Install	Ea.	29.50	27.50		57	dimmer switch. Wiring is not included.
	Demolish and Install	Ea.	29.50	32.70		62.20	
	Reinstall	Ea.		22.02		22.02	
	Clean	Ea.		2		2	
	Minimum Charge	Job		234		234	
Plate							
	Demolish	Ea.		2.60		2.60	Includes material and labor to install
	Install	Ea.	.42	5.85		6.27	a one gang brown wall switch plate.
	Demolish and Install	Ea.	.42	8.45		8.87	
	Reinstall	Ea.		4.68		4.68	
	Clean	Ea.	.08	.40		.48	
	Minimum Charge	Job		234		234	
With Wiring							
Single							
	Demolish	Ea.		26		26	Includes material and labor to install
	Install	Ea.	13.55	27.50		41.05	single switch and plate including up to
	Demolish and Install	Ea.	13.55	53.50		67.05	20' of romex cable.
	Reinstall	Ea.		21.89		21.89	
	Clean	Ea.		2		2	
	Minimum Charge	Job		234		234	
Double							
	Demolish	Ea.		26		26	Includes material and labor to install
	Install	Ea.	30.50	47		77.50	double switch and plate including up
	Demolish and Install	Ea.	30.50	73		103.50	to 20' of romex cable.
	Reinstall	Ea.		37.44		37.44	
	Clean	Ea.	.08	6.40		6.48	
	Minimum Charge	Job		234		234	
Triple							
	Demolish	Ea.		39		39	Includes material and labor to install
	Install	Ea.	34	52.50		86.50	triple switch and plate including up to
	Demolish and Install	Ea.	34	91.50		125.50	20' of romex cable.
	Reinstall	Ea.		42.11		42.11	
	Clean	Ea.	.08	9.60		9.68	
	Minimum Charge	Job		234		234	
Dimmer							
	Demolish	Ea.		26		26	Includes material and labor to install
	Install	Ea.	35	32		67	dimmer switch and cover plate
	Demolish and Install	Ea.	35	58		93	including up to 20' of romex cable.
	Reinstall	Ea.		25.73		25.73	
	Clean	Ea.		2		2	
	Minimum Charge	Job		234		234	

263

Finish Electrical

Cover for Outlet / Switch

	Unit	Material	Labor	Equip.	Total	Specification
High Grade						
Demolish	Ea.		2.60		2.60	Includes material and labor to install
Install	Ea.	2.78	5.85		8.63	wall plate, stainless steel, 1 gang.
Demolish and Install	Ea.	2.78	8.45		11.23	
Reinstall	Ea.		4.68		4.68	
Clean	Ea.	.08	.40		.48	
Minimum Charge	Job		234		234	
Deluxe Grade						
Demolish	Ea.		2.60		2.60	Includes material and labor to install
Install	Ea.	4.61	5.85		10.46	wall plate, brushed brass, 1 gang.
Demolish and Install	Ea.	4.61	8.45		13.06	
Reinstall	Ea.		4.68		4.68	
Clean	Ea.	.08	.40		.48	
Minimum Charge	Job		234		234	

Residential Light Fixture

	Unit	Material	Labor	Equip.	Total	Specification
Ceiling						
Good Quality						
Demolish	Ea.		10.85		10.85	Includes material and labor to install
Install	Ea.	41.50	11.70		53.20	standard quality incandescent ceiling
Demolish and Install	Ea.	41.50	22.55		64.05	light fixture. Wiring is not included.
Reinstall	Ea.		9.36		9.36	
Clean	Ea.	.10	26.50		26.60	
Minimum Charge	Job		234		234	
Better Quality						
Demolish	Ea.		10.85		10.85	Includes material and labor to install
Install	Ea.	103	24.50		127.50	custom quality incandescent ceiling
Demolish and Install	Ea.	103	35.35		138.35	light fixture. Wiring is not included.
Reinstall	Ea.		19.71		19.71	
Clean	Ea.	.10	26.50		26.60	
Minimum Charge	Job		234		234	
Premium Quality						
Demolish	Ea.		10.85		10.85	Includes material and labor to install
Install	Ea.	300	24.50		324.50	deluxe quality incandescent ceiling
Demolish and Install	Ea.	300	35.35		335.35	light fixture. Wiring is not included.
Reinstall	Ea.		19.71		19.71	
Clean	Ea.	.10	26.50		26.60	
Minimum Charge	Job		234		234	
Recessed Ceiling						
Demolish	Ea.		21.50		21.50	Includes material and labor to install
Install	Ea.	51.50	15.60		67.10	standard quality recessed eyeball
Demolish and Install	Ea.	51.50	37.10		88.60	spotlight with housing. Wiring is not
Reinstall	Ea.		12.48		12.48	included.
Clean	Ea.	.04	3.34		3.38	
Minimum Charge	Job		234		234	
Recessed Eyeball						
Demolish	Ea.		21.50		21.50	Includes material and labor to install
Install	Ea.	77	16.70		93.70	custom quality recessed eyeball
Demolish and Install	Ea.	77	38.20		115.20	spotlight with housing. Wiring is not
Reinstall	Ea.		13.37		13.37	included.
Clean	Ea.	.04	3.34		3.38	
Minimum Charge	Job		234		234	

Finish Electrical

Residential Light Fixture	Unit	Material	Labor	Equip.	Total	Specification
Recessed Shower Type						
Demolish	Ea.		21.50		21.50	Includes material and labor to install
Install	Ea.	64	15.60		79.60	deluxe quality recessed eyeball
Demolish and Install	Ea.	64	37.10		101.10	spotlight with housing. Wiring is not
Reinstall	Ea.		12.48		12.48	included.
Clean	Ea.	.04	3.34		3.38	
Minimum Charge	Job		234		234	
Run Wiring						
Install	Ea.	17.70	18.70		36.40	Includes labor and material to install a
Minimum Charge	Job		234		234	electric fixture utility box with
						non-metallic cable.
Fluorescent						
Good Quality						
Demolish	Ea.		23.50		23.50	Includes material and labor to install
Install	Ea.	42	67		109	standard quality 12" wide by 48" long
Demolish and Install	Ea.	42	90.50		132.50	decorative surface mounted fluorescent
Reinstall	Ea.		53.49		53.49	fixture w/acrylic diffuser.
Clean	Ea.	.04	3.34		3.38	
Minimum Charge	Job		234		234	
Better Quality						
Demolish	Ea.		23.50		23.50	Includes material and labor to install
Install	Ea.	86	75.50		161.50	an interior fluorescent lighting fixture.
Demolish and Install	Ea.	86	99		185	
Reinstall	Ea.		60.39		60.39	
Clean	Ea.	.04	3.34		3.38	
Minimum Charge	Job		234		234	
Premium Quality						
Demolish	Ea.		23.50		23.50	Includes material and labor to install
Install	Ea.	89	88.50		177.50	deluxe quality 24" wide by 48" long
Demolish and Install	Ea.	89	112		201	decorative surface mounted fluorescent
Reinstall	Ea.		70.64		70.64	fixture w/acrylic diffuser.
Clean	Ea.	.04	3.34		3.38	
Minimum Charge	Job		234		234	
Run Wiring						
Install	Ea.	17.70	18.70		36.40	Includes labor and material to install a
Minimum Charge	Job		234		234	electric fixture utility box with
						non-metallic cable.
Exterior						
Good Quality						
Demolish	Ea.		21		21	Includes material and labor to install
Install	Ea.	53	29.50		82.50	standard quality incandescent outdoor
Demolish and Install	Ea.	53	50.50		103.50	light fixture. Wiring is not included.
Reinstall	Ea.		23.40		23.40	
Clean	Ea.	.20	13.35		13.55	
Minimum Charge	Job		234		234	
Better Quality						
Demolish	Ea.		21		21	Includes material and labor to install
Install	Ea.	98	29.50		127.50	custom quality incandescent outdoor
Demolish and Install	Ea.	98	50.50		148.50	light fixture. Wiring is not included.
Reinstall	Ea.		23.40		23.40	
Clean	Ea.	.20	13.35		13.55	
Minimum Charge	Job		234		234	
Premium Quality						
Demolish	Ea.		21		21	Includes material and labor to install
Install	Ea.	200	117		317	deluxe quality incandescent outdoor
Demolish and Install	Ea.	200	138		338	light fixture. Wiring is not included.
Reinstall	Ea.		93.60		93.60	
Clean	Ea.	.20	13.35		13.55	
Minimum Charge	Job		234		234	

Finish Electrical

Residential Light Fixture	Unit	Material	Labor	Equip.	Total	Specification
Outdoor w / Pole						Includes material and labor to install
Demolish	Ea.		21		21	post lantern type incandescent outdoor
Install	Ea.	262	117		379	light fixture. Wiring is not included.
Demolish and Install	Ea.	262	138		400	
Reinstall	Ea.		93.60		93.60	
Clean	Ea.	.20	13.35		13.55	
Minimum Charge	Job		234		234	
Run Wiring						
Install	Ea.	17.70	18.70		36.40	Includes labor and material to install a
Minimum Charge	Job		234		234	electric fixture utility box with
						non-metallic cable.
Track Lighting						
Demolish	L.F.		7.20		7.20	Includes material and labor to install
Install	L.F.	18.35	19.50		37.85	track lighting.
Demolish and Install	L.F.	18.35	26.70		45.05	
Reinstall	L.F.		15.60		15.60	
Clean	L.F.	.20	6.40		6.60	
Minimum Charge	Job		234		234	

Commercial Light Fixture	Unit	Material	Labor	Equip.	Total	Specification
Fluorescent						
2 Bulb, 2'						
Demolish	Ea.		21		21	Includes material and labor to install a
Install	Ea.	37	58.50		95.50	2' long surface mounted fluorescent
Demolish and Install	Ea.	37	79.50		116.50	light fixture with two 40 watt bulbs.
Reinstall	Ea.		46.80		46.80	
Clean	Ea.	1.01	23		24.01	
Minimum Charge	Job		234		234	
2 Bulb, 4'						
Demolish	Ea.		21		21	Includes material and labor to install a
Install	Ea.	69.50	67		136.50	4' long surface mounted fluorescent
Demolish and Install	Ea.	69.50	88		157.50	light fixture with two 40 watt bulbs.
Reinstall	Ea.		53.49		53.49	
Clean	Ea.	1.01	23		24.01	
Minimum Charge	Job		234		234	
3 Bulb, 4'						
Demolish	Ea.		21		21	Includes material and labor to install a
Install	Ea.	105	67		172	4' long pendant mounted fluorescent
Demolish and Install	Ea.	105	88		193	light fixture with three 34 watt bulbs.
Reinstall	Ea.		53.49		53.49	
Clean	Ea.	1.01	23		24.01	
Minimum Charge	Job		234		234	
4 Bulb, 4'						
Demolish	Ea.		21		21	Includes material and labor to install a
Install	Ea.	95.50	72		167.50	4' long pendant mounted fluorescent
Demolish and Install	Ea.	95.50	93		188.50	light fixture with four 34 watt bulbs.
Reinstall	Ea.		57.60		57.60	
Clean	Ea.	1.01	23		24.01	
Minimum Charge	Job		234		234	
2 Bulb, 8'						
Demolish	Ea.		26		26	Includes material and labor to install a
Install	Ea.	107	88.50		195.50	8' long surface mounted fluorescent
Demolish and Install	Ea.	107	114.50		221.50	light fixture with two 110 watt bulbs.
Reinstall	Ea.		70.64		70.64	
Clean	Ea.	1.01	23		24.01	
Minimum Charge	Job		234		234	

Finish Electrical

Commercial Light Fixture		Unit	Material	Labor	Equip.	Total	Specification
Run Wiring							
	Install	Ea.	17.70	18.70		36.40	Includes labor and material to install a
	Minimum Charge	Job		234		234	electric fixture utility box with
							non-metallic cable.
Ceiling, Recessed							
Eyeball Type							
	Demolish	Ea.		21.50		21.50	Includes material and labor to install
	Install	Ea.	77	16.70		93.70	custom quality recessed eyeball
	Demolish and Install	Ea.	77	38.20		115.20	spotlight with housing. Wiring is not
	Reinstall	Ea.		13.37		13.37	included.
	Clean	Ea.	.04	3.34		3.38	
	Minimum Charge	Job		234		234	
Shower Type							
	Demolish	Ea.		21.50		21.50	Includes material and labor to install
	Install	Ea.	64	15.60		79.60	deluxe quality recessed eyeball
	Demolish and Install	Ea.	64	37.10		101.10	spotlight with housing. Wiring is not
	Reinstall	Ea.		12.48		12.48	included.
	Clean	Ea.	.04	3.34		3.38	
	Minimum Charge	Job		234		234	
Run Wiring							
	Install	Ea.	17.70	18.70		36.40	Includes labor and material to install a
	Minimum Charge	Job		234		234	electric fixture utility box with
							non-metallic cable.
Ceiling Grid Type							
2 Tube							
	Demolish	Ea.		30.50		30.50	Cost includes material and labor to
	Install	Ea.	55	88.50		143.50	install 2 lamp fluorescent light fixture
	Demolish and Install	Ea.	55	119		174	in 2' x 4' ceiling grid system including
	Reinstall	Ea.		70.64		70.64	lens and tubes.
	Clean	Ea.	1.01	23		24.01	
	Minimum Charge	Job		234		234	
4 Tube							
	Demolish	Ea.		34.50		34.50	Cost includes material and labor to
	Install	Ea.	63.50	99.50		163	install 4 lamp fluorescent light fixture
	Demolish and Install	Ea.	63.50	134		197.50	in 2' x 4' ceiling grid system including
	Reinstall	Ea.		79.66		79.66	lens and tubes.
	Clean	Ea.	1.01	23		24.01	
	Minimum Charge	Job		234		234	
Acrylic Diffuser							
	Demolish	Ea.		5.40		5.40	Includes material and labor to install
	Install	Ea.	74.50	14.20		88.70	fluorescent light fixture w/acrylic
	Demolish and Install	Ea.	74.50	19.60		94.10	diffuser.
	Reinstall	Ea.		11.35		11.35	
	Clean	Ea.	.65	4.01		4.66	
	Minimum Charge	Job		234		234	
Louver Diffuser							
	Demolish	Ea.		6.50		6.50	Includes material and labor to install
	Install	Ea.	83	14.20		97.20	fluorescent light fixture w/louver
	Demolish and Install	Ea.	83	20.70		103.70	diffuser.
	Reinstall	Ea.		11.35		11.35	
	Clean	Ea.	.65	4.01		4.66	
	Minimum Charge	Job		234		234	
Run Wiring							
	Install	Ea.	17.70	18.70		36.40	Includes labor and material to install a
	Minimum Charge	Job		234		234	electric fixture utility box with
							non-metallic cable.

Finish Electrical

Commercial Light Fixture

Commercial Light Fixture	Unit	Material	Labor	Equip.	Total	Specification
Track Lighting						
Demolish	L.F.		7.20		7.20	Includes material and labor to install
Install	L.F.	18.35	19.50		37.85	track lighting.
Demolish and Install	L.F.	18.35	26.70		45.05	
Reinstall	L.F.		15.60		15.60	
Clean	L.F.	.20	6.40		6.60	
Minimum Charge	Job		234		234	
Emergency						
Demolish	Ea.		37		37	Includes material and labor to install
Install	Ea.	157	117		274	battery-powered emergency lighting
Demolish and Install	Ea.	157	154		311	unit with two (2) lights, including
Reinstall	Ea.		93.60		93.60	wiring.
Clean	Ea.	.51	23		23.51	
Minimum Charge	Job		234		234	
Run Wiring						
Install	Ea.	17.70	18.70		36.40	Includes labor and material to install a
Minimum Charge	Job		234		234	electric fixture utility box with non-metallic cable.

Fan

Fan	Unit	Material	Labor	Equip.	Total	Specification
Ceiling Paddle						
Good Quality						
Demolish	Ea.		29		29	Includes material and labor to install
Install	Ea.	103	47		150	standard ceiling fan.
Demolish and Install	Ea.	103	76		179	
Reinstall	Ea.		37.44		37.44	
Clean	Ea.	.41	20		20.41	
Minimum Charge	Job		234		234	
Better Quality						
Demolish	Ea.		29		29	Includes material and labor to install
Install	Ea.	156	47		203	better ceiling fan.
Demolish and Install	Ea.	156	76		232	
Reinstall	Ea.		37.44		37.44	
Clean	Ea.	.41	20		20.41	
Minimum Charge	Job		234		234	
Premium Quality						
Demolish	Ea.		29		29	Includes material and labor to install
Install	Ea.	370	58.50		428.50	deluxe ceiling fan.
Demolish and Install	Ea.	370	87.50		457.50	
Reinstall	Ea.		46.80		46.80	
Clean	Ea.	.41	20		20.41	
Minimum Charge	Job		234		234	
Light Kit						
Install	Ea.	45	58.50		103.50	Includes labor and material to install a
Minimum Charge	Job		234		234	ceiling fan light kit.
Bathroom Exhaust						
Ceiling Mounted						
Demolish	Ea.		24		24	Cost includes material and labor to
Install	Ea.	58	46.50		104.50	install 60 CFM ceiling mounted
Demolish and Install	Ea.	58	70.50		128.50	bathroom exhaust fan, up to 10' of
Reinstall	Ea.		37.33		37.33	wiring with one wall switch.
Clean	Ea.	.20	8		8.20	
Minimum Charge	Job		234		234	

Finish Electrical

Fan		Unit	Material	Labor	Equip.	Total	Specification
Wall Mounted							
	Demolish	Ea.		24		24	Cost includes material and labor to
	Install	Ea.	73.50	46.50		120	install 110 CFM wall mounted
	Demolish and Install	Ea.	73.50	70.50		144	bathroom exhaust fan, up to 10' of
	Reinstall	Ea.		37.33		37.33	wiring with one wall switch.
	Clean	Ea.	.20	8		8.20	
	Minimum Charge	Job		234		234	
Lighted							
	Demolish	Ea.		24		24	Cost includes material and labor to
	Install	Ea.	53	46.50		99.50	install 50 CFM ceiling mounted lighted
	Demolish and Install	Ea.	53	70.50		123.50	exhaust fan, up to 10' of wiring with
	Reinstall	Ea.		37.33		37.33	one wall switch..
	Clean	Ea.	.20	8		8.20	
	Minimum Charge	Job		234		234	
Blower Heater w / Light							
	Demolish	Ea.		24		24	Includes material and labor to install
	Install	Ea.	113	78		191	ceiling blower type ventilator with
	Demolish and Install	Ea.	113	102		215	switch, light and snap-on grill. Includes
	Reinstall	Ea.		62.21		62.21	1300 watt/120 volt heater.
	Clean	Ea.	.20	8		8.20	
	Minimum Charge	Job		234		234	
Fan Heater w / Light							
	Demolish	Ea.		24		24	Includes material and labor to install
	Install	Ea.	154	78		232	circular ceiling fan heater unit, 1500
	Demolish and Install	Ea.	154	102		256	watt, surface mounted.
	Reinstall	Ea.		62.21		62.21	
	Clean	Ea.	.20	8		8.20	
	Minimum Charge	Job		234		234	
Whole House Exhaust							
36" Ceiling Mounted							
	Install	Ea.	1025	117		1142	Includes material and labor to install a
	Clean	Ea.	.06	5.85		5.91	whole house exhaust fan.
	Minimum Charge	Job		234		234	
Kitchen Exhaust							
Standard Model							
	Install	Ea.	83	31		114	Includes labor and materials to install
	Clean	Ea.	.06	5.85		5.91	a bathroom or kitchen vent fan.
	Minimum Charge	Job		234		234	
Low Noise Model							
	Install	Ea.	103	31		134	Includes labor and materials to install
	Clean	Ea.	.06	5.85		5.91	a bathroom or kitchen vent fan, low
	Minimum Charge	Job		234		234	noise model.

Low Voltage Systems		Unit	Material	Labor	Equip.	Total	Specification
Smoke Detector							
Pre-wired							
	Demolish	Ea.		10.85		10.85	Includes material and labor to install
	Install	Ea.	22.50	88		110.50	AC type smoke detector including
	Demolish and Install	Ea.	22.50	98.85		121.35	wiring.
	Reinstall	Ea.		70.24		70.24	
	Clean	Ea.	.08	10		10.08	
	Minimum Charge	Job		234		234	

Finish Electrical

Low Voltage Systems		Unit	Material	Labor	Equip.	Total	Specification
Run Wiring							
	Install	Ea.	17.70	18.70		36.40	Includes labor and material to install a
	Minimum Charge	Job		234		234	electric fixture utility box with
							non-metallic cable.
Door Bell / Chimes							
Good Quality							
	Demolish	Ea.		32.50		32.50	Includes material and labor to install
	Install	Ea.	55	117		172	surface mounted 2 note door bell.
	Demolish and Install	Ea.	55	149.50		204.50	Wiring is not included.
	Reinstall	Ea.		93.60		93.60	
	Clean	Ea.	.20	10		10.20	
	Minimum Charge	Job		234		234	
Better Quality							
	Demolish	Ea.		32.50		32.50	Includes material and labor to install
	Install	Ea.	80	117		197	standard quality surface mounted 2
	Demolish and Install	Ea.	80	149.50		229.50	note door bell. Wiring is not included.
	Reinstall	Ea.		93.60		93.60	
	Clean	Ea.	.20	10		10.20	
	Minimum Charge	Job		234		234	
Premium Quality							
	Demolish	Ea.		32.50		32.50	Includes material and labor to install
	Install	Ea.	109	117		226	deluxe quality surface mounted 2 note
	Demolish and Install	Ea.	109	149.50		258.50	door bell. Wiring is not included.
	Reinstall	Ea.		93.60		93.60	
	Clean	Ea.	.20	10		10.20	
	Minimum Charge	Job		234		234	
Run Wiring							
	Install	Ea.	17.70	18.70		36.40	Includes labor and material to install a
	Minimum Charge	Job		234		234	electric fixture utility box with
							non-metallic cable.
Intercom System							
Intercom (master)							
	Demolish	Ea.		86.50		86.50	Includes material and labor to install
	Install	Ea.	635	234		869	master intercom station with AM/FM
	Demolish and Install	Ea.	635	320.50		955.50	music and room monitoring. Wiring is
	Reinstall	Ea.		187.20		187.20	not included.
	Clean	Ea.	.20	26.50		26.70	
	Minimum Charge	Job		234		234	
Intercom (remote)							
	Demolish	Ea.		52		52	Includes material and labor to install
	Install	Ea.	58	58.50		116.50	remote station for master intercom
	Demolish and Install	Ea.	58	110.50		168.50	system. Wiring is not included.
	Reinstall	Ea.		46.80		46.80	
	Clean	Ea.	.20	10		10.20	
	Minimum Charge	Job		234		234	
Security System							
Alarm Panel							
	Demolish	Ea.		104		104	Includes material and labor to install a
	Install	Ea.	164	234		398	6 zone burglar alarm panel.
	Demolish and Install	Ea.	164	338		502	
	Reinstall	Ea.		187.20		187.20	
	Clean	Ea.	.20	10		10.20	
	Minimum Charge	Job		234		234	

Low Voltage Systems	Unit	Material	Labor	Equip.	Total	Specification
Motion Detector						
Demolish	Ea.		74.50		74.50	Includes material and labor to install a
Install	Ea.	250	203		453	ultrasonic motion detector for a
Demolish and Install	Ea.	250	277.50		527.50	security system.
Reinstall	Ea.		162.78		162.78	
Clean	Ea.	.20	10		10.20	
Minimum Charge	Job		234		234	
Door Switch						
Demolish	Ea.		32.50		32.50	Includes material and labor to install a
Install	Ea.	152	88.50		240.50	door / window contact for a security
Demolish and Install	Ea.	152	121		273	system.
Reinstall	Ea.		70.64		70.64	
Clean	Ea.	.20	3.20		3.40	
Minimum Charge	Job		234		234	
Window Switch						
Demolish	Ea.		32.50		32.50	Includes material and labor to install a
Install	Ea.	152	88.50		240.50	door / window contact for a security
Demolish and Install	Ea.	152	121		273	system.
Reinstall	Ea.		70.64		70.64	
Clean	Ea.	.20	3.20		3.40	
Minimum Charge	Job		234		234	
Satellite System						
Dish						
Demolish	Ea.		144		144	Includes material, labor and
Install	Ea.	1275	390		1665	equipment to install 10' mesh dish.
Demolish and Install	Ea.	1275	534		1809	
Reinstall	Ea.		312		312	
Clean	Ea.	4.03	40		44.03	
Minimum Charge	Job		234		234	
Motor						
Demolish	Ea.		72		72	Includes material and labor to install a
Install	Ea.	400	195		595	television satellite dish motor unit.
Demolish and Install	Ea.	400	267		667	
Reinstall	Ea.		156		156	
Clean	Ea.	.20	10		10.20	
Minimum Charge	Job		234		234	
Television Antenna						
40' Pole						
Demolish	Ea.		81.50		81.50	Includes material and labor to install
Install	Ea.	30.50	146		176.50	stand-alone 1"-2" metal pole, 10' long.
Demolish and Install	Ea.	30.50	227.50		258	Cost does not include antenna.
Reinstall	Ea.		117		117	
Clean	Ea.	.80	40		40.80	
Paint	Ea.	8.95	46		54.95	
Minimum Charge	Job		234		234	
Rotor Unit						
Demolish	Ea.		65		65	Includes material and labor to install a
Install	Ea.	84	58.50		142.50	television antenna rotor.
Demolish and Install	Ea.	84	123.50		207.50	
Reinstall	Ea.		46.80		46.80	
Clean	Ea.	.80	40		40.80	
Minimum Charge	Job		234		234	
Single Booster						
Demolish	Ea.		65		65	Includes material and labor to install
Install	Ea.	41.50	58.50		100	standard grade VHF television signal
Demolish and Install	Ea.	41.50	123.50		165	booster unit and all hardware required
Reinstall	Ea.		46.80		46.80	for connection to TV cable.
Clean	Ea.	.04	5		5.04	
Minimum Charge	Job		234		234	

Gazebo   Gutter   Shutter

Window Treatment	Unit	Material	Labor	Equip.	Total	Specification
Drapery						
Good Grade						
Install	L.F.	45.50	6.40		51.90	Includes material and labor to install
Reinstall	L.F.		5.13		5.13	good quality drapery.
Clean	L.F.	2.85	.16		3.01	
Minimum Charge	Job		160		160	
Premium Grade						
Install	L.F.	80.50	6.40		86.90	Includes material and labor to install
Reinstall	L.F.		5.13		5.13	premium quality drapery.
Clean	L.F.	2.85	.18		3.03	
Minimum Charge	Job		160		160	
Lining						
Install	L.F.	19.90	6.40		26.30	Includes material and labor to install
Reinstall	L.F.		5.13		5.13	drapery lining.
Clean	L.F.	1.43	.09		1.52	
Minimum Charge	Job		160		160	
Valance Board						
Demolish	L.F.		1.78		1.78	Includes material and labor to install a
Install	L.F.	4.98	12.80		17.78	drapery valance board.
Demolish and Install	L.F.	4.98	14.58		19.56	
Reinstall	L.F.		10.25		10.25	
Clean	L.F.	1.43	.32		1.75	
Minimum Charge	Job		160		160	
Rod						
Demolish	L.F.		4.45		4.45	Includes material and labor to install
Install	L.F.	7.55	7.30		14.85	standard traverse drapery hardware.
Demolish and Install	L.F.	7.55	11.75		19.30	
Reinstall	L.F.		5.86		5.86	
Clean	L.F.	.08	.29		.37	
Paint	L.F.	.07	.71		.78	
Minimum Charge	Job		160		160	
Blinds						
Mini-type						
Demolish	S.F.		.94		.94	Includes material and labor to install
Install	S.F.	5.30	.73		6.03	horizontal 1" slat blinds.
Demolish and Install	S.F.	5.30	1.67		6.97	
Reinstall	S.F.		.59		.59	
Clean	S.F.	.54	.03		.57	
Minimum Charge	Job		160		160	

Improvements / Appliances / Treatments

Window Treatment		Unit	Material	Labor	Equip.	Total	Specification
Vertical Type							
	Demolish	S.F.		.94		.94	Includes material and labor to install
	Install	S.F.	8.60	.94		9.54	vertical 3" - 5" cloth or PVC blinds.
	Demolish and Install	S.F.	8.60	1.88		10.48	
	Reinstall	S.F.		.75		.75	
	Clean	S.F.	.29	.03		.32	
	Minimum Charge	Job		160		160	
Vertical Type per L.F.							
	Demolish	L.F.		1.48		1.48	Includes material and labor to install
	Install	L.F.	51	4.27		55.27	vertical 3" - 5" cloth or PVC blinds x
	Demolish and Install	L.F.	51	5.75		56.75	72" long.
	Reinstall	L.F.		3.42		3.42	
	Clean	L.F.	2.02	.22		2.24	
	Minimum Charge	Job		160		160	
Venetian Type							
	Demolish	S.F.		.94		.94	Includes material and labor to install
	Install	S.F.	8.40	.73		9.13	horizontal 2" slat blinds.
	Demolish and Install	S.F.	8.40	1.67		10.07	
	Reinstall	S.F.		.59		.59	
	Clean	S.F.	.29	.03		.32	
	Minimum Charge	Job		160		160	

Wood Shutter

27" x 36", 4 Panel

		Unit	Material	Labor	Equip.	Total	Specification
	Demolish	Ea.		30		30	Includes material and labor to install
	Install	Pr.	99	25.50		124.50	moveable louver, up to 33" x 36", 4
	Demolish and Install	Pr.	99	55.50		154.50	panel shutter.
	Reinstall	Pr.		20.33		20.33	
	Clean	Ea.	.08	9.75		9.83	
	Paint	Ea.	1.43	26.50		27.93	
	Minimum Charge	Job		216		216	

33" x 36", 4 Panel

		Unit	Material	Labor	Equip.	Total	Specification
	Demolish	Ea.		30		30	Includes material and labor to install
	Install	Pr.	99	25.50		124.50	moveable louver, up to 33" x 36", 4
	Demolish and Install	Pr.	99	55.50		154.50	panel shutter.
	Reinstall	Pr.		20.33		20.33	
	Clean	Ea.	.08	9.75		9.83	
	Paint	Ea.	1.50	28.50		30	
	Minimum Charge	Job		216		216	

39" x 36", 4 Panel

		Unit	Material	Labor	Equip.	Total	Specification
	Demolish	Ea.		30		30	Includes material and labor to install
	Install	Pr.	108	25.50		133.50	moveable louver, up to 47" x 36", 4
	Demolish and Install	Pr.	108	55.50		163.50	panel shutter.
	Reinstall	Pr.		20.33		20.33	
	Clean	Ea.	.08	9.75		9.83	
	Paint	Ea.	1.50	28.50		30	
	Minimum Charge	Job		216		216	

47" x 36", 4 Panel

		Unit	Material	Labor	Equip.	Total	Specification
	Demolish	Ea.		30		30	Includes material and labor to install
	Install	Pr.	108	25.50		133.50	moveable louver, up to 47" x 36", 4
	Demolish and Install	Pr.	108	55.50		163.50	panel shutter.
	Reinstall	Pr.		20.33		20.33	
	Clean	Ea.	.08	9.75		9.83	
	Paint	Ea.	1.56	31		32.56	
	Minimum Charge	Job		216		216	

Improvements / Appliances / Treatments

Stairs		Unit	Material	Labor	Equip.	Total	Specification
Concrete Steps							
Precast							
	Demolish	Ea.		62	45	107	Includes material and labor to install
	Install	Flight	470	149	43	662	precast concrete front entrance stairs,
	Demolish and Install	Flight	470	211	88	769	4' wide, with 48" platform and 2
	Clean	Ea.		4.45		4.45	risers.
	Paint	Ea.	4.73	46		50.73	
	Minimum Charge	Job		385		385	
Metal							
Concrete Filled							
	Demolish	Ea.		17.80		17.80	Includes material and labor to install
	Install	Riser	615	70.50	5.20	690.70	steel, cement filled metal pan stairs
	Demolish and Install	Riser	615	88.30	5.20	708.50	with picket rail.
	Clean	Ea.	.12	2.74		2.86	
	Paint	Ea.	.69	2.74		3.43	
	Minimum Charge	Job		261		261	
Landing							
	Demolish	S.F.		4.45		4.45	Includes material and labor to install
	Install	S.F.	130	8.30	.61	138.91	pre-erected conventional steel pan
	Demolish and Install	S.F.	130	12.75	.61	143.36	landing.
	Clean	S.F.	.12	.57		.69	
	Paint	S.F.	.24	.79		1.03	
	Minimum Charge	Job		261		261	
Railing							
	Demolish	L.F.		2.46		2.46	Includes material and labor to install
	Install	L.F.	17.05	12.05	.89	29.99	primed steel pipe.
	Demolish and Install	L.F.	17.05	14.51	.89	32.45	
	Clean	L.F.	.80	2		2.80	
	Paint	L.F.	.86	6.15		7.01	
	Minimum Charge	Job		261		261	

Elevator		Unit	Material	Labor	Equip.	Total	Specification
2 Stop Residential							
	Install	Ea.	12300	6500		18800	Includes labor, material and
	Clean	Ea.	.87	20		20.87	equipment to install 2 stop elevator for
	Minimum Charge	Job		650		650	residential use.
2 Stop Commercial							
	Install	Ea.	44100	13000		57100	Includes labor, material and
	Clean	Ea.	.87	20		20.87	equipment to install 2 stop elevator for
	Minimum Charge	Job		650		650	apartment or commercial building with
3 Stop Commercial							2,000 lb/13 passenger capacity.
	Install	Ea.	55500	20000		75500	Includes labor, material and
	Clean	Ea.	.87	20		20.87	equipment to install 3 stop elevator for
	Minimum Charge	Job		650		650	apartment or commercial building with
							2,000 lb/13 passenger capacity.
4 Stop Commercial							
	Install	Ea.	67500	27100		94600	Includes labor, material and
	Clean	Ea.	.87	20		20.87	equipment to install 4 stop elevator for
	Minimum Charge	Job		650		650	apartment or commercial building with
							2,000 lb/13 passenger capacity.

Improvements / Appliances / Treatments

Elevator

	Unit	Material	Labor	Equip.	Total	Specification
5 Stop Commercial						
Install	Ea.	79000	34200		113200	Includes labor, material and
Clean	Ea.	.87	20		20.87	equipment to install 5 stop elevator for
Minimum Charge	Job		650		650	apartment or commercial building with
						2,000 lb/13 passenger capacity.

Rangetop

	Unit	Material	Labor	Equip.	Total	Specification
4-burner						
Demolish	Ea.		32.50		32.50	Cost includes material and labor to
Install	Ea.	320	78		398	install 4-burner electric surface unit.
Demolish and Install	Ea.	320	110.50		430.50	
Reinstall	Ea.		62.40		62.40	
Clean	Ea.	.06	29.50		29.56	
Minimum Charge	Job		80		80	
6-burner						
Demolish	Ea.		32.50		32.50	Includes material and labor to install a
Install	Ea.	2100	93.50		2193.50	6-burner cooktop unit.
Demolish and Install	Ea.	2100	126		2226	
Reinstall	Ea.		74.88		74.88	
Clean	Ea.	.06	29.50		29.56	
Minimum Charge	Job		80		80	
Premium Brand w / Grill						
Demolish	Ea.		32.50		32.50	Includes material and labor to install
Install	Ea.	1100	93.50		1193.50	electric downdraft cooktop with grill.
Demolish and Install	Ea.	1100	126		1226	
Reinstall	Ea.		74.88		74.88	
Clean	Ea.	.06	29.50		29.56	
Minimum Charge	Job		80		80	

Rangehood

	Unit	Material	Labor	Equip.	Total	Specification
Vented						
30″						
Demolish	Ea.		29.50		29.50	Includes material and labor to install a
Install	Ea.	76.50	93.50		170	vented range hood.
Demolish and Install	Ea.	76.50	123		199.50	
Reinstall	Ea.		74.88		74.88	
Clean	Ea.	.06	8.35		8.41	
Minimum Charge	Job		80		80	
36″						
Demolish	Ea.		29.50		29.50	Includes material and labor to install a
Install	Ea.	177	93.50		270.50	vented range hood.
Demolish and Install	Ea.	177	123		300	
Reinstall	Ea.		74.88		74.88	
Clean	Ea.	.06	8.35		8.41	
Minimum Charge	Job		80		80	
42″						
Demolish	Ea.		29.50		29.50	Includes material and labor to install a
Install	Ea.	183	110		293	vented range hood.
Demolish and Install	Ea.	183	139.50		322.50	
Reinstall	Ea.		87.84		87.84	
Clean	Ea.	.06	8.35		8.41	
Minimum Charge	Job		80		80	

Improvements / Appliances / Treatments

Rangehood	Unit	Material	Labor	Equip.	Total	Specification
Ventless						
30"						
Demolish	Ea.		29.50		29.50	Includes material and labor to install a
Install	Ea.	93.50	58.50		152	ventless range hood.
Demolish and Install	Ea.	93.50	88		181.50	
Reinstall	Ea.		46.80		46.80	
Clean	Ea.	.06	8.35		8.41	
Minimum Charge	Job		80		80	
36"						
Demolish	Ea.		29.50		29.50	Includes material and labor to install a
Install	Ea.	174	93.50		267.50	ventless range hood.
Demolish and Install	Ea.	174	123		297	
Reinstall	Ea.		74.88		74.88	
Clean	Ea.	.06	8.35		8.41	
Minimum Charge	Job		80		80	
42"						
Demolish	Ea.		29.50		29.50	Includes material and labor to install a
Install	Ea.	205	78		283	ventless range hood.
Demolish and Install	Ea.	205	107.50		312.50	
Reinstall	Ea.		62.40		62.40	
Clean	Ea.	.06	8.35		8.41	
Minimum Charge	Job		80		80	

Oven	Unit	Material	Labor	Equip.	Total	Specification
Free Standing						
Demolish	Ea.		32.50		32.50	Cost includes material and labor to
Install	Ea.	560	64		624	install 30" free standing electric range
Demolish and Install	Ea.	560	96.50		656.50	with self-cleaning oven.
Reinstall	Ea.		51.26		51.26	
Clean	Ea.	.06	29.50		29.56	
Minimum Charge	Job		80		80	
Single Wall Oven						
Demolish	Ea.		32.50		32.50	Includes material and labor to install a
Install	Ea.	690	117		807	built-in oven.
Demolish and Install	Ea.	690	149.50		839.50	
Reinstall	Ea.		93.60		93.60	
Clean	Ea.	.06	29.50		29.56	
Minimum Charge	Job		80		80	
Double Wall Oven						
Demolish	Ea.		32.50		32.50	Includes material and labor to install a
Install	Ea.	1425	216		1641	conventional double oven.
Demolish and Install	Ea.	1425	248.50		1673.50	
Reinstall	Ea.		172.80		172.80	
Clean	Ea.	.06	29.50		29.56	
Minimum Charge	Job		80		80	
Drop-in Type w / Range						
Demolish	Ea.		32.50		32.50	Includes material and labor to install a
Install	Ea.	745	78		823	built-in cooking range with oven.
Demolish and Install	Ea.	745	110.50		855.50	
Reinstall	Ea.		62.40		62.40	
Clean	Ea.	.06	29.50		29.56	
Minimum Charge	Job		80		80	

Improvements / Appliances / Treatments

Oven	Unit	Material	Labor	Equip.	Total	Specification
Hi/Lo w / Range, Microwave						
Demolish	Ea.		32.50		32.50	Includes material and labor to install a
Install	Ea.	1950	430		2380	double oven, one conventional, one
Demolish and Install	Ea.	1950	462.50		2412.50	microwave.
Reinstall	Ea.		345.60		345.60	
Clean	Ea.	.06	29.50		29.56	
Minimum Charge	Job		80		80	
Hi/Lo w/ Range / Double Oven						
Demolish	Ea.		32.50		32.50	Includes material and labor to install a
Install	Ea.	1425	216		1641	conventional double oven.
Demolish and Install	Ea.	1425	248.50		1673.50	
Reinstall	Ea.		172.80		172.80	
Clean	Ea.	.06	29.50		29.56	
Minimum Charge	Job		80		80	
Countertop Microwave						
Demolish	Ea.		11.15		11.15	Includes material and labor to install a
Install	Ea.	161	40		201	1.0 cubic foot microwave oven.
Demolish and Install	Ea.	161	51.15		212.15	
Reinstall	Ea.		32.04		32.04	
Clean	Ea.	.06	14.65		14.71	
Minimum Charge	Job		80		80	
Cabinet / Wall Mounted Microwave						
Demolish	Ea.		22.50		22.50	Includes material and labor to install a
Install	Ea.	770	117		887	space saver microwave oven.
Demolish and Install	Ea.	770	139.50		909.50	
Reinstall	Ea.		93.60		93.60	
Clean	Ea.	.06	14.65		14.71	
Minimum Charge	Job		80		80	

Dryer	Unit	Material	Labor	Equip.	Total	Specification
Basic Grade						
Demolish	Ea.		14.85		14.85	Includes material and labor to install
Install	Ea.	450	251		701	electric or gas dryer. Vent kit not
Demolish and Install	Ea.	450	265.85		715.85	included.
Reinstall	Ea.		201.17		201.17	
Clean	Ea.	.06	29.50		29.56	
Minimum Charge	Job		80		80	
Good Grade						
Demolish	Ea.		14.85		14.85	Includes material and labor to install
Install	Ea.	560	251		811	electric or gas dryer. Vent kit not
Demolish and Install	Ea.	560	265.85		825.85	included.
Reinstall	Ea.		201.17		201.17	
Clean	Ea.	.06	29.50		29.56	
Minimum Charge	Job		80		80	
Premium Grade						
Demolish	Ea.		14.85		14.85	Includes material and labor to install
Install	Ea.	1625	375		2000	electric or gas dryer. Vent kit not
Demolish and Install	Ea.	1625	389.85		2014.85	included.
Reinstall	Ea.		301.76		301.76	
Clean	Ea.	.06	29.50		29.56	
Minimum Charge	Job		80		80	

Improvements / Appliances / Treatments

Dryer

Dryer	Unit	Material	Labor	Equip.	Total	Specification
Washer / Dryer Combination Unit						Includes material and labor to install electric washer/dryer combination unit, 27" wide, stackable or unitized.
Demolish	Ea.		14.85		14.85	
Install	Ea.	1150	64		1214	
Demolish and Install	Ea.	1150	78.85		1228.85	
Reinstall	Ea.		51.26		51.26	
Clean	Ea.	.06	29.50		29.56	
Minimum Charge	Job		80		80	

Washer

Washer	Unit	Material	Labor	Equip.	Total	Specification
Basic Grade						Includes material and labor to install washing machine. New hoses not included.
Demolish	Ea.		14.85		14.85	
Install	Ea.	530	167		697	
Demolish and Install	Ea.	530	181.85		711.85	
Reinstall	Ea.		133.76		133.76	
Clean	Ea.	.06	29.50		29.56	
Minimum Charge	Job		80		80	
Good Grade						Includes material and labor to install washing machine. New hoses not included.
Demolish	Ea.		14.85		14.85	
Install	Ea.	865	251		1116	
Demolish and Install	Ea.	865	265.85		1130.85	
Reinstall	Ea.		200.64		200.64	
Clean	Ea.	.06	29.50		29.56	
Minimum Charge	Job		80		80	
Premium Grade						Includes material and labor to install washing machine with digital computer readouts and large capacity. New hoses not included.
Demolish	Ea.		14.85		14.85	
Install	Ea.	1650	500		2150	
Demolish and Install	Ea.	1650	514.85		2164.85	
Reinstall	Ea.		401.28		401.28	
Clean	Ea.	.06	29.50		29.56	
Minimum Charge	Job		80		80	
Washer / Dryer Combination Unit						Includes material and labor to install electric washer/dryer combination unit, 27" wide, stackable or unitized.
Demolish	Ea.		14.85		14.85	
Install	Ea.	1150	64		1214	
Demolish and Install	Ea.	1150	78.85		1228.85	
Reinstall	Ea.		51.26		51.26	
Clean	Ea.	.06	29.50		29.56	
Minimum Charge	Job		80		80	

Refrigerator

Refrigerator	Unit	Material	Labor	Equip.	Total	Specification
12 Cubic Foot						Includes material and labor to install a refrigerator.
Demolish	Ea.		44.50		44.50	
Install	Ea.	460	64		524	
Demolish and Install	Ea.	460	108.50		568.50	
Reinstall	Ea.		51.26		51.26	
Clean	Ea.	.06	29.50		29.56	
Minimum Charge	Job		80		80	
16 Cubic Foot						Includes material and labor to install a refrigerator.
Demolish	Ea.		44.50		44.50	
Install	Ea.	550	71		621	
Demolish and Install	Ea.	550	115.50		665.50	
Reinstall	Ea.		56.96		56.96	
Clean	Ea.	.06	29.50		29.56	
Minimum Charge	Job		80		80	

Improvements / Appliances / Treatments

Refrigerator	Unit	Material	Labor	Equip.	Total	Specification
18 Cubic Foot						
Demolish	Ea.		44.50		44.50	Includes material and labor to install a
Install	Ea.	725	80		805	refrigerator.
Demolish and Install	Ea.	725	124.50		849.50	
Reinstall	Ea.		64.08		64.08	
Clean	Ea.	.06	29.50		29.56	
Minimum Charge	Job		80		80	
21 Cubic Foot						
Demolish	Ea.		44.50		44.50	Includes material and labor to install a
Install	Ea.	1050	91.50		1141.50	refrigerator.
Demolish and Install	Ea.	1050	136		1186	
Reinstall	Ea.		73.23		73.23	
Clean	Ea.	.06	29.50		29.56	
Minimum Charge	Job		80		80	
24 Cubic Foot						
Demolish	Ea.		44.50		44.50	Includes material and labor to install a
Install	Ea.	1400	91.50		1491.50	refrigerator.
Demolish and Install	Ea.	1400	136		1536	
Reinstall	Ea.		73.23		73.23	
Clean	Ea.	.06	29.50		29.56	
Minimum Charge	Job		80		80	
27 Cubic Foot						
Demolish	Ea.		44.50		44.50	Includes material and labor to install a
Install	Ea.	2750	64		2814	refrigerator.
Demolish and Install	Ea.	2750	108.50		2858.50	
Reinstall	Ea.		51.26		51.26	
Clean	Ea.	.06	29.50		29.56	
Minimum Charge	Job		80		80	
Ice Maker						
Install	Ea.	65.50	62.50		128	Includes labor and material to install
Minimum Charge	Job		80		80	an automatic ice maker in a refrigerator.

Freezer	Unit	Material	Labor	Equip.	Total	Specification
15 Cubic Foot						
Demolish	Ea.		44.50		44.50	Cost includes material and labor to
Install	Ea.	665	64		729	install 15 cubic foot freezer.
Demolish and Install	Ea.	665	108.50		773.50	
Reinstall	Ea.		51.26		51.26	
Clean	Ea.	.06	29.50		29.56	
Minimum Charge	Job		80		80	
18 Cubic Foot						
Demolish	Ea.		44.50		44.50	Cost includes material and labor to
Install	Ea.	885	64		949	install 18 cubic foot freezer.
Demolish and Install	Ea.	885	108.50		993.50	
Reinstall	Ea.		51.26		51.26	
Clean	Ea.	.06	29.50		29.56	
Minimum Charge	Job		80		80	
21 Cubic Foot						
Demolish	Ea.		44.50		44.50	Includes material and labor to install a
Install	Ea.	800	64		864	15 to 23 cubic foot deep freezer.
Demolish and Install	Ea.	800	108.50		908.50	
Reinstall	Ea.		51.26		51.26	
Clean	Ea.	.06	29.50		29.56	
Minimum Charge	Job		80		80	

Improvements / Appliances / Treatments

Freezer		Unit	Material	Labor	Equip.	Total	Specification
24 Cubic Foot							
	Demolish	Ea.		44.50		44.50	Includes material and labor to install a
	Install	Ea.	890	128		1018	24 cubic foot deep freezer.
	Demolish and Install	Ea.	890	172.50		1062.50	
	Reinstall	Ea.		102.53		102.53	
	Clean	Ea.	.06	29.50		29.56	
	Minimum Charge	Job		80		80	
Chest-type							
	Demolish	Ea.		44.50		44.50	Cost includes material and labor to
	Install	Ea.	665	64		729	install 15 cubic foot freezer.
	Demolish and Install	Ea.	665	108.50		773.50	
	Clean	Ea.	.06	29.50		29.56	
	Minimum Charge	Job		80		80	

Dishwasher		Unit	Material	Labor	Equip.	Total	Specification
4 Cycle							
	Demolish	Ea.		35.50		35.50	Includes material and labor to install
	Install	Ea.	405	155		560	good grade automatic dishwasher.
	Demolish and Install	Ea.	405	190.50		595.50	
	Reinstall	Ea.		123.72		123.72	
	Clean	Ea.	.06	29.50		29.56	
	Minimum Charge	Job		80		80	

Garbage Disposal		Unit	Material	Labor	Equip.	Total	Specification
In Sink Unit							
	Demolish	Ea.		35		35	Cost includes material and labor to
	Install	Ea.	163	62		225	install 1/2 HP custom disposal unit.
	Demolish and Install	Ea.	163	97		260	
	Reinstall	Ea.		49.49		49.49	
	Clean	Ea.	.03	8.35		8.38	
	Minimum Charge	Job		80		80	

Trash Compactor		Unit	Material	Labor	Equip.	Total	Specification
4 to 1 Compaction							
	Demolish	Ea.		32.50		32.50	Includes material and labor to install a
	Install	Ea.	935	86.50		1021.50	trash compactor.
	Demolish and Install	Ea.	935	119		1054	
	Reinstall	Ea.		69.12		69.12	
	Clean	Ea.	.06	20		20.06	
	Minimum Charge	Job		80		80	

Kitchenette Unit		Unit	Material	Labor	Equip.	Total	Specification
Range, Refrigerator and Sink							
	Demolish	Ea.		130		130	Includes material and labor to install
	Install	Ea.	1750	515		2265	range/refrigerator/sink unit, 72"
	Demolish and Install	Ea.	1750	645		2395	wide, base unit only.
	Reinstall	Ea.		412.40		412.40	
	Clean	Ea.	1.01	14.65		15.66	
	Minimum Charge	Job		80		80	

Improvements / Appliances / Treatments

Bath Accessories		Unit	Material	Labor	Equip.	Total	Specification
Towel Bar							
	Demolish	Ea.		7.40		7.40	Includes material and labor to install
	Install	Ea.	59.50	18		77.50	towel bar up to 24″ long.
	Demolish and Install	Ea.	59.50	25.40		84.90	
	Reinstall	Ea.		14.40		14.40	
	Clean	Ea.		4.01		4.01	
	Minimum Charge	Job		216		216	
Toothbrush Holder							
	Demolish	Ea.		7.40		7.40	Includes material and labor to install a
	Install	Ea.	13.85	21.50		35.35	surface mounted tumbler and
	Demolish and Install	Ea.	13.85	28.90		42.75	toothbrush holder.
	Reinstall	Ea.		17.28		17.28	
	Clean	Ea.		4.01		4.01	
	Minimum Charge	Job		216		216	
Grab Rail							
	Demolish	Ea.		11.15		11.15	Includes material and labor to install a
	Install	Ea.	34	18.80		52.80	24″ long grab bar. Blocking is not
	Demolish and Install	Ea.	34	29.95		63.95	included.
	Reinstall	Ea.		15.03		15.03	
	Clean	Ea.	.41	6.70		7.11	
	Minimum Charge	Job		216		216	
Soap Dish							
	Demolish	Ea.		7.40		7.40	Includes material and labor to install a
	Install	Ea.	6.20	21.50		27.70	surface mounted soap dish.
	Demolish and Install	Ea.	6.20	28.90		35.10	
	Reinstall	Ea.		17.28		17.28	
	Clean	Ea.		4.01		4.01	
	Minimum Charge	Job		216		216	
Toilet Paper Roller							
	Demolish	Ea.		7.40		7.40	Includes material and labor to install a
	Install	Ea.	19.60	14.40		34	surface mounted toilet tissue dispenser.
	Demolish and Install	Ea.	19.60	21.80		41.40	
	Reinstall	Ea.		11.52		11.52	
	Clean	Ea.	.41	10		10.41	
	Minimum Charge	Job		216		216	
Dispenser							
Soap							
	Demolish	Ea.		9.90		9.90	Includes material and labor to install a
	Install	Ea.	51	21.50		72.50	surface mounted soap dispenser.
	Demolish and Install	Ea.	51	31.40		82.40	
	Reinstall	Ea.		17.28		17.28	
	Clean	Ea.	.41	10		10.41	
	Minimum Charge	Job		216		216	
Towel							
	Demolish	Ea.		11.15		11.15	Includes material and labor to install a
	Install	Ea.	49	27		76	surface mounted towel dispenser.
	Demolish and Install	Ea.	49	38.15		87.15	
	Reinstall	Ea.		21.60		21.60	
	Clean	Ea.	.41	13.35		13.76	
	Minimum Charge	Job		216		216	
Seat Cover							
	Demolish	Ea.		7.40		7.40	Includes material and labor to install a
	Install	Ea.	38	29		67	surface mounted toilet seat cover
	Demolish and Install	Ea.	38	36.40		74.40	dispenser.
	Reinstall	Ea.		23.04		23.04	
	Clean	Ea.	.41	10		10.41	
	Minimum Charge	Job		216		216	

Improvements / Appliances / Treatments

Bath Accessories

Bath Accessories		Unit	Material	Labor	Equip.	Total	Specification
Sanitary Napkin							Includes material and labor to install a surface mounted sanitary napkin dispenser.
	Demolish	Ea.		18.75		18.75	
	Install	Ea.	35	45.50		80.50	
	Demolish and Install	Ea.	35	64.25		99.25	
	Reinstall	Ea.		36.38		36.38	
	Clean	Ea.	.20	13.35		13.55	
	Minimum Charge	Job		216		216	
Partition							
Urinal							Includes material and labor to install a urinal screen.
	Demolish	Ea.		22.50		22.50	
	Install	Ea.	253	108		361	
	Demolish and Install	Ea.	253	130.50		383.50	
	Reinstall	Ea.		86.40		86.40	
	Clean	Ea.	.61	8.90		9.51	
	Minimum Charge	Job		216		216	
Toilet							Includes material and labor to install baked enamel standard size partition, floor or ceiling mounted with one wall and one door.
	Demolish	Ea.		66		66	
	Install	Ea.	650	173		823	
	Demolish and Install	Ea.	650	239		889	
	Reinstall	Ea.		138.24		138.24	
	Clean	Ea.	4.03	20		24.03	
	Minimum Charge	Job		216		216	
Handicap							Includes material and labor to install baked enamel handicap partition, floor or ceiling mounted with one wall and one door.
	Demolish	Ea.		66		66	
	Install	Ea.	975	173		1148	
	Demolish and Install	Ea.	975	239		1214	
	Reinstall	Ea.		138.24		138.24	
	Clean	Ea.	4.03	20		24.03	
	Minimum Charge	Job		216		216	

Fire Prevention / Protection

Fire Prevention / Protection		Unit	Material	Labor	Equip.	Total	Specification
Fire Extinguisher							
5# Carbon Dioxide							Includes labor and material to install one wall mounted 5 lb. carbon dioxide factory charged unit, complete with hose, horn and wall mounting bracket.
	Install	Ea.	205			205	
10# Carbon Dioxide							Includes labor and material to install one wall mounted 10 lb. carbon dioxide factory charged unit, complete with hose, horn and wall mounting bracket.
	Install	Ea.	295			295	
15# Carbon Dioxide							Includes labor and material to install one wall mounted 15 lb. carbon dioxide factory charged unit, complete with hose, horn and wall mounting bracket.
	Install	Ea.	380			380	

Improvements / Appliances / Treatments

Fire Prevention / Protection	Unit	Material	Labor	Equip.	Total	Specification
5# Dry Chemical						
Install	Ea.	55			55	Includes labor and material to install one wall mounted 5 lb. dry chemical factory charged unit, complete with hose, horn and wall mounting bracket.
20# Dry Chemical						
Install	Ea.	147			147	Includes labor and material to install one wall mounted 20 lb. dry chemical factory charged unit, complete with hose, horn and wall mounting bracket.

Gutters	Unit	Material	Labor	Equip.	Total	Specification
Galvanized						
Demolish	L.F.		1.48		1.48	Cost includes material and labor to install 5" galvanized steel gutter with enamel finish, fittings, hangers, and corners.
Install	L.F.	2.34	3.85		6.19	
Demolish and Install	L.F.	2.34	5.33		7.67	
Reinstall	L.F.		3.08		3.08	
Clean	L.F.		.43		.43	
Paint	L.F.	.24	1.14		1.38	
Minimum Charge	Job		241		241	
Aluminum						
Demolish	L.F.		1.48		1.48	Cost includes material and labor to install 5" aluminum gutter with enamel finish, fittings, hangers, and corners.
Install	L.F.	2.87	3.85		6.72	
Demolish and Install	L.F.	2.87	5.33		8.20	
Reinstall	L.F.		3.08		3.08	
Clean	L.F.		.43		.43	
Paint	L.F.	.24	1.14		1.38	
Minimum Charge	Job		241		241	
Copper						
Demolish	L.F.		1.48		1.48	Cost includes material and labor to install 5" half-round copper gutter with fittings, hangers, and corners.
Install	L.F.	8.45	3.85		12.30	
Demolish and Install	L.F.	8.45	5.33		13.78	
Reinstall	L.F.		3.08		3.08	
Clean	L.F.		.43		.43	
Minimum Charge	Job		241		241	
Plastic						
Demolish	L.F.		1.48		1.48	Cost includes material and labor to install 4" white vinyl gutter fittings, hangers, and corners.
Install	L.F.	1.31	3.76		5.07	
Demolish and Install	L.F.	1.31	5.24		6.55	
Reinstall	L.F.		3.01		3.01	
Clean	L.F.		.43		.43	
Paint	L.F.	.24	1.14		1.38	
Minimum Charge	Job		241		241	

Downspouts	Unit	Material	Labor	Equip.	Total	Specification
Galvanized						
Demolish	L.F.		1.02		1.02	Cost includes material and labor to install 4" diameter downspout with enamel finish.
Install	L.F.	2.87	3.32		6.19	
Demolish and Install	L.F.	2.87	4.34		7.21	
Reinstall	L.F.		2.66		2.66	
Clean	L.F.		.43		.43	
Paint	L.F.	.24	1.14		1.38	
Minimum Charge	Job		241		241	

Improvements / Appliances / Treatments

Downspouts		Unit	Material	Labor	Equip.	Total	Specification
Aluminum							
	Demolish	L.F.		1.02		1.02	Includes material and labor to install
	Install	L.F.	3.17	3.44		6.61	aluminum enameled downspout.
	Demolish and Install	L.F.	3.17	4.46		7.63	
	Reinstall	L.F.		2.75		2.75	
	Clean	L.F.		.43		.43	
	Paint	L.F.	.24	1.14		1.38	
	Minimum Charge	Job		241		241	
Copper							
	Demolish	L.F.		1.02		1.02	Includes material and labor to install
	Install	L.F.	9.30	2.54		11.84	round copper downspout.
	Demolish and Install	L.F.	9.30	3.56		12.86	
	Reinstall	L.F.		2.03		2.03	
	Clean	L.F.		.43		.43	
	Paint	L.F.	.24	1.14		1.38	
	Minimum Charge	Job		241		241	
Plastic							
	Demolish	L.F.		1.02		1.02	Cost includes material and labor to
	Install	L.F.	2.29	2.29		4.58	install 2" x 3" vinyl rectangular
	Demolish and Install	L.F.	2.29	3.31		5.60	downspouts.
	Reinstall	L.F.		1.83		1.83	
	Clean	L.F.		.43		.43	
	Paint	L.F.	.24	1.14		1.38	
	Minimum Charge	Job		241		241	

Shutters		Unit	Material	Labor	Equip.	Total	Specification
Exterior							
25" High							
	Demolish	Ea.		11.15		11.15	Includes material and labor to install
	Install	Pr.	194	43		237	pair of exterior shutters 25" x 16",
	Demolish and Install	Pr.	194	54.15		248.15	unpainted, installed as fixed shutters
	Reinstall	Pr.		43.20		43.20	on concrete or wood frame.
	Clean	Ea.	.08	9.75		9.83	
	Paint	Ea.	1.90	19.85		21.75	
	Minimum Charge	Job		216		216	
39" High							
	Demolish	Ea.		11.15		11.15	Includes material and labor to install
	Install	Pr.	262	43		305	pair of shutters 39" x 16", unpainted,
	Demolish and Install	Pr.	262	54.15		316.15	installed as fixed shutters on concrete
	Reinstall	Pr.		43.20		43.20	or wood frame.
	Clean	Ea.	.08	9.75		9.83	
	Paint	Ea.	2.96	27		29.96	
	Minimum Charge	Job		216		216	
51" High							
	Demolish	Ea.		11.15		11.15	Includes material and labor to install
	Install	Pr.	325	43		368	pair of shutters 51" x 16", unpainted,
	Demolish and Install	Pr.	325	54.15		379.15	installed as fixed shutters on concrete
	Reinstall	Pr.		43.20		43.20	or wood frame.
	Clean	Ea.	.08	9.75		9.83	
	Paint	Ea.	3.84	28		31.84	
	Minimum Charge	Job		216		216	

Improvements / Appliances / Treatments

Shutters	Unit	Material	Labor	Equip.	Total	Specification
59″ High						
Demolish	Ea.		11.15		11.15	Includes material and labor to install
Install	Pr.	430	43		473	pair of shutters 59″ x 16″, unpainted,
Demolish and Install	Pr.	430	54.15		484.15	installed as fixed shutters on concrete
Reinstall	Pr.		43.20		43.20	or wood frame.
Clean	Ea.	.08	9.75		9.83	
Paint	Ea.	4.43	30.50		34.93	
Minimum Charge	Job		216		216	
67″ High						
Demolish	Ea.		11.15		11.15	Includes material and labor to install
Install	Pr.	455	48		503	pair of shutters 67″ x 16″, unpainted,
Demolish and Install	Pr.	455	59.15		514.15	installed as fixed shutters on concrete
Reinstall	Pr.		48		48	or wood frame.
Clean	Ea.	.08	9.75		9.83	
Paint	Ea.	5.05	34		39.05	
Minimum Charge	Job		216		216	
Interior Wood						
23″ x 24″, 2 Panel						
Demolish	Ea.		11.15		11.15	Cost includes material and labor to
Install	Ea.	86	25.50		111.50	install 23″ x 24″, 4 panel interior
Demolish and Install	Ea.	86	36.65		122.65	moveable pine shutter, 1-1/4″ louver,
Reinstall	Ea.		20.33		20.33	knobs and hooks and hinges.
Clean	Ea.	.08	9.75		9.83	
Paint	Ea.	1.43	26.50		27.93	
Minimum Charge	Job		216		216	
27″ x 24″, 4 Panel						
Demolish	Ea.		11.15		11.15	Cost includes material and labor to
Install	Ea.	86	25.50		111.50	install 27″ x 24″, 4 panel interior
Demolish and Install	Ea.	86	36.65		122.65	moveable pine shutter, 1-1/4″ louver,
Reinstall	Ea.		20.33		20.33	knobs and hooks and hinges.
Clean	Ea.	.08	9.75		9.83	
Paint	Ea.	1.43	26.50		27.93	
Minimum Charge	Job		216		216	
31″ x 24″, 4 Panel						
Demolish	Ea.		11.15		11.15	Cost includes material and labor to
Install	Ea.	94.50	25.50		120	install 31″ x 24″, 4 panel interior
Demolish and Install	Ea.	94.50	36.65		131.15	moveable pine shutter, 1-1/4″ louver,
Reinstall	Ea.		20.33		20.33	knobs and hooks and hinges.
Clean	Ea.	.08	9.75		9.83	
Paint	Ea.	1.43	26.50		27.93	
Minimum Charge	Job		216		216	
35″ x 24″, 4 Panel						
Demolish	Ea.		11.15		11.15	Cost includes material and labor to
Install	Ea.	101	25.50		126.50	install 35″ x 24″, 4 panel interior
Demolish and Install	Ea.	101	36.65		137.65	moveable pine shutter, 1-1/4″ louver,
Reinstall	Ea.		20.33		20.33	knobs and hooks and hinges.
Clean	Ea.	.08	9.75		9.83	
Paint	Ea.	1.43	26.50		27.93	
Minimum Charge	Job		216		216	
39″ x 24″, 4 Panel						
Demolish	Ea.		11.15		11.15	Cost includes material and labor to
Install	Ea.	112	25.50		137.50	install 39″ x 24″, 4 panel interior
Demolish and Install	Ea.	112	36.65		148.65	moveable pine shutter, 1-1/4″ louver,
Reinstall	Ea.		20.33		20.33	knobs and hooks and hinges.
Clean	Ea.	.08	9.75		9.83	
Paint	Ea.	1.43	26.50		27.93	
Minimum Charge	Job		216		216	

Improvements / Appliances / Treatments

Shutters	Unit	Material	Labor	Equip.	Total	Specification
47" x 24", 4 Panel						
Demolish	Ea.		11.15		11.15	Cost includes material and labor to
Install	Ea.	128	25.50		153.50	install 47" x 24", 4 panel interior
Demolish and Install	Ea.	128	36.65		164.65	moveable pine shutter, 1-1/4" louver,
Reinstall	Ea.		20.33		20.33	knobs and hooks and hinges.
Clean	Ea.	.08	9.75		9.83	
Paint	Ea.	1.50	28.50		30	
Minimum Charge	Job		216		216	

Awning	Unit	Material	Labor	Equip.	Total	Specification
Standard Aluminum						
36" Wide x 30" Deep						
Demolish	Ea.		11.15		11.15	Includes material and labor to install
Install	Ea.	209	36		245	one aluminum awning with
Demolish and Install	Ea.	209	47.15		256.15	weather-resistant finish.
Reinstall	Ea.		28.80		28.80	
Clean	Ea.		13.35		13.35	
Minimum Charge	Job		216		216	
48" Wide x 30" Deep						
Demolish	Ea.		11.15		11.15	Includes material and labor to install
Install	Ea.	216	43		259	one aluminum awning with
Demolish and Install	Ea.	216	54.15		270.15	weather-resistant finish.
Reinstall	Ea.		34.56		34.56	
Clean	Ea.		13.35		13.35	
Minimum Charge	Job		216		216	
60" Wide x 30" Deep						
Demolish	Ea.		22.50		22.50	Includes material and labor to install
Install	Ea.	252	48		300	one aluminum awning with
Demolish and Install	Ea.	252	70.50		322.50	weather-resistant finish.
Reinstall	Ea.		38.40		38.40	
Clean	Ea.		13.35		13.35	
Minimum Charge	Job		216		216	
72" Wide x 30" Deep						
Demolish	Ea.		22.50		22.50	Includes material and labor to install
Install	Ea.	288	54		342	one aluminum awning with
Demolish and Install	Ea.	288	76.50		364.50	weather-resistant finish.
Reinstall	Ea.		43.20		43.20	
Clean	Ea.		13.35		13.35	
Minimum Charge	Job		216		216	
Roll-up Type						
Demolish	S.F.		.80		.80	Includes material and labor to install
Install	S.F.	15.20	4.32		19.52	an aluminum roll-up awning.
Demolish and Install	S.F.	15.20	5.12		20.32	
Reinstall	S.F.		3.46		3.46	
Clean	S.F.	.04	.67		.71	
Minimum Charge	Job		216		216	
Canvas						
30" Wide						
Demolish	Ea.		6.70		6.70	Includes material and labor to install a
Install	Ea.	202	36		238	canvas window awning.
Demolish and Install	Ea.	202	42.70		244.70	
Reinstall	Ea.		28.80		28.80	
Clean	Ea.		4.01		4.01	
Minimum Charge	Job		216		216	

Improvements / Appliances / Treatments

Awning	Unit	Material	Labor	Equip.	Total	Specification
36″ Wide						
Demolish	Ea.		6.70		6.70	Includes material and labor to install a
Install	Ea.	223	43		266	canvas window awning.
Demolish and Install	Ea.	223	49.70		272.70	
Reinstall	Ea.		34.56		34.56	
Clean	Ea.		4.39		4.39	
Minimum Charge	Job		216		216	
42″ Wide						
Demolish	Ea.		6.70		6.70	Includes material and labor to install a
Install	Ea.	237	54		291	canvas window awning.
Demolish and Install	Ea.	237	60.70		297.70	
Reinstall	Ea.		43.20		43.20	
Clean	Ea.		5.20		5.20	
Minimum Charge	Job		216		216	
48″ Wide						
Demolish	Ea.		6.70		6.70	Includes material and labor to install a
Install	Ea.	249	61.50		310.50	canvas window awning.
Demolish and Install	Ea.	249	68.20		317.20	
Reinstall	Ea.		49.37		49.37	
Clean	Ea.		6.05		6.05	
Minimum Charge	Job		216		216	
Cloth Canopy Cover						
8′ x 10′						
Demolish	Ea.		365		365	Includes material and labor to install
Install	Ea.	405	216		621	one 8′ x 10′ cloth canopy patio cover
Demolish and Install	Ea.	405	581		986	with front bar and tension support
Reinstall	Ea.		172.80		172.80	rafters and 9″ valance.
Clean	Ea.	3.22	53.50		56.72	
Minimum Charge	Job		430		430	
8′ x 15′						
Demolish	Ea.		365		365	Includes material and labor to install
Install	Ea.	500	216		716	one 8′ x 15′ cloth canopy patio cover
Demolish and Install	Ea.	500	581		1081	with front bar and tension support
Reinstall	Ea.		172.80		172.80	rafters and 9″ valance.
Clean	Ea.	3.22	80		83.22	
Minimum Charge	Job		430		430	

Vent	Unit	Material	Labor	Equip.	Total	Specification
Small Roof Turbine						
Demolish	Ea.		11.15		11.15	Includes material and labor to install
Install	Ea.	71	43.50		114.50	spinner ventilator, wind driven,
Demolish and Install	Ea.	71	54.65		125.65	galvanized, 4″ neck diam, 180 CFM.
Reinstall	Ea.		34.69		34.69	
Clean	Ea.		7.10		7.10	
Minimum Charge	Job		251		251	
Large Roof Turbine						
Demolish	Ea.		8.90		8.90	Includes material and labor to install
Install	Ea.	82	62		144	spinner ventilator, wind driven,
Demolish and Install	Ea.	82	70.90		152.90	galvanized, 8″ neck diam, 360 CFM.
Reinstall	Ea.		49.55		49.55	
Clean	Ea.		8		8	
Minimum Charge	Job		251		251	

Vent		Unit	Material	Labor	Equip.	Total	Specification
Gable Louvered							
	Demolish	Ea.		22.50		22.50	Includes material and labor to install a
	Install	Ea.	49.50	14.40		63.90	vinyl gable end vent.
	Demolish and Install	Ea.	49.50	36.90		86.40	
	Reinstall	Ea.		11.52		11.52	
	Clean	Ea.		4.27		4.27	
	Paint	Ea.	1.20	5.70		6.90	
	Minimum Charge	Job		216		216	
Ridge Vent							
	Demolish	L.F.		1.15		1.15	Includes material and labor to install a
	Install	L.F.	3.28	3.11		6.39	mill finish aluminum ridge vent strip.
	Demolish and Install	L.F.	3.28	4.26		7.54	
	Minimum Charge	Job		216		216	
Foundation							
	Demolish	Ea.		8		8	Includes material and labor to install
	Install	Ea.	17.80	14.15		31.95	galvanized foundation block vent.
	Demolish and Install	Ea.	17.80	22.15		39.95	
	Reinstall	Ea.		11.33		11.33	
	Clean	Ea.	.20	8		8.20	
	Minimum Charge	Job		216		216	
Frieze							
	Demolish	L.F.		.79		.79	Includes material and labor to install
	Install	L.F.	1.34	1.73		3.07	pine frieze board.
	Demolish and Install	L.F.	1.34	2.52		3.86	
	Reinstall	L.F.		1.38		1.38	
	Clean	L.F.	.04	.27		.31	
	Minimum Charge	Job		216		216	
Water Heater Cap							
	Demolish	Ea.		17.40		17.40	Includes material and labor to install a
	Install	Ea.	37	60		97	galvanized steel water heater cap.
	Demolish and Install	Ea.	37	77.40		114.40	
	Reinstall	Ea.		48.16		48.16	
	Clean	Ea.	1.41	20		21.41	

Cupolas		Unit	Material	Labor	Equip.	Total	Specification
22" x 22"							
	Demolish	Ea.		210		210	Includes material and labor to install a
	Install	Ea.	370	108		478	cedar cupola with aluminum roof
	Demolish and Install	Ea.	370	318		688	covering.
	Reinstall	Ea.		86.40		86.40	
	Minimum Charge	Job		216		216	
29" x 29"							
	Demolish	Ea.		210		210	Includes material and labor to install a
	Install	Ea.	505	108		613	cedar cupola with aluminum roof
	Demolish and Install	Ea.	505	318		823	covering.
	Reinstall	Ea.		86.40		86.40	
	Minimum Charge	Job		216		216	
35" x 35"							
	Demolish	Ea.		210		210	Includes material and labor to install a
	Install	Ea.	920	144		1064	cedar cupola with aluminum roof
	Demolish and Install	Ea.	920	354		1274	covering.
	Reinstall	Ea.		115.20		115.20	
	Minimum Charge	Job		216		216	

Improvements / Appliances / Treatments

Cupolas

	Unit	Material	Labor	Equip.	Total	Specification
47" x 47"						
Demolish	Ea.		210		210	Includes material and labor to install a
Install	Ea.	1800	216		2016	cedar cupola with aluminum roof
Demolish and Install	Ea.	1800	426		2226	covering.
Reinstall	Ea.		172.80		172.80	
Minimum Charge	Job		216		216	
Weather Vane						
Install	Ea.	166	54		220	Includes minimum labor and
Minimum Charge	Job		216		216	equipment to install residential type weathervane.

Aluminum Carport

	Unit	Material	Labor	Equip.	Total	Specification
20' x 20' Complete						
Demolish	Ea.		223		223	Includes material, labor and
Install	Ea.	8800	710	183	9693	equipment to install an aluminum
Demolish and Install	Ea.	8800	933	183	9916	carport. Foundations are not included.
Reinstall	Ea.		567.84	146.50	714.34	
Clean	Ea.	.21	80		80.21	
Minimum Charge	Job		430		430	
24' x 24' Complete						
Demolish	Ea.		223		223	Includes material, labor and
Install	Ea.	12700	945	244	13889	equipment to install an aluminum
Demolish and Install	Ea.	12700	1168	244	14112	carport. Foundations are not included.
Reinstall	Ea.		757.12	195.33	952.45	
Clean	Ea.	.21	160		160.21	
Minimum Charge	Job		430		430	
Metal Support Posts						
Demolish	Ea.		2.97		2.97	Includes material and labor to install
Install	Ea.	29	54		83	metal support posts for a carport.
Demolish and Install	Ea.	29	56.97		85.97	
Reinstall	Ea.		43.20		43.20	
Clean	Ea.	.21	3.34		3.55	
Paint	Ea.	.21	7.40		7.61	
Minimum Charge	Job		430		430	

Storage Shed

	Unit	Material	Labor	Equip.	Total	Specification
Aluminum						
Pre-fab (8' x 10')						
Demolish	Ea.		64.50		64.50	Includes material and labor to install
Install	Ea.	2025	630		2655	an aluminum storage shed.
Demolish and Install	Ea.	2025	694.50		2719.50	
Clean	Ea.	1.34	40		41.34	
Minimum Charge	Ea.		520		520	
Pre-fab (10' x 12')						
Demolish	Ea.		122		122	Includes material and labor to install
Install	Ea.	2550	630		3180	an aluminum storage shed.
Demolish and Install	Ea.	2550	752		3302	
Clean	Ea.	1.34	44.50		45.84	
Minimum Charge	Ea.		520		520	

Improvements / Appliances / Treatments

Storage Shed		Unit	Material	Labor	Equip.	Total	Specification
Wood							
Pre-fab (8' x 10')							
	Demolish	Ea.		64.50		64.50	Includes material and labor to install a
	Install	Ea.	1925	630		2555	pre-fabricated wood storage shed.
	Demolish and Install	Ea.	1925	694.50		2619.50	
	Clean	Ea.	1.34	40		41.34	
	Minimum Charge	Ea.		520		520	
Pre-fab (10' x 12')							
	Demolish	Ea.		122		122	Includes material and labor to install a
	Install	Ea.	2425	630		3055	pre-fabricated wood storage shed.
	Demolish and Install	Ea.	2425	752		3177	
	Clean	Ea.	1.34	44.50		45.84	
	Minimum Charge	Ea.		520		520	

Gazebo		Unit	Material	Labor	Equip.	Total	Specification
Good Grade							
	Demolish	S.F.		3.56		3.56	Includes material and labor to install a
	Install	S.F.	48.50	32.50		81	gazebo.
	Demolish and Install	S.F.	48.50	36.06		84.56	
	Reinstall	S.F.		25.92		25.92	
	Clean	S.F.	.17	2.14		2.31	
	Minimum Charge	Job		216		216	
Custom Grade							
	Demolish	S.F.		3.56		3.56	Includes material and labor to install a
	Install	S.F.	68	32.50		100.50	gazebo.
	Demolish and Install	S.F.	68	36.06		104.06	
	Reinstall	S.F.		25.92		25.92	
	Clean	S.F.	.17	2.14		2.31	
	Minimum Charge	Job		216		216	
Bench Seating							
	Demolish	L.F.		5.95		5.95	Includes material and labor to install
	Install	L.F.	2.21	21.50		23.71	pressure treated bench seating.
	Demolish and Install	L.F.	2.21	27.45		29.66	
	Reinstall	L.F.		17.28		17.28	
	Clean	L.F.	.17	1.60		1.77	
	Paint	L.F.	.67	2.96		3.63	
	Minimum Charge	Job		216		216	
Re-screen							
	Install	S.F.	1.77	1.73		3.50	Includes labor and material to
	Minimum Charge	Job		216		216	re-screen wood frame.

Pool		Unit	Material	Labor	Equip.	Total	Specification
Screen Enclosure							
Re-screen							
	Install	SF Wall	.03	5.20		5.23	Includes material and labor to install a
	Minimum Charge	Job		216		216	screen enclosure for a pool.
Screen Door							
	Demolish	Ea.		8.55		8.55	Includes material and labor to install
	Install	Ea.	360	72		432	wood screen door with aluminum cloth
	Demolish and Install	Ea.	360	80.55		440.55	screen. Frame and hardware not
	Reinstall	Ea.		57.60		57.60	included.
	Clean	Ea.	.15	11.70		11.85	
	Paint	Ea.	4.99	14.80		19.79	
	Minimum Charge	Job		216		216	

Improvements / Appliances / Treatments

Pool		Unit	Material	Labor	Equip.	Total	Specification
Heater / Motor							
	Demolish	Ea.		44.50		44.50	Includes material and labor to install
	Install	Ea.	2500	555		3055	swimming pool heater, not incl. base
	Demolish and Install	Ea.	2500	599.50		3099.50	or pad, elec., 12 kW, 4,800 gal
	Reinstall	Ea.		443.37		443.37	pool, incl. pump.
	Clean	Ea.	4.03	40		44.03	
	Minimum Charge	Job		255		255	
Filter System							
	Demolish	Ea.		71		71	Includes material, labor and
	Install	Total	1275	400		1675	equipment to install sand filter system
	Demolish and Install	Total	1275	471		1746	tank including hook-up to existing
	Reinstall	Total		321.02		321.02	equipment. Pump and motor not
	Minimum Charge	Job		251		251	included.
Pump / Motor							
	Demolish	Ea.		44.50		44.50	Includes material and labor to install a
	Install	Ea.	910	100		1010	22 GPM pump.
	Demolish and Install	Ea.	910	144.50		1054.50	
	Reinstall	Ea.		80.26		80.26	
	Clean	Ea.	4.03	40		44.03	
	Minimum Charge	Job		255		255	
Pump Water							
	Install	Day		445	93	538	Includes labor and equipment to pump
	Minimum Charge	Job		200		200	water from a swimming pool.
Replaster							
	Install	SF Surf	1.50	10.30		11.80	Includes labor and material to
	Minimum Charge	Job		200		200	replaster gunite pool with a surface
Solar Panels							area of 500 to 600 S.F.
	Demolish	S.F.		1.86		1.86	Includes material and labor to install
	Install	S.F.	34	3.30		37.30	solar panel.
	Demolish and Install	S.F.	34	5.16		39.16	
	Reinstall	S.F.		2.64		2.64	
	Minimum Charge	Ea.		520		520	

Construction Clean-up	Unit	Material	Labor	Equip.	Total	Specification
Final						
Clean	S.F.		.28		.28	Includes labor for final site/job
Minimum Charge	Job		160		160	clean-up including detail cleaning.

Location Factors

Costs shown in *RSMeans Residential Cost Data* are based on national averages for materials and installation. To adjust these costs to a specific location, simply multiply the base cost by the factor for that city. The data is arranged alphabetically by state and postal zip code numbers. For a city not listed, use the factor for a nearby city with similar economic characteristics.

STATE	CITY	Residential
ALABAMA		
350-352	Birmingham	.86
354	Tuscaloosa	.78
355	Jasper	.72
356	Decatur	.76
357-358	Huntsville	.85
359	Gadsden	.75
360-361	Montgomery	.76
362	Anniston	.76
363	Dothan	.74
364	Evergreen	.72
365-366	Mobile	.81
367	Selma	.72
368	Phenix City	.73
369	Butler	.72
ALASKA		
995-996	Anchorage	1.22
997	Fairbanks	1.24
998	Juneau	1.22
999	Ketchikan	1.26
ARIZONA		
850,853	Phoenix	.86
851,852	Mesa/Tempe	.85
855	Globe	.82
856-857	Tucson	.84
859	Show Low	.86
860	Flagstaff	.86
863	Prescott	.81
864	Kingman	.83
865	Chambers	.83
ARKANSAS		
716	Pine Bluff	.78
717	Camden	.69
718	Texarkana	.73
719	Hot Springs	.69
720-722	Little Rock	.80
723	West Memphis	.77
724	Jonesboro	.75
725	Batesville	.72
726	Harrison	.73
727	Fayetteville	.69
728	Russellville	.75
729	Fort Smith	.80
CALIFORNIA		
900-902	Los Angeles	1.09
903-905	Inglewood	1.06
906-908	Long Beach	1.05
910-912	Pasadena	1.04
913-916	Van Nuys	1.07
917-918	Alhambra	1.08
919-921	San Diego	1.03
922	Palm Springs	1.04
923-924	San Bernardino	1.05
925	Riverside	1.07
926-927	Santa Ana	1.05
928	Anaheim	1.06
930	Oxnard	1.08
931	Santa Barbara	1.07
932-933	Bakersfield	1.06
934	San Luis Obispo	1.07
935	Mojave	1.05
936-938	Fresno	1.10
939	Salinas	1.13
940-941	San Francisco	1.24
942,956-958	Sacramento	1.11
943	Palo Alto	1.18
944	San Mateo	1.22
945	Vallejo	1.16
946	Oakland	1.21
947	Berkeley	1.23
948	Richmond	1.23
949	San Rafael	1.22
950	Santa Cruz	1.15
951	San Jose	1.21
952	Stockton	1.11
953	Modesto	1.10

STATE	CITY	Residential
CALIFORNIA (CONT'D)		
954	Santa Rosa	1.19
955	Eureka	1.11
959	Marysville	1.11
960	Redding	1.11
961	Susanville	1.11
COLORADO		
800-802	Denver	.89
803	Boulder	.91
804	Golden	.87
805	Fort Collins	.88
806	Greeley	.85
807	Fort Morgan	.89
808-809	Colorado Springs	.86
810	Pueblo	.88
811	Alamosa	.84
812	Salida	.87
813	Durango	.88
814	Montrose	.86
815	Grand Junction	.91
816	Glenwood Springs	.88
CONNECTICUT		
060	New Britain	1.11
061	Hartford	1.10
062	Willimantic	1.11
063	New London	1.10
064	Meriden	1.10
065	New Haven	1.11
066	Bridgeport	1.11
067	Waterbury	1.11
068	Norwalk	1.12
069	Stamford	1.12
D.C.		
200-205	Washington	.94
DELAWARE		
197	Newark	1.02
198	Wilmington	1.02
199	Dover	1.01
FLORIDA		
320,322	Jacksonville	.82
321	Daytona Beach	.87
323	Tallahassee	.78
324	Panama City	.77
325	Pensacola	.81
326,344	Gainesville	.80
327-328,347	Orlando	.87
329	Melbourne	.87
330-332,340	Miami	.86
333	Fort Lauderdale	.86
334,349	West Palm Beach	.86
335-336,346	Tampa	.90
337	St. Petersburg	.80
338	Lakeland	.87
339,341	Fort Myers	.86
342	Sarasota	.89
GEORGIA		
300-303,399	Atlanta	.87
304	Statesboro	.73
305	Gainesville	.77
306	Athens	.76
307	Dalton	.75
308-309	Augusta	.81
310-312	Macon	.79
313-314	Savannah	.80
315	Waycross	.79
316	Valdosta	.74
317,398	Albany	.77
318-319	Columbus	.80
HAWAII		
967	Hilo	1.18
968	Honolulu	1.22

Location Factors

STATE	CITY	Residential
STATES & POSS.		
969	Guam	.93
IDAHO		
832	Pocatello	.87
833	Twin Falls	.81
834	Idaho Falls	.85
835	Lewiston	.99
836-837	Boise	.88
838	Coeur d'Alene	.97
ILLINOIS		
600-603	North Suburban	1.19
604	Joliet	1.22
605	South Suburban	1.19
606-608	Chicago	1.22
609	Kankakee	1.13
610-611	Rockford	1.11
612	Rock Island	.98
613	La Salle	1.12
614	Galesburg	1.04
615-616	Peoria	1.07
617	Bloomington	1.04
618-619	Champaign	1.05
620-622	East St. Louis	1.04
623	Quincy	1.03
624	Effingham	1.05
625	Decatur	1.05
626-627	Springfield	1.05
628	Centralia	1.04
629	Carbondale	1.02
INDIANA		
460	Anderson	.91
461-462	Indianapolis	.93
463-464	Gary	1.06
465-466	South Bend	.91
467-468	Fort Wayne	.90
469	Kokomo	.92
470	Lawrenceburg	.88
471	New Albany	.88
472	Columbus	.92
473	Muncie	.92
474	Bloomington	.94
475	Washington	.91
476-477	Evansville	.91
478	Terre Haute	.90
479	Lafayette	.93
IOWA		
500-503,509	Des Moines	.91
504	Mason City	.77
505	Fort Dodge	.75
506-507	Waterloo	.82
508	Creston	.84
510-511	Sioux City	.87
512	Sibley	.74
513	Spencer	.76
514	Carroll	.80
515	Council Bluffs	.86
516	Shenandoah	.81
520	Dubuque	.86
521	Decorah	.78
522-524	Cedar Rapids	.93
525	Ottumwa	.86
526	Burlington	.88
527-528	Davenport	.97
KANSAS		
660-662	Kansas City	.98
664-666	Topeka	.78
667	Fort Scott	.89
668	Emporia	.83
669	Belleville	.81
670-672	Wichita	.79
673	Independence	.89
674	Salina	.80
675	Hutchinson	.79
676	Hays	.82
677	Colby	.83
678	Dodge City	.81
679	Liberal	.80
KENTUCKY		
400-402	Louisville	.92
403-405	Lexington	.90

STATE	CITY	Residential
KENTUCKY (CONT'D)		
406	Frankfort	.89
407-409	Corbin	.83
410	Covington	.94
411-412	Ashland	.95
413-414	Campton	.88
415-416	Pikeville	.92
417-418	Hazard	.87
420	Paducah	.89
421-422	Bowling Green	.90
423	Owensboro	.91
424	Henderson	.92
425-426	Somerset	.85
427	Elizabethtown	.88
LOUISIANA		
700-701	New Orleans	.86
703	Thibodaux	.82
704	Hammond	.75
705	Lafayette	.83
706	Lake Charles	.83
707-708	Baton Rouge	.82
710-711	Shreveport	.78
712	Monroe	.74
713-714	Alexandria	.76
MAINE		
039	Kittery	.92
040-041	Portland	.97
042	Lewiston	.97
043	Augusta	.93
044	Bangor	.96
045	Bath	.92
046	Machias	.96
047	Houlton	.97
048	Rockland	.96
049	Waterville	.91
MARYLAND		
206	Waldorf	.90
207-208	College Park	.88
209	Silver Spring	.90
210-212	Baltimore	.90
214	Annapolis	.89
215	Cumberland	.88
216	Easton	.83
217	Hagerstown	.87
218	Salisbury	.82
219	Elkton	.89
MASSACHUSETTS		
010-011	Springfield	1.07
012	Pittsfield	1.07
013	Greenfield	1.05
014	Fitchburg	1.13
015-016	Worcester	1.14
017	Framingham	1.16
018	Lowell	1.16
019	Lawrence	1.17
020-022, 024	Boston	1.21
023	Brockton	1.16
025	Buzzards Bay	1.14
026	Hyannis	1.13
027	New Bedford	1.16
MICHIGAN		
480,483	Royal Oak	1.02
481	Ann Arbor	1.03
482	Detroit	1.05
484-485	Flint	.96
486	Saginaw	.93
487	Bay City	.93
488-489	Lansing	.94
490	Battle Creek	.93
491	Kalamazoo	.92
492	Jackson	.94
493,495	Grand Rapids	.91
494	Muskegon	.90
496	Traverse City	.86
497	Gaylord	.89
498-499	Iron mountain	.91
MINNESOTA		
550-551	Saint Paul	1.11
553-555	Minneapolis	1.13
556-558	Duluth	1.06

Location Factors

STATE	CITY	Residential
MINNESOTA (CONT'd)		
559	Rochester	1.04
560	Mankato	1.00
561	Windom	.93
562	Willmar	.97
563	St. Cloud	1.05
564	Brainerd	.96
565	Detroit Lakes	.95
566	Bemidji	.94
567	Thief River Falls	.94
MISSISSIPPI		
386	Clarksdale	.74
387	Greenville	.81
388	Tupelo	.76
389	Greenwood	.78
390-392	Jackson	.82
393	Meridian	.81
394	Laurel	.77
395	Biloxi	.80
396	Mccomb	.75
397	Columbus	.76
MISSOURI		
630-631	St. Louis	1.03
633	Bowling Green	.96
634	Hannibal	.93
635	Kirksville	.90
636	Flat River	.96
637	Cape Girardeau	.89
638	Sikeston	.88
639	Poplar Bluff	.87
640-641	Kansas City	1.05
644-645	St. Joseph	.98
646	Chillicothe	.97
647	Harrisonville	.99
648	Joplin	.90
650-651	Jefferson City	.93
652	Columbia	.92
653	Sedalia	.92
654-655	Rolla	.97
656-658	Springfield	.89
MONTANA		
590-591	Billings	.90
592	Wolf Point	.87
593	Miles City	.88
594	Great Falls	.91
595	Havre	.84
596	Helena	.88
597	Butte	.88
598	Missoula	.88
599	Kalispell	.87
NEBRASKA		
680-681	Omaha	.90
683-685	Lincoln	.87
686	Columbus	.87
687	Norfolk	.89
688	Grand Island	.88
689	Hastings	.90
690	Mccook	.83
691	North Platte	.89
692	Valentine	.84
693	Alliance	.84
NEVADA		
889-891	Las Vegas	1.03
893	Ely	1.02
894-895	Reno	.95
897	Carson City	.96
898	Elko	.93
NEW HAMPSHIRE		
030	Nashua	.98
031	Manchester	.98
032-033	Concord	.97
034	Keene	.88
035	Littleton	.92
036	Charleston	.86
037	Claremont	.87
038	Portsmouth	.97

STATE	CITY	Residential
NEW JERSEY		
070-071	Newark	1.14
072	Elizabeth	1.16
073	Jersey City	1.13
074-075	Paterson	1.14
076	Hackensack	1.13
077	Long Branch	1.13
078	Dover	1.13
079	Summit	1.14
080,083	Vineland	1.11
081	Camden	1.12
082,084	Atlantic City	1.15
085-086	Trenton	1.13
087	Point Pleasant	1.10
088-089	New Brunswick	1.15
NEW MEXICO		
870-872	Albuquerque	.83
873	Gallup	.83
874	Farmington	.83
875	Santa Fe	.85
877	Las Vegas	.83
878	Socorro	.83
879	Truth/Consequences	.82
880	Las Cruces	.81
881	Clovis	.83
882	Roswell	.83
883	Carrizozo	.83
884	Tucumcari	.83
NEW YORK		
100-102	New York	1.34
103	Staten Island	1.28
104	Bronx	1.30
105	Mount Vernon	1.12
106	White Plains	1.15
107	Yonkers	1.16
108	New Rochelle	1.16
109	Suffern	1.13
110	Queens	1.30
111	Long Island City	1.33
112	Brooklyn	1.34
113	Flushing	1.32
114	Jamaica	1.31
115,117,118	Hicksville	1.20
116	Far Rockaway	1.31
119	Riverhead	1.21
120-122	Albany	.98
123	Schenectady	.99
124	Kingston	1.05
125-126	Poughkeepsie	1.16
127	Monticello	1.05
128	Glens Falls	.91
129	Plattsburgh	.95
130-132	Syracuse	.98
133-135	Utica	.94
136	Watertown	.92
137-139	Binghamton	.97
140-142	Buffalo	1.06
143	Niagara Falls	1.02
144-146	Rochester	.99
147	Jamestown	.90
148-149	Elmira	.92
NORTH CAROLINA		
270,272-274	Greensboro	.85
271	Winston-Salem	.86
275-276	Raleigh	.86
277	Durham	.85
278	Rocky Mount	.81
279	Elizabeth City	.80
280	Gastonia	.85
281-282	Charlotte	.86
283	Fayetteville	.89
284	Wilmington	.86
285	Kinston	.81
286	Hickory	.80
287-288	Asheville	.83
289	Murphy	.82
NORTH DAKOTA		
580-581	Fargo	.79
582	Grand Forks	.73
583	Devils Lake	.77
584	Jamestown	.71
585	Bismarck	.78

Location Factors

STATE	CITY	Residential
NORTH DAKOTA (CONT'D)		
586	Dickinson	.75
587	Minot	.82
588	Williston	.75
OHIO		
430-432	Columbus	.95
433	Marion	.90
434-436	Toledo	.98
437-438	Zanesville	.90
439	Steubenville	.95
440	Lorain	.96
441	Cleveland	1.00
442-443	Akron	.98
444-445	Youngstown	.95
446-447	Canton	.93
448-449	Mansfield	.91
450	Hamilton	.92
451-452	Cincinnati	.92
453-454	Dayton	.92
455	Springfield	.93
456	Chillicothe	.96
457	Athens	.90
458	Lima	.91
OKLAHOMA		
730-731	Oklahoma City	.82
734	Ardmore	.78
735	Lawton	.80
736	Clinton	.80
737	Enid	.76
738	Woodward	.79
739	Guymon	.79
740-741	Tulsa	.78
743	Miami	.85
744	Muskogee	.74
745	Mcalester	.75
746	Ponca City	.78
747	Durant	.77
748	Shawnee	.76
749	Poteau	.76
OREGON		
970-972	Portland	.99
973	Salem	.98
974	Eugene	.99
975	Medford	.97
976	Klamath Falls	.97
977	Bend	1.00
978	Pendleton	.98
979	Vale	.96
PENNSYLVANIA		
150-152	Pittsburgh	1.01
153	Washington	.96
154	Uniontown	.95
155	Bedford	.91
156	Greensburg	.97
157	Indiana	.94
158	Dubois	.92
159	Johnstown	.92
160	Butler	.94
161	New Castle	.93
162	Kittanning	.94
163	Oil City	.91
164-165	Erie	.94
166	Altoona	.88
167	Bradford	.91
168	State College	.91
169	Wellsboro	.92
170-171	Harrisburg	.97
172	Chambersburg	.90
173-174	York	.93
175-176	Lancaster	.92
177	Williamsport	.85
178	Sunbury	.94
179	Pottsville	.94
180	Lehigh Valley	1.02
181	Allentown	1.04
182	Hazleton	.93
183	Stroudsburg	.92
184-185	Scranton	.98
186-187	Wilkes-Barre	.95
188	Montrose	.92
189	Doylestown	1.06

STATE	CITY	Residential
PENNSYLVANIA (CONT'D)		
190-191	Philadelphia	1.16
193	Westchester	1.10
194	Norristown	1.10
195-196	Reading	.98
PUERTO RICO		
009	San Juan	.75
RHODE ISLAND		
028	Newport	1.09
029	Providence	1.10
SOUTH CAROLINA		
290-292	Columbia	.86
293	Spartanburg	.86
294	Charleston	.94
295	Florence	.82
296	Greenville	.85
297	Rock Hill	.80
298	Aiken	.97
299	Beaufort	.79
SOUTH DAKOTA		
570-571	Sioux Falls	.76
572	Watertown	.73
573	Mitchell	.74
574	Aberdeen	.75
575	Pierre	.77
576	Mobridge	.73
577	Rapid City	.78
TENNESSEE		
370-372	Nashville	.85
373-374	Chattanooga	.83
375,380-381	Memphis	.84
376	Johnson City	.72
377-379	Knoxville	.75
382	Mckenzie	.73
383	Jackson	.77
384	Columbia	.78
385	Cookeville	.71
TEXAS		
750	Mckinney	.72
751	Waxahackie	.78
752-753	Dallas	.84
754	Greenville	.70
755	Texarkana	.73
756	Longview	.68
757	Tyler	.74
758	Palestine	.75
759	Lufkin	.78
760-761	Fort Worth	.83
762	Denton	.75
763	Wichita Falls	.78
764	Eastland	.75
765	Temple	.77
766-767	Waco	.78
768	Brownwood	.72
769	San Angelo	.73
770-772	Houston	.85
773	Huntsville	.77
774	Wharton	.72
775	Galveston	.83
776-777	Beaumont	.81
778	Bryan	.74
779	Victoria	.71
780	Laredo	.75
781-782	San Antonio	.80
783-784	Corpus Christi	.79
785	Mc Allen	.76
786-787	Austin	.78
788	Del Rio	.73
789	Giddings	.78
790-791	Amarillo	.79
792	Childress	.80
793-794	Lubbock	.80
795-796	Abilene	.76
797	Midland	.80
798-799,885	El Paso	.74
UTAH		
840-841	Salt Lake City	.80
842,844	Ogden	.79
843	Logan	.79

Location Factors

STATE	CITY	Residential
UTAH (CONT'D)		
845	Price	.77
846-847	Provo	.79
VERMONT		
050	White River Jct.	.90
051	Bellows Falls	.97
052	Bennington	1.01
053	Brattleboro	.96
054	Burlington	.95
056	Montpelier	.94
057	Rutland	.94
058	St. Johnsbury	.91
059	Guildhall	.91
VIRGINIA		
220-221	Fairfax	1.02
222	Arlington	1.04
223	Alexandria	1.06
224-225	Fredericksburg	1.02
226	Winchester	1.01
227	Culpeper	1.02
228	Harrisonburg	.87
229	Charlottesville	.90
230-232	Richmond	.96
233-235	Norfolk	.98
236	Newport News	.97
237	Portsmouth	.91
238	Petersburg	.94
239	Farmville	.85
240-241	Roanoke	.96
242	Bristol	.84
243	Pulaski	.84
244	Staunton	.87
245	Lynchburg	.93
246	Grundy	.81
WASHINGTON		
980-981,987	Seattle	1.02
982	Everett	1.04
983-984	Tacoma	1.01
985	Olympia	.99
986	Vancouver	.97
988	Wenatchee	.94
989	Yakima	.98
990-992	Spokane	.97
993	Richland	.97
994	Clarkston	.92
WEST VIRGINIA		
247-248	Bluefield	.94
249	Lewisburg	.93
250-253	Charleston	.97
254	Martinsburg	.89
255-257	Huntington	.98
258-259	Beckley	.93
260	Wheeling	.95
261	Parkersburg	.93
262	Buckhannon	.94
263-264	Clarksburg	.94
265	Morgantown	.94
266	Gassaway	.94
267	Romney	.93
268	Petersburg	.94
WISCONSIN		
530,532	Milwaukee	1.08
531	Kenosha	1.03
534	Racine	1.02
535	Beloit	1.01
537	Madison	.99
538	Lancaster	.97
539	Portage	.97
540	New Richmond	.99
541-543	Green Bay	1.02
544	Wausau	.96
545	Rhinelander	.96
546	La Crosse	.96
547	Eau Claire	.99
548	Superior	.97
549	Oshkosh	.96
WYOMING		
820	Cheyenne	.80
821	Yellowstone Nat. Pk.	.80
822	Wheatland	.77

STATE	CITY	Residential
WYOMING (CONT'D)		
823	Rawlins	.81
824	Worland	.80
825	Riverton	.80
826	Casper	.75
827	Newcastle	.81
828	Sheridan	.80
829-831	Rock Springs	.84
CANADIAN FACTORS (reflect Canadian currency)		
ALBERTA		
	Calgary	1.13
	Edmonton	1.12
	Fort McMurray	1.14
	Lethbridge	1.12
	Lloydminster	1.07
	Medicine Hat	1.07
	Red Deer	1.07
BRITISH COLUMBIA		
	Kamloops	1.05
	Prince George	1.05
	Vancouver	1.07
	Victoria	1.05
MANITOBA		
	Brandon	1.06
	Portage la Prairie	1.02
	Winnipeg	1.00
NEW BRUNSWICK		
	Bathurst	.95
	Dalhousie	.95
	Fredericton	1.00
	Moncton	.96
	Newcastle	.95
	St. John	1.03
NEWFOUNDLAND		
	Corner Brook	.99
	St Johns	1.04
NORTHWEST TERRITORIES		
	Yellowknife	1.09
NOVA SCOTIA		
	Bridgewater	.98
	Dartmouth	1.00
	Halifax	1.01
	New Glasgow	1.00
	Sydney	.99
	Truro	.97
	Yarmouth	1.00
ONTARIO		
	Barrie	1.14
	Brantford	1.15
	Cornwall	1.14
	Hamilton	1.12
	Kingston	1.14
	Kitchener	1.07
	London	1.10
	North Bay	1.15
	Oshawa	1.13
	Ottawa	1.11
	Owen Sound	1.13
	Peterborough	1.12
	Sarnia	1.15
	Sault Ste Marie	1.07
	St. Catharines	1.09
	Sudbury	1.06
	Thunder Bay	1.11
	Timmins	1.11
	Toronto	1.13
	Windsor	1.10
PRINCE EDWARD ISLAND		
	Charlottetown	.92
	Summerside	.94
QUEBEC		
	Cap-de-la-Madeleine	1.13
	Charlesbourg	1.13
	Chicoutimi	1.15
	Gatineau	1.13
	Granby	1.13

Location Factors

STATE	CITY	Residential
QUEBEC (CONT'D)		
	Hull	1.13
	Joliette	1.13
	Laval	1.13
	Montreal	1.14
	Quebec	1.13
	Rimouski	1.15
	Rouyn-Noranda	1.13
	Saint Hyacinthe	1.13
	Sherbrooke	1.13
	Sorel	1.13
	St Jerome	1.13
	Trois Rivieres	1.17
SASKATCHEWAN		
	Moose Jaw	.95
	Prince Albert	.93
	Regina	1.07
	Saskatoon	1.05
YUKON		
	Whitehorse	.98

Abbreviations

A	Area
ASTM	American Society for Testing and Materials
B.F.	Board feet
Carp.	Carpenter
C.F.	Cubic feet
CWJ	Composite wood joist
C.Y.	Cubic yard
Ea.	Each
Equip.	Equipment
Exp.	Exposure
Ext.	Exterior
F	Fahrenheit
Ft.	Foot, feet
Gal.	Gallon
Hr.	Hour
in.	Inch, inches
Inst.	Installation
Int.	Interior
Lb.	Pound
L.F.	Linear feet
LVL	Laminated veneer lumber
Mat.	Material
Max.	Maximum
MBF	Thousand board feet
MBM	Thousand feet board measure
MSF	Thousand square feet
Min.	Minimum
O.C.	On center
O&P	Overhead and profit
OWJ	Open web wood joist
Oz.	Ounce
Pr.	Pair
Quan.	Quantity
S.F.	Square foot
Sq.	Square, 100 square feet
S.Y.	Square yard
V.L.F.	Vertical linear feet
'	Foot, feet
"	Inch, inches
o	Degrees

Index

302

Index

RSMeans Building Construction Cost Data 2014

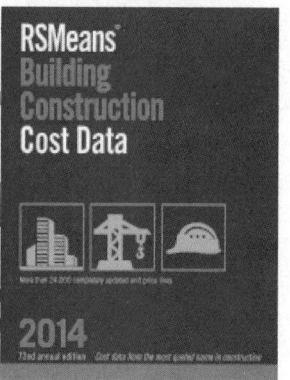

Offers you unchallenged unit price reliability in an easy-to-use format. Whether used for verifying complete, finished estimates or for periodic checks, it supplies more cost facts better and faster than any comparable source. More than 24,000 unit prices have been updated for 2014. The City Cost Indexes and Location Factors cover more than 930 areas, for indexing to any project location in North America. Order and get *RSMeans Quarterly Update Service* FREE.

$194.95 | Available Sept. 2013 | Catalog no. 60014

RSMeans Mechanical Cost Data 2014

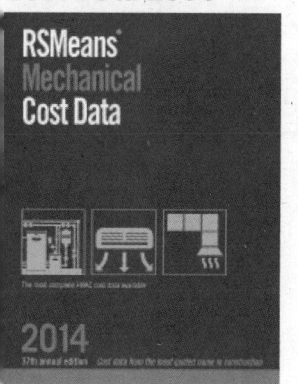

Total unit and systems price guidance for mechanical construction . . . materials, parts, fittings, and complete labor cost information. Includes prices for piping, heating, air-conditioning, ventilation, and all related construction.

Plus new 2014 unit costs for:

- Thousands of installed HVAC/controls assemblies components
- "On-site" Location Factors for more than 930 cities and towns in the U.S. and Canada
- Crews, labor, and equipment

$191.95 | Available Oct. 2013 | Catalog no. 60024

RSMeans Square Foot Costs 2014
Accurate and Easy-to-Use

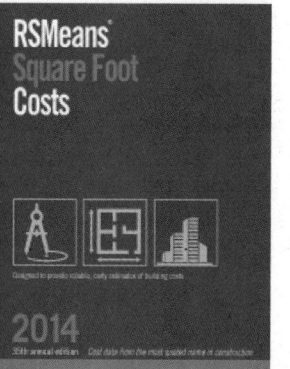

- **Updated price information** based on nationwide figures from suppliers, estimators, labor experts, and contractors
- New green building models
- Realistic graphics, offering true-to-life illustrations of building projects
- Extensive information on using square foot cost data, including sample estimates and alternate pricing methods

$205.95 | Available Oct. 2013 | Catalog no. 60054

RSMeans Green Building Cost Data 2014

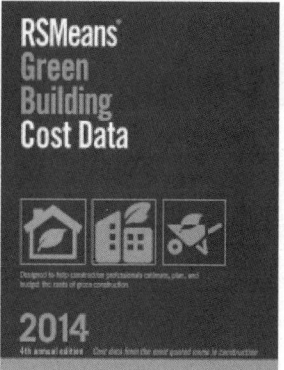

Estimate, plan, and budget the costs of green building for both new commercial construction and renovation work with this fourth edition of *RSMeans Green Building Cost Data*. More than 10,000 unit costs for a wide array of green building products plus assemblies costs. Easily identified cross references to LEED and Green Globes building rating systems criteria.

$160.95 | Available Nov. 2013 | Catalog no. 60554

RSMeans Facilities Construction Cost Data 2014

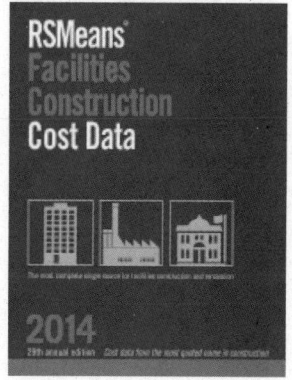

For the maintenance and construction of commercial, industrial, municipal, and institutional properties. Costs are shown for new and remodeling construction and are broken down into materials, labor, equipment, and overhead and profit. Special emphasis is given to sections on mechanical, electrical, furnishings, site work, building maintenance, finish work, and demolition.

More than 49,000 unit costs, plus assemblies costs and a comprehensive Reference Section are included.

$496.95 | Available Nov. 2013 | Catalog no. 60204

RSMeans Commercial Renovation Cost Data 2014
Commercial/Multifamily Residential

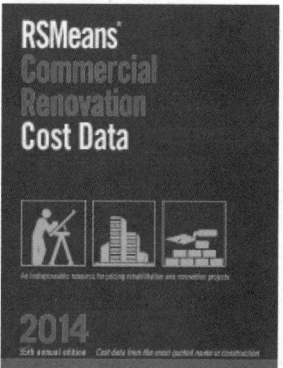

Use this valuable tool to estimate commercial and multifamily residential renovation and remodeling.

Includes: New costs for hundreds of unique methods, materials, and conditions that only come up in repair and remodeling, PLUS:

- Unit costs for more than 19,000 construction components
- Installed costs for more than 2,000 assemblies
- More than 930 "on-site" localization factors for the U.S. and Canada

$156.95 | Available Oct. 2013 | Catalog no. 60044

RSMeans Electrical Cost Data 2014

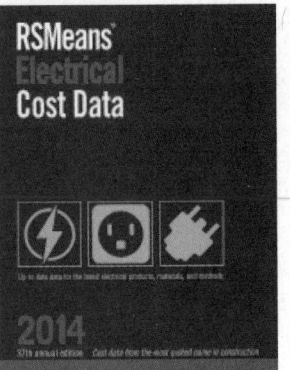

Pricing information for every part of electrical cost planning. More than 13,000 unit and systems costs with design tables; clear specifications and drawings; engineering guides; illustrated estimating procedures; complete labor-hour and materials costs for better scheduling and procurement; and the latest electrical products and construction methods.

- A variety of special electrical systems, including cathodic protection
- Costs for maintenance, demolition, HVAC/mechanical, specialties, equipment, and more

$196.95 | Available Oct. 2013 | Catalog no. 60034

RSMeans Electrical Change Order Cost Data 2014

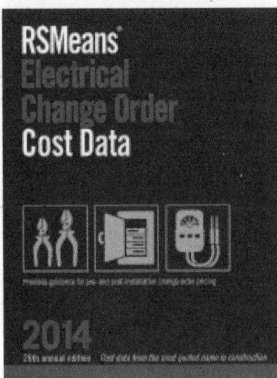

RSMeans Electrical Change Order Cost Data provides you with electrical unit prices exclusively for pricing change orders—based on the recent, direct experience of contractors and suppliers. Analyze and check your own change order estimates against the experience others have had doing the same work. It also covers productivity analysis and change order cost justifications. With useful information for calculating the effects of change orders and dealing with their administration.

$187.95 | Available Dec. 2013 | Catalog no. 60234

RSMeans Assemblies Cost Data 2014

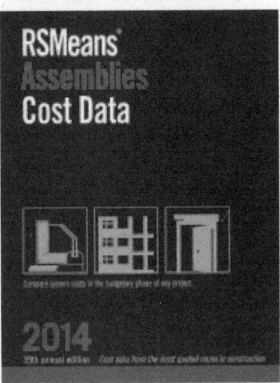

RSMeans Assemblies Cost Data takes the guesswork out of preliminary or conceptual estimates. Now you don't have to try to calculate the assembled cost by working up individual component costs. We've done all the work for you.

Presents detailed illustrations, descriptions, specifications, and costs for every conceivable building assembly— over 350 types in all—arranged in the easy-to-use UNIFORMAT II system. Each illustrated "assembled" cost includes a complete grouping of materials and associated installation costs, including the installing contractor's overhead and profit.

$315.95 | Available Sept. 2013 | Catalog no. 60064

RSMeans Open Shop Building Construction Cost Data 2014

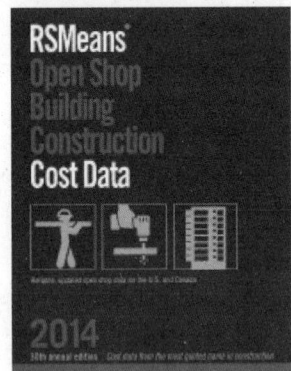

The latest costs for accurate budgeting and estimating of new commercial and residential construction . . . renovation work . . . change orders . . . cost engineering.

RSMeans Open Shop "BCCD" will assist you to:

- Develop benchmark prices for change orders
- Plug gaps in preliminary estimates and budgets
- Estimate complex projects
- Substantiate invoices on contracts
- Price ADA-related renovations

$165.95 | Available Dec. 2013 | Catalog no. 60154

RSMeans Residential Cost Data 2014

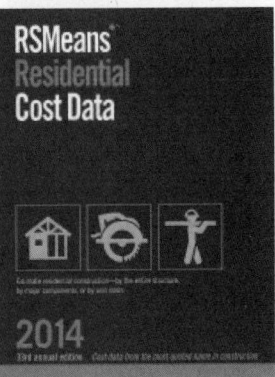

Contains square foot costs for 28 basic home models with the look of today, plus hundreds of custom additions and modifications you can quote right off the page. Includes costs for more than 700 residential systems. Complete with blank estimating forms, sample estimates, and step-by-step instructions.

Contains line items for cultured stone and brick, PVC trim lumber, and TPO roofing.

$139.95 | Available Oct. 2013 | Catalog no. 60174

RSMeans Site Work & Landscape Cost Data 2014

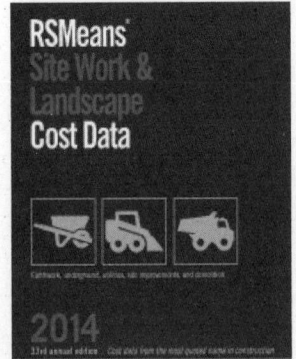

Includes unit and assemblies costs for earthwork, sewerage, piped utilities, site improvements, drainage, paving, trees and shrubs, street openings/repairs, underground tanks, and more. Contains 78 types of assemblies costs for accurate conceptual estimates.

Includes:

- Estimating for infrastructure improvements
- Environmentally-oriented construction
- ADA-mandated handicapped access
- Hazardous waste line items

$187.95 | Available Dec. 2013 | Catalog no. 60284

RSMeans Facilities Maintenance & Repair Cost Data 2014

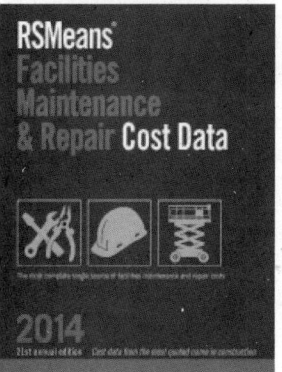

RSMeans Facilities Maintenance & Repair Cost Data gives you a complete system to manage and plan your facility repair and maintenance costs and budget efficiently. Guidelines for auditing a facility and developing an annual maintenance plan. Budgeting is included, along with reference tables on cost and management, and information on frequency and productivity of maintenance operations.

The only nationally recognized source of maintenance and repair costs. Developed in cooperation with the Civil Engineering Research Laboratory (CERL) of the Army Corps of Engineers.

$434.95 | Available Nov. 2013 | Catalog no. 60304

RSMeans Concrete & Masonry Cost Data 2014

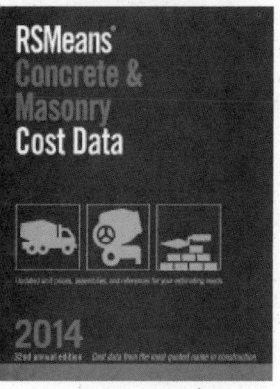

Provides you with cost facts for virtually all concrete/masonry estimating needs, from complicated formwork to various sizes and face finishes of brick and block—all in great detail. The comprehensive Unit Price Section contains more than 8,000 selected entries. Also contains an Assemblies [Cost] Section, and a detailed Reference Section that supplements the cost data.

$177.95 | Available Dec. 2013 | Catalog no. 60114

RSMeans Construction Cost Indexes 2014

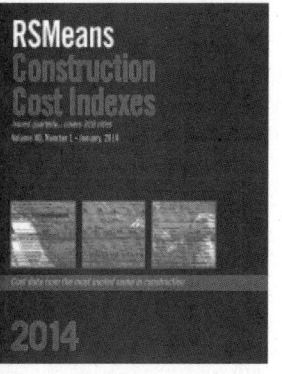

What materials and labor costs will change unexpectedly this year? By how much?

- Breakdowns for 318 major cities
- National averages for 30 key cities
- Expanded five major city indexes
- Historical construction cost indexes

$362.00 per year (subscription) | Catalog no. 50144
$93.50 individual quarters | Catalog no. 60144 A,B,C,D

RSMeans Light Commercial Cost Data 2014

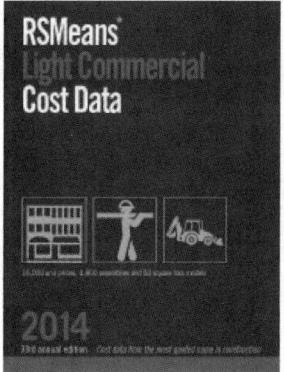

Specifically addresses the light commercial market, which is a specialized niche in the construction industry. Aids you, the owner/designer/contractor, in preparing all types of estimates—from budgets to detailed bids. Includes new advances in methods and materials.

Assemblies Section allows you to evaluate alternatives in the early stages of design/planning.

More than 15,000 unit costs ensure that you have the prices you need . . . when you need them.

$144.95 | Available Nov. 2013 | Catalog no. 60184

RSMeans Labor Rates for the Construction Industry 2014

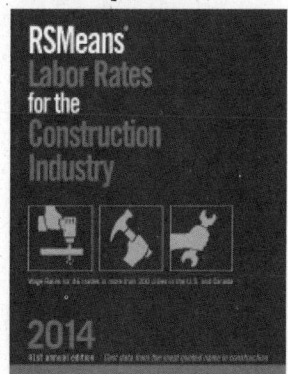

Complete information for estimating labor costs, making comparisons, and negotiating wage rates by trade for more than 300 U.S. and Canadian cities. With 46 construction trades listed by local union number in each city, and historical wage rates included for comparison. Each city chart lists the county and is alphabetically arranged with handy visual flip tabs for quick reference.

$424.95 | Available Dec. 2013 | Catalog no. 60124

RSMeans Interior Cost Data 2014

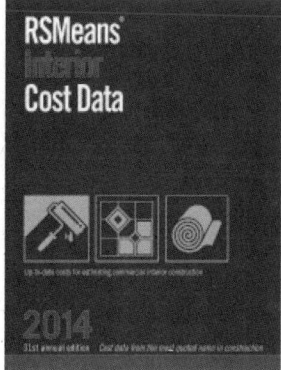

Provides you with prices and guidance needed to make accurate interior work estimates. Contains costs on materials, equipment, hardware, custom installations, furnishings, and labor costs . . . for new and remodel commercial and industrial interior construction, including updated information on office furnishings, and reference information.

$196.95 | Available Nov. 2013 | Catalog no. 60094

Annual Cost Guides

For more information visit the RSMeans website at **www.rsmeans.com**

Unit prices according to the latest MasterFormat!

RSMeans Heavy Construction Cost Data 2014

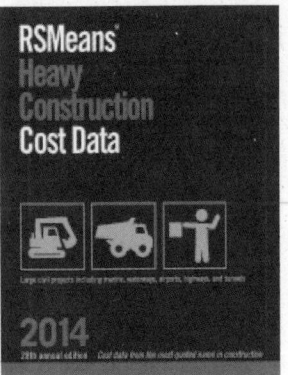

A comprehensive guide to heavy construction costs. Includes costs for highly specialized projects such as tunnels, dams, highways, airports, and waterways. Information on labor rates, equipment, and materials costs is included. Features unit price costs, systems costs, and numerous reference tables for costs and design.

$192.95 | Available Dec. 2013 | Catalog no. 60164

RSMeans Plumbing Cost Data 2014

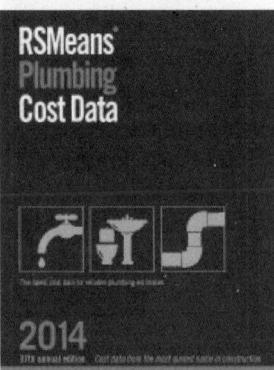

Comprehensive unit prices and assemblies for plumbing, irrigation systems, commercial and residential fire protection, point-of-use water heaters, and the latest approved materials. This publication and its companion, *RSMeans Mechanical Cost Data*, provide full-range cost estimating coverage for all the mechanical trades.

Now contains updated costs for potable water and radiant heat systems and high efficiency fixtures.

$194.95 | Available Oct. 2013 | Catalog no. 60214

2014 RSMeans Seminar Schedule

Note: call for exact dates and details.

Location	Dates	Location	Dates
Seattle, WA	January and August	Jacksonville FL	September
Dallas/Ft. Worth, TX	January	Dallas, TX	September
Austin, TX	February	Charleston, SC	October
Anchorage, AK	March and September	Houston, TX	October
Las Vegas, NV	March and October	Atlanta, GA	November
Washington, DC	April and September	Baltimore, MD	November
Phoenix, AZ	April	Orlando, FL	November
Kansas City, MO	April	San Diego, CA	December
Toronto	May	San Antonio, TX	December
Denver, CO	May	Raleigh, NC	December
San Francisco, CA	June		
Bethesda, MD	June		
Columbus, GA	June		
El Segundo, CA	August		

1-800-334-3509, Press 1

Professional Development

For more information visit the RSMeans website at **www.rsmeans.com**

eLearning Training Sessions

Learn how to use *RSMeans Online*™ or *RSMeans CostWorks*® CD from the convenience of your home or office. Our eLearning training sessions let you join a training conference call and share the instructors' desktops, so you can view the presentation and step-by-step instructions on your own computer screen. The live webinars are held from 9 a.m. to 4 p.m. eastern standard time, with a one-hour break for lunch.

For these sessions, you must have a computer with high speed Internet access and a compatible Web browser. Learn more at www.rsmeansonline.com or call for a schedule: 1-800-334-3509 and press 1. Webinars are generally held on selected Wednesdays each month.

RSMeans Online™
$299 per person

RSMeans CostWorks® **CD**
$299 per person

Professional Development

For more information visit the RSMeans website at **www.rsmeans.com**

RSMeans Online™ Training

Construction estimating is vital to the decision-making process at each state of every project. RSMeansOnline works the way you do. It's systematic, flexible and intuitive. In this one day class you will see how you can estimate any phase of any project faster and better.

Some of what you'll learn:
- Customizing RSMeansOnline
- Making the most of RSMeans "Circle Reference" numbers
- How to integrate your cost data
- Generate reports, exporting estimates to MS Excel, sharing, collaborating and more

Also available: RSMeans Online™ training webinar

Facilities Construction Estimating

In this *two-day* course, professionals working in facilities management can get help with their daily challenges to establish budgets for all phases of a project.

Some of what you'll learn:
- Determining the full scope of a project
- Identifying the scope of risks and opportunities
- Creative solutions to estimating issues
- Organizing estimates for presentation and discussion
- Special techniques for repair/remodel and maintenance projects
- Negotiating project change orders

Who should attend: facility managers, engineers, contractors, facility tradespeople, planners, and project managers.

Scheduling with Microsoft Project

Two days of hands-on training gives you a look at the basics to putting it all together with MS Project to create a complete project schedule. Learn to work better and faster, manage changes and updates, enhance tracking, generate actionable reports, and boost control of your time and budget.

Some of what you'll learn:
- Defining task/activity relationships: link tasks, establish predecessor/successor relationships and create logs
- Baseline scheduling: the essential what/when
- Using MS Project to determine the critical path
- Integrate RSMeans data with MS Project
- The dollar-loaded schedule: enhance the reliability of this "must-know" technique for scheduling public projects.

Who should attend: contractors' project-management teams, architects and engineers, project owners and their representatives, and those interested in improving their project planning and scheduling and management skills.

Maintenance & Repair Estimating for Facilities

This *two-day* course teaches attendees how to plan, budget, and estimate the cost of ongoing and preventive maintenance and repair for existing buildings and grounds.

Some of what you'll learn:
- The most financially favorable maintenance, repair, and replacement scheduling and estimating
- Auditing and value engineering facilities
- Preventive planning and facilities upgrading
- Determining both in-house and contract-out service costs
- Annual, asset-protecting M&R plan

Who should attend: facility managers, maintenance supervisors, buildings and grounds superintendents, plant managers, planners, estimators, and others involved in facilities planning and budgeting.

Practical Project Management for Construction Professionals

In this *two-day* course, acquire the essential knowledge and develop the skills to effectively and efficiently execute the day-to-day responsibilities of the construction project manager.

Covers:
- General conditions of the construction contract
- Contract modifications: change orders and construction change directives
- Negotiations with subcontractors and vendors
- Effective writing: notification and communications
- Dispute resolution: claims and liens

Who should attend: architects, engineers, owner's representatives, project managers.

Mechanical & Electrical Estimating

This *two-day* course teaches attendees how to prepare more accurate and complete mechanical/electrical estimates, avoiding the pitfalls of omission and double-counting, while understanding the composition and rationale within the RSMeans mechanical/electrical database.

Some of what you'll learn:
- The unique way mechanical and electrical systems are interrelated
- M&E estimates—conceptual, planning, budgeting, and bidding stages
- Order of magnitude, square foot, assemblies, and unit price estimating
- Comparative cost analysis of equipment and design alternatives

Who should attend: architects, engineers, facilities managers, mechanical and electrical contractors, and others who need a highly reliable method for developing, understanding, and evaluating mechanical and electrical contracts.

Professional Development

Unit Price Estimating

This interactive *two-day* seminar teaches attendees how to interpret project information and process it into final, detailed estimates with the greatest accuracy level.

The most important credential an estimator can take to the job is the ability to visualize construction and estimate accurately.

Some of what you'll learn:

- Interpreting the design in terms of cost
- The most detailed, time-tested methodology for accurate pricing
- Key cost drivers—material, labor, equipment, staging, and subcontracts
- Understanding direct and indirect costs for accurate job cost accounting and change order management

Who should attend: corporate and government estimators and purchasers, architects, engineers, and others who need to produce accurate project estimates.

RSMeans CostWorks® CD Training

This one-day course helps users become more familiar with the functionality of *RSMeans CostWork*s program. Each menu, icon, screen, and function found in the program is explained in depth. Time is devoted to hands-on estimating exercises.

Some of what you'll learn:

- Searching the database using all navigation methods
- Exporting RSMeans data to your preferred spreadsheet format
- Viewing crews, assembly components, and much more
- Automatically regionalizing the database

This training session requires you to bring a laptop computer to class.

When you register for this course you will receive an outline for your laptop requirements.

Also offering web training for CostWorks CD!

Facilities Est. Using RSMeans CostWorks® CD

Combines hands-on skill building with best estimating practices and real-life problems. Brings you up-to-date with key concepts, and provides tips, pointers, and guidelines to save time and avoid cost oversights and errors.

Some of what you'll learn:

- Estimating process concepts
- Customizing and adapting RSMeans cost data
- Establishing scope of work to account for all known variables
- Budget estimating: when, why, and how
- Site visits: what to look for—what you can't afford to overlook
- How to estimate repair and remodeling variables

This training session requires you to bring a laptop computer to class.

Who should attend: facility managers, architects, engineers, contractors, facility tradespeople, planners, project managers and anyone involved with JOC, SABRE, or IDIQ.

Conceptual Estimating Using RSMeans CostWorks® CD

This *two day* class uses the leading industry data and a powerful software package to develop highly accurate conceptual estimate for your construction projects. All attendees must bring a laptop computer loaded with the current year *Square Foot Model Costs* and the *Assemblies Cost Data* CostWorks titles.

Some of what you'll learn:

- Introduction to conceptual estimating
- Types of conceptual estimates
- Helpful hints
- Order of magnitude estimating
- Square foot estimating
- Assemblies estimating

Who should attend: architects, engineers, contractors, construction estimators, owner's representatives, and anyone looking for an electronic method for performing square foot estimating.

Assessing Scope of Work for Facility Construction Estimating

This *two-day* practical training program addresses the vital importance of understanding the SCOPE of projects in order to produce accurate cost estimates for facility repair and remodeling.

Some of what you'll learn:

- Discussions of site visits, plans/specs, record drawings of facilities, and site-specific lists
- Review of CSI divisions, including means, methods, materials, and the challenges of scoping each topic
- Exercises in SCOPE identification and SCOPE writing for accurate estimating of projects
- Hands-on exercises that require SCOPE, take-off, and pricing

Who should attend: corporate and government estimators, planners, facility managers, and others who need to produce accurate project estimates.

Unit Price Est. Using RSMeans CostWorks® CD

Step-by-step instruction and practice problems to identify and track key cost drivers—material, labor, equipment, staging, and subcontractors—for each specific task. Learn the most detailed, time-tested methodology for accurately "pricing" these variables their impact on each other and on total cost.

Some of what you'll learn:

- Unit price cost estimating
- Order of magnitude, square foot, and assemblies estimating
- Quantity takeoff
- Direct and indirect construction costs
- Development of contractor's bill rates
- How to use *RSMeans Building Construction Cost Data*

This training session requires you to bring a laptop computer to class.

Who should attend: architects, engineers, corporate and government estimators, facility managers, and government procurement staff.

Professional Development

Registration Information

Register early . . . Save up to $100! Register 30 days before the start date of a seminar and save $100 off your total fee. *Note: This discount can be applied only once per order. It cannot be applied to team discount registrations or any other special offer.*

How to register Register by phone today! The RSMeans toll-free number for making reservations is **1-800-334-3509, Press 1.**

Two day seminar registration fee - $935. One-day *RSMeans CostWorks®* **training registration fee - $375.** To register by mail, complete the registration form and return, with your full fee, to: RSMeans Seminars, 700 Longwater Drive, Norwell, MA 02061.

Government pricing All federal government employees save off the regular seminar price. Other promotional discounts cannot be combined with the government discount.

Team discount program for two to four seminar registrations. Call for pricing: 1-800-334-3509, Press 1

Multiple course discounts When signing up for two or more courses, call for pricing.

Refund policy Cancellations will be accepted up to ten business days prior to the seminar start. There are no refunds for cancellations received later than ten working days prior to the first day of the seminar. A $150 processing fee will be applied for all cancellations. Written notice of cancellation is required. Substitutions can be made at any time before the session starts. **No-shows are subject to the full seminar fee.**

AACE approved courses Many seminars described and offered here have been approved for 14 hours (1.4 recertification credits) of credit by the AACE International Certification Board toward meeting the continuing education requirements for recertification as a Certified Cost Engineer/Certified Cost Consultant.

AIA Continuing Education We are registered with the AIA Continuing Education System (AIA/CES) and are committed to developing quality learning activities in accordance with the CES criteria. Many seminars meet the AIA/CES criteria for Quality Level 2. AIA members may receive (14) learning units (LUs) for each two-day RSMeans course.

Daily course schedule The first day of each seminar session begins at 8:30 a.m. and ends at 4:30 p.m. The second day begins at 8:00 a.m. and ends at 4:00 p.m. Participants are urged to bring a hand-held calculator, since many actual problems will be worked out in each session.

Continental breakfast Your registration includes the cost of a continental breakfast, and a morning and afternoon refreshment break. These informal segments allow you to discuss topics of mutual interest with other seminar attendees. (You are free to make your own lunch and dinner arrangements.)

Hotel/transportation arrangements RSMeans arranges to hold a block of rooms at most host hotels. To take advantage of special group rates when making your reservation, be sure to mention that you are attending the RSMeans seminar. You are, of course, free to stay at the lodging place of your choice. **(Hotel reservations and transportation arrangements should be made directly by seminar attendees.)**

Important Class sizes are limited, so please register as soon as possible.

Note: Pricing subject to change.

Registration Form

ADDS-1000

Call 1-800-334-3509, Press 1 to register or FAX this form 1-800-632-6732. Visit our website: www.rsmeans.com

Please register the following people for the RSMeans construction seminars as shown here. We understand that we must make our own hotel reservations if overnight stays are necessary.

☐ Full payment of $_____ enclosed.

☐ Bill me.

Please print name of registrant(s).

(To appear on certificate of completion)

_____

_____

_____

_____

P.O. #:_____
GOVERNMENT AGENCIES MUST SUPPLY PURCHASE ORDER NUMBER OR TRAINING FORM.

Firm name_____

Address_____

City/State/Zip_____

Telephone no._____ Fax no._____

E-mail address_____

Charge registration(s) to: ☐ MasterCard ☐ VISA ☐ American Express

Account no._____ Exp. date_____

Cardholder's signature_____

Seminar name_____

Seminar City_____

Please mail check to: RSMeans Seminars, 700 Longwater Drive, Norwell, MA 02061 USA

New Titles - Reference Books

Solar Energy: Technologies & Project Delivery for Buildings

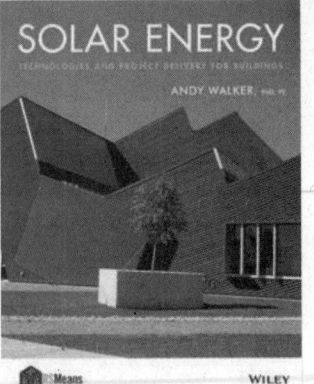

by Andy Walker

An authoritative reference on the design of solar energy systems in building projects, with applications, operating principles, and simple tools for the construction, engineering, and design professionals, the book simplifies the solar design and engineering process and provides sample documentation for the complete design of a solar energy system for buildings.

$85.00 | 320 pages, hardover | Catalog no. 67365

Project Scheduling & Management for Construction, 4th Edition

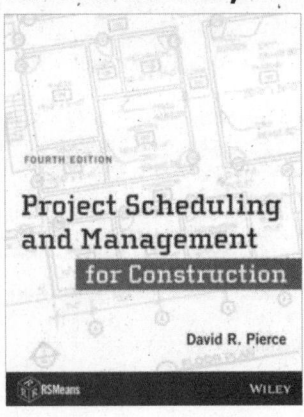

by David R. Pierce

First published in 1988 by RSMeans, the new edition of *Project Scheduling and Management for Construction* has been substantially revised for both professionals and students enrolled in construction management and civil engineering programs. While retaining its emphasis on developing practical, professional-level scheduling skills, the new edition is a relatable, real world case study.

$95.00 | 272 pages, softcover | Catalog no. 67367

Estimating Building Costs, 2nd Edition
For the Residential & Light Commercial Construction Professional

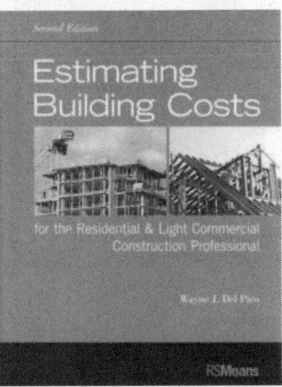

by Wayne J. Del Pico

This book guides readers through the entire estimating process, explaining in detail how to put together a reliable estimate that can be used not only for budgeting, but also for developing a schedule, managing a project, dealing with contingencies, and ultimately making a profit.

Completely revised and updated to reflect the CSI MasterFormat 2010 system, this practical guide describes estimating techniques for each building system and how to apply them according to the latest industry standards.

$75.00 | 398 pages, softcover | Catalog no. 67343A

Project Control: Integrating Cost & Schedule in Construction

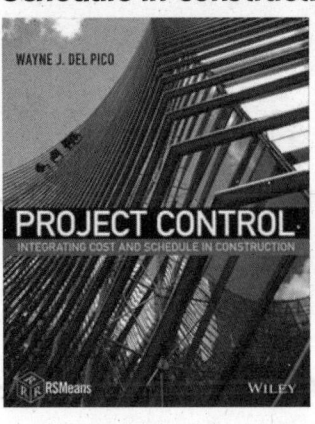

by Wayne J. Del Pico

Written by a seasoned professional in the field, *Project Control: Integrating Cost and Schedule in Construction* fills a void in the area of project control as applied in the construction industry today. It demonstrates how productivity models for an individual project are created, monitored, and controlled, and how corrective actions are implemented as deviations from the baseline occur.

$95.00 | 240 pages, softcover | Catalog no. 67366

How to Estimate with Means Data & CostWorks, 4th Edition

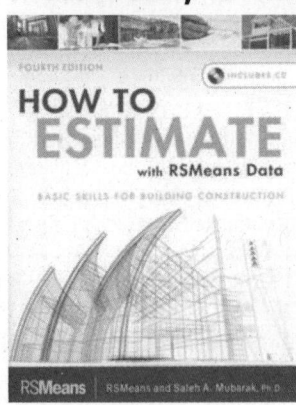

by RSMeans and Saleh A. Mubarak, Ph.D.

This step-by-step guide takes you through all the major construction items with extensive coverage of site work, concrete and masonry, wood and metal framing, doors and windows, and other divisions. The only construction cost estimating handbook that uses the most popular source of construction data, RSMeans, this indispensible guide features access to the instructional version of CostWorks in electronic form, enabling you to practice techniques to solve real-world estimating problems.

$75.00 | 292 pages, softcover | Includes CostWorks CD
Catalog no. 67324C

RSMeans Cost Data, Student Edition

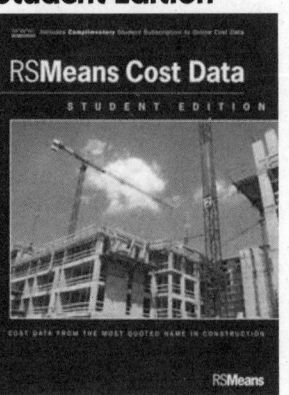

This book provides a thorough introduction to cost estimating in a self-contained print and online package. With clear explanations and a hands-on, example-driven approach, it is the ideal reference for students and new professionals.

Features include:

- Commercial and residential construction cost data in print and online formats
- Complete how-to guidance on the essentials of cost estimating
- A supplemental website with plans, problem sets, and a full sample estimate

$99.00 | 512 pages, softcover | Catalog no. 67363

Reference Books

Value Engineering: Practical Applications
For Design, Construction, Maintenance & Operations

by Alphonse Dell'Isola, PE

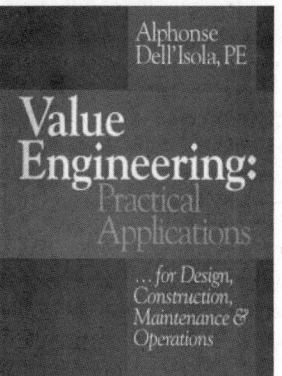

A tool for immediate application—for engineers, architects, facility managers, owners, and contractors. Includes making the case for VE—the management briefing; integrating VE into planning, budgeting, and design; conducting life cycle costing; using VE methodology in design review and consultant selection; case studies; VE workbook; and a life cycle costing program on disk.

$85.00 | Over 450 pages, illustrated, softcover | Catalog no. 67319A

Complete Book of Framing, 2nd Edition

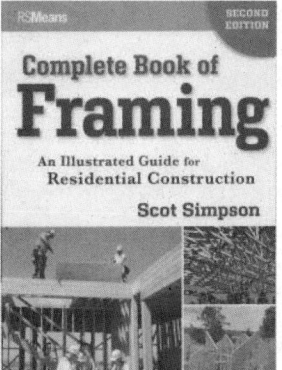

by Scot Simpson

This updated, easy-to-learn guide to rough carpentry and framing is written by an expert with more than thirty years of framing experience. Starting with the basics, this book begins with types of lumber, nails, and what tools are needed, followed by detailed, fully illustrated steps for framing each building element. Framer-Friendly Tips throughout the book show how to get a task done right—and more easily.

$29.95 | 352 pages, softcover | Catalog no. 67353A

Risk Management for Design & Construction

Introduces risk as a central pillar of project management and shows how a project manager can prepare to deal with uncertainty. Experts in the field use clear, straightforward terminology to demystify the concepts of project uncertainty and risk. Includes:

- Integrated cost and schedule risk analysis
- An introduction to a ready-to-use system of analyzing a project's risks and tools to proactively manage risks
- A methodology that was developed and used by the Washington State Department of Transportation
- Case studies and examples on the proper application of principles
- Information about combining value analysis with risk analysis

$125.00 | Over 250 pages, softcover | Catalog no. 67359

Green Home Improvement

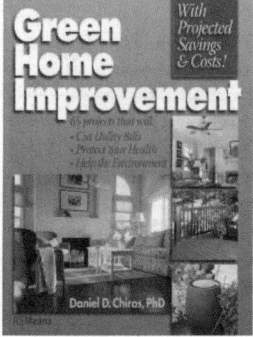

by Daniel D. Chiras, PhD

With energy costs rising and environmental awareness increasing, people are looking to make their homes greener. This book, with 65 projects and actual costs and projected savings help homeowners prioritize their green improvements.

Projects range from simple water savers that cost only a few dollars, to bigger-ticket items such as HVAC systems. With color photos and cost estimates, each project compares options and describes the work involved, the benefits, and the savings.

$34.95 | 320 pages, illustrated, softcover | Catalog no. 67355

How Your House Works, 2nd Edition

by Charlie Wing

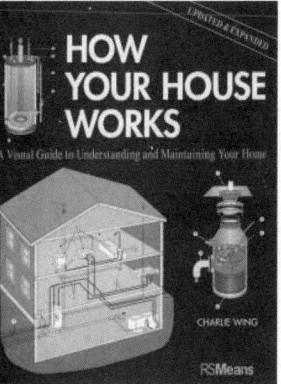

Knowledge of your home's systems helps you control repair and construction costs and makes sure the correct elements are being installed or replaced. This book uncovers the mysteries behind just about every major appliance and building element in your house. See-through, cross-section drawings in full color show you exactly how these things should be put together and how they function, including what to check if they don't work. It just might save you having to call in a professional.

$22.95 | 192 pages, softcover | Catalog no. 67351A

Life Cycle Costing for Facilities

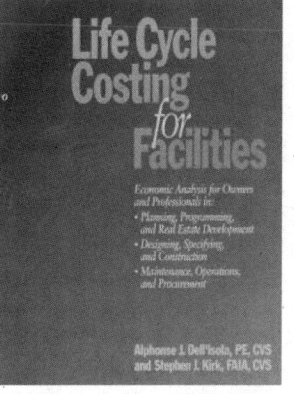

by Alphonse Dell'Isola and Dr. Steven Kirk

Guidance for achieving higher quality design and construction projects at lower costs! Cost-cutting efforts often sacrifice quality to yield the cheapest product. Life cycle costing enables building designers and owners to achieve both. The authors of this book show how LCC can work for a variety of projects — from roads to HVAC upgrades to different types of buildings.

$99.95 | 396 pages, hardcover | Catalog no. 67341

Reference Books

For more information visit the RSMeans website at www.rsmeans.com

Unit prices according to the latest MasterFormat!

Builder's Essentials: Plan Reading & Material Takeoff

For Residential and Light Commercial Construction

by Wayne J. DelPico

A valuable tool for understanding plans and specs, and accurately calculating material quantities. Step-by-step instructions and takeoff procedures based on a full set of working drawings.

$45.00 | Over 420 pages, softcover | Catalog no. 67307

Means Unit Price Estimating Methods, 4th Edition

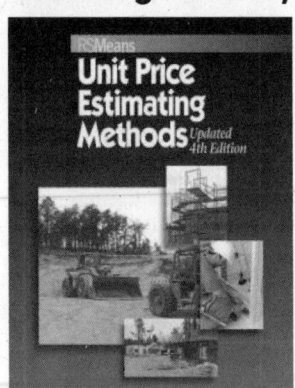

Includes cost data and estimating examples, updated to reflect changes to the CSI numbering system and new features of RSMeans cost data. It describes the most productive, universally accepted ways to estimate, and uses checklists and forms to illustrate shortcuts and timesavers. A model estimate demonstrates procedures. A new chapter explores computer estimating alternatives.

$75.00 | Over 350 pages, illustrated, softcover | Catalog no. 67303B

Concrete Repair & Maintenance Illustrated

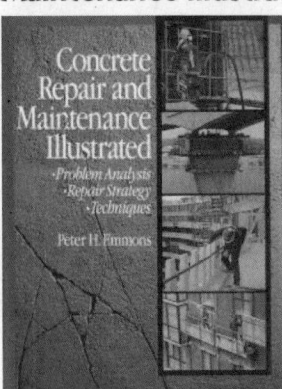

by Peter Emmons

Hundreds of illustrations show users how to analyze, repair, clean, and maintain concrete structures for optimal performance and cost effectiveness. From parking garages to roads and bridges to structural concrete, this comprehensive book describes the causes, effects, and remedies for concrete wear and failure. Invaluable for planning jobs, selecting materials, and training employees, this book is a must-have for concrete specialists, general contractors, facility managers, civil and structural engineers, and architects.

$75.00 | 300 pages, illustrated, softcover | Catalog no. 67146

Square Foot & UNIFORMAT Assemblies Estimating Methods, 3rd Edition

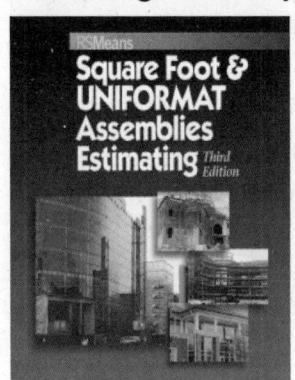

Develop realistic square foot and assemblies costs for budgeting and construction funding. The new edition features updated guidance on square foot and assemblies estimating using UNIFORMAT II. An essential reference for anyone who performs conceptual estimates.

$75.00 | Over 300 pages, illustrated, softcover | Catalog no. 67145B

Electrical Estimating Methods, 3rd Edition

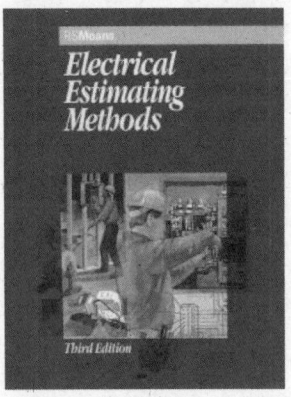

Expanded edition includes sample estimates and cost information in keeping with the latest version of the CSI MasterFormat and UNIFORMAT II. Complete coverage of fiber optic and uninterruptible power supply electrical systems, broken down by components, and explained in detail. Includes a new chapter on computerized estimating methods. A practical companion to *RSMeans Electrical Cost Data.*

$75.00 | Over 325 pages, hardcover | Catalog no. 67230B

Residential & Light Commercial Construction Standards, 3rd Edition

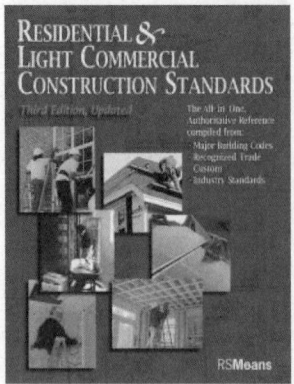

Updated by RSMeans and contributing authors

This book provides authoritative requirements and recommendations compiled from leading professional associations, industry publications, and building code organizations. This all-in-one reference helps establish a standard for workmanship, quickly resolve disputes, and avoid defect claims. Updated third edition includes new coverage of green building, seismic, hurricane, and mold-resistant construction.

$65.00 | Over 550 pages, illustrated, softcover | Catalog no. 67322B

Reference Books

Construction Business Management

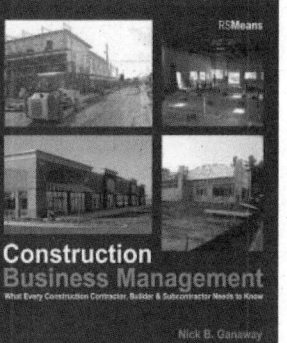

by Nick Ganaway

Only 43% of construction firms stay in business after four years. Make sure your company thrives with valuable guidance from a pro with 25 years of success as a commercial contractor. Find out what it takes to build all aspects of a business that is profitable, enjoyable, and enduring. With a bonus chapter on retail construction.

$55.00 | 200 pages, softcover | Catalog no. 67352

The Practice of Cost Segregation Analysis

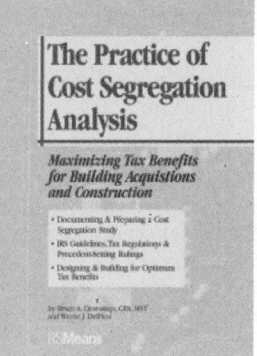

by Bruce A. Desrosiers and Wayne J. DelPico

This expert guide walks you through the practice of cost segregation analysis, which enables property owners to defer taxes and benefit from "accelerated cost recovery" through depreciation deductions on assets that are properly identified and classified.

With a glossary of terms, sample cost segregation estimates for various building types, key information resources, and updates via a dedicated website, this book is a critical resource for anyone involved in cost segregation analysis.

$105.00 | Over 225 pages | Catalog no. 67345

Green Building: Project Planning & Cost Estimating, 3rd Edition

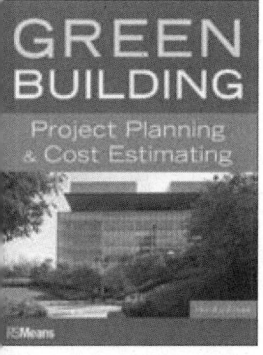

Since the widely read first edition of this book, green building has gone from a growing trend to a major force in design and construction.

This new edition has been updated with the latest in green building technologies, design concepts, standards, and costs. Full-color with all new case studies—plus a new chapter on commercial real estate.

110.00 | Over 450 pages, softcover | Catalog no. 67338B

Project Scheduling & Management for Construction, 3rd Edition

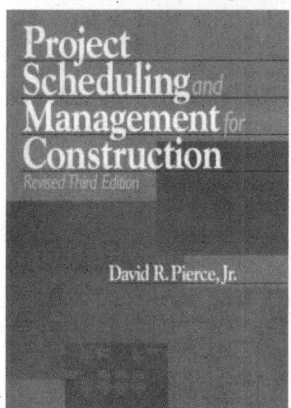

by David R. Pierce, Jr.

A comprehensive yet easy-to-follow guide to construction project scheduling and control—from vital project management principles through the latest scheduling, tracking, and controlling techniques. The author is a leading authority on scheduling, with years of field and teaching experience at leading academic institutions. Spend a few hours with this book and come away with a solid understanding of this essential management topic.

$64.95 | Over 300 pages, illustrated, hardcover | Catalog no. 67247B

Preventive Maintenance for Multi-Family Housing

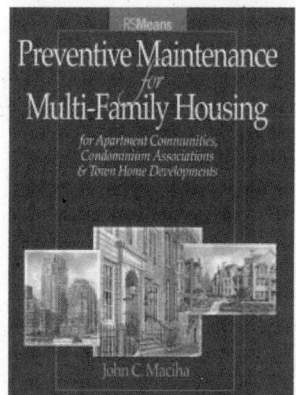

by John C. Maciha

Prepared by one of the nation's leading experts on multi-family housing.

This complete PM system for apartment and condominium communities features expert guidance, checklists for buildings and grounds maintenance tasks and their frequencies, a reusable wall chart to track maintenance, and a dedicated website featuring customizable electronic forms. A must-have for anyone involved with multi-family housing maintenance and upkeep.

$95.00 | 225 pages | Catalog no. 67346

Job Order Contracting: Expediting Construction Project Delivery

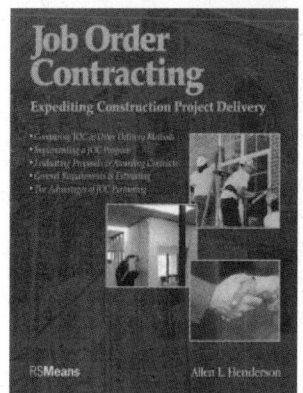

by Allen L. Henderson

Expert guidance to help you implement JOC—fast becoming the preferred project delivery method for repair and renovation, minor new construction, and maintenance projects in the public sector and in many states and municipalities. The author, a leading JOC expert and practitioner, shows how to:

- Establish a JOC program
- Evaluate proposals & award contracts
- Handle general requirements and estimating
- Partner for maximum benefits

$89.95 | 192 pages, illustrated, hardcover | Catalog no. 67348

Reference Books

For more information visit the RSMeans website at **www.rsmeans.com**

Construction Supervision

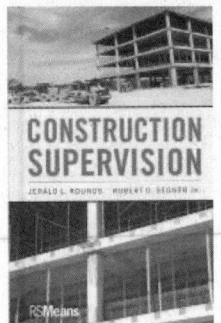

This brand new title inspires supervisory excellence with proven tactics and techniques applied by thousands of construction supervisors over the past decade. Recognizing the unique and critical role the supervisor plays in project success, the book's leadership guidelines carve out a practical blueprint for motivating work performance and increasing productivity through effective communication.

Features:

- A unique focus on field supervision and crew management
- Coverage of supervision from the foreman to the superintendent level
- An overview of technical skills whose mastery will build confidence and success for the supervisor
- A detailed view of "soft" management and communication skills

$95.00 | Over 450 pages, softcover | Catalog no. 67358

The Homeowner's Guide to Mold

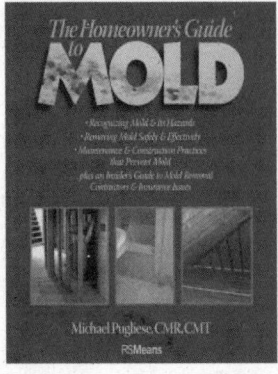

By Michael Pugliese

Expert guidance to protect your health and your home.

Mold, whether caused by leaks, humidity or flooding, is a real health and financial issue—for homeowners and contractors.

This full-color book explains:

- Construction and maintenance practices to prevent mold
- How to inspect for and remove mold
- Mold remediation procedures and costs
- What to do after a flood
- How to deal with insurance companies

$21.95 | 144 pages, softcover | Catalog no. 67344

Landscape Estimating Methods, 5th Edition

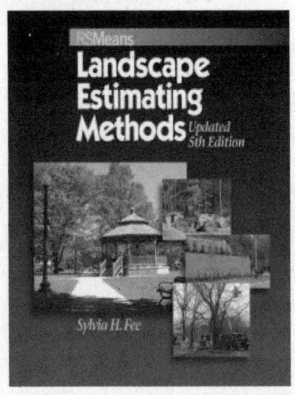

Answers questions about preparing competitive landscape construction estimates, with up-to-date cost estimates and the new MasterFormat classification system. Expanded and revised to address the latest materials and methods, including new coverage on approaches to green building. Includes:

- Step-by-step explanation of the estimating process
- Sample forms and worksheets that save time and prevent errors

$75.00 | Over 350 pages, softcover | Catalog no. 67295C

Building & Renovating Schools

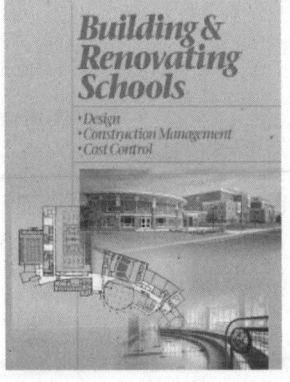

This all-inclusive guide covers every step of the school construction process—from initial planning, needs assessment, and design, right through moving into the new facility. A must-have resource for anyone concerned with new school construction or renovation. With square foot cost models for elementary, middle, and high school facilities, and real-life case studies of recently completed school projects.

The contributors to this book—architects, construction project managers, contractors, and estimators who specialize in school construction—provide start-to-finish, expert guidance on the process.

$99.95 | Over 425 pages, hardcover | Catalog no. 67342

Universal Design Ideas for Style, Comfort & Safety

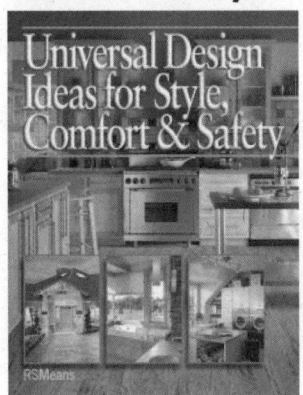

by RSMeans and Lexicon Consulting, Inc.

Incorporating universal design when building or remodeling helps people of any age and physical ability more fully and safely enjoy their living spaces. This book shows how universal design can be artfully blended into the most attractive homes. It discusses specialized products like adjustable countertops and chair lifts, as well as simple ways to enhance a home's safety and comfort. With color photos and expert guidance, every area of the home is covered. Includes budget estimates that give an idea how much projects will cost.

$21.95 | 160 pages, illustrated, softcover | Catalog no. 67354

Plumbing Estimating Methods, 3rd Edition

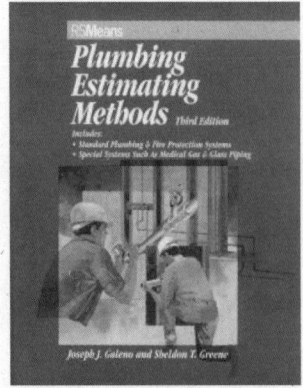

by Joseph J. Galeno and Sheldon T. Greene

Updated and revised! This practical guide walks you through a plumbing estimate, from basic materials and installation methods through change order analysis. *Plumbing Estimating Methods* covers residential, commercial, industrial, and medical systems, and features sample takeoff and estimate forms and detailed illustrations of systems and components.

$65.00 | 330+ pages, softcover | Catalog no. 67283B

Reference Books

For more information visit the RSMeans website at **www.rsmeans.com**

Understanding & Negotiating Construction Contracts

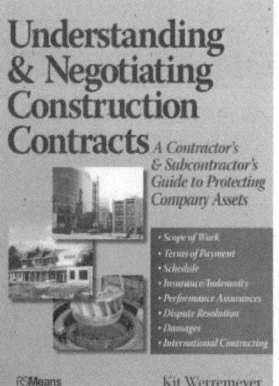

by Kit Werremeyer

Take advantage of the author's 30 years' experience in small-to-large (including international) construction projects. Learn how to identify, understand, and evaluate high risk terms and conditions typically found in all construction contracts—then negotiate to lower or eliminate the risk, improve terms of payment, and reduce exposure to claims and disputes. The author avoids "legalese" and gives real-life examples from actual projects.

$80.00 | 300 pages, softcover | Catalog no. 67350

Means Illustrated Construction Dictionary

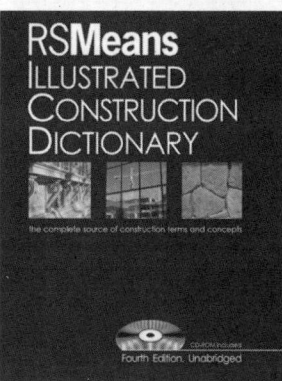

Unabridged 4th Edition, with CD-ROM

Long regarded as the industry's finest, *Means Illustrated Construction Dictionary* is now even better. With nearly 20,000 terms and more than 1,400 illustrations and photos, it is the clear choice for the most comprehensive and current information. The companion CD-ROM that comes with this new edition adds extra features such as: larger graphics and expanded definitions.

$99.95 | Over 790 pages, illust., hardcover | Catalog no. 67292B

The Gypsum Construction Handbook

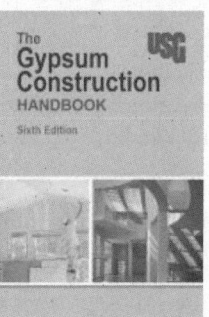

by USG

An invaluable reference of construction procedures for gypsum drywall, cement board, veneer plaster, and conventional plaster. This new edition includes the newest product developments, installation methods, fire- and sound-rated construction information, illustrated framing-to-finish application instructions, estimating and planning information, and more. Great for architects and engineers; contractors, builders, and dealers; apprentices and training programs; building inspectors and code officials; and anyone interested in gypsum construction. Features information on tools and safety practices, a glossary of construction terms, and a list of important agencies and associations. Also available in Spanish.

$40.00 | Over 575 pages, illustrated, softcover | Catalog no. 67357A

RSMeans Estimating Handbook, 3rd Edition

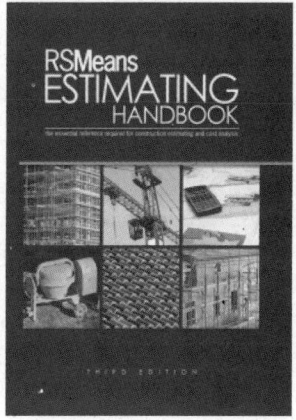

Widely used in the industry for tasks ranging from routine estimates to special cost analysis projects, this handbook has been completely updated and reorganized with new and expanded technical information.

RSMeans Estimating Handbook will help construction professionals:

- Evaluate architectural plans and specifications
- Prepare accurate quantity takeoffs
- Compare design alternatives and costs
- Perform value engineering
- Double-check estimates and quotes
- Estimate change orders

$110.00 | Over 900 pages, hardcover | Catalog No. 67276B

Mechanical Estimating Methods, 4th Edition

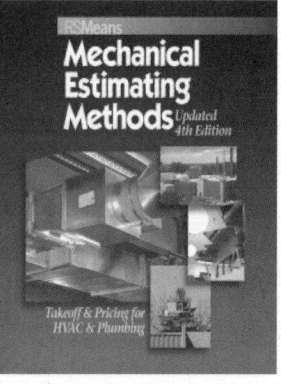

Completely updated, this guide assists you in making a review of plans, specs, and bid packages, with suggestions for takeoff procedures, listings, substitutions, and pre-bid scheduling for all components of HVAC. Includes suggestions for budgeting labor and equipment usage. Compares materials and construction methods to allow you to select the best option.

$70.00 per copy | Over 350 pages, illustrated, softcover | Catalog no. 67294B

2014 Order Form

ORDER TOLL FREE 1-800-334-3509 OR FAX 1-800-632-6732

For more information visit the RSMeans website at **www.rsmeans.com**

Unit prices according to the latest MasterFormat!

Qty.	Book no.	COST ESTIMATING BOOKS	Unit Price	Total
	60064	Assemblies Cost Data 2014	$315.95	
	60014	Building Construction Cost Data 2014	194.95	
	60044	Commercial Renovaion Cost Data 2014	156.95	
	60114	Concrete & Masonry Cost Data 2014	177.95	
	50144	Construction Cost Indexes 2014 (subscription)	362.00	
	60144A	Construction Cost Index–January 2014	93.50	
	60144B	Construction Cost Index–April 2014	93.50	
	60144C	Construction Cost Index–July 2014	93.50	
	60144D	Construction Cost Index–October 2014	93.50	
	60344	Contr. Pricing Guide: Resid. R & R Costs 2014	39.95	
	60234	Electrical Change Order Cost Data 2014	187.95	
	60034	Electrical Cost Data 2014	196.95	
	60204	Facilities Construction Cost Data 2014	496.95	
	60304	Facilities Maintenance & Repair Cost Data 2014	434.95	
	60554	Green Building Cost Data 2014	160.95	
	60164	Heavy Construction Cost Data 2014	192.95	
	60094	Interior Cost Data 2014	196.95	
	60124	Labor Rates for the Const. Industry 2014	424.95	
	60184	Light Commercial Cost Data 2014	144.95	
	60024	Mechanical Cost Data 2014	191.95	
	60154	Open Shop Building Const. Cost Data 2014	165.95	
	60214	Plumbing Cost Data 2014	194.95	
	60174	Residential Cost Data 2014	139.95	
	60284	Site Work & Landscape Cost Data 2014	187.95	
	60054	Square Foot Costs 2014	205.95	
	62013	Yardsticks for Costing (2013)	185.95	
	62014	Yardsticks for Costing (2014)	189.95	
		REFERENCE BOOKS		
	67329	Bldrs Essentials: Best Bus. Practices for Bldrs	40.00	
	67307	Bldrs Essentials: Plan Reading & Takeoff	35.95	
	67342	Building & Renovating Schools	99.95	
	67261A	The Building Prof. Guide to Contract Documents	75.00	
	67339	Building Security: Strategies & Costs	95.00	
	67353A	Complete Book of Framing, 2nd Ed.	29.95	
	67146	Concrete Repair & Maintenance Illustrated	75.00	
	67352	Construction Business Management	55.00	
	67364	Construction Law	110.00	
	67358	Construction Supervision	95.00	
	67363	Cost Data Student Edition	99.00	
	67314	Cost Planning & Est. for Facil. Maint.	95.00	
	67230B	Electrical Estimating Methods, 3rd Ed.	75.00	
	67343A	Est. Bldg. Costs for Resi. & Lt. Comm., 2nd Ed.	75.00	
	67276B	Estimating Handbook, 3rd Ed.	110.00	
	67318	Facilities Operations & Engineering Reference	115.00	
	67301	Facilities Planning & Relocation	89.95	
	67338B	Green Building: Proj. Planning & Cost Est., 3rd Ed.	110.00	
	67355	Green Home Improvement	34.95	
	67357A	The Gypsum Construction Handbook	40.00	
	67148	Heavy Construction Handbook	110.00	
	67308E	Home Improvement Costs–Int. Projects, 9th Ed.	24.95	
	67309E	Home Improvement Costs–Ext. Projects, 9th Ed.	24.95	

Qty.	Book no.	REFERENCE BOOKS (Cont.)	Unit Price	Total
	67344	Homeowner's Guide to Mold	21.95	
	67324C	How to Est.w/Means Data & CostWorks, 4th Ed.	75.00	
	67351A	How Your House Works, 2nd Ed.	22.95	
	67282A	Illustrated Const. Dictionary, Condensed, 2nd Ed.	65.00	
	67292B	Illustrated Const. Dictionary, w/CD-ROM, 4th Ed.	99.95	
	67362	Illustrated Const. Dictionary, Student Ed.	55.00	
	67348	Job Order Contracting	89.95	
	67295C	Landscape Estimating Methods, 5th Ed.	75.00	
	67341	Life Cycle Costing for Facilities	99.95	
	67294B	Mechanical Estimating Methods, 4th Ed.	70.00	
	67283B	Plumbing Estimating Methods, 3rd Ed.	65.00	
	67345	Practice of Cost Segregation Analysis	105.00	
	67366	Project Control: Integrating Cost & Sched.	95.00	
	67346	Preventive Maint. for Multi-Family Housing	95.00	
	67367	Project Scheduling & Manag. for Constr., 4th Ed.	95.00	
	67322B	Resi. & Light Commercial Const. Stds., 3rd Ed.	65.00	
	67359	Risk Management for Design & Construction	125.00	
	67365	Solar Energy: Technology & Project Delivery	85.00	
	67145B	Sq. Ft. & Assem. Estimating Methods, 3rd Ed.	75.00	
	67321	Total Productive Facilities Management	85.00	
	67350	Understanding and Negotiating Const. Contracts	80.00	
	67303B	Unit Price Estimating Methods, 4th Ed.	75.00	
	67354	Universal Design	21.95	
	67319A	Value Engineering: Practical Applications	85.00	

MA residents add 6.25% state sales tax _____

Shipping & Handling** _____

Total (U.S. Funds)* _____

Prices are subject to change and are for U.S. delivery only. *Canadian customers may call for current prices. **Shipping & handling charges: Add 7% of total order for check and credit card payments. Add 9% of total order for invoiced orders.

Send order to: ADDV-1000

Name (please print) _____

Company _____

☐ Company

☐ Home Address _____

_____

City/State/Zip _____

Phone # _____ P.O. # _____

(Must accompany all orders being billed)

Mail to: RSMeans, 700 Longwater Drive, Norwell, MA 02061